Reader's Digest

CONDENSED BOOKS

READER'S DIGEST

Volume IV·1967

CONDENSED BOOKS

Autumn Selections

The Reader's Digest Association

Pleasantville, New York

The original editions of the books in this volume
are published and copyrighted as follows:

Christy, published at $6.95 by McGraw-Hill Book Co.
© 1967 by Catherine Marshall LeSourd

The Best of Clarence Day, published at $5.95 by Alfred A. Knopf, Inc.
Copyright 1920, 1922, 1923, 1924, 1928, 1931, 1932, 1933, 1934, 1935
by Clarence Day
Copyright 1936 by The Curtis Publishing Co.
Copyright 1933, 1935, 1936, 1937 by the Estate of Clarence Day
Copyright 1948 by Katherine B. Day

The Fox and the Hound, published at $4.95 by E. P. Dutton & Co., Inc.
© 1967 by Daniel P. Mannix

Nicholas and Alexandra: An Intimate Account of the Last of the Romanovs
and the Fall of Imperial Russia, published at $10.00 by Atheneum Publishers
© 1967 by Robert K. Massie

The Gabriel Hounds, published in the U.S.A. at $5.95
by M. S. Mill & Company, Inc., an affiliate of William Morrow & Co., Inc.
© 1967 by Mary Stewart

Quotation from "Everybody's Doin' It Now," by Irving Berlin, on page 69
© Copyright 1911, Irving Berlin. Copyright renewed.
Reprinted by permission of Irving Berlin Music Corporation.

Photograph of Easter egg on page 358
Courtesy of the Forbes Magazine Collection of Fabergé

CONTENTS

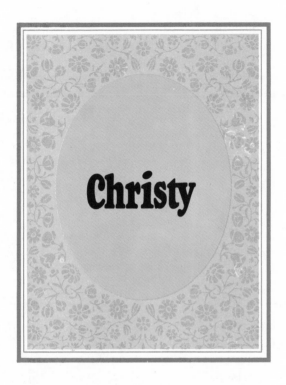

Christy

A CONDENSATION OF THE BOOK BY

CATHERINE MARSHALL

ILLUSTRATED BY HOWARD SANDEN

For many years, Catherine Marshall, the distinguished author of *A Man Called Peter* and other inspirational books, listened to her mother's stories of her experiences as a young mission teacher in eastern Tennessee. Mrs. Marshall went with her parents—her father had been a Presbyterian minister in the same settlement—to the wild, beautiful mountains and saw the humor, courage and saltiness of the mountain people for herself.

Gradually, the need to tell her mother's story in the form of a novel took hold. *Christy*—a moving, authentic drama of mountain life—is the inspiring result. Around the character of Christy, a spirited young girl in search of her own identity and a deeper religious faith, Catherine Marshall has brought to life the whole Appalachian world with its feuds, its fun, its humanity, and its proud independence.

In the end, young Christy finds a new understanding of God through suffering—and she finds, too, her lifetime love.

Prologue

ON THAT November afternoon when I first saw Cutter Gap, the crumbling chimney of Alice Henderson's cabin stood stark against the sky, blackened by the flames that had consumed the house. The encroaching weeds: field grass and chickweed and penny-royal had all but obliterated even the outline of the foundations.

The old mission house was still there, high on its rise of ground, with the mountain towering behind it. Once painted a proud white, it was gray and sagging, the front porch gone. There were no other buildings left at the mission. The church-schoolhouse had long since been moved to another location; David Grantland's cabin had been demolished.

Nonetheless, I was standing with my mother on the spot I had always longed to see—the site of the adventures recounted so vividly by my parents during my growing-up years. These years had brought changes to Cutter Gap: "brought-on" clothes, canned food, autos, radios over which blared hillbilly music.

But many of Appalachia's economic problems had never been solved, so the federal government had stepped in. In 1936, the towering scenery of Cutter Gap was incorporated into the Cherokee National Forest, and the families who lived there sold their small holdings to the government. By the time I saw the Cove, cabin after cabin stood vacant. Forest rangers and tourists roamed the Gap, and bear and deer, raccoon and bobcat, fox and wild boar were returning to these Tennessee forests.

But mother was surprised to find that certain things had not changed. The way in, for instance, was still a bumpy trail with washouts and gullies and fords over a tumbling mountain stream. When the car finally stopped in the mission yard, mother got out and stood and looked—and looked—trying to see everything at once. A young family now lived in what had been the old mission house, and they had invited us to stay for the night.

We explored room after room. The dining room was still much the same, mother said—tan tongue-and-groove walls—only now there was a mail-order stove (providing the only heat in the house) with a pipe through the ceiling. We found that there was still no running water and the old telephone was in its place on the wall. "Remember my telling you about bringing the wires in?" mother asked. Yes, I remembered.

She stopped in the parlor doorway, her face aglow. "The Lyon and Healy! Imagine!" The huge grand piano still stood there, though the ivory was missing from most of the keys.

We were given the front bedroom upstairs. There were fluffy clean curtains at the windows. "How did they know," mother said, "that this was once my room?" She was eager for more reconnoitering. "Catherine, would you walk down the road with me?" she said eagerly. "I want to find out if—well, a lot of things."

As we walked along, I sensed excitement rising in her. She was the nineteen-year-old Christy Huddleston again, exploring this same road wearing the shoes she had bought at the Bon Marché in Asheville. ("Ice-pick toes," David Grantland had teasingly called them.)

Presently we were standing by the O'Teale cabin she knew so well. No one was around. It was like walking into an empty stage setting or into one's own dream. Clumps of old English boxwood in the yard were surrounded by rotting tires, pieces of twisted metal, old newspapers. We walked up the creaking stairs at one end of the porch and stood in the doorway. Everyone was gone, and on the floor was a snowstorm of slips of paper—receipts for pay from a South Carolina cotton mill. Mother shook her head in disbelief at the dates. "They're so many years back," she said. "The children must have left the mountains to work in a mill and sent most of their pay home." I watched her turning the slips of paper over and over in her hands as if trying to make them speak to her. She said, "I lost my supper that first night after I had seen the half-witted epileptic boy who lived here. It was Miss Alice who comforted me. Miss Alice . . ." Mother's blue eyes held a faraway look.

I thought of tall, blonde, patrician Alice Henderson as she had been described to me. In spite of her eager, adventurous mind, her religious beliefs had been as settled as the nineteen-year-old Christy's had been unsure. She had been at the center of all the drama that had been acted out on this gigantic stage, with the brooding, unchanging mountains as the backdrop.

It was then that I got my first clear glimpse of the book I had always wanted to write about the mountains—my mountains. For I had been born among mountains like these. All of my life the windswept heights had challenged me—and steadied me.

As if reading my thoughts, mother said shyly, "The story aches to be told, Catherine. The secrets of the human spirit that Alice Henderson knew are needed today. And my mountain friends—I want people to know them as they really were."

And suddenly, I understood how the story should be written—through mother's eyes, as I had seen it all along. Only—from the beginning, my imagination had taken hold of the true incidents and had shaped them so that now I scarcely knew where truth stopped and fiction began. Therefore, though so much of the story really happened, I would set it down in the form of fiction. As much as she could tell me, I would write. I said to her now, "I've never understood why your parents let you come here."

She laughed softly. "Oh, teaching in a mission school sounded so safe; and Dr. Ferrand was so solid, so reliable. . . . Father was certain he could entrust me to Dr. Ferrand."

Down in the valley,
valley so low;
Hang your head over,
hear the wind blow.
Hear the wind blow, love,
hear the wind blow;
Hang your head over,
hear the wind blow....

Christy's Story

CHAPTER 1

ONLY MY father saw me to the Asheville station that January morning in 1912. Mother had gotten up early to fix us a hot breakfast and that moment would always be sharp and real in my mind: the look of love and longing in mother's eyes; the smell of the starch in her crisp apron; the hissing of the pine rosin in the big iron stove; the lake of melted butter in the steaming mound of hominy grits on my plate. Then father called, "Time to start!" and my brother, George, said a sleepy good-by from the stairs.

In the gray light, the railroad station had a wraithlike look. I saw with a leap of heart that the train would be pulled by *Old Buncombe,* a favorite engine on the East-Tennessee-Virginia-and-Georgia Railroad. It was green, with gold trim, and there were big brass ornaments on its headlight. The billows of smoke pouring out of its smokestack looked blacker than usual against the background of new-fallen snow.

Father tried to be jovial, teasing me as if I were nine and not nineteen. He considered me too young to teach school in a mountain cove, and I had battled long and hard with him and mother for the chance to do this. Impulsively I stuck my right hand into his overcoat pocket, and his left hand covered it.

"Girlie," he asked gruffly, "do you really have enough money to get you through until payday? Twenty-five a month won't go far."

I was trying to sound gay. "But there won't be any temptation to spend money. It will be good for me."

We mounted the steps to the train. There was the smell of coal dust that railroad cars had then; grime in every crevice; brass spittoons; a potbellied stove in the rear; sacks of grain and produce piled toward the back. I sank down on the red plush seat, with my valise on the floor beside me. The whistle blew. Father reached out for me; his tweed coat was rough against my cheek. "Don't forget to write." He pinched my cheek—and was gone.

I saw him on the platform, talking to the old conductor. I knew from long experience what he was saying. "My daughter's in there. Take care of my girl." It was embarrassing.

The conductor waved his arms, shouting, "All a-boarrd!" *Old Buncombe* sputtered and wheezed with the familiar chuff . . . chuff . . . chuff. Our car jerked forward. The conductor began moving down the aisle gathering tickets.

It would mortify me before the other passengers if he told me that he would take good care of me, so I turned to the window and pretended to be looking at the rising hills. What I actually saw reflected in the glass was a figure so slender that it should have belonged to a much younger girl. I threw back my shoulders, trying to fill out my new fawn-colored coat suit. The blue eyes beneath the piled-up dark hair stared back quizzically.

"Ticket, please. You're Christy Huddleston, aren't you?"

I nodded, hoping I'd managed a dignified expression. After all, I had often taken the train to Flora MacDonald College in Red Springs, and once I had taken the sleeper to my aunt's home in Charleston.

"I'm Javis McGovern," the conductor said. "So you're bound for El Pano, young lady. Your father said you were going to teach school in Cutter Gap." Mr. McGovern rubbed his chin whiskers. "I oughten to be tellin' you, but that Cutter Gap is right rough country."

Then he went on gathering tickets, and I thought of the talk the past summer on which I had based my future in Cutter Gap. It

13

was at a church conference in Montreat, North Carolina, where my family spent a part of every summer. I remembered the big auditorium; the ladies in voile or crepe de chine; the cardboard fans advertising religious publishing houses or pulpit furniture; a pleasant hum of whispering voices. Then Dr. Ferrand, a man with a white goatee and a resonant voice, began to speak.

During the War Between the States he had ridden horseback through the Cumberland Mountains on his way to join the Confederate Army. He had been impressed with how poor, yet how intelligent, the mountain people were. Years later, a successful doctor in Arkansas, he had become desperately ill with scarlet fever. He vowed that if he lived, he would help the Appalachian people. Upon recovering, he sacrificed his fine practice to start mission work in Arkansas, Kentucky, and finally in the Great Smokies, where he met Miss Alice Henderson, a Quaker from Ardmore, Pennsylvania, who had braved hardship and danger to serve where she saw need. A year ago Miss Henderson had placed her own three schools under the auspices of his American Inland Mission, to strengthen the work.

Then Dr. Ferrand talked about the need for recruits. "Beyond the great mountains, outstretched hands and beseeching voices cry, 'Come over and help us,' " he said. He spoke of Branner Bill, who had been the feuding terror of Cataleechie Cove until he had heard the gospel story and became a changed man; of Rob Allen who wanted book learning so much that he came to school barefooted through deep snow. Dr. Ferrand's mission had only one other worker and three hundred and sixty dollars. "Will you hear and help," he said, "or will you leave them to their distress and ignorance?" And with that, the little doctor sat down.

I had heard about need in places like China and Africa, but I had had no idea that such awful conditions existed right in our own mountains. As we sang the closing hymn, "Just As I Am," my feeling of exhilaration grew so strong that I could scarcely sing. After the benediction, I made my way down the aisle. Dr. Ferrand gripped my hand warmly, and my voice shook a little as I told him, "You asked for volunteers. You are looking at one."

Then I had gone back to our hotel to begin the long task of persuading father and mother. And I had never wavered since, through all their weeks of pleas and arguments, for up in the mountains were children who at least should have the chance of learning to read.

The screeching of the train lurching to a stop broke my reverie. I got out for a breath of fresh air, and saw men putting levers under rocks on the roadbed. I could see nothing around us but snow-drifted mountains, with wisps of clouds trailing off the tallest peaks like banners in the gray sky. It was a lonely landscape.

The wind was rising, a whimpering, sobbing wind, with pain in it. Then smoke began puffing rhythmically out of *Old Buncombe's* smokestack. The rocks had been sent crashing down the mountainside.

I climbed back inside and, as the train started, opened the little wicker basket mother had given me. There was chicken breast and buttered slices of salt-rising bread, an apple, fresh buttermilk, spice cake, and Nabisco wafers. As I munched, memories came sweeping over me, and I thought of our big old kitchen, with its wonderful fragrances. Why had smells—pleasant and unpleasant—always been so important to me? Sometimes the bad ones were torture, but the nice ones—like honeysuckle or grapes or mother's bread—more than made up for it.

Was I being foolish to leave my wonderful home? I only knew that it was an experiment I had to make. Sunday after Sunday I had sat in the First Presbyterian Church of Asheville, with its blue carpets and tall, carved pulpit chairs. Our preachers had all been good men, kind men. I had seldom been able to keep my mind on what they were saying, but I had thought the trouble lay with me. Now I had discovered something about religion which had not come through to me before. That was why I had had to explore for myself—as Tennyson said, *Life piled on life.*

The winter twilight was coming fast. The train began to slow down and the engineer blew a long warning whistle. *Old Buncombe's* wheels ground to a stop. Hastily I put on my coat, picked up my moleskin muff and my valise, and started down the aisle.

"Let me help you with that." Mr. McGovern swung my valise to the ground. "Miss Huddleston," he said earnestly, "watch yourself out there at Cutter Gap!"

"Thank you, Mr. McGovern." I tried to sound confident.

My eyes searched the dusk—just a tiny station and four or five houses. I had hoped that someone would meet me. How often I'd pictured the scene. . . . "Miss Huddleston?" he would ask. "We've been anticipating your arrival. How very nice—" And his eyes would say, We were expecting a young girl, but you're a grown woman. And I would be very gracious and extend my hand in greeting. . . . But no one was approaching at all. There was the "All a-boarrd," and I watched as the train got under way. I felt fear rising in me. Everything dear and familiar was disappearing over the horizon with that train. *Old Buncombe's* whistle blew—far away. Then even the sound was gone. I swallowed the lump in my throat, took a firm grip on my valise, and blindly headed for the little station.

The ticket agent, wearing a green eyeshade, looked up as I approached.

"Is there anywhere in El Pano to spend the night?" I asked.

"Well, let's see now. Maybe Miz Tatum's. You just—guess it's easier to show you." He ducked out through a door beside the cage, and I followed him into the stinging cold. He pointed across the tracks. "Second house down. Just tell her I sent you."

I thanked him, and he disappeared inside the warm station.

It was not easy to carry my valise and hold up my skirts in the snow at the same time, but I struggled on until a second Victorian frame house loomed out of the darkness. I set my valise on the porch and twirled the bell. The tall big-boned woman who opened the door almost filled the opening.

"Mrs. Tatum, I'm Christy Huddleston from Asheville. I'm the new teacher at Cutter Gap. The station man told me that you could put me up for the night."

"Sure could. C'mon in. Here, let me take that valise—you can bring the lamp. Right on up. That room just ahead."

It was a plain room with a shiny brass bed, but everything was

16

clean. "Now, you make yourself to home, and I'll fix you a bite. Come on down when you're ready."

I changed as quickly as I could, then I picked up the lamp and groped my way down the stairs. Mrs. Tatum had put on a large calico apron. "C'mon in, child. There's spareribs, pickled beans, and sourwood honey and apple butter to put on the biscuit bread. Think that's enough to keep body and soul on speakin' terms?"

"Plenty, thanks. My mother packed me some food for the trip."

"If I may ask," the voice was hesitant, "how did your mother take it, your comin' to teach in the Cove?"

This was not something I wanted to discuss. "Oh, it was all right with my parents. After all, I'm nineteen."

"I don't think you know what you're gettin' yourself into. You come from a highfalutin' home, easy to tell that."

"Mrs. Tatum, I'm not afraid of plain living."

"Have you ever had to wash your clothes by beatin' 'em on a battlin' block? Did you ever sleep in a bed with the quilts held down by rocks to keep the wind from blowing them off?"

Thinking she was exaggerating, I smiled. Yet her attitude started little shivers up and down my spine.

"I don't want nothin' to happen to you. I'm not speakin' of your gettin' shot at. When a body minds his own business, he generally needn't be afraid. It's your *feelin's*. They don't take much stock in foreigners in the Cove. And they don't like to be beholden. It's goin' to be well-nigh impossible for you to help them. Only person I ever saw that could do that is Miz Alice Henderson."

Eager to change the subject from my probable failure, I pounced on the name. "Oh, would you tell me about her?"

"She's a character right enough. Imagine a high-toned Quaker lady livin' up there in the mountains by herself! There's lots of talk about how she come there in the first place. Some say she was runnin' away from a broken heart."

"How far is Cutter Gap from here?" I asked.

"Seven mile, more or less. Come mornin', talk to Ben Pentland at the General Store. He carries the mail to the Cove." She apparently decided to make one last try. "Look, maybe you don't like somebody you never saw afore buttin' in, but my advice is get yourself right back to your own folks. There now, I've said it."

"Mrs. Tatum," I explained, "I've given my word about teaching school. A promise is a promise. Thanks a lot for the supper, and please don't worry about me."

As I turned to go up to bed, she was standing staring after me, looking distressed.

CHAPTER 2

AT THE El Pano General Store next morning, I was greeted first by smells: coal oil, cheese, leather, bacon, tobacco. A group of men were gathered around the stove. Their whittling and rocking left off as eyes followed me across the creaky floor. "Excuse me," I said to a woman arranging spools of thread in a cabinet. "I was told that I might find Mr. Pentland here."

The woman called, "Ben Pentland, com'here—willya?"

A man looked up from the high boots he had been lacing and grunted, then like a jackknife unfolded to well over six feet. He had a long, slim weather-creased face, thin firm lips, deep-set eyes and bushy eyebrows. As he ambled in our direction, I stuck out a mittened hand. "I'm Christy Huddleston. Mr. Pentland, I'm trying to find a way to get out to the Cove. Mrs. Tatum said you carry mail out there."

"Yep. But ain't nobody been in or out the Cove since a couple days. Snow was too deep. But I'm startin' out there now. Letters are pilin' up something fearful." (This meant, I found later, that he had six to deliver.)

"Could I walk out there with you today?" I asked.

"Nope. It jest wouldn't be fitten for a gal-woman to go along with the U-nited States mail." Abruptly, he took a step backward, dramatically placing his hand over his heart. He intoned, " 'Neither rain—nor snow—nor heat—nor gloom of night—will stay these couriers from the swift completion of their appointed rounds.' Ain't that *beautiful?* Just been told us by the gov-ment in Washington. Now I figure if none of those things are meant to stay us couriers, then we shorely can't have no gal-woman stayin' us." And he turned to rejoin his companions.

I ran after him. "Mr. Pentland, *please*. I promise that I won't interfere. *Please?*"

He seemed to take my measure. "Look, it's not easy a-walkin' in the snow— And what about your go-away satchel?"

I leaped at the straw he held out. "I've only one small valise with me. The rest of my things are coming by trunk. May I, may I come with you?"

"Wal— Kin you be ready in a hip and a hurry?"

"I'll be ready." And I ran out of the store.

TWENTY minutes later a still incredulous Mrs. Tatum was telling me good-by on her front porch. Impulsively she took my face between her hands. "Don't forget I've got good broad shoulders if ever ye need cryin' posts." She held me off at arm's length, looking at me. "You're a sight on the eyes," she said approvingly. "They've never seen the likes of you." As I turned to go join Mr. Pentland, waiting on the road, she thrust a paper poke into my hands. "No good walkin' on an empty stummick."

For the first half mile or so, Mr. Pentland, carrying my valise along with his mail pack, set a brisk pace along a wide, well-traveled lane between snowy fields. Beyond the fields were foothills, and beyond them, the mountains. Over the farthest range hung a soft smoky-blue mantle. When Mr. Pentland noticed that I was having trouble keeping up with his long strides, he said, "Reckon I'd better whittle my walk down a mite. You'll be nippety-tuck to keep up with me. Hell's Banjer! Wimmin's skirts ain't the best for snow."

I discovered that all of his speech was quaint. "The sunball" . . . "afeard" . . . "mought." Twilight, he called "the aidge of dark." And there was a natural courtesy about him that I liked.

I said, "What's your first mail stop, Mr. Pentland?"

"Becks' mailbox is first. I've got a letter from Mistress Beck's aunt in Jonesboro. Her littlest settin'-along child's been poorly

19

for some time. Guess she's a-lettin' Mistress Beck know the news."

We walked in silence to the Becks'. Then I asked how many families lived around Cutter Gap. The mailman thought a moment. "Jedgmatically, I don't know. Maybe 'bout seventy."

"Most of them farm, don't they? What do they raise?"

"Young'uns," he answered drily.

"And do most of the children go to the mission school?"

"Wal-l, hit de-pends. Not all of 'em got religion, and there's some families just p'int blank won't go near it. But most everyone likes the new preacher, David Grantland. He's got good wind in the pulpit and can shore tote a tune."

"Is he married?"

"No-o-o." Mr. Pentland looked at me and chuckled.

I changed the subject. "Do you know Miss Alice Henderson?"

"Everybody knows Miz Alice Henderson. Tangy as an unripe persimmon. Dauncy. Rides a horse all over the mountains, side-saddle, long skirt. Keeps busier than a honeybee 'round a rosey-bush—a-teachin', a-preachin', nursin' the sick, a-comfortin' the dyin'. Has a heap o' light hair, leetle gray in it now. Wears it in braids folded 'round her head, like—like a crown.

"She talks about God lovin' folks—says He wants us all happy. She don't put no stock in long-faced persons even when they *think* they've got religion." He chuckled. "At Christmas in the mountains we shoot rifle-guns up chimneys and blow up tree stumps to celebrate. Last Christmas Miz Henderson sent to Philadelfy for a big box of boughten fireworks. My, but them fireworks was shorely a sight to be-hold."

After we had delivered two more letters, the trail began winding upward. It grew colder. My eyes watered and I could no longer feel my toes inside my rubber boots. Even my eyelashes were beaded with wet snow falling from the trees.

At last we turned downhill and reached a large creek in a valley. There was no bridge across the creek—only two huge uneven logs with an occasional thin board nailed across. They swayed precariously six feet or more above the water. Mr. Pentland said, "I'll go first to see if hit's slippery-like."

Halfway across he paused. Below him water sprayed over boulders where the stream was not frozen. He called back, "Hit ain't bad. Wait until I get acrost, so you won't get no sway."

I never had liked heights, and standing on the bank, I felt sick. Then I heard Mr. Pentland's voice above the roar of the water. "Stomp your feet to get 'em warm. Then come on—but first scrape your boots and hoist your skirts." Mechanically I did as he directed, then took a deep breath and put a foot on a swaying log. I took a few steps, shut my eyes, then opened them. Another step. I heard Mr. Pentland's voice. "You're doin' fine. Not far now."

The logs were swaying, tilting. . . . I dropped to my knees and began crawling dizzily. Mr. Pentland was shouting, "Only a few more steps. Stand up now. I'll catch you." Unsteadily, I stood. . . . Step—getting closer now—only a few more feet.

At last I saw Mr. Pentland's grinning face below me. "Guess you ain't crossed the likes of that before." He held out a gnarled hand and almost lifted me off the end of the log.

Another hour of steady walking brought us to a second mountain and a sliced-out path. At one side, the ledge appeared to drop off into space. "Lonesome Pine Ridge," Mr. Pentland called to me. "There's another way that's shorter. But it's so up-tilted, you could stand straight up and bite the ground."

I wondered as I panted after him if any piece of land could be more up-tilted than this. I was beginning to understand why the mailman had not wanted to bring me. This morning seemed like days and days ago. Before long it was five hundred feet to the valley floor below; somewhere down there I could hear a cowbell tinkling. The gusts of wind were so strong I was sure we would be blown off the cliff. Mr. Pentland must have sensed that I was afraid because he called back over his shoulder, "You must be bodaciously tired. Not much farther to the Spencers'. We could set a spell by their fire, maybe have a bite to eat."

THE SPENCERS' cabin was made of mud-chinked logs. In their clearing inside a split-rail fence were some clumps of English boxwood, an immense black pot, a pile of firewood, chickens pecking in the snow, and a crude sled. An unshaved, red-blond man in black felt hat and overalls appeared on the porch and called out, "Howdy!" Hounds raced toward us, yapping.

Mr. Pentland called, "Howdy. How you doin'?"

" 'Bout like common."

In spite of his shabby clothing, there was something debonair about him. The front of his hat was pinned up with a long thorn, and a sprig of balsam was stuck jauntily into the hatband. "Git out of the way till you git more sense," he called to the hounds, and they slunk out of sight around the cabin.

"Jeb Spencer, this here's Miz Huddleston. New teacher from Asheville-way."

"Howdy do, ma'am." The man's greeting was almost courtly. He led us through the doorway into a ruddy glow of firelight. I saw several beds piled high with quilts and a tall woman with an assortment of towheaded children. Mr. Spencer said, "C'mon and see the stranger. Don't know as I can handle her name. This here's my woman. And that there's John. And this'uns Zady. And that's Clara. And that's Lulu." His voice took on more warmth. "And that thar's the least'un." He pointed to a tiny boy.

I smiled at the children and then held out my hand to Mrs. Spencer. But she only touched my fingers shyly and said, "Would you like to rest your wrap and set a spell?" Her voice was low-toned and musical, and she was beautiful in an artless way. In her early thirties, I guessed, yet with all these children. . . . She was wearing only a calico dress and was barefooted in this cold.

Mr. Pentland handed her the lunch Mrs. Tatum had given me. I held my cold hands to the fire and looked around the cabin. There were two rooms side by side with rough puncheon floors and fireplaces. This room was both living and sleeping quarters; the smaller one was the kitchen. A narrow ladder led to a loft. Garments of various kinds and a worn saddle hung from wall pegs. A long-barreled rifle was laid across an elk-horn rack, and flatirons were lined up on the hearth near an ancient cradle.

The "least'un" came up to me shyly, and I was just beginning to make friends with him when we gathered for dinner around a plank table. No mention was made of washing hands. Mr. Spencer asked the blessing: "Thank Thee, Lord, for providin' this bounty. Bless us and bind us. Amen." And out of the corner of one eye I saw a small gray pig come through the open door.

Clara spoke up eagerly. "That thar's Belinda, our pet pig—all our'n." She picked up the pig and put him in her lap while I tried not to show surprise.

Mrs. Tatum's poke dinner had been placed on a tin plate in the middle of the table beside a big pot of steaming cabbage. I hated to part with all of my lunch since I knew that it at least was clean. Nevertheless I asked Clara if she would like a sandwich. All the children nodded eagerly—and soon my food was gone.

"Can I give you some pot likker?" Mrs. Spencer asked over my shoulder. Without waiting for an answer, she ladled some onto the wooden plate in front of me. Jeb and John Spencer were already using pieces of corn bread to sop up the cabbage mixture. The only other thing on the table was a bowl of sauerkraut.

Mrs. Spencer moved quietly and gracefully to and from the kitchen, bringing the family more corn pone and coffee. Her features were delicate, and her eyes were wistful. The oldest girl looked like her except that she was a bit round-shouldered, as if already she was carrying burdens too heavy for her. She had her mother's low-pitched voice with that melancholy note in it.

These were the faces of pioneers, a certain Spartan quality to them all. The grave look was there even at moments when dry humor was flowing, as when Mr. Spencer commented about a widow-woman who thought herself extra pious. " 'Course she ain't much of a hand to housekeep: slut's wool all over the place. When yer mind is that fixated on things above, dirt's bound to settle below." I had a strange feeling, as if, in crossing the mountains, I had crossed into another century and the days of the American frontier. Daniel Boone might walk into this cabin any moment— or Davy Crockett.

Suddenly, a man rushed into the cabin, out of breath. "It's Bob Allen," he gasped. "Hurt bad! They're carryin' him here. He was a-comin' to El Pano to fetch on the new teacher."

23

A YOUNG MAN, unconscious, his head bloody, was carried into the cabin on a stretcher of branches and laid on a bed. The words whirled in my head, "Comin' to fetch on the new teacher. . . ." Because of me this had happened.

Mrs. Spencer's voice was gentle, as if she sensed how I felt. "Miz Henderson's been a-pesterin' Bob to carry word to you. But it were snowin' too heavy on Sunday for him to journey."

"What 'n' all happened?" I heard Mr. Pentland ask.

One of the stretcher-bearers said, "Bob was cuttin' acrost Pebble Mountain when a high wind come up and a big tulip poplar tree got wind-throwed. Fumped him right on the head. We was huntin' squirrels and the old hound dog nosed him out in the bresh, tree still on him. Doc MacNeill's a-comin'."

Within what seemed like minutes, the strangest group of people I had ever seen began crowding into the Spencer cabin—neighbors and Allen relatives. I was never to fathom how news traveled so fast in those mountains.

Then Dr. MacNeill arrived. He appeared to be in his thirties, with rugged features and unkempt reddish hair. He took off his coat and rolled up his shirt sleeves. His arms were muscular. He made his examination by lamplight, for although it was early afternoon the cabin was dark. His fingers slid over Mr. Allen's head—feeling, probing. He checked the pulse; opened the eyelids and looked intently into the eyes; checked the reflexes. Something about his fingers reminded me of my father's hands, only these were rough and work-worn. Finally he straightened up. "Mary Allen," he said, "I'm needing to talk to you and Bob's brother Ault. Mary, I'd best speak plain. Bob's bad off."

Mary's face was rigid with fear. "Be it a—mortalizing—wound, Doc?" she whispered.

"Mary," the Doctor said gently, "Bob's pulse is slow, reflexes bad, one eye doesn't respond to light. It's getting almost impossible for him to breathe. There's some bleeding inside Bob's skull. If I leave it there, Bob will die." He paused and I saw the tears in his eyes. "There's one chance of bringing him round. That's to bore a 'burr hole' in the skull to let the bad blood out.

I'll tell you true—I've never tried this operation, but I saw it done once by a professor of mine, Starr Gatlin. It's chancy. Mary, it's up to you and Ault. Will you let me try?"

In the stillness, we heard Bob's labored breathing. Mary Allen rocked soundlessly on her heels, laboring with her stark alternatives; yet no whimper escaped her. The grief of the inarticulate cuts so much deeper than the wailing of the self-pitying.

"I say naw. I stand against it," Ault Allen, a heavily bearded man, exclaimed. "Life and death is in the hands of the Lord. We've no call to tamper with it."

Then Mary spoke. "No, Ault, ye're wrong. We've no cause to let go so long as there's one livin' breath left in Bob. Try it, Doc! We've got six young'uns. Will ye try, Doc?"

The Doctor looked at Ault. "Ault . . . ?"

"We-ll—" Ault pulled at his beard. "Hit's up to you, but I don't like meddlin' with the Lord's business." He shrugged.

The Doctor himself wavered for another moment. I thought I understood his cruel dilemma. There was not much hope for Mr. Allen and if the patient died during the operation some of these people would surely blame him. At last he said tersely, "We'll go ahead. Jeb Spencer and John Holcombe, I need your help."

I knew that Dr. MacNeill had made a courageous decision. But looking at his tousled hair and rumpled shirt sleeves as he directed the preparations, I wondered if it was not a foolhardy one. A mountain cabin; dirty pots and pans by the hearth; a baby crying in its mother's arms; the foul air in the crowded room. . . . Surely the Doctor would ask these staring people to leave.

But he said only, "We'll use that kitchen table. Fairlight, will you and Lizzie scrub it? And Jeb, do you have a razor and a straight awl and hammer? Ben Pentland, will you get water from the spring? Better start a fire under the washpot. And Jeb, you don't have another table, do you? . . . Then get me a couple of sawhorses and some boards for an instrument table. And hurry!"

At last came the announcement I had been waiting for. "The whole kit and caboodle of you best leave," the Doctor said gruffly. His eyes swept the room and he noticed me for the first time since he had entered the cabin. An intense light seemed to burn suddenly in his deep-set eyes. He stared at me without speaking, fingers plucking the unkempt hair on his neck. I felt he was seeing me as the cause of the accident.

Finally he turned to the others. "If you close-kin feel called on to stay, then stand off. And no crying or wailing."

The people respected the Doctor, I could see that; yet only a few left. I wanted to slip out, but I was penned in by the crowd.

From his saddlebags, the Doctor had brought muslin bags with bandages, sutures and instruments. He put Mr. Spencer's tools and the instruments into a pot of boiling water. After a time he began laying supplies out on a clean cloth spread on the saw-horse table. Why try to sterilize instruments, I thought, not six feet from an anything but sterile audience?

As some of the men lifted Bob Allen onto the makeshift operating table, I heard a scuffle at the door and turned to see Bob's wife rushing toward the still form with an axe in her hands. She gave it a mighty heave and I stifled a scream. With a crash the axe bit deep into the floor under the table. Then with shaking hands she tied a string around one of her husband's wrists.

I was too stunned to move. To my surprise, Dr. MacNeill took this behavior calmly. "All right," he said, "that should be helpful. Now, will someone take care of Mary until this is over?"

The sickly odor of ether soon hung in the close air. I managed to slip by people and out the door. Outside I breathed deeply. I saw I was where I did not belong, where people still believed in witchcraft. I had been born in another century. Could anything but evil come of this meeting of two worlds?

The ether began to drive other people into the yard, including Mrs. Spencer. I moved closer to her. "The Doctor called you Fairlight," I said. "That's a lovely name."

She nodded, but seemed preoccupied. Her eyes were focused with intense concentration on the sun, which was setting behind a tall pinnacle opposite. When suddenly the sun dipped and the shadow of the mountain fell across us like a dark hand, I felt Fairlight cringe, I said to lighten the moment, "The sun sinks in a hurry here, doesn't it?" But she did not hear me. The eyes in her lovely face were glazed, turned toward that peak across the valley, seeing some specter I could not glimpse.

A long time passed. Finally Mr. Pentland's voice spoke from the shadows. "You must be real tired," he said kindly. "I'll take you on to the mission. It's not far."

"But Mr. Allen— How is he? Is he—"

"Still livin' and breathin'. Doc MacNeill found the blood clots. He says Bob has a fightin' chance."

"Oh, I'm *so* glad." I was weak with relief. Mr. Pentland had my valise and was already starting. I had had all the walking I wanted, but there was no alternative except to follow him.

I had not realized what a toll the day had taken until we were at the mission house. Then I could feel tears of exhaustion just under the surface. The door opened, and through a haze of fatigue, I saw a young man with friendly brown eyes and a wide smile. A firm hand welcomed me. A tall, gaunt, older woman led me upstairs. "This will be your room. Are you hungry?"

"No, thank you. I'm fine." As she left, I fell into bed. The last thing I remember was the sound of a mountain stream somewhere close—flowing—flowing into the night.

CHAPTER 3

I SLID OUT of bed late next morning, stiff and sore. There was no luxury here: only a washstand with a china pitcher and bowl; a dresser with a cracked mirror; two straight chairs; net curtains; and rag rugs on the floor. I hobbled stiffly to a window.

Mountain ranges met my eyes, folded one behind the other. In the foreground, snow-covered, then with patches of green, beyond, deeper green. On the blue of the farthest summits clouds rested like wisps of cotton. I counted eleven ranges rising up and up toward the vault of the sky. The Great Smokies . . .

As I lifted my eyes to those summits, involuntarily I took a deep breath, wondering about Mr. Allen. In the face of tragedy, these mountains were whispering to me, and from that moment this became *my* view, a source of peace and strength.

The woman I had seen the night before appeared at my door. She was a tense, plain woman with sparse gray hair. She worked her thumbs restlessly back and forth against her fingers. "I'm Ida Grantland, David's sister," she said. "Did you sleep well?"

"Like a rock. Miss Grantland, tell me— How is Mr. Allen?"

"Dr. MacNeill spent the night there. Miss Henderson too. When you get, ah—changed—" and she looked pointedly at the crumpled dress I had slept in "—come on down. Miss Henderson would like to see you after breakfast." She smiled at me as she left, but the smile seemed wooden.

As I ate breakfast—hot oatmeal, buckwheat cakes and maple syrup—Miss Grantland delivered a message: "My brother David's at the Low Gap School. The school's closed, and there were some old desks we could use here." She pointed out the window to a building with an unfinished steeple. "David's working on the steeple. He can build anything he sets his hand to." That puppet's smile again. It made me feel uncomfortable. "That building will be used for school on weekdays, church on Sundays. Some of the men promised to help David haul the desks today. And believe me, he has to grab the help of these mountain men when he can get it."

David, she said, slept in a tiny bunkhouse close to the creek below—Cutter Branch—but took his meals here at the big house; Miss Alice did too, when she was in Cutter Gap and not at one of the other missions. "David begged me to keep house for him," she told me proudly. "Said he couldn't get along without me. I doubt anybody else could cook to suit him."

The side door banged and David Grantland stood in the doorway. A girl with a shock of snarled red hair peered from behind him. He crossed the room quickly, thrusting out his hand. "Miss Huddleston, great that you're here. This is Ruby Mae Morrison. She's staying with us for a while." I learned later that her stepfather had ordered her out of the cabin in a fit of anger. Since she had nowhere else to go, the mission had taken her in.

29

"Coffee, David?" his sister said.

"Shouldn't." He glanced at me and smiled. "All right, five minutes off." He eased his tall lean frame into a chair beside me. "That was quite a walk you had," he said with admiration. His brown eyes looked me over carefully, missing, I guessed, not much. Ruby Mae Morrison, too, kept her eyes on me while Mr. Grantland's five minutes stretched to ten. Then he left, saying that he would see me later.

AT MY knock, the door of Miss Henderson's cabin swung open. I saw a woman of slightly above average height, with clear, beautifully cut features. As she stared into my face, an odd look leaped into her eyes and for an instant she stood motionless. Then she realized that I was standing in the cold. "I'm so sorry," she said. "Do come in."

I was surprised at the room before me. Firelight gleamed on polished brass and the gray satin of pewter; the turkey reds and cobalt blues of handloomed materials were set off by old pine and cherry furniture. A bank of windows all across the back of the room let the towering peaks in like a gigantic mural. I had not realized how homesick I was until I felt relief pouring through me. So there was some beauty and order in the Cove!

"Let me hang up your coat, child. Does my cabin surprise you?" There was a trace of amusement in her voice.

"It's so beautiful that I want to hug it—if you could hug a room," I said. "It's like—well, like coming home."

"That's the nicest compliment my cabin's ever had. Here, sit by the fire." She sat down opposite me, still with a puzzled crease between her eyes as she regarded me. Her eyes, in which there were traces of fatigue, were a fathomless deep gray.

"Miss Henderson, how is Mr. Allen?"

"About seven this morning he opened his eyes and asked about his ailing hound dog. I think he's going to be all right. Now—tell me, why did you come to Cutter Gap?"

Surely she must be joking? But her face told me that she was not. "I thought Dr. Ferrand told you. I came to teach."

"Dr. Ferrand is a great man," she answered calmly. "But no judge of the female. What's *your* version? Why *are* you here?"

I found myself resisting the way the question was put. I told her about hearing Dr. Ferrand at Montreat, and about being so moved that I had volunteered.

"Looking back," she asked me, "do you think you were carried away by the emotion of the moment?"

"Somewhat, perhaps. But I've had plenty of time to think it over. I'd like my life to count for something more than just staying home, getting married, having babies."

Did I read cynicism in the gray eyes? No. But a down-to-earth quality that I was not accustomed to in people in religious work; too much realism for comfort. An eloquent silence now filled the room, and in that creative, listening stillness—a Quaker silence?— my mind went back to my life in Asheville. A good enough life of parties and picnics, only what did it all mean? There must be more to life than that. Or was there—for a woman? I couldn't wait until after college to find out. I had to know.

As if there had been no pause at all, Miss Henderson asked gently, "So it seemed to you that teaching school here was the next step in making your life count?"

"Well, yes. I had no other idea of anything I could do."

Miss Henderson made no comment, but I was squirming under the level gaze from those gray eyes. There was no malice in them, just a calm weighing and measuring. I longed to tell her about that feeling I'd had of some special mission to perform. *But I can't lay my fingers on what the mission is yet. So how can I talk about it?* I want my life to be full. I want to laugh—and love. Help others to the limit of my ability. But I said none of this.

As abruptly as she had embarked on the uncomfortable questions, Miss Henderson changed the subject. "You'll need some facts about your new job," she said. "School opens next Monday. Perhaps you'd like to know more about the staff and the mountain people. By the way, they dislike being called mountaineers. Better say mountain people or highlanders. Also, my friends all call me Miss Alice. Now, with your coming, we have an

31

official staff of three—David Grantland, you and me, with Dr. Ferrand in overall charge. David just graduated from seminary. He's a Pennsylvanian like me."

"How long have *you* been here, Miss Alice?"

"Almost ten years in the Smokies. And when I finally saw Cutter Gap, I loved it. I built this cabin partly to show these people how to use native materials and the old crafts of their Scottish ancestors to create beauty. I wanted a quiet spot too, where people could talk out their problems. There are plenty to talk out. The religious background here is mostly strict Calvinism. It breeds steel in folks—it's better than a wishy-washy religion that really has no convictions at all. But it's bequeathed to these people a lot of heart scalds. Fears, taboos—you can't do this and you mustn't do that or you'll go to hell."

"I hate a religion of fears," I said with feeling.

"I do too." Miss Henderson sighed. "One of our tasks here is to show folks a God who wants to give them joy. How they need joy! They have such hard lives. . . ."

"That hardness is all I've seen so far," I said.

She nodded. "At first I couldn't see anything but the dirt and the poverty either. But then something else began to come through. One day I came upon a mountain girl playing a dulcimer with a goose quill. She sang one ballad after another. Once I began to notice, I heard the old ballads everywhere, and I began to catch seventeenth-century words—a lot of them straight out of Shakespeare. These people have a fine heritage."

Mrs. Tatum had said that Miss Alice was the only person who had been able to help these proud mountain people. I saw why. She had uncovered a legitimate source of pride, and built on it.

"They have sharp minds," she was saying. "Only they haven't had much of a chance." Then she told me about some of the older mountain teachers. One had refused to believe that the earth was round; another had used just one sentence written on the blackboard—"Where will you spend eternity?"—to teach both reading and spelling.

"The people have exceptional awareness," she went on. "It

could be used to create and appreciate beauty. Instead, it is used for smallness, like easily hurt feelings. They are people with proud self-reliance and an iron will. But this will is now used mainly to keep feuds alive. We've had a lot of violence. The first thing I did here was to buy a gun and learn to shoot."

"You did! I thought Quakers believed in non-violence?"

"Of course. But I had to meet these men on their own ground, talk straight to them about pride and family loyalty. I'm a better shot than a lot of them, and they know it and respect it."

As I rose to go, Miss Alice held out her hand to me. "Christy Huddleston, I think thee will do." The warmth in her voice brought quick tears to my eyes.

CHAPTER 4

FOR THE first day of school Mr. Grantland put away his working clothes. The Tuesday before I had watched in admiration as he sat astride the rafters of the unfinished schoolhouse, driving in nails with powerful blows and shouting down orders to the few volunteers helping him. Then he had supervised the placing of the secondhand benches, battered school desks and potbellied stove. He was only seven years older than I was but he seemed a thousand years older in experience and self-assurance.

Now he wore a shirt and tie. But his heavy boots were laced almost to his knees. The dainty heels and pointed toes of my kid-and-patent-leather shoes were ludicrous in contrast as I picked my way along the boardwalk with him.

"Those are silly shoes. Ice-pick toes." His voice was teasing. "Hold on! Steady!" he exclaimed as I slipped. I could feel the warmth of his hand even through my coat.

The yard was swarming with children. They stared at me, and I saw with shock that many of them were barefooted in the snow. Suddenly I was painfully self-conscious about my foolish shoes.

A little boy came running to us. He had carrot-red hair with a

33

cowlick and gentian-blue eyes. "Teacher, I've come to swap howdys," he said.

Mr. Grantland said solemnly, "This is Little Burl Allen, a son of Bob Allen, the man who had the operation."

I reached down for the cold little hand. "I'm delighted to swap howdys with you, Little Burl." He was *so* little! I longed to pick him up and get him warm. As David Grantland and I went into the school I whispered, "Why hasn't the mission *done* something about their bare feet?"

A smile tugged at his mouth. "These youngsters have gone barefoot all their lives. And they're healthy as pigs."

The schoolroom smelled of varnish and woodsmoke, wet wool, cedar pencils and chalk. Most of the children filed up to my desk and stood gazing at me. When Mr. Grantland managed to send them away, the girls, to my surprise, seated themselves on one side of the room, the boys on the other. I found later that this was a tradition, even for adults in church.

I stood beside the battered desk on its dais and surveyed my pupils. Several—including three of the boys—seemed to be older than I was; yet there were some tiny ones, surely not more than five years old. Many had faces like tired old men and women, and several were cross-eyed. There were sixty-three children in the room. How could any teacher handle them?

Mr. Grantland introduced me, and I moved in front of the desk. "I—I'm glad to be here," I said. "Mr. Grantland, I know you have many things to do, so we won't ask you to stay."

I saw amusement in his eyes. He asked softly, "Sure you don't want me to stay?" For a moment I wavered, noticing the big boys at the back of the room. "Lundy Taylor," Mr. Grantland said, indicating a big, sullen boy, "has never been to school before—not with *Allen* children."

I did not know what he meant, but I did know that it was important that I grapple with this situation myself. I tried to put finality into my voice as I said, "Thank you."

Mr. Grantland nodded and left. I took a deep breath. All at once the children seemed like giants. I leaned against the desk for support. A little boy in the front row whispered behind his hand, "She's narvious. Look at her shakin'." He was right.

Custom required that each school day begin with a reading of Scripture and a prayer. I opened my Bible and, in a voice as firm as I could make it, read from the Twenty-fourth Psalm.

> *"Who shall ascend into the hill of the Lord?*
> *Or who shall stand in his holy place?*
> *He that hath clean hands, and a pure heart . . ."*

Then I plunged into a prayer: "We thank Thee for those who cared enough to fix up this beautiful school for us. Be with us as we begin to learn. Amen. And now we'll sing," I announced. "Let's start off with 'America.' "

"Don't recollect that 'un," said a small voice.

"You're teasing me! It goes—" Still a little trembly, I cleared my throat and sang: *"My coun-try 'tis of thee—"*

Several children were shaking their heads. "No ma'am, we're not throwin' off on you. Jest never learnt hit."

It scarcely seemed possible but this was no time to make an issue of it. "Well then, 'America the Beautiful.' "

"Vow and declare, Teacher, never heerd tell of it."

"Then what songs *do* you know?" I said desperately.

" 'When the Roll Is Called Up Yonder,' " an older girl answered. " 'Froggie Went A-Courtin' ' "—from a little fellow. " 'Oh, for a Faith That Will Not Shrink,' " said a bigger boy. " 'Sourwood Mountain,' " said another.

A chorus of yeses. "Teacher, that's the *sweepingest* song!"

Someone in the room went "Fa-sol-la" to give the pitch and they were off, the singing quite out of my hands:

> *"I've got a gal in the Sourwood Moun-tain*
> *She's so good and kind,*
> *She's broke the heart of many a poor fellow,*
> *But she's never broke this'un of mine."*

Feet tapped, fingers drummed on desks. These mountain children sang with unselfconscious charm and skill. Some sang parts:

35

> *"I've got a gal in the Buffalo Hollow,*
> *Hey-tank-toddle all the day,*
> *Oh, she won't come and I won't follow,*
> *And a hey-tank-toddle all the day."*

The children smiled broadly, and I found myself smiling back at the fun of the mountain songs. But after all the songs—innumerable verses of each one—I remembered reluctantly that my next task was to get an attendance roll. I beckoned to the mission boarder, redheaded Ruby Mae, and to two other girls. I asked them to help me get the full names of the pupils, their ages, parents' names, and where they lived. "Let's each take a row," I said. "You watch me with the first name and then you'll understand."

I began with a flaxen-haired boy who looked to be about a second-grader. He had the firmest mouth I had ever seen on a youngster. "Your name?" I said.

"Front name be Sam Houston." Long pause. "Back name be Holcombe."

"And your father's and mother's names?"

"He be John Swanson Holcombe. She's just Mama. But wimmin folks call her Lizzie."

"But she has a name. What's her *real* name?"

The small brow wrinkled. "Let me study on hit. Oh, shorely. Elizabeth Teague Holcombe," he intoned triumphantly.

I glanced at my helpers, watching me, and pushed resolutely on. Sam Houston was nine. He had never before been to school. There were five other children in the family. "Last question, Sam Houston— Your address? Tell me where you live."

"Wal— First ye cross Burning Branch. Then ye cut acrost Lonesome Pine Ridge and down. At the third fork in the trail, ye scoot under the fence and head for Pigeonroost Gap. Then ye spy our cabin, about two mile from the Spencers'."

Acutely conscious of the girls watching me, I scribbled something that made no sense even to me. Then I nodded to the girls, and they started down their rows as I went on with mine.

Although this was a somewhat unconventional roll call, it was valuable to me because the children volunteered all sorts of information. John Spencer, fifteen, had a battered plane-geometry book on his desk. "Teacher, I worked all these figgers. Could you git me a harder book?"

"I'll surely try. Have you always been good at math?"

"Yes'm. Plumb crazy about workin' figgers."

"Well, that's *great*," I said looking at him with interest as I went on to the next boy. He said that his name was Zacharias Jehoshaphat Holt—to snickers all around him.

"Now tell me your real name," I said.

"Zacharias Jehoshaphat—" His right ear jerked violently.

"Teacher, he be a-packin' lies," the boy in back of him said. "Jest look at his ear. All them Holts, when they tell a whopper, their ears twitch."

I turned again to Zacharias. "Tell me your real name."

"Zacharias"—he snickered—"Jehoshaphat—" Once again, the ear wiggled. But now I saw a string over it. Slightly unnerved, I reached over to remove it, but the boy in back jerked the string away and stuffed it in his desk.

Incensed, I marched to the desk and reached in, only to have my fingers meet a mass of wriggling fur. As I squealed and stepped backward, a raccoon clambered onto the desk and sat there looking at me from behind his funny mask of a face, one end of the cord in his mouth. Then with one paw, like a small hand, he delicately extracted the string and began scolding me.

My schoolroom was now bedlam, but the boy with the coon kept a straight face. He seemed a reincarnation of Tom Sawyer: overalls, bare feet, tousled hair, freckles. He had masterminded the whole thing, I suspected. "What's your name?" I said.

"Creed Josiah Allen. This be my pet coon, Scalawag."

"Might be a good name for you too. How old is he, Creed?"

"Got him from a kit last summer. That's like a nest, where young'uns are. Coons are the main best pets in the world. If ye'd like one fer yerself, maybe we'uns could git one for ye."

"Thanks, Creed. It's very nice of you." I wanted to make friends this first morning. "Now—about Scalawag and school—"

What could I say? Suddenly I had an inspiration. "Scalawag is such a 'specially fine coon— Let's make a pact. You leave him home after this, then bring him to the big social just before school closes. We'll make Scalawag part of the entertainment."

His face shone. "That be a sealed bargin. Land o' livin'! Pretty nigh everybody in the Cove'll see Scalawag!"

Feeling rather proud of the way I'd handled that, I went on with the roll. Zacharias Jehoshaphat was really Zacharias Holt, and the directions for getting to his cabin took an entire paragraph. Then came several O'Teales.

The last note I made for each boy was what school supplies and books he had. There was pathetically little to put down. In my row, I saw one worn copy of *Red Riding Hood,* one plane geometry, one Fowler's *Arithmetic,* a *Jack and the Beanstalk,* and a Smith's *Primary Grammar.* Obviously the matter of books and supplies was urgent, yet the parents could contribute almost nothing. And David Grantland had already brought over the few tattered textbooks that the mission owned.

As THE morning went on, I grew uneasy about the Lundy Taylor David Grantland had mentioned. Resentment of some sort smoldered in Lundy. He never joined in anything and seemed to dislike me. I forced myself to look instead at the bright, appealing children, like Little Burl Allen who twice slipped up to my desk to touch admiringly the embroidery on my shirtwaist. "Teacher, hit's a wondery sight to be-hold!" On his second trip he entreated, "Teacher, when will ye set up and sup with us? Our house is over furrenist the crik, over the ridge and down. Ye can cut through the nigh way."

"Of course I'll come," I said. "How is your father?"

"Oh Paw's head be mendin' fine now. Doc MacNeill shore fixed it good. If'n ye'll come and sup, I'll ask my Mama to make ye a Scripture cake." The blue, blue eyes were pleading.

"I'm so glad about your father. And I *will* come soon."

All morning I was conscious of the musical lilt of voices. "Teacher, ever-who seen such pretty wearin'-clothes as yours!" . . .

"Teacher, the day long you're makin' this a thronged day." ...
How could I unravel bad grammar from the picturesque idiom
that it would be a shame to change?

Next in that "thronged day" came noon recess, which the children called "the dinner spell." Even before they opened their
dinner pails, some of them organized a singing game. Their voices
were high and sweet in the crisp cold air:

"Here come five dukes, a-rovin', a-rovin', a-rovin',
Here come five dukes a-rovin', with a heigh a-ransomtee. ...

We're quite as good as you sires, one of us, sires, one of us
sires,
Pray will you have one of us sires, with a heigh a-ransomtee. ..."

"Dukes" and "sires" in these isolated mountains!

After I had eaten my basket dinner, I watched the children.
They had oak-split baskets or lard buckets with large soda biscuits, sometimes with a slice of pork between, more often with
sugar heavily sprinkled on the bread; cold roasted sweet potatoes
which they peeled and ate like bananas; corn bread; an occasional apple. Everyone drank from the same gourd in the cedar
water bucket at the back of the room. I must put a stop to that.

I began a list on a scrap of paper:

Books: Write father. Are there books from our library which the
children could use?
Solve matter of communal water bucket.
Write our minister's wife in Asheville. Perhaps ladies' societies
would help us buy textbooks and help with shoes.
Problem: How to go about grading the school?
Problem: Is sex segregation good or bad? Think through.

Suddenly I heard a screech of pain. I ran out to find tiny Vella
Holt crumpled on the ground, sobbing. "Has a pump knot on her
head," a voice volunteered as I took her in my arms.

A girl's voice added softly, "She got hit." The girl thrust a ball
into my hands. It was made of strips of cloth bound with thread.
I pushed a thumb through and found a rock at the center. I saw

Lundy Taylor and Smith O'Teale slinking into the schoolhouse.

"Did Lundy or Smith throw this?" The children did not answer, but their eyes told me the truth. As we put cloths wrung out in snow on Vella's "pump knot," I felt chilled and frightened.

From then on, the day did not go too well. For one thing, I had used up my lesson plans for the day soon after dinner. One of the chief differences between the veteran teacher and the recruit must be that the experienced can never find enough time, whereas the recruit struggles to fill the school hours.

What subjects had we not touched on today? *Penmanship!* I would put some sentences on the blackboard to be copied.

Halfway across the floor, I almost stepped on some marbles. Automatically, I stopped to pick them up. But Little Burl hurled himself toward me. "Teacher, them marbles will burn ye!"

"They was put in the stove, ma'am," John Spencer said. "Warn't me," he added. "Guess it was just foolery." Calmly, he took a rag from his pocket, picked up the marbles, and left them on my desk. In the back of the room, I heard Lundy's "He! He!"

"Look, a prank's a prank," I said. "But this wasn't funny. There are tiny, barefoot children in this room."

"And that isn't the kind of prank we're going to put up with here," David Grantland said from the doorway. He strode toward my desk, and for me, his presence filled the room. Suddenly I realized how drained I was. He stood by my side protectingly. "Recess time for you, Teacher," he said quietly.

As I gratefully turned to go, he said, "Girls and boys, I have a letter from Dr. Ferrand for the opening of school. . . ."

CHAPTER 5

I HAD BEEN teaching school for four weeks and my troubles were multiplying faster than the freckles on Ruby Mae's face. In order to handle so many children, I needed to seat the pupils of each grade together; yet over and over I was told, "No'm, I can't sit by no boy. My paw'll take me out if'n ye make this a courtin' school."

And the parents—stubborn Scots with a sprinkling of Irish and German—were equally "sot" in their insistence on Latin, when the children really needed elementary subjects. They were convinced that anyone without Latin "didn't have no l'arnin' a-tall." I had supposed that a year and a half of college would enable me to teach in a one-room country schoolhouse. Now I was terrified at the prospect of Latin.

Then there were other problems—like the pigs rooting and grunting around and under the school; the tobacco juice which marred the freshly painted walls of the schoolhouse; the crude obscene drawings on the walls of the privies. Increasingly, evidence pointed to three boys as our chief troublemakers, Lundy Taylor, Wraight Holt and Smith O'Teale.

After school I desperately needed some time to myself to take my mind off them—and Latin—but privacy was as hard to come by as four-leaf clovers in a dandelion patch, chiefly because Ruby Mae Morrison was always appearing at my bedroom door. She would stare at me and talk ceaselessly, while she fingered my possessions. If I fled from my room to escape her, she would trail me around like a devoted collie. And when I washed my clothes in the mission-house kitchen, Miss Ida Grantland would stand there, gazing at me steadily, rubbing her thumbs against her fingers, disapproval shrieking from her silence.

Mr. Grantland—now David to me—did not take his sister too seriously, and neither should I, he told me. His light approach to everything helped me hang on to my sense of humor.

At the supper table after my first school day, I had admitted my discouragement. "Well," David told me as he helped himself to more corn pudding, "I'll take over the Bible classes on top of the mathematics classes—and your advanced Latin classes. *There* you have a magnificent offer, with all I have to do. I must call on sixty families a month. Build schoolhouse-churches, barns, springhouses, roads. Preach, organize Sunday schools. Set up hayrides and stir-offs for the young folks. Shall I go on?"

"No need. I'm impressed," I told him. And I was. I asked, "Where are the barns you built?"

41

"Afraid you'd ask about that." He leaned close to me with a smile. "No barns. Just thought I'd try tossing that in for effect. Now—do you want my help?"

"As my students say, 'I do! And thank you kindly.' "

But even with David's help, I felt I had to face the fact that the school was too much for an inexperienced teacher. Perhaps I had made a mistake.

ONE AFTERNOON after an especially exhausting day, I thought that a walk would clear my head. The snow was beautiful, a pristine white, pure and sparkling, until just ahead of me on the road I saw dark blobs marring the whiteness. As I got closer, I saw that some poor little rabbit had been caught by another animal and literally torn to bits.

I skirted the spot and walked on down the road, wishing my mind were a slate so that with one swipe I could wipe off what I had just seen. Instead, a train of kindred memories came rushing in—like a tomcat streaking across our lawn in Asheville with a baby squirrel in his mouth, the squirrel crying in pathetic, high-pitched squeals of protest at death. Why did nature have such a vicious, tooth-and-claw aspect? I tried to think of other things. . . .

I was passing the O'Teales' barn then and Mrs. O'Teale hallooed. I was in no mood to pay a call, but there was no escaping.

The O'Teale cabin was even more unkempt than the others I had seen. There were rags and junk in the yard, and no effort had been made to stack the firewood which lay in wild disarray where it had been tossed. There was human filth along with the animal. *Isn't there an outhouse?* I thought. *Aren't they teaching the children anything?*

Mrs. O'Teale (whose first name, Swannie, did not seem to suit her) was obviously flattered by what she thought a deliberate visit from the new teacher. "Come in and set," she said warmly. She was tall and slender, with stringy, dirty blond hair.

Inside the cabin there was a terrible stench. I saw a penned-off area in a corner, as if for some pet animal. The back door slammed, and a hulking boy in his teens shuffled into the room, staring at me with vacant eyes. He wore only a tattered sweater that came almost to his knees and his hair was long and matted. Empty desolation looked out of his eyes. "That thar's Wilmer, my firstborn," Mrs. O'Teale said matter-of-factly.

The boy pointed to some corn bread. "Um-humh. Oo-anh."

"Hongry? Wal, don't squawk." Swannie O'Teale thrust the plate into his hands, and he crammed a fistful of corn bread into his mouth. "Wal now," she said, "that should keep Wilmer from starvin'. And how are my young'uns doin' in school?"

I hedged. "It's probably a little too soon to tell. It takes a while to get accustomed to a new teacher."

"Aye. One teacher from the level lands left, sayin' she weren't gonna put up with boy-persons a-flashin' knives at her."

There was a loud clatter, and I jumped. Wilmer had finished and dropped the tin plate. He bared his teeth in a caricature of a grin. I was revolted and then ashamed of my revulsion. The boy shuffled across the room to a pile of glistening rocks and pieces of metal and glass beside the pen.

"'Course sometimes Wilmer takes a notion to run off," Mrs. O'Teale said. "Then we'uns have a time findin' him. Don't want him to git ahold of a rifle-gun or fall off'n the moun-tain. When he takes fits like that, we fence him in." Animal grunts came from the corner as Wilmer sat on the floor playing with his rocks.

I risked a question. "Has he always been like this?"

"Yes'm. Since he was birthed. But he's a good boy."

I could not sort out my feelings. Compassion for Mrs. O'Teale and for her boy rose in me. Yet I dared not express it, for she would wonder *why* I felt sorry for her. I swallowed a nauseous lump in my throat and rose. "I must be going," I said. "Next time I'll be able to tell you more about the schoolwork."

I left, and the minute I was out of sight, I lifted my skirts and ran wildly down the road, detouring the dead rabbit. At the mission house, I dashed up to my bedroom, changed all my clothes, and brushed my hair by an open window so the clean mountain air could pour through it. Then I washed my face and hands over and over before I went down to supper.

There was nothing wrong with Miss Ida's salmon croquettes, but tonight my stomach was churning. Through a haze I saw Miss Alice looking at me questioningly. I managed to blurt out, "Excuse me—" as I fled toward the yard. Moments later I felt Miss Alice's firm cool hands on my head. "Go ahead, be sick, Christy. Thee will feel better." When it was finally over, she asked, "Where were you this afternoon?"

"O'Teales'." My voice sounded weak and far away.

"Oh—no wonder. That's the worst place of all."

She came back with me to my bedroom. When she sat down on the edge of the bed, I blurted out, "Father was right. I don't belong here. I'm going back home. Miss Alice, I'm sorry about the children." Then I started crying.

She let me sob, not protesting my leaving or asking questions. In the end, her silence was eloquent. I lifted my head and tossed my tousled hair out of my wet eyes to look at her. The gray eyes looked back calmly. "Am I wrong to feel this way?" I asked, suddenly unsure of myself.

"Any sensitive person would feel exactly as thee feels." The voice was crisp. "Now is a good time to decide whether you'll go home or not—provided you make your decision on the way life really is."

"Not much of life can be as bad as what I saw today."

"You'd be surprised. Every bit of life, every single one of us has a dark side," she retorted. "When we leave home, we are venturing out of our ivory tower. And a lot of us want to run back to a shelter in a hurry."

"Did *you* ever want to run back?"

"Certainly. At sixteen I had, shall we say, a difficult experience—so difficult that I didn't ever again want to see dirt, or blood, or disease, or cruelty, or death. But ever since God has been gently prying my hands off my eyes, plunging me over and over into situations where I had to see reality."

"Bad situations? Really bad?"

"Yes, really bad. Like the crippled nine-year-old girl who was beaten, then raped, by her mother's lover. She died next day."

My horror must have shown, but Miss Alice took no notice. "Or the day I discovered a woman swinging from the rafters in a cabin on Hog Back Mountain. When I asked her imbecile husband why he had done it, he said, 'A woman what can't stand hangin' a few hours ain't no woman a-tall.'

"You're sensitive. Remember, I said it was God who was prying my hands off my eyes. As if He were saying, 'You've got to see life as it really is before you can *do* anything about evil.' He is always there beside me, looking at the dreadful sights with compassion and heartbreak."

"How *could* God stand by and watch a little girl raped and a woman hanged? How could He?"

"I think God *had* to give us free choice—the privilege of going His way or refusing. And He's specific about going His way." She ticked the points off on her fingers: "Do good. Be merciful. And best of all, *Give, and it shall be given unto you; good measure, pressed down, and shaken together, and running over* . . . But all that plenty doesn't become ours until we drive in our stake, on a particular promise to indicate that we *accept* that gift. That, Christy, is called claiming."

A wonderful smile lit her face. "Christy, if we're going to work on God's side, we have to open our hearts to grief and pain, for He suffers more than any of us. And at the point where His ultimate in love meets His total capacity to feel our agony—there the miracle happens—and the exterior situation changes. I've *seen* that miracle." Looking at my puzzled expression, she added quietly, "Christy, all of us have watched love's mending power in small situations. What I'm talking about is a vast multiplication of that power."

She smiled at me and fell into one of her Quaker silences. I wished I knew how she had come to terms with life. She said at last, "You're terribly important. Each of us is. We're all unique. If you don't do the work that's been given you to do, that work may never be done." She rose to go. "It's late and you're tired. But here's the question for you to sleep on. Were you supposed to come here, Christy? Or were you running away from home?"

I AWOKE TO A sunshiny morning, feeling so happy that I had trouble remembering what I had been so gloomy about the night before. Somehow, some way in the night behind me, I had decided that this Cove was my Cove. These children were my children. Little as I had to give, I had to give it here. I rested my forehead on the cold wood of the window frame and looked out at the far peaks. I said inside myself, "Dear God, maybe I *was* partly running off from home for freedom and adventure. But if You can use me here in this Cove, well, here I am."

I went to the schoolroom eagerly. In an effort to understand "my" children better, I had assigned the older ones a theme: "What I Want to Do When I Grow Up." That morning I found that the themes were even more revealing than I had imagined.

Clara Spencer wrote:

> . . . When I grow up, I want to have a lot of shoes. Three pairs even. And I want a fine house with enough pans to cook in and a rug on the floor to sink my toes in.

Rob Allen had different dreams:

> . . . Sometimes I get to feeling lonesome. I want to tell my thoughts, my good thoughts on the inside, to somebody without being laughed at. It would pleasure me to know the right way to put things like that on paper for other people too. . . ."

Ruby Mae wanted to have lots of pretty shirtwaists like "Teacher," and Smith O'Teale wanted to go to the level lands and get a fine job. But Wraight Holt's theme sounded a false note:

> I disgust being a slickfaced boy and want to be a masterest man-person now. I wud be proud for a woman grown something like you are to claim me for her feller . . .

Hastily, I thrust it under some papers. But color had flooded my face, and the three boys at the back of the room were smirking.

Why were these boys in school anyway? I knew that the Allens and Taylors had been feuding for a long time, and that this was the first time Bird's-Eye Taylor, Lundy's father, had let Lundy come to school with Allen children. David had said that Miss Alice's teaching about forgiveness might finally be making a dent, but I had a reluctant conviction that something else was afoot.

Meanwhile, the themes dramatized the poverty of the Cove. And the mission reflected this poverty. One day I walked through the mission house, notebook and pencil in hand, making lists—for there had always been the thought of taking in a few pupils as boarders for the worst months when snow and sleet made attendance spotty. But I found that we would need mattresses, blankets, kitchen supplies—even money to buy food.

My thoughts went on to the yard. The mission did not own a horse—only old Theo, the mule. Buying a horse could not be postponed much longer, but a good one cost about a hundred dollars.

That night, my thoughts about our needs carried over into my own kind of prayer. . . . "Lord, Miss Alice said that if we give, it shall be given unto us. Well, I don't have her faith, Lord, in You. Can You help me with my faith (I hope it isn't wrong to ask this) by giving unto the mission 'good measure'? Maybe even a horse? Or—or anything else on the list?"

Three days later Mr. Pentland brought me a letter postmarked Plainfield, New Jersey. As I opened it, a check for one hundred and six dollars dropped into my lap. Wonderingly, I read:

Dear Miss Huddleston:

I have just returned from a visit in Asheville, where I met your mother at a tea. She told me—most charmingly—about your fascinating pupils and their needs. On the journey home, I could not get them off my mind. Then waiting for me at home was an unexpected dividend check!

My husband and I are tithing this year as we feel led, and my heart tells me that the enclosed check belongs to your work. I send it with real joy.

Yours most sincerely,
Lucy Mae Furnam

It was for the horse! I heard David's voice in the kitchen and ran there. I showed him the check. "Isn't it *great!*" I said. Then I added shyly, "David, it's—well, you see, Miss Alice believes that the things that are promised in the Bible are there for us to claim. So—I found a special promise and I asked God to send us a horse. So David, this is it. This is *it!*"

David's voice was gentle. "Christy, do you honestly think Mrs. Furnam sent this check as the direct result of your prayers? It's only a coincidence. Nice though. Hope we *can* use it for a horse."

When I told Miss Alice that David thought the check was just a coincidence, she said, "No. I think you reached out for faith in the best way you knew. And I think you got your answer."

"Oh, Miss Alice!" I hugged her.

NOT LONG afterward David and Sam Houston's father, John Holcombe, a sharp trader, bought Prince, a black stallion with a white star on his forehead, a long silky mane and a flowing tail.

"Roughly three dollars more than the check," David reported to me later. "If we were going by the gospel according to Christy, Prince plus his saddle should have cost *exactly* one hundred and six dollars, not one penny more. Some angel got his figures garbled. Anyway, I made up the small difference."

But David's teasing could not deflate me. From being weak, my faith now knew no bounds. Mother had been sending me her *Ladies' Home Journal* each month, and one night as I browsed through an idea struck me. What about asking the advertisers to contribute some of their products to our mission? After many tries, I evolved a letter describing our work, and over the next few days, I wrote firms that manufactured needed items from mattresses to soap. I asked Bell Telephone to donate equipment for a telephone, and I wrote to Lyon & Healy for a piano. I hoped that I was not overdoing it.

THE NEXT night, Ruby Mae Morrison was sitting in my bed-room while I tried to comb out her tangled red hair. "How long has it been since you combed this hair, Ruby Mae?" I said.

"Factually, I lost my onliest tuckin' comb," she answered sadly. "Be tickled with braids. But ye'd have t'learn me how."

"Braiding's easy. I'll teach you."

And that was not the only thing I'd have to teach her. She washed her face and hands a few times a week—never a full bath—with the result that it was not pleasant to be near her. I had dodged and fled her until I realized that there was no escape. One of the sayings from Miss Alice's Quaker Meeting was apropos: "That person is meant to be my bundle." Ruby Mae was clearly my bundle.

Even more disturbing to me than her slovenliness was her chattering. I remembered another of Miss Alice's teachings: "God can use even our annoyances to bring us a blessing. Thank Him for whatever happens, no matter how disagreeable it seems."

I decided to try it. Feeling foolish, I made myself say, "I thank You that Ruby Mae talks so much." And to my astonishment, I began to *hear* what she was saying. It was a priceless opportunity to get inside the mountain mind.

To Ruby Mae, Miss Alice was incredibly wealthy. "Independent rich, she is. Paid cash-money for this land. Built this here mission house—so tall, one house a-top another house same as a stack cake. And swear to Josh-way, if she didn't put shiny glass windows in her cabin too, to let the sun through."

Even more wonderful to Ruby Mae were the deep wells for the mission and Miss Alice's cabin, with pumps beside the kitchen sinks! Miss Alice had insisted on other unprecedented things, like having yard springs covered over. She told the mountain people they could get sick from dirty water, might even get the dread typhoid.

And Miss Alice, a woman, had started a worship service. "First off, folks was scandalized," Ruby Mae reminisced. "Old men used t'snort, 'Nothin' outside the house and yard be fittin' for wimmin.' But Miz Henderson paid them no mind, and in no time folks said, 'The string of her talk is good. I confidence the way she jest talks quiet but faces us down. She says things I can think on while I'm a-doin' up my work.'" For a few, Miss Alice's concept that happiness was not a sin or a "worldly pleasure" was taking root. Timidly, some of the women were reaching out for a God of love.

CHAPTER 6

FROM UPSTAIRS I heard a banging on the door. As I ran downstairs, Ruby Mae called, "This here's Bessie Coburn's paw." Bessie was Ruby Mae's best friend.

"Howdy, ma'am," Mr. Coburn said. "Stopped to tell ye about Tom McHone's baby—she quit breathin' last night. Opal's carryin' on right bad. Miss Henderson's over to the Big Lick Spring mission, so Opal says would ye fix up the baby real pretty?"

Me? But I had never even seen anyone who had died, let alone prepared a body. I stammered, "Of course I'll come."

I found a baby dress in the mission's used-clothing box, and some ribbons that had decorated going-away gifts from friends in Asheville. I added a cake of soap, clean rags, safety pins, a needle and thread, and set out with Ruby Mae.

The McHones' cabin stood in the horseshoe bend of a wide creek, near several immense old trees. It was built on posts, in two sections, with a dogtrot in between. We walked across the listing porch and Mrs. McHone, a spare, drawn young woman, received us warmly, eager to talk. "The baby cried somethin' awful all night, so we thought it was liver-growed."

"Mrs. McHone, what's liver-grown?"

"Lots of babies has it. You take the baby by the left heel and right hand and make them tetch. Then you take the left hand and right heel. If'n they won't tetch, you know hit's liver-growed. Then you got to force the hand and heel to tetch. When I pulled, the baby hollered and went limp as a rag doll. Give her tea all night long, but nothin' holped. Jest afore the sunball come up, she quit breathin'." She was crying quietly now, wiping her eyes with her apron. She led us inside the house and pointed to the little body lying on a large bed.

The horror sickened me. The baby must have had cruel internal injuries. Yet Opal McHone had acted out of love. For the first time in my life, I knew grief. I had had childish disappointments, hurt pride, even a sense of loss. But these had been super-ficial emotions because they were self-centered. This was the first bitter taste of a grief not my own.

Tom McHone diffidently shook my hand. Then an older man, Uncle Bogg, Tom's father, smiled at me. I had heard of Uncle Bogg. He was shiny-bald on top, but what hair remained was long and curled jauntily over his ears, giving him a puckish look. A Roman nose, deep creases around his eyes, and stubble on his chin completed an amazing picture.

Opal McHone sat on the edge of the bed and watched while Ruby Mae and I washed the ivory body. The baby's eyelids were transparently thin with the fine lines of blue veins still showing. The little mouth was open slightly. "Hit was the Lord's will," Opal said. "The Lord giveth and the Lord taketh away. . . ."

I bit my lips to keep from saying what I was thinking. As I took one of the tiny hands in mine to wash it, I wanted to lash out against something, somebody. Dr. MacNeill—why wasn't he *teaching* these mothers?

Three men appeared at the cabin door. "We've come to see the fancy layin' out," one said thickly. All three were obviously drunk. Trying to ignore them, I turned back to my task.

"Come on in, if'n ye must," Uncle Bogg said, "but don't bother Miz Christy." He made no effort to introduce them.

"Now ain't them ribbons purty!" The tallest man, heavily bearded, leaned over the bed. He smelled of home-brewed liquor. I recognized Bob Allen's brother Ault.

The room was growing dark, but no one thought of lighting lamps. When I had dressed the baby, Mrs. McHone cradled the little body in her arms. "No baby in the Cove has ever had ribbons afore. So purty! Oh, Miz Christy, I'm obleeged to you!"

I groped for something comforting to say. "Maybe—maybe you'll have another baby girl sometime."

Ault Allen laughed uproariously. "That oughten to be hard. Breedin's easy for Tom."

"You can jest shut up," Uncle Bogg said. "You're drunk. This ain't no time for talk like that."

I said, "If there's nothing else I can do . . ."

"I'll see ye to the aidge of the woods," Uncle Bogg said. He watched the drunken men slip out the door. Then he lit a lantern and took a rifle from its rack, and we started out. At the edge of the clearing, he stood listening intently. I heard nothing unusual, but he said with sudden vehemence, "I'm a-goin' with ye to the mission." And he set off, walking briskly between Ruby Mae and me. Soon we saw that he was taking a different way back to the mission, through great pillared tulip trees, the bare branches ghostly in the twilight. He kept throwing the lantern light to one side, then to the other, his eyes searching the woods.

A twig snapped to our left. The old man stopped and put the lantern down, his gun instantly in position. But our straining ears heard only the eerie cry of a hoot owl. "Thought I heerd a varmint," he explained.

"Thought I seen a shadder movin'—there!" Ruby Mae whispered, sidling closer to Uncle Bogg.

The old man raised the lantern. "Lots of shadders. C'mon." He quickened his pace. "Miz Christy, onybody told ye about our tall cornstalk?"

"No." I was delighted to sense a tall tale coming.

"Wal—our family was all out on the porch 'bout the crack of dawn one mornin' shellin' a turn of seed corn when Opal called us to breakfast. I drapped my ear of corn off'n the porch, and after we'd et, I saw the corn had fell into the pig trough. Water had done swelled up one of the grains to 'bout as big as a small apple. I put that big one in my pocket.

"Went on down to the field to plant the seed corn. Swear-r-r, that grain had swelled big as a ball. Set it at the aidge of the field. Got all the corn in and went to look at that grain. Hit had swelled so, looked big as a pumpkin. Must have weighed nigh on thirty pound." The story was rolling out exuberantly now, and I realized that he was deliberately trying to divert us.

"Wal—I dug a good-size hole for it, rolled that grain in, stomped the dirt down on it, turned to go, when a-whammity-bang, heard somethin' behind me. That stalk of corn had shot out'n the ground and was already ten foot or so in the air. In two weeks hit was as tall as a oak. Every blade was 'bout a hundred foot from the ground. Come cuttin' time me and Tom and Jeb Spencer spent all day hackin' at that cornstalk. 'Bout sundown it started a-fallin'. Heard the stalk hit the ground about midnight.

" 'Bout day-bust, we walked up to see which-a-way it had fell. Couldn't see the end of it. That cornstalk was lyin' yander acrost the Tennessey-North Carolina line and the county sheriffs were gatherin'. We run home like streaks of greased lightnin'. . . . Mission house jest around the bend," Uncle Bogg ended blithely. He had brought us all through the woods without our knowing it.

As we reached the mission yard, David came striding out. "*Am* I glad to see you! Uncle Bogg, thanks for walking them home."

The old man set the lantern on the ground and let go a stream of tobacco juice. "While Miz Christy was layin' out Opal's baby, some neighbor-men come in. And then some—"

"Hold the story a minute, Uncle Bogg." David turned to us. "Girls, Ida has waited supper for you." As we went in, I heard them talking, but what they were saying, we could not hear.

DAVID and I set out through the woods and along cliffs to the Lufty Branch Church, where he was going to preach. I was riding Theo, the mission mule, for Prince was too spirited for me. My long riding skirt was draped over the mule's belly, amost dragging the ground, and David grinned at me as we rode. But when he spoke, his tone was serious. "Christy, don't take any more trips away from the mission without me. The other night, it wasn't those drunks who followed you through the woods. It was men Uncle Bogg had never seen here before."

"But what would strangers want in Cutter Gap?"

"That's what I intend to find out," David said grimly.

We rode on in silence, across a dangerously narrow ledge and through stands of virgin timber—tulip trees, giant beeches and red spruce. When we came to Big Spoon Creek, plunging down the mountain across our path, David halted on the bank. "I'll go first," he said, "and hope Prince will set an example for old Theo."

The stallion stepped confidently into the water, paused to drink. Then he plunged on and splashed up the opposite bank.

I urged Theo after him, and everything went well until we were almost in the middle of the creek. Then suddenly I felt icy water on my legs as the mule's legs slid from under him. Finally I jumped off, and with water almost to my waist and my wet skirts tugging me downstream, I managed to struggle to shore. David pulled me up on the bank. My teeth were chattering, and he began rubbing my hands between his. "We've got to do something for you in a hurry. Doc MacNeill's cabin is somewhere near." By now Theo was across the creek. We went up the narrow trail and came to the Doctor's cabin, silvery gray against the shadows of Green Ridge.

The door opened and Dr. MacNeill appeared. He was wearing brown corduroys and a plaid hunting shirt, open at the neck. I got the same impression of overflowing vitality that I'd had in the Spencers' cabin. "Anything wrong?" he said at once.

"Nothing serious. Christy got soaked in the creek. Could we dry her out by your fire?"

Again that curious look he had had when he first saw me came into the Doctor's eyes. "Come on in," he said.

Inside, I saw that this was strictly a man's place. There were deer heads on the walls, a bearskin rug on the hearth, and a great many framed pictures, mostly men. "Those clothes mustn't dry on you," the Doctor said. "Let's see what I can find." He turned abruptly toward a closed door, took a key out of his pocket, unlocked the door, entered and closed the door behind him.

I sank down on a stool by the fire and looked around the room. On a table was a man's pipe. I picked it up and looked at a wide silver band on the stem. It was engraved: *Tha mo chos air ceann mo naimhdean.* Puzzled, I laid the pipe down. On the other side of the fireplace was a woman's low chair with a dainty spindled back. On the mantel, a clock was inscribed: *London—1783.*

"Think you could get into this?" Dr. MacNeill had come back and was holding up a flower-sprigged muslin dress; other garments were over his arm. The door had been closed again.

56

"Oh, yes!" With difficulty I restrained my curiosity.

"Better slip out of those wet shoes too. Here's a pair of my carpet slippers."

I went to the room he indicated, and he shut the door after me. It was his bedroom. There was a pine four-poster bed with a gray-white homespun spread hastily pulled up over the voluminous featherbed, a cherry chest of drawers, an open cupboard with medical books, a small wooden chest, and a hooked rug.

I spread the garments on the bed. The dainty underclothes were of fine lawn trimmed with handmade lace and ribbon. They fitted as though they had been made for me. As I put on the dress, a fragrance of woodruff came from it. Back in the living room, I said, "These are perfect!" I put my wet clothes to dry by the fire.

David said, "Christy, you can't go out in this weather in a muslin dress. You stay here and I'll make excuses for you at Lufty Branch. By the time I get back, your skirt will be dry." I agreed reluctantly, and David left.

ALONE with Dr. MacNeill, I felt ill at ease, for there were contradictions in this man and his surroundings. He seemed of the mountains, yet strangely not of them. Why did he practice medicine here, and yet let things go on as before—like that liver-grown superstition that had killed the McHone baby? Why the locked door in a community where most people scarcely bothered to shut their front doors? And to whom had these clothes belonged?

"You're a silent one, for a female." The deep voice broke into my thoughts. "I'm going to fix you a hot grog."

"Please don't! I don't like the taste."

"Then call it medicine, insurance against any effects from your swim in the creek."

It was useless to protest; Dr. MacNeill had a dominating way about him. As he took a pewter jug from a shelf, mixed the grog and placed it close to the fire, I studied his face. In profile it was as rugged as if the features had been chiseled out of stone. But the hazel eyes were perceptive, their corners crisscrossed with smile lines, and he had a sensitive mouth.

"Drink that." He thrust the pewter mug at me.

Dutifully I raised the mug to my lips but did not drink the bitter stuff. "Dr. MacNeill, I'm confused about something."

A smile pulled at his mouth. "What do you mean?"

Now that I had taken the plunge, I was embarrassed. "Oh, lots of things. Like the McHone baby dying," I blurted out.

Suddenly the Doctor seemed preoccupied with filling his pipe. His deliberation was maddening. "You've a lot to learn about the mountain people," he said finally. "I've known Opal all my life. Her granny was revered here as an herbalist. Some of her knowledge was sound enough, some of it nonsense—like the liver-grown ailment. But granny's word is gospel. Opal won't listen to me when my word crosses granny's." He paused. There was an almost imperceptible change in his expression. "I can guess your next question. About the dress. It belonged to my wife. She died three years ago in childbirth with the baby—typhoid complications."

"Oh, I'm sorry." I wanted to ask if the locked room had been hers, but his manner told me the subject was closed.

"As for me," he went on, "I'm a hillbilly, born in this cabin like my parents and my grandparents. When I was sixteen, a group of New York physicians came here on a hunting trip. My uncle was their guide and I helped carry their gear. For some reason they took a liking to me. When they found out that I had ambitions to be a doctor, they made college and medical school possible. I went to Jefferson Medical College, then got my bedside training at Jefferson Hospital. Those pictures are of some of the doctors. Great men. I owe them everything."

I rose to look at the pictures and the Doctor came and stood just behind me. I felt his breath on my neck. Abruptly, I walked over to the pictures on the other wall. "And this one?"

"That's Starr Gatlin who demonstrated the brain surgery I performed on Bob Allen. Isn't often tried now, but it was used fairly often by pioneer doctors for survivors of Indian scalpings."

"I didn't know anybody survived Indian scalpings."

"Oh, a few. The frontier doctors bored a series of holes with a straight awl until they drew blood to the surface. That caused the scalp to grow again—in time. They did it without ether. Anyone who lived through being scalped was strong enough to stand a little more."

I had had enough of scalping. "When Mary Allen hove that axe into the floor, what was that about?" I asked.

He smiled. "An axe is supposed to keep a person from hemorrhaging. The string around Bob's wrist was to keep disease away." He tapped the tobacco out of his pipe. "Let's get back to the medical situation in the Cove," he said. "I'm here because of a rainy May afternoon I spent with Starr Gatlin. I had three offers for a beginning practice, and I was torn about where my duty lay. But by the time I had talked myself out with Starr Gatlin, I knew what I had to do. I knew how desperately these people needed a doctor—last year I was out on calls one hundred and seventy-four nights—and I wouldn't have been happy anywhere else. Some of the men I interned with will probably be as famous as Gatlin. I follow their careers with interest, rejoice in their success." He indicated the pictures again. "They're the ones who make it possible for me to supply necessary drugs and medicine to my patients."

He rose and put another log on the fire. Then he stood on the hearth, absently squeezing his hair in his fingertips. "You wonder why I'm not reforming things around here. You're young, and you feel things strongly. Well, I know things are bad—but these people can't be changed all at once. They have their own timing. Last week Uncle Bogg was talking to me about a Northern lumber company which is trying to buy up land. 'All the trouble them outlanders are makin' for us tryin' to git our land, that ain't so bad by itself,' Uncle Bogg said. 'But hit's comin' right on top of the Civil War that seems more'n we can stand.'"

I couldn't help laughing, and the Doctor went on, "Anyway, we've a worse problem here than dirt, and that's rooting out the hates that lead to killings. Take the Taylor-Allen feud. It started in 1879 with a land-boundary dispute. Since then nine men have been killed. And out of nine murders and several woundings, nobody's been convicted." He smiled at me. "Your eyes are very expressive, Miss Huddleston. They tell me you don't believe me."

I was trying to absorb this. "But—how did they get off?"

"Because family loyalty comes before everything else here—including the law. Families plot for years to get one of their clan elected a judge, sheriff, or what we call a county squire—the local title for a justice of the peace. If the squire lets a case get to trial, juries put family ahead of everything else too. The El Pano district has elected the same county squire for eighteen years and there hasn't been a sentence for murder in all that time. He's Uncle Bogg McHone."

I was shocked. "You can't be serious! He seems so likable."

"I like him too. But he thinks our family quarrels are our own business. If he didn't feel that way, he'd never have been re-elected seventeen times." The Doctor walked over to look out the front window. "If you really want reform here, stopping the feuding is a fertile field for your mission." There was something close to contempt in his voice as he said "your mission," as if it was far removed from his sphere of activity. "I agree with you," he added, "that it would be pleasant for me to teach mothers how to take care of babies instead of my having to suture slashed abdomens and operate on half-gouged-out eyes."

He heated some coffee in an old white enamelware coffeepot, and as we drank it, David walked in. I was startled that so much time had passed. I dressed again in my own clothes and David insisted that I ride Prince across Big Spoon Creek. On the trail home, I asked David how much he knew about the murders.

"Enough," he said. "The Doc is right. My mind's been wrestling about the mission's responsibility. I may have to rip open the subject from the pulpit soon, though that could be—dangerous."

"David, about Dr. MacNeill. I still don't see how he can go into these cabins year after year and leave them in such bad shape as always. He's a strange one. I don't think I like him."

"That's not fair, Christy. I've spent some evenings with Neil MacNeill, talking. Good talk, too. His ancestors, incidentally, were a distinguished family—the MacNeills of the Island of Barra. Their castle is still there. Get Miss Alice to tell you the story."

SIX OF Miss Ida's hot buckwheat cakes—David was enjoying his breakfast. I poured him a second cup of coffee. "When you have something important to say to a man," my mother said, "never say it to a hungry one." This should be the moment.

"David," I said, "I've gotten notice of some shipments at El Pano—for the mission." I tried to sound casual. "Just a few things." I traced the pattern in the tablecloth with a finger. "A Harvester wagon, and, uh—a grand piano."

"A *what?*" He pushed his chair back and looked at me. "Get that pleading look out of those big eyes! Now what is this about?"

I told him about writing to businessmen about donating products, and that I never expected Lyon & Healy to send a *concert* grand. When I finished, David laughed. "How many letters have you written, Christy?"

"Thirty-eight. I've had—let me think—twenty donations. Mattresses, soap, paints, window shades, soup . . ."

Poor David! For the next few weeks, hauling freight from El Pano took most of his time and the steeple-building was delayed. Three bedsteads arrived, and soon Miss Ida complained that she couldn't get around the kitchen because of the cases of soup, evaporated milk, baked beans, and cocoa. "David," she fumed, "you've got to find somewhere else to dump all this paraphernalia."

But the back porch was already heaped high with the cartons of pins, insulators, and the wire from the telephone company. A lot of wire was needed for seven miles.

Then the piano arrived. It took two pairs of oxen hitched to the new wagon to pull it, and David and three mountain men spent two days getting it across the mountains. It was given a place of honor in the almost empty living room.

After supper that day, Miss Alice said to me, "Christy, I'm forced to tell you that Dr. Ferrand and I don't like begging. We believe that people must freely choose, without pressure, to make a gift. Most of those never-ending pleas for funds from charitable organizations and pulpits are trying to pry money out of people by riding roughshod over their right of choice. And Christy, all of us had the right to be consulted about procedure here. I don't think this going ahead on your own was good teamwork."

I gulped back several explanations, for I knew she was right. I had gone running off on my own, and David had said that if he was expected to string telephone wire across two mountains, a creek and a river, I might at least have talked it over with him before writing the Bell Company. I had just thought that if David could build a school, he would have no problem installing one little telephone.

Woefully, I acknowledged I had been impulsive and thoughtless, but that did not stop boxes and barrels from continuing to arrive. Evening after evening we unpacked them.

One evening it was several boxes of secondhand books and clothing from my Asheville church. David unpacked the books first, and they were fine; most could be used at the school. Then he began pulling out clothes. He held up a heavily beaded party dress. "Oh-h! It's beau-ti-ful." Ruby Mae reached out eager hands for it.

"*Perfect* for hoeing," David said. "What have we next?" He pulled out a pink corset with many stays and teasingly draped it prominently over a chair. Next came a swallowtail coat and—as I felt increasingly let down—a series of ladies' hats, with aigrettes, velvets, veiling. David twirled one on his finger—a straw with red roses so wired that a cluster towered above the hat. "Hey, model this, Christy," he said and shoved it down on my hair.

The brim was over my eyes and I could feel the tower of roses vibrating in the air. It was a relief to laugh, and soon all of us—including Miss Alice—were caught up in the hilarity. Each item out of that barrel was more ludicrous than the last: a moth-eaten muff; a ruffled nightcap; a pillow top, souvenir of Niagara Falls; ladies' chemises; and men's vests.

The third barrel was better, with lots of children's shoes; but mixed in with them were ladies' shoes with high heels and pointed toes, some satin.

Miss Alice said that it would not do to give any of the clothes away, since mountain people didn't want to be beholden; so David decided to set up store in his little house, one afternoon a week. We could charge seventy-five cents for a good suit or dress. And since cash was so short in the Cove, we could take produce in exchange when it was necessary.

The store caused immediate excitement. To our astonishment, the first items to go were the ones we had thought useless. Every woman wanted a fancy city dress, every man a vest to wear on top of faded, patched overalls. Bob Allen wore a swallowtail coat as he tended mill, and high-heeled satin shoes filled with sand were used as door stops in many a mountain cabin. Soon the mission was drowning in sorghum and sauerkraut, which became the principal media of exchange. There were nights when David stealthily buried gallons of sauerkraut in the backyard.

EVERY Monday morning handed me problems for which no teacher's training course could ever have prepared me. First of all were the smells—the odor of children who did not take baths during the cold months and who, if they owned any underwear, usually had it sewn on for the winter. I carried a perfumed handkerchief up my sleeve and pulled it out to dab at my nose when they came too near. How I rued that sensitive nose of mine! I felt like crying out, "Please, God, change my nose—or help me get the children clean in a hurry."

Finally, I sent away for hygiene textbooks, and gave the class a health lesson each day. We talked about the necessity of washing, getting down to *how* to bathe since most of them had only a granite tub or pan to use in front of a fire. Another day the lesson would be about drinking water and the dangers of typhoid and hookworm. The children often went to the bathroom in a mountain stream, so I spoke candidly.

When I saw how much the girls were copying me, I tried to be even more meticulous about grooming. Soon Lizette Holcombe, Bessie Coburn, Ruby Mae and Clara Spencer were asking me if they could take a bath or wash clothes in the mission house. Since

Miss Ida did not take kindly to this, they used my room and I kept a can of violet-scented talc on hand for them.

As time went on, I came to know the children and to think of them as persons rather than names. When I began to love them, the odors ("funks," my children said) were no longer so much of a problem for me. When love came in the front door, my preoccupation with bad smells crept out the rathole.

A problem of a different sort was the plight of those pupils, like Lundy Taylor, who were far behind their age group in everything. And I felt equally sorry about a child like Mountie O'Teale. When Mountie tried to speak, she grunted and croaked like an animal. She never showed any emotion whatever. She seemed dead inside.

One afternoon I caught Creed Allen and her own brother Smith teasing her. On the playground they bent a sycamore sapling into a bow, lured her by, then released the branch to hit her in the face. When she started crying they chanted in unison:

> *"Mush-mouthed Millie,*
> *Can't even speak. . . ."*

Since I was trying not to interfere too often on the playground, I waited to see what would happen. Mountie did not tell on the boys, but I saw misery staring out of her eyes. So she *was* able to feel, feel deeply. Perhaps Mountie might turn out to be the white lamb of the O'Teale family. But what to do for her?

It may be that my wondering constituted a sort of prayer. But prayer—that is, the kind that asks for help with some particular problem—was still new to me.

I waited for an opportunity to do something special for her, and the chance came one day when I noticed that the shabby coat she wore to school had no buttons. During recess, I dashed to the mission house, got some buttons from Miss Ida's button box, sewed them on, then hung the coat back on the peg.

After school, Mountie came bouncing up to my desk, gleefully pointing to the buttons. "Teacher, see my pretty buttons!"

I could scarcely believe it. The child was speaking plainly for the first time. As I pondered this, I wondered if Mountie's speech defect had an emotional basis. Perhaps what she needed was to be sure that someone loved her for herself.

I decided to give her—privately, after school—a red scarf my mother had knitted for me, to tell Mountie that she was a very special person to me. It conveyed the message all right. She laughed delightedly and hugged me and did an impromptu dance, waving the scarf. Then we practiced. "See my buttons?" "Pretty red scarf!" Each time I told Mountie she was doing better, she would try even harder, for Teacher cared about *her*. Her reading ability grew astonishingly fast, and though the speech defect was by no means over, Mountie came out highest of all in the reading tests that year.

Mountie taught me that what these mountain children needed most was love, instead of lives governed, as the adult lives were, by fear and hate. My pupils were hungry for love expressed in physical contact. They were forever touching me. And there was a link between this need and a child's ability to learn. When beginners were having trouble, I would take them one by one on my lap to give them a reading lesson. They learned twice as fast. With sixty-seven pupils, it was hard to find time for such individual attention, so I appointed Junior Teachers to help me, among them Bob Allen, John Spencer and Lizette and John Holcombe. They profited from the experience.

Meantime, I could not like, much less love, some of the mountain adults—and children—who would not work and wanted no part of anyone's ideas or leadership. ("Let Tennessey man-power its own roads. Hit disconfits me t'work.") I comforted myself with the thought that it was my privilege not to like everyone.

Then Little Burl helped me understand that it was my privilege to *try* to like everyone, to see the good in each individual.

One morning we had interrupted a spelling lesson to watch the birds at our school feeding station. Juncos, titmice and a pair of cardinals were stuffing themselves on sunflower seeds. Looking at the cardinals' red plumage, I said, "God must have cared about birds or He wouldn't have made them so beautiful. But He loves everything He's made, and He loves *you* extra specially."

As the children turned back to work, I noticed two men crossing the school yard toward the back of the building. Shortly they retraced their steps in the direction of the road, striding, not sauntering as most mountain men did. This time I saw their faces and felt sure that they were strangers. I tucked the incident into my mind to tell David sometime, then turned back to the class.

Little Burl was sitting at his desk staring up at the ceiling, his funny little face puckered into a look of intense concentration. I had reached down to get some paper out of my desk drawer when I felt arms around my neck, hugging me fiercely. Little Burl locked his hands behind my neck and looked me full in the eyes. "Teacher, hain't it true that if God loves ever'body, then we'uns got to love ever'body too?"

I looked at him in astonishment. "Yes, Little Burl, it *is* true."

When I gave up my privilege of disliking anyone I chose, compassion grew in me: more love for the children and, as time passed, for the older mountain people too.

CHAPTER 8

MY NEW life was a stretching process all the way. I had always thought of myself as shy, but Miss Alice now asked me to visit the families of my schoolchildren. I wondered if these calls would be more than a gesture, for the reserve of the mountain people was not easy to penetrate. Highlanders held their hands quietly at their sides while they appraised me, an "outlander." And if they had nothing to say worth saying, they said—nothing.

My first call was on Ruby Mae's parents. I found a man with a white beard and a much younger woman sitting idly on the porch, the man's feet on the railing. "I'm Christy Huddleston, the new teacher," I began. "Are you Mr. Morrison?"

There was no answer. My words might as well have been dropped into a bottomless hole. Finally they struck bottom. "I'm Duggin Morrison," the man said.

"I've gotten to know your stepdaughter well," I said.

The feet remained on the railing. "Settin' chair over yan."

I picked up the chair and set it beside the woman. She was barefooted and had hard lines in her face. "Mr. Morrison," I said, "your daughter wants you to forgive her, let her come home."

"She's stiff-necked. Needs to be took down a peg."

"Well, I think you'd find her different now. It would be nice if you could get back together." No reply. I tried another direction. "Mrs. Morrison, have you seen our new school building?"

"Naw."

"How about you, Mr. Morrison? Do come see us at the mission."

"I don't go round no church-houses. And don't take no stock in a brought-on city fellow a-tellin' us how to live."

As a caller, I was a catastrophe. I rose, but still they did not move from their chairs. "It was nice to meet you," I said, and got away from there as quickly as I could.

DAVID offered to go along on my visit to the Spencer cabin. He was afraid I would never find it on Lonesome Pine Ridge.

There was a warm touch of spring in the air this last week of March. The willows by the streams were a whisper of green lace, and here and there in the valley, spicewood bushes waved yellow plumes.

All around the Spencers' high sunlit cabin were the rich odors of sun-baked earth and pine and spruce and balsam; and within the cabin was charm. Fairlight had arranged galax leaves in two old pewter bowls, and in a chipped cup she had put trillium and violets. Unselfconsciously she reached out slender fingers to caress the flowers. "The very first. The least'uns of the springtime."

There was grace in the gesture and in the long tapering fingers, even though they were red and rough. They were the hands of an aristocrat. Nor could I see any trace of that Fairlight, rigid with fear, who had stood beside me watching the sun sink during Bob Allen's operation. Today she was eager to show me everything. There was an unusual quilt with a moon-and-star motif on the quilting frame near the hearth. So while David talked with fifteen-year-old John, I asked about it. Fairlight pointed to a window high in the wall. "See that lookout? I get a heap of joy from that. When I'm lonesome-like, it pearts me up to look up there and see the sun-ball or the moon and stars. So thrice one night I drawed me picture-pretties of the new moon and a star."

I looked at her in astonishment. "You drew the new moon at three different positions for your quilt?"

She nodded. "Weren't much work. Seems right nice to have the starry heavens on my counterpin."

Then Clara and Zady came into the room carrying heaping plates of gingerbread, and John produced a cedar pail filled with roasted chestnuts. And Mr. Spencer appeared with a dulcimer under his arm. I realized that this was to be a real party—one the Spencers must have planned for days. No sitting and staring here!

Jeb Spencer gave me a courtly "Howdy-do, ma'am." Then he shook David's hand vigorously. "Howdy, Preacher. How's the steeple-makin'?"

"I've got to knock off on the steeple for a while to string telephone wire. How about giving me a hand?"

"Aye. Been thinkin' I mought lend you a hand-up. I'd kinder like to speak into that newfangled contraption myself."

Jeb began plying the goose quill back and forth across the strings of the dulcimer. Its flutelike, plaintive quality would never take the place of the fiddle for foot-tapping rhythms, but I could see that it was the perfect accompaniment for the half-singing, half-talking ballads:

> *"O rise you up, ye sev'n breth-e-rens,*
> *And bring your sister down;*
> *It nev-er shall be said that a Stu-art's son*
> *Had taken her out of town.*
> *He mounted her on a milk-white steed,*
> *He rode a dap-ple gray.*
>
> *He swung a bug-le horn about his neck*
> *And so went blowing away. . . ."*

68

The girls were squealing with delight, and Jeb was exuberant as he watched the witchery of the old tales capture us all. The ballads re-created other centuries for us—snow-white steeds, and swords, fair maidens at casement windows, and the peel towers of the English border country; and then the American frontier—corn bread and biscuits, raccoons and mules—and always blood flowing and men being hanged, for life in seventeenth- and eighteenth-century Britain and on the frontier had its gory side.

David injected a new note. "Now I'll match you with one of the latest tunes. I'll sing it once, Jeb, then you pick it up: *Ev'rybody's doin' it, doin' it, doin' it. . . .*"

"Oh, a *foolery* song!" Clara cried. Soon the children were singing with David. And then the concert ended with Jeb singing a song that was going to haunt me forever:

> *"Down in the valley,*
> *valley so low;*
> *Hang your head over,*
> *hear the wind blow.*
>
> *Hear the wind blow, love,*
> *hear the wind blow;*
> *Hang your head over,*
> *hear the wind blow. . . ."*

How is it that a song will wing its way into mind and heart to lodge there like a homing bird? In those lines someone had captured what I felt so deeply—the plight of the mountain women.

As David and I were leaving, Fairlight said timidly, "Miz Christy, is there anything I can do to help you, like clean up the school yan? I'm a good hand to work." The words were spoken with gentle dignity, and I realized that Fairlight was not just volunteering to help; she was holding out the gift of her friendship. Among the mountain people, this was the most cherished gift of all.

I said, "That's the nicest offer anyone has made me. I'll accept it—if you'll let me be your friend. And maybe there'll be something I can do for you too."

"Aye, you can holp, Miz Christy," she said shyly. "Would you—learn me to read?"

I wanted to teach this woman to read more than I'd ever wanted to do anything before. "I'd love to do that, Mrs. Spencer. Could you come to the mission house, maybe Saturday?"

"For shore and sartin, I'll be there," she said joyously. "And would you—handle my front name, Fairlight?"

As WE walked back to the mission I was so gratified that I felt like skipping; but I hated to act like a little girl when I was with David. I said, "David, do men like girls to be, well, reserved?" David looked at me quizzically. "What I'm trying to get at is that we're taught to be modest and not too talkative, but sometimes I feel like a hypocrite when I try to act demure."

"Well then, be yourself. I like you that way."

"All right, I will. You see, David, there are so many things I want to *do* something about. Like the women around here—the hard life they have, and the way the men sort of use them."

David let his hand fall on my shoulder. "Christy, you're full of fire, aren't you? Why, I can see you marching down the street with a suffragette sign saying, 'Women Have Rights.' But I wouldn't try it in the Cove—not for a while." He let his hand slide off my shoulder—I thought, almost reluctantly. I felt secure and, yes, exhilarated walking beside him.

FAIRLIGHT arrived at the mission Saturday before we had finished breakfast. I took her over to the empty schoolhouse where we sat at two desks pulled side by side before an open window. I had cut out some landscapes from magazines, and pasted some figures of people onto cardboard bases so that they could stand upright. I had a copy of the alphabet in large clear letters, a ruled pad and some pencils.

First I picked up the Bible. "There are lots and lots of words in this book, Fairlight, but all the words in it use only these twenty-six letters." I pointed. "So after you've learned just twenty-six letters and know how to put them together—you can read!"

Her eyes shone, and after we had read the alphabet aloud twice, she became so intent on learning it that she almost forgot I was there. At last she looked at me. "Think I've got it . . . A-B-C-D—" on she went, making only one mistake.

Next we propped up a picture of a sunlit landscape. "Now, Fairlight, pick out one of the paper people." She stood a dapper-looking man up before the landscape, and we learned MAN and then TREE, GRASS, SUN, SKY, LIGHT. . . . Then I opened the Bible again. "Fairlight, the words on this page are just ideas marching. Like this one, *And God said, Let there be light* . . ."

"L-I-G-H-T! I *see* it." Her slender finger was on the word. "LIGHT! Oh, I love the light! Don't you? I hate the darkness."

Let there be light . . . I sat there thinking that I had never seen light dawn so quickly for anyone as for this woman.

ONE SATURDAY morning I was invited to Miss Alice's sewing circle: she wanted me to prepare to take charge of it when she had to be away. As I headed down the hill I thought again how unmistakably her cabin bore the flavor of her personality. In both the woman and her home there was harmony, never a straining for effect. Miss Alice accepted herself as she was and therefore accepted others. The secret of her calm seemed to be that she was not trying to prove anything. She was—that was all.

There had been times recently when I had found her Quaker calmness maddening, as I fretted and pawed the ground in my reforming zeal. Her stance toward life seemed to say: God is— and that is enough. How could Miss Alice be so sure that He had the world in His hand?

I reached the cabin just behind an old woman in a black skirt and a faded calico shirtwaist. Her cornflower-blue eyes were sunk deep in a wrinkled, parchment face. Miss Alice opened the door.

"Aunt Polly Teague and Christy—have you met? I thought not. Come in. How have you been, Aunt Polly?"

"Tole'able, tole'able. Old bones be cold bones, I guess."

"Aunt Polly has a rare distinction," Miss Alice said. "She's the oldest woman in the Cove. Ninety-two. Is that right?"

"Ninety-two, ninety-three, I cain't be bothered!" Aunt Polly snapped. "When my eighteenth young'un was birthed on my fiftieth name day, jest took a notion to drapp all birth dates out'n my head. They are jest a botheration." I looked at her in astonishment. Eighteen children! A baby when she was fifty!

But the rest of the group was arriving. They included Fairlight, Ruby Mae, Lizette Holcombe and Clara Spencer. There were also two I had not met before—the Cove midwife, Granny Barclay, and Liz Ann Robertson, who was certainly not more than fifteen, but was already married and obviously in a family way.

Miss Alice served sassafras tea and sugar cookies, using Limoges china. When the tea was gone, Fairlight nestled the beautiful teacup in her hands. "Feels like silk to the skin," she said.

"Now while you sew," Miss Alice observed, "Miss Christy and I could read to you from the Bible."

"That would be purely a delight," Aunt Polly said; and Granny Barclay broke in, "And would ye pray for the folks with miseries? Eyes are worse than ordinary. But Doc's a-studyin' on it."

Clara asked, "Granny, you be seein' a lot of Doc. Is it true that thar's a room at his place he won't let nobody see?"

"Aye, lassie, for a fact." Granny smacked her lips.

I could see that Miss Alice was eager to turn off this gossip. "Lizette, didn't I hear that your mother had a new baby?"

"Four month back that was. Ailin' now. Cries a heap."

"Was the young'un a gal-baby?" Aunt Polly asked.

"Yes, it was a gal." The girl paused a moment, her face immobile. "And it's a gal yit."

The women started to work on their quilt pieces and I started to read the Bible at the place Miss Alice pointed out. I was self-conscious about reading aloud to grown-ups from the Bible, but I soon realized that the women were listening not to me but to the stories. I too got caught up in the familiar parable of the Prodigal Son:

"But when he was yet a great way off, his father saw him, and had compassion, and ran, and fell on his neck, and kissed

him. . . . Let us eat, and be merry: for this my son was dead, and is alive again; he was lost, and is found. . . ."

When I ended, there was only the faint hissing of the apple logs on the fire.

Miss Alice, who had settled herself in a wing chair, now took the Bible. It was soon apparent that she had selected the passages with one thought in mind: she wanted these women to hear for themselves the scriptural assurance of God's love for them. She seemed to think that if the poverty-stricken highlanders gripped this fact, then in time their fear and poverty and ignorance would end. Then she closed the Bible and began the prayers. They were directed at God's adequacy to meet human problems. The needs of these women were as real and solid as the dirt in which they dug; as substantial as the mountains that towered over them; as near as pain and disease and childbirth.

"Aaa-*men*," Granny Barclay pronounced resoundingly. "Miz Henderson, your talk would put heart in a hollow log."

"Aye, makes my soul happy," Aunt Polly agreed. "All my born days them preacher-men made me think I was on the slippery path to hell. But when I hit my seventieth name day and still couldn't feel no singein' from them fires, I calculated I'd jest pearten up, and let the fires roar on without me."

Granny Barclay shook her finger at the old woman. "Pollyanne Teague, ye has a sassy tongue in your head."

"Better than bein' a say-nothingin' person."

Tactfully Miss Alice changed the subject. "Granny, I want to show Miss Christy your quilt."

I leaned over to have a look. "Is it an old pattern?"

"Aye. Hearts and Gizzards. Most patterns was handed down."
"It's beautiful!"

"But weavin' is purtier than quiltin'," Fairlight said. "Sittin' on the weavin' bench, watchin' the blossoms come out and smile at you from the kiverlid."

Her words made the older women nostalgic. Weaving was almost a lost art in the Cove. "You know, store-boughten clothes don't wear a-tall," Aunt Polly said. "Thar's something about a-settin' and trompin' the treadles—nothing can fret a-body then."

"Got a foot-power loom still," Granny said.

"And in my loft," Fairlight said eagerly, "I've got a heap of drafts—belonged to my mama and her mama before her. They're the paper patterns for the de-signs. Tell you how to make Queen Anne's De-light, Trailin' Vine, Young Man's Fancy, Whig Rose, Road-in-the-Wilderness."

Miss Alice said, "Some of my friends in Pennsylvania and Miss Christy's in Asheville would leap at the chance to buy hand-woven things. Would you do some weaving to sell?"

"If you mean for cash-money," Mrs. McHone answered, "that would shorely be welcome."

"What about the dyeing?" young Clara asked.

"Ain't hard," Granny said. "Walnut and butternut hulls for browns and blacks. Pokeberries make lavender. Hic'kry bark for the lastingest yeller. Madder for red and pink, and for blue—"

Aunt Polly interrupted her. "We'd have t'put off till August to set the blue pot. Indigo don't bloom till then. Wal, got to take my foot in hand and git along home."

The meeting broke up with the women still chattering, full of plans for the future. As I helped Miss Alice clear up afterward, I asked about Granny Barclay's eyes.

"I'm afraid it's trachoma. There's a surprising amount of it—along with hookworm and typhoid and consumption. Dr. Mac-Neill helped to start the temporary eye hospital in Lyleton. Many a Saturday Neil takes a wagonload of patients there."

"Oh! That reminds me," I said. "David told me to ask you sometime about the Doctor's ancestors in Scotland."

She smiled at me. "Of course! Let's sit by the fire."

As THE story unfolded, it carried us out of the quiet room in Tennessee, back . . . back through time to 1745. It seemed that Neil MacNeill, an ancestor of Doctor Neil MacNeill, was visiting cousins in America that year. While he was away, Bonnie Prince Charlie tried to win back the throne of England and Scotland for the Stuarts. The Highlanders were defeated by the English in the bloody massacre of Culloden Moor in April 1746.

When Neil MacNeill returned to Scotland in November of 1746, his father was gone and his frail grandfather, a price on his head, had had to flee the castle to live in a cave in the mountains. In fact, Argyllshire was full of clansmen hiding out, a price on every head. But the people were intensely loyal; they would not betray kinsfolk.

The Duke of Cumberland's men, under order, roamed the countryside, burning homesteads and grain, driving away cattle. Their aim was to destroy the economy—and they succeeded. Many women and children were actually starving. Prince Charles, with the help of many, including Flora MacDonald—still a heroine among these mountain folk—had escaped to France. A reward of thirty thousand pounds was placed on his head, but none of the poverty-stricken Highlanders would touch it.

Neil went to London to see if he could get any relief for the Highlanders. He did not succeed, but his solicitor pointed out that since he had been out of the country during the rebellion, his own fortune could not be touched by the English government.

He decided to buy a ship and offer to transport to North Carolina any of his countrymen who wanted to emigrate, and in the spring of 1747 four hundred and eighty Scottish men and women sailed in Neil's ship, *The Curlew*, for America—and freedom.

Neil stayed behind. His grandfather had died, and Neil put his estate into the hands of trustees, to be used to bring more immigrants to America. "With him, when *The Curlew* next sailed," Miss Alice went on, "Neil brought mementos of the family castle. They are in his namesake's cabin—a cherry chest, a spindle-back chair, a mantel clock, that pipe of his with the silver band inscribed in Gaelic.

"In all, *The Curlew* made four round trips. Neil was personally responsible for bringing some eighteen hundred Scottish folk to the North Carolina coast. But soon his exiles were homesick for the sight of a mountain, and a place of their own for their 'ain folk.' So in 1750 Neil led them into the virgin forest of what later became Tennessee, and when they lifted their eyes to the smoky blue of these mountains—when once again they saw valleys thick with morning mist—when they listened to the tumbling mountain streams—they wept. They had come home again. Never would they forget their ballads, their superstitions. Always their men would be quick to take offense, slow to forgive. They would hand down their personal loyalties, their stubbornness, their distrust of governments. These are their strengths, their glory—and sometimes, Christy, their damnation."

Miss Alice had finished. No wonder Dr. MacNeill had said, "These are my people. I love them."

It was not until I had left that I realized that Miss Alice had told the story as though somehow, sometime she had lived so completely into the MacNeill family that she had made it her own.

CHAPTER 9

MANY MOUNTAIN schools were in session only about twelve weeks of the year—six in the winter, after harvest time, and six in the summer, after spring planting. Highlanders had firm traditions about spring-planting time. Beans must be planted on Good Friday. (No one could tell me why.) Corn should go in when the oak leaves were as large as a squirrel's ear; late corn and cabbage on the Fourth of July.

Our six-week Spring Planting Holiday, beginning March 29, was a welcome recess because it gave me time to think. Teaching Fairlight—and now Opal McHone wanted lessons—had brought into focus my dreams for the Cove. When women were hungry to learn to read, when Fairlight was so athirst for beauty that she kept arranging flowers in a chipped crockery cup—who could deny them? But if we were to have adult classes in reading and in household arts, we were going to need another teacher. Then too, I still had a long list of supplies we would need if we were to take in boarders. All of it added up to money. Was there some new way to obtain funds?

I was trying to select an exciting story from the Bible one evening for my daily Scripture reading the next day when in the Book of Esther I read the superlative drama of the way a woman had dedicated her beauty and femininity, as well as her intelligence, to the freedom of the Jews. (She was a perfect example of my mother's belief that dowdiness did not help God's cause.) Thinking of Esther, I had an idea. What we lacked was someone to dramatize our needs to people outside. I could do that!

Knoxville was our nearest large city and the wealthiest man in Knoxville was Hazen L. Smith. His firm supplied retail grocery stores all over East Tennessee. He was an acquaintance of my father's, but I decided not to use that as an entrée. I wanted to test out a growing conviction that if one had a dream that was *right*—in the sense of being honest and unselfish—then a way could always be found.

I wrote a letter to Mr. Smith telling him that I was a school-teacher in the mission school in Cutter Gap and requesting an interview. I received a brief reply setting up an interview for April 16. This time—chastened by Miss Alice's criticism of my businessmen letters—I discussed my plan with her. She gave me her permission, but warned me to stay within Dr. Ferrand's philosophy of fund raising: no pressure on anyone. I did not confide in David—this trip might be just a waste of time, and he did make fun of me sometimes.

I FOUND Knoxville bewildering. The people walked so fast! And everyone was so dressed up—the ladies sweeping along the board sidewalks, their heads held so proudly. And almost every woman wore a hat and gloves. Beautiful, elaborate hats . . .

I looked down at my black broadcloth suit. What I needed was a dramatic hat to set it off. Soon, in a store, I found what I sought—a beautiful black hat, faced with white velvet, with swooping ostrich plumes. I would have to carry my head high and sweep into Mr. Hazen L. Smith's office to bring this hat off, but it was exactly right. I was flabbergasted when I saw the price tag: twenty-five dollars. My Queen Esther plan was almost lost forever! However, businessmen like my father said you had to spend money to make money, so, impetuously, I bought it. And from the moment it rested on my dark hair, there was no problem about feeling queenly. That hat was magic!

At the Smith Building, I followed a young man with a celluloid collar down an immense room filled with rows upon rows of stenographers' desks. As I swept down the long aisle formed by the desks, I was thinking of Queen Esther and her unfaltering walk across that vast marble pavement. For her, there must have been a moment when the king on his golden throne looked so far away that she might as well have been seeing him through the wrong end of a telescope.

I was shown into a large, carpeted office where a heavy-set man, beginning to gray at the temples, sat behind an enormous desk. He stood as I entered. "You, a missionary! I don't believe it. Why haven't they sent out missionaries like you before?" Warm, kindly eyes looked at me. "Let's sit down."

I tried hard not to show the embarrassment his frank admiration stirred. I had to shift his interest from me to the cause.

Too many solicitors, I knew, present only a need. Need is appealing, especially to the sentimental, but the improvident and the lazy will always be with us, so sketching in the *potential* in the Cove seemed important. I described the conditions there. Then I told him of John Spencer and the plane-geometry book, of Bessie Coburn, who had worked her way through a second-year Latin book by herself, and of Lizette Holcombe, who could add complicated figures in her head as fast as we could read them to her.

I knew I had him interested, and I was becoming more exuberant by the minute. "Who knows what children like that could do? They *must* have a chance for more education."

"Did you say," Mr. Smith asked, "that you're trying to handle sixty-seven children all by yourself in one room?"

"That's right. But, Mr. Smith, don't feel sorry for me. I'd always thought that lumping all grades would slow everybody down. But instead, the younger children finish their own work, then listen enthusiastically to the recitations of the older ones. They think lessons are a treat. In fact, it's been a shock comparing them with my friends back in Asheville. We took school for granted."

"I know just what you mean," Mr. Smith said. "Mrs. Smith and I have a fourteen-year-old son." He turned and stared out the window, then looked straight at me. "Am I the first person you've come to for help?"

"The very first." I hesitated, then took the plunge. "You're a businessman; I think you'd like me to be honest. Mr. Smith, I've recently learned something exciting. It's that a Christian has no business being satisfied with mediocrity. Because he has God's help he can reach for the stars. Educating boys and girls takes lots of money. And who's the most successful businessman in East Tennessee? You. I was told to reach for the stars, so I walked in on *you*."

Mr. Smith laughed delightedly. "That's refreshing candor all right, even if it is a trifle materialistic."

The word materialistic made me remember Dr. Ferrand's philosophy of giving. Had I overstepped again? "I don't want you to give a single dollar to this work unless your conscience lays it on you," I said. "I'll respect a resounding 'No.'"

"I believe you mean that." He looked at me thoughtfully. "I like what you've told me, Miss Huddleston, and I like your way of telling it. I'll help all right. I want to, very much. That is my decision—with no pressure from you."

MOTHER and father had urged me to use the coming holiday for a visit home, but I made excuses. I was beginning to enjoy my new life too much to want to leave.

We found many ways of having fun. Of an evening, we gathered around the new piano. Miss Ida was a good pianist and I played, though poorly. David would produce his ukulele. He already had a reputation in the Cove as a "song-followin' man." With his nimble fingers, he had a ready-made way into all hearts, for the highlanders had a song for all occasions—for hunting, or hoeing, for churning, or rocking the baby. Children asked

David shyly for a "gettin'-goin' tune" and older people pleaded for gospel hymns like "Just As I Am" or "Wondrous Love."

One evening soon after I got back from Knoxville, some of the older boys from school heard us singing and stopped in. "Be tickled to death," Wraight Holt requested of David, "if ye'd take a runago at one of them whittleding songs."

"Dizzifyin' music, that's what we want," chimed in Ruby Mae. So David started in on "Oh, You Beautiful Doll," and as I tried to pick it out on the piano, the boys clapped, wheeled and clogged. "Look at them rambunctious boys a-flaxing east and west," Ruby Mae exulted. "Feel gaily as bucks, don't they!"

After that, with apples roasting in the fire and corn popping, we had a party. Word soon "got norated around" about the fun to be had at the mission house, and we had to limit the open houses to two a week to leave us time for schoolwork.

One evening when we were by ourselves, I tried to play "Down by the Old Mill Stream" on the piano. Every few bars I hit a screeching discord, while Ruby Mae dramatically clapped her hands to her ears, "Ol-oo-whee-ee-ee law! Scrapes my eardrums!"

"It would scrape anybody's." Miss Ida appeared in the doorway, sucking in her lower lip and looking at us as if she were a bird about to pounce. She advanced on me and handed me a letter, looking at me piercingly. "This came earlier today."

"It's from Mr. Smith!" I tore it open eagerly.

Dear Miss Huddleston:

Enclosed please find a cheque for two hundred dollars to be used toward your boarding school and other projects. There will be more from time to time. I want to give considerable thought to what my part should be in your work, keep in touch with you, and go slowly. I have shipped you two boxes of textbooks and some maps.

By the way, are you related to John L. Huddleston? I've known him for many years. Mrs. Smith looks forward to meeting you one day and joins me in good wishes.

Sincerely yours,
Hazen L. Smith

David was watching me. "Her eyes are bright. Her cheeks are glowing. Must be good news. Want to share? Or is it a secret?"

I tossed the letter at him. "Of *course* I'll share. It's great news!" I did a little waltz around his chair, waving the check in the air. "*Whirl and twirl, tiddley-um— This old girl feels frolicsome!*"

David finished the letter and laughed. "May I have this dance?" We went waltzing around and I heard a snort as Miss Ida strode out of the room.

The next day she sought me out to ask, "Christy, where is David? I need him to put up a clothesline."

"I haven't seen him, Miss Ida."

She clucked irritably. "You see more of him than *I* do. You got notions about him. Made that apparent last night."

I knew that I should not let this one pass. "Miss Ida, if I had nothing on my mind but getting a husband, do you think I would have picked Cutter Gap?"

She dropped the conversation.

AUNT POLLY TEAGUE sent for David and me to come see her. After ninety-three years, Dr. MacNeill told us, her tired heart was failing.

We found her in her dollhouse of a cabin, sitting in a chair like a queen on a throne, wearing a flannel nightgown with a shawl around her shoulders and a black stocking cap pulled down almost to her eyes. A quilt was draped across her legs like a lap robe. The bright blue eyes in the wrinkled face lighted with pleasure as we walked in and she lifted gnarled hands to grasp both of David's. "Praise the Lord! You come in time." She turned her blazing blue eyes on me. "And Miz Christy, I asked for you because I hankered to see yer fresh young face once more, and that white neck of your'n holdin' yer head up so proud-like."

David said, "Come on now, you're not about to die!"

"Son, that rattletrap talk won't fool yerself or me. Now, first off, I want you to read out'n the Good Book. Read them certain-sure words about the life to come. There 'tis." She pointed to a worn family Bible on a table and David picked it up. "Find that spot where it says 'bout many mansions." She waited expectantly.

"The Gospel of John, I believe," David said. "Yes, here it is:

Let not your heart be troubled . . . In my Father's house are
many mansions . . . I go to prepare a place for you. . . ."

Aunt Polly was nodding. "Now I want to ask you a question straight out, Preacher. What do *you* believe is gonna happen when my heart gives out? Is my speerit gonna see Him right off?"

"I guess lots of people have wanted to know that, Aunt Polly. We used to discuss it a lot at seminary."

Please, David! I thought. *Not that abstract way.*

"Preacher, I ain't needin' to know what you gabbled about when you had time on yer hands. Tell me what 'n'all you *know*."

"Aunt Polly, we can't experience death while we're living, so we cannot *know*—the way you mean. Even Scripture seems confusing."

My heart was sinking into my shoe tops. *David, David . . .*

Aunt Polly was silent, her face so expressionless that David looked at her curiously. He said, "Some think at physical death we go first into a state of unconsciousness, then—"

Aunt Polly held up one hand, her eyes snapping fire. "Ye mean that some folks think that when we die, our speerit gits kept in a sort of icehouse till the trump sounds at the last day? Wal, son, shorely, you can't disremember about Jesus tellin' that thief on the cross beside Him, *This day thou shalt be with me in paradise.* Those men were *a-dyin'!* Weren't no time for foolin'-around talk. *This day* means just what it says."

David looked hurt and embarrassed. "I'm sorry, Aunt Polly. It's just that I'm trying to be intellectually honest with you."

"Poor man-person!" Her voice had a smile in it. "Had no call to heave my load onto your young shoulders. Got a little gimp left myself." She paused. "I'll tell ye a true tale. Be ye listenin'?"

David and I nodded, not knowing what to expect.

"Nigh onto sixty years ago 'twas. Freeman and I owned a big scope of land, and as the babies came, Freeman had to keep addin' onto our cabin. 'Twas pretty, with a big black walnut tree crowdin' it and honeysuckle all acrost the porch. The crik was like a necklace round it and the everlastin' hills closed us in cozy, like in the holler of a cup. The work was everlastin' too. I'd commence long afore the crack of dawn and still be at it by firelight.

"Wal, finally my heart give out. The nighest doctor said if'n I didn't rest I would die sure. But sakes alive! There wasn't a natural blessed thing I could do about restin' with a houseful of little shavers stacked right up to the loft. So when the queer spells would come on, I'd go out and querl up on the grass under the walnut tree, a-drinkin' in the strength of the earth till the spell passed, then go back to my work. And I didn't die.

"But something worse was ailin' my heart, only the Doc didn't know about *that:* It was starvin' to death. The Cove didn't have no church-house then and the longin' inside me ached and cried for something, I didn't rightly know what. Then one day I was goin' along the path windin' through the blackberry brambles. And at one certain spot on that path—I could show you where—somethin' happened to me. He met me. It was simple-like, but clear as mornin' light. I says to Him, 'Lord,' I says, 'I don't rightly know whether I'm gonna live or die, but it don't make no differ. From here on, my life belongs to You.'

"And it did too, for a fact. From that day I could feel His love a-feedin' my starvin', thirstin' soul. And the more I tried givin' His love away to my young'uns and my man and the neighbor-folks, the more love He gave back to me. Then Freeman had a huntin' acci-dent and went on afore me. And no sooner had he gone from his body, than he was in the room with us'uns. Not that I could see him, but I shorely could feel him, laughin' easy-like, tellin' us clear that everything was all right, not to worry a mite.

"I've been livin' with my Lord for over sixty year now, and the second I take my leave of this wore-out flesh, He'll be a-waitin' for me. Rest yer soul on that, son. And now I aim to give you and Miz Christy my blessin'. And I'm that beholden to you for bringin' yer brightness to take away some of an old lady's lonesomeness. Thank ye, lassie."

I reached down to hug Aunt Polly, but I could not speak. The cheek I pressed against hers was moist with tears.

I WAS seeing more and more of Fairlight Spencer. In the beginning I had thought of teaching her to read as just another do-good project. (I admit it, to my shame.) But in a few short weeks I had begun to love this mountain woman.

What the record time is for learning to read, I do not know, but the prize probably belongs to Fairlight. She "practiced" all the time—on the old newspapers pasted on the cabin walls, on the family Bible, on the labels of jars and bottles. Within a few weeks, she was borrowing books two or three at a time and reading while doing her housework: a book propped on the windowsill while she washed dishes; a book on a chair at her side while she was churning, spinning, or stringing beans.

She taught me something important about the use of time and how to enjoy life. On the first fine spring day, she always dropped her housework: "The house, it's been a-settin' here for a hundred years. It'll be right here tomorrow"—and made for a spot she knew in the woods. There she would brush aside the dead leaves and gaze wonderingly on the first blossoms of the trailing arbutus. Often she found time to pause in her work to "lift her heart" with a sunset, or to call the children to see the grandeur of thunderheads piling up over the peaks. And there was always leisure for the family to gather on the porch "to sing the moon up."

The highlanders were often accused of being lazy and shiftless. As I got to know them better, my conclusion was: relaxed, yes; shiftless, a few of them; greedy, scarcely ever.

Human life is short. Are we going to go through our so few years with little time for our family and friends, with unseeing eyes for the beauties around us? I began to wonder if the mountain values were not more civilized than civilization's.

I also realized now why these people were shy. They had never learned the citified arts of hiding feelings or of smiling when the heart was cold. Friendship was dangerous to them because once they let you in, it must be for life. Mountain friendship came from a time when there was no more final bond than a man's pledged word; when every family connection was firm and strong, forged in the past, stretching into the future. And now I began to understand a little about the feuds. When a member of one's family was betrayed, the betrayal bit deeper than it would have with people whose relationships were more shallow. To forgive it seemed to the highlander to cut across the integrity of life itself.

ONE DAY Fairlight and I had agreed to meet on Pebble Mountain to watch Jeb, David and some other men string the telephone wire. The telephone was a big event, for it would be the Cove's first real link with civilization.

Fairlight was at the edge of a clearing waiting for me. I could tell by her childishly eager look that she had something to show me. "Pyxie lichen." She pointed to a delicate moss. "Jest a-waitin' here I spied nine kinds. That thar's reindeer moss. And that's beard lichen." Fairlight also knew where to find "monkey-jugs," as she called wild ginger, and "sang"—the ginseng so prized in the Orient. She had favorite spots for all the herbs she needed for her family doctoring: mullein for cough syrup, for instance; crab-apple bark for asthma; and witch-hazel bark to make a salve for burns.

She pointed now at the hill. "Men-persons jest yonder."

We scrambled through the bushes and found the men lifting a tall pole into a hole. David looked almost as dirty and sweaty as the rest, yet there was no question as to who was directing the operation. His voice was, as usual, loud and booming; I wondered if he realized how abrupt and overbearing his orders sounded.

I was puzzled to notice Ozias Holt, father of the eight Holt children, slumped behind a tree trunk, whittling. So much work was involved in the wire stringing that David was paying his helpers twenty cents an hour. Eleven men had been hired, but David never knew when they would show up. And here was Mr. Holt, taking it easy, unnoticed by David.

"Men, we've got to get at least six more poles in the ground before dark," David was announcing in a voice that would have reached a congregation of two thousand.

At that moment, Ozias Holt stretched himself full length on the ground, hands under his head. The movement caught David's eye and he strode over. "What ails you, Ozias?"

Holt did not stir. "Rev'end, I'm bodaciously tired out."

"Tired out! Ozias Holt, I won't pay you one red cent for loafing around here all day. Start working—or quit."

Mr. Holt answered nothing. Finally he rose, stretched, yawned, and slouched off through the woods while David watched him go, obviously seething. Silently, the rest of the men turned back to their tasks.

Fairlight whispered to me, "Don't like preacher-person tanglin' with Ozias Holt. He's a mean'un. Don't want nothin' t'happen."

A BIG shipment of books and maps arrived from Mr. Smith. David and I spent most of the night unpacking them, and next day at school I could scarcely wait to get through the opening exercises and announce the big surprise. My pupils were entranced with the beauty of the wall maps. At once, we found Tennessee and stuck in a pin at the approximate location of Cutter Gap. Now, at last, I had tools to help me convey some notion of the world beyond the Cove.

I was the only person in the classroom who had ever before seen books with fresh covers and not a page missing. I made a speech about taking care of them.

John Spencer turned the pages of the calculus book, looking as if he had been handed a gift of the moon, and after I read Coleridge's "Kubla Khan" from one of our new copies of *English Romantic Poets*, Isaak McHone learned the whole poem by heart, rolling the rhythms over his tongue.

Friday morning I started for school early to prepare for the end-of-the-week spelling bee. When I opened the door, I drew in my breath sharply. The room was wrecked. Our beautiful new books and maps had been ripped and slashed and thrown around wildly. I looked around through a blur of tears, and then hot anger rose in me. I don't understand, I thought. I just don't understand. Are people mad at the school? But why? . . .

Most of the children were subdued, suddenly remote, that day. We spent much of the morning putting torn books and maps back together as best we could. Then I realized how chilly the room was, and went over to poke up the fire. I had no sooner opened the iron grating than a series of explosions spit sparks and flame into my face and onto my hair and dress. With a cry I backed away, slapping at the sparks, while Ruby Mae, sitting in the nearest seat, rushed to me and frantically raked burning pieces of something out of my hair. I stood there, my dress scorched, a painful burn on my neck, looking at my class. Finally, with a shaking voice, I asked, "What was it that exploded?"

There was a long silence. Some of the children would not look at me. Finally Joshua Bean Beck spoke up, "Hit be buckeyes in the ashes, Teacher. They git hot and then pop and fly all t'pieces when the air hits 'em." I opened my mouth for the obvious question but Joshua Bean was ahead of me. "No ma'am. Not me. I wouldn't do that to ye."

Then who? Haven't I gotten through to these youngsters at all? . . . No, you're angry and you're going too far. Only a few are to blame, and anger is not the way to handle anything.

To get control of myself I turned to the blackboard to write down the spelling words. At once I heard a steady noise at the back of the room. I whirled just in time to see Lundy stalking down the aisle, poking a stick into little Mountie's back and he-heeing. The sneer on his face made me suspect that he was responsible for the buckeyes. "Lundy," I said, managing to speak calmly, "do you know anything about that explosion?"

The huge boy stood there gawking at me, his mouth slack, his eyes empty. Then fire leaped to his eyes. "No gal-woman's goin' tell me what to do," he snarled.

Momentarily I was startled, then fury took over. The fact that the boy towered above me mattered not at all. "You'll do what I tell you to," I said, almost shrieking. I reached up and grabbed his shock of hair with all the strength I had, dragged him down

and shook him. The yank took him by surprise and he blinked back tears. But then the next moment he doubled his fists and Fairlight's son John forced his way between us.

"Lundy—go—to—your—seat, or I'm the one you'll fight!" a stern masculine voice said. It was David who had arrived for the mathematics lessons.

The boy slunk down immediately. Suddenly I was shaking, and the next instant David was by my side propelling me to my desk. "Sit down," he whispered. "I'll take over."

THAT evening, in front of Miss Alice's fireplace, David and I told her the story of the book slashing. "Who would deliberately tear up new books? And why?" I asked.

Miss Alice's eyes were thoughtful. "Perhaps because to a certain type, anything new and strange poses a threat. New schoolhouse. . . . New books. . . . New starry-eyed teacher with lots of plans for the future. I'm only guessing, but for some, that may add up to a threat to the only way of life they've ever known."

She paused. "Christy, you mentioned your anger over this. Perhaps it would help if you recognized *why* you got so furious. I believe it was because the new books are a tangible token of a personal triumph—a triumph of self. Therefore, when the books were slashed, it was as if *you yourself* were slashed."

David was looking at Miss Alice as if he wanted to argue. But her words had hit home with me. I wondered again if I really belonged in that schoolhouse.

Miss Alice smiled. "No need to be discouraged, Christy. What you've undertaken in your schoolroom isn't a state of perfection to be arrived at suddenly. It's like a baby learning to walk, falling, and trying again. We Friends say that all discouragement is from an evil source and can only end in more evil. Thee fell into a temper! So thee is human. Thank God for thy humanness."

LUNDY did not come back to school, and gossip began to reach me that his father, Bird's-Eye, was plotting revenge on me. Ruby Mae told me, "Ye see, Teacher, what happened in school that day ain't lost a bitty-bit in the tellin'. I'm afeered Mr. Taylor has heerd that ye did things ye didn't do."

I would have to seek out Bird's-Eye and tell him the truth. I dreaded this, for Ruby Mae described him as "fractious," but for the sake of the school, the Lundy matter must be resolved.

David and Miss Alice were engrossed in the completion of our telephone installation in the mission house so I decided to slip off.

The Taylor cabin was perched like an eagle's nest on the top of a mountain. So steep was the final ascent that I tethered Theo to a tree two hundred feet below the cabin to climb the rest of the way on foot.

I paused first to "Hallo." No sooner was the call out of my mouth than the doorway was filled with a man's figure, shotgun in hand. I knew that he had been watching me. "I want to talk to you, Mr. Taylor," I called. "May I come up?"

"Come up then," he said grudgingly.

The path was steep and slippery and ended at the door in a level spot about a yard wide. I introduced myself, and he said, "What d'ye want with us?" The eyes looking into mine were cold, and a slit of a mouth was set in a grizzled face which had not known a razor in days.

"Just wanted to talk about Lundy. May I come in?"

"Ain't no place fer a woman. Jest Lundy and me here."

"I understand. But I'd like to talk to you."

He seemed surprised at my persistence, but finally moved to one side, disclosing what seemed more a cave than a cabin. In fact, I had the impression that an entrance in back might lead to a cave in the mountain ledges. "Come in and set then," Bird's-Eye said. He moved aside, and for the first time, I saw Lundy standing behind his father.

"Hello, Lundy," I tried to put as much warmth as possible into my voice. "When are you coming back to school?"

"Dunno." He ogled me, and for the first time I was afraid, since no one at the mission knew where I was.

"Mought as well tell ye," Bird's-Eye said. "Don't want wimmin teachers a-whoppin' my young'un."

"Mr. Taylor, I didn't whip Lundy. He's bigger than I am. How do you think I could whip him?"

Lundy was sidling toward the door. His father's hand shot out, but the boy ducked. "Consarned fool. Ye lied t'me."

"Ah, Pap, I jest—"

"I'm a-goin' to smoke yer britches till the fire catches."

But Lundy was already out the door.

"Don't be too hard on him," I said. "Lundy was just testing me. I had a little trouble with him, and I jerked him by the hair. I hope you'll send him back."

There was something close to a thaw on Bird's-Eye's face. He did not seem to think yanking Lundy's hair a bad idea. He said, "Dunno if schoolin's any use to Lundy. He may be twitter-witted. His Mam was. Fitified and addlepated. I pulled out and left her in North Carolina. That's why I'm a-raisin' Lundy."

"I see. Well then, it seems to me you need help. That's what the mission's here for—to help."

"Churches ain't fer us. Always been a sinner myself, and ain't never lied to the Lord about it."

"But I'm a sinner too. Everybody is. As I understand it, that's what church is all about—to save sinners."

"Don't want savin'. And I disgust churches."

There seemed little point in pursuing this. "Mr. Taylor, I'd better be going. You'll send Lundy back to school?"

"I'll study on it."

"And drop by the mission house yourself. We'd like to be friends." I hurried quickly down the slope. I had the feeling that Lundy was spying on me from behind a bush.

A WEEK later I looked up from my desk and there stood Lundy. "Could I clean the blackboard for ye, Teacher?"

He seemed like a new Lundy. He came up to my desk as often as he dared; he hung around after school, talking and ogling. He was hostile to David, however, and greeted him each day with scowls. David, on his side, still did not trust Lundy.

The following Friday I was at my desk during recess when I

heard shouts from the playground. I rushed out. "Hit's Teacher!" someone cried. "Better stop it!" As the children stood back, I saw Festus Allen and Lundy fighting. Festus, only eleven, was using feet as well as fists, but he was getting the worse of it.

"Quit that!" I thrust myself between the two boys, barely missing a fist in my face.

Then I saw Festus' brother Little Burl unconscious on the ground. Frantically, my hands felt for his heart. Beating, thank God! I could see no cuts or bruises on his face. Then I lifted his shirt. There was a round red mark on his stomach. I took him in my arms, putting his head lower than his body. It seemed a long time before his eyelids fluttered open. "My stummick hurts," he moaned.

"I know. Just lie still." I looked up. "One of you tell Lundy I want to see him. Ruby Mae, how did this happen?"

Ruby Mae looked frightened. "Lundy seed Little Burl a-scroungin' around under the schoolhouse. Give a panther-shriek, pulled him out, started kickin' him."

"Ruby Mae, you'd better ask Mr. Grantland to come here."

Finally Little Burl felt better, though his stomach still hurt. I helped him to his feet and we walked slowly into the schoolhouse. I was relieved to find Lundy there by himself. "Lundy," I said, "get in your seat and stay there. I'll be back in a minute."

Outside, I met Ruby Mae and David. I told him about the fight, ending with, "But David, why would Lundy get that angry over Little Burl crawling under the schoolhouse?"

"Christy, I think you'd better let me handle this. I'm going to have to do some quizzing."

I was relieved. "That's fine with me, David."

All afternoon I waited for some report from him. Toward dusk I decided to investigate for myself. As I reached the playground, a pig, walking oddly, crossed near me. I had never seen a pig look like that. And something else was odd too: there was no noise of pigs under the schoolhouse. At the schoolhouse steps there was a strong smell, but not of pigs. Suddenly, I was panicky about what I might be about to find. I ran back to the big house.

David met me on the porch. "What's the hurry, Christy?"

"Something's wrong at the schoolhouse. Will you have a look?"

I trailed his long strides across the yard and up the hill. At the back of the building, I almost stumbled over a broken jug. Nearby were several hogs, sound asleep. They were breathing heavily and did not stir as we approached.

David crouched over and made his way under the building. Then he whistled loudly. "Holy thunder! Christy, somebody's fixed a storage room under the schoolhouse floor. There are a lot of jugs here. Moonshine whiskey. I'll hand them out one at a time."

He thrust a heavy jug into my hands; then another, and another, and another. Finally he came out, rubbing dust off his hands. "So this was what Lundy didn't want Little Burl to find! But Christy, this can't be all Lundy's doing. Blockaders—moonshiners—must be involved."

"What did Lundy say when you talked to him?"

"I never got the chance. He'd slipped away."

"David, I think you should see Bird's-Eye's cabin. I think it is built against a cave where he could store a *hundred* jugs."

David said, between clenched teeth, "If you're right, Christy, then the blockaders are trying to make me look like an ass. They think the church-schoolhouse I built is my pride and joy, so they store their moonshine practically under the altar! Well, I'll show them!" David began to uncork jugs and pour the liquor on the ground. "I'd like to pickle their brains in this!" His hands were trembling. "I'll put the empty jugs back in their hiding place. Then we'll watch people's reactions."

"David, those pigs still haven't moved."

"You know horses won't drink a drop of water with mash in it, but pigs like nothing better. Those hogs are drunk."

"Drunk pigs! How funny!"

"The pigs are funny," David said, "but the situation isn't."

That Sunday evening after supper, David tapped me on the shoulder. "How about a walk?"

Outside it was a clear moonlit night. Silently David took my arm and steered me down to gurgling, singing Cutter Branch.

Then he said, "I found Lundy up near his cabin. He was defensive. Sullen. Wouldn't say much, but I pried out a little. Two other boys are in on the secret room under the school: Wraight Holt and Smith O'Teale."

"But Smith's only fourteen!" I thought of the undersized boy whose black eyes always seemed to be pleading for something.

"I know. I warned Lundy that he and his two friends might have to leave school. Told him that their punishment would have to be decided by their parents and the mission staff. At the mention of parents, he started smirking. It was a dead giveaway: adults are managing the setup.

"Remember Uncle Bogg was pretty sure the men who followed you through the woods that night were not Cutter Gap men? Well, I'm afraid we've got a little blockading business going on right under our noses with schoolboys as go-betweens." The moonlight put deep hollows in David's cheeks, gave him a gaunt look.

"David, it seems too small an operation for strangers."

"Right now there's very strict law enforcement for blockaders in North Carolina, so Tennessee whiskey is in great demand. What's more, I've made it easier to get the stuff to the state line by improving our road. We'll have to talk this out with Miss Alice as soon as possible. And then I'm going to have to find out which men are behind these boys, maybe go after the still."

Suddenly I was afraid for David. As if sensing this, he reached for my hand. "Do you have to go after the moonshiners yourself, David? That's dangerous."

"I know. But I can't get federal marshals on the case without more evidence. These mountain men can guzzle all the liquor they please, but when they start involving our schoolchildren . . ."

NEXT EVENING I suddenly remembered that two weeks before I had seen three strange men riding past the mission property. It had not seemed important at the time, but now, with all that had happened, David should know about it.

He had gone off to his bunkhouse, so I started down the walk toward it. I noticed that his lamps were lit, with all the shades drawn tight. Then, as I got closer, I saw a movement in the bushes by the little building. I ducked behind a laurel thicket and held my breath, listening. Not a sound except the gurgle of the stream and a low hum of voices inside the bunkhouse.

Clouds cast murky shadows as I parted two branches and peered through. A shadow moved and a pebble rolled down to the road. Just then the clouds parted and moonlight bathed the foliage. I saw Lundy skulking in the bushes.

At that instant the bunkhouse door opened and Bob Allen came out and went briskly down the road. With Lundy nearby, this did not seem the time to talk to David. I went back to the big house.

Next morning, David strode in looking weary, his riding clothes and boots muddy. "Any hot coffee?"

I poured him a cup and told him about the strange men and my trip to his cabin.

David looked startled. "Did Lundy see Bob Allen?"

"Yes, I'm sure he did."

"Then thank God I didn't find the still this morning, or Bob Allen would be a dead man."

Lundy did not come back to school that week.

IT WAS the following Tuesday, during our regular weekly conference with Miss Alice, that I learned about the still.

Miss Alice made these Tuesday evenings a refreshing oasis in her peaceful cabin. She flouted the accepted custom of covering her tabletops with doilies; the patina of the lovely old wood was all the decoration needed. In a pewter bowl she would arrange well-polished apples and some nuts, or a piece of quartz along with some unusual leaves and berries. Though David, manlike, noticed none of these details, he nevertheless responded to the atmosphere they created.

On this particular Tuesday night, he sank gratefully into the easy chair. "I've found the still," he began abruptly, "but the men weren't there. Yesterday afternoon Prince and I started out for Big Lick Gap. Well, at Coldsprings Branch Prince stopped to drink, then he snorted and backed away. I dismounted and scooped up some water. You couldn't miss the smell of mash. I started up the stream and found the path trampled. Also—and this was odd—small branches had been broken at more or less regular intervals and left dangling all along the path. Then I saw a piece of copper tubing lying in the leaves. I decided it was time to bring the federal marshals in. I didn't dare use our new telephone—too public—so I rode to the telephone exchange in Lyleton and phoned the federal office in Knoxville. Within an hour they had two of their men on the train to El Pano. They told me where to pick up horses, and at a little past midnight, I guided them to Coldsprings Branch, and rode on home in the moonlight.

"One of the marshals, Gentry Long, telephoned today. Told me they had gone a mile or so upstream when they found a dummy stuffed with straw, hanging from a branch—the usual warning to revenue men. There was nothing else there but some pieces of copper tubing. Somebody had warned the blockaders."

"David," I said, "*who* warned them?"

"I've no idea. Mountain people stick together against 'revs.'"

Miss Alice broke in. "David, I want to change the subject to your run-in with Ozias Holt when you were putting in the telephone lines. Fairlight told me about it."

"Anything I said to Ozias he deserved."

Miss Alice was mild. "I'm not passing judgment on that. But now you can demonstrate to Ozias the strength in forgiveness."

"I fail to see how forgiving Ozias for being a lazy bum would demonstrate anything to him except weakness."

"David, no Christian ever has a right to sever any relationship out of anger. I bring this up now because with the blockading problem unsolved, this is no time for misunderstandings. I suggest you talk to Ozias in friendship. When people don't talk, they sever what may have been God's only route into a man's heart."

"I guess you're right," said David slowly. He rose to end the conversation. "I'll walk to the big house, Christy, if you're ready to leave too."

He had little to say as we went up the hill.

CHAPTER 11

FROM THE parlor I could hear a man talking to David at the door. "Here to give ye and Miz Christy an in-vite to the workin', come Satur-day." Whoever it was sounded ill at ease. "Aim to clear part of Deer Moun-tain, back of our place."

"Thanks, Ozias." David's voice was a little too hearty. "Appreciate that. We'll sure be there. Thanks again."

David looked puzzled as he walked into the parlor. "Did you hear that? Ozias Holt. I haven't done a thing about following Miss Alice's advice, and when mountain men are mad at you, they never invite you to eat with them. I think Ozias intends this working to be a challenge. What these men want to know is, can I handle a crosscut saw or an axe? How good a shot am I? Can I use my fists?" David looked like a child about to face his first examination.

"And *can* you do all those things?"

"I doubt it." A smile crinkled his face. "Bareknuckle fighting and target practice weren't requirements at seminary."

"That's because they didn't know Cutter Gap."

A "WORKING," I knew, was a carry-over from pioneer times when a man's only chance to get his land cleared, a roof over his family's head, or a barn built was to ask for the help of his neighbors. All the way from the Appalachians to Abraham Lincoln's Illinois and on into the great West, an acre of land could be cleared or a cabin or a barn "raised" in a day with a working.

When we headed for the Holt cabin Saturday, David had his tools over his shoulder. By the time we got there, some of the men were already toiling side by side up the slope, each having been given a vertical strip to clear. The hillside was a tangle of huckleberry, poison hemlock, scrub oak, rhododendron, small pine and tough little locusts to be grubbed out.

Ozias dropped his mattock. "Howdy, Miz Christy. Mornin',

Preacher." He seemed to gloat a bit as he pointed with a crusty forefinger to the strip they had saved for David. The other men—among them Bird's-Eye Taylor—said nothing. Their silence created an ominous atmosphere.

David prepared to go to work, and Rebecca Holt beckoned to me from the cabin door. The room was already so crowded that I wondered how space would be found for the men's noon meal.

The women welcomed me but there was something different today. For one thing, I missed Aunt Polly Teague. I kept expecting to see her balmoral petticoats come sweeping through the door. But her premonition had been right: the week after David and I visited her, she had died, with a look of heaven on her face.

However, her absence was not the only difference today: there was something else, a sense of restraint in the cabin? Why?

I decided to test it out. "I'm sorry Mary Allen isn't here. I wanted to ask her about Little Burl. He hasn't been at school since he got hit. Has anybody heard how he is?"

Silence hung heavy. Fairlight's eyes grew wary, with pleading in them, as she looked at me. "I heard Burl can't eat much. Reckon he'll make out though."

What did the pleading look mean? That I should not talk about the Allens? On which side *were* they in the moonshining situation? How much better it would be if only these people would air their doubts and fears instead of suppressing them!

By the time the men had been called to the midday meal, the tension in the room was unmistakable. It was the custom for the men to eat first and for the women to serve them, then the women ate at what was called "second table." As soon as the men were seated at the trestle table, Ozias asked David to say the grace.

David looked beaten. His broad shoulders were sagging, his shirt wet with perspiration. But his deep voice filled the room. "For the bounty of this table, for the hands that prepared this food, for this home, for friends to help us, Lord, we give Thee our thanks. Amen."

He said little as the men ate. Usually workings were also jollifications, with fiddling and ballad singing. But today there was lit-

tle fun, though Uncle Bogg told a few jokes and tall tales. When the meal was over David got to his feet, his shoulders still sagging, and went out. I started clearing the dishes, but my mind was in the yard, wondering what would happen.

Later that afternoon I left the quilt piecing inside the cabin to see how the outside work was progressing. Several of the men had already finished their strips, but David still had almost half of his to clear. No one offered to lend him a hand, and if they had offered, he would have refused. For it had become increasingly obvious to him that the mountain men would listen to what he had to say from the pulpit only if first he proved himself to them, by their own standards, as a man.

I brought David a dipper of cool water, and as he drank thirstily, I was concerned to see that the palm of his right hand was now bloody. When I asked about bandaging it, he shook his head grimly. "You can doctor me this evening." Then he picked up his mattock again.

About an hour later, I heard a disturbance. I rushed out. David had almost reached the top of his strip. Bird's-Eye was shouting up at him, his voice slurred and thick.

"Ain't been treated so fine today, have ye?" he taunted. "That's what we think of folks that pester with other folks' business." He spat contemptuously on the ground. "Religion ain't got nothing to do with blockadin' or feudin' or gredges no-way. Oh, you're a good enough hand to work. But Preacher, you mind your own play-pretties and we'll mind our'n—less'n you want to see your great-great-grandmammy real soon."

As he raised his rifle, I clapped my hand over my mouth to stifle a scream. Three shots spattered into the ground at David's feet; the fourth whistled within inches of his head. Then Bird's-Eye stood there, his head cocked tantalizingly over the trigger which would release a fifth cartridge.

I could feel my heart beating wildly. Jeb Spencer, Tom McHone and several other men looked embarrassed, but most of the faces were immobile, registering nothing. Not a man moved. David was ashen, but he was looking Bird's-Eye calmly in the face, his brown eyes unblinking. Under his unwavering gaze, Bird's-Eye slowly lowered the rifle. The silence in the yard was so intense that the mooing of a cow on a distant mountainside sounded like a bugle call.

Slowly David's eyes traveled the circle of men, as if trying to see how many friends he had. At last he spoke. "If any of you would like to hear my answer, come to church tomorrow."

Then he turned his back and attacked the last of the bushes on his strip.

ON SUNDAYS the schoolroom was usually half to three-quarters full of worshipers; today it was crowded. I got to the service early and found an inconspicuous place toward the back.

As I had bandaged David's raw hands the night before, his eyes had had a "No Trespassing" look, as though he had to be alone to think things out for himself. Once during the night, a noise had wakened me and I had gotten out of bed to look out the front window. It was David, walking back and forth near his bunk-house. At breakfast, though he had seemed weary, there had been a determined set to his jaw. Too determined, if he was to communicate with these people.

Soon the first hymn was in full swing—and I mean swing. This was no medieval cathedral, but a raw wood church, with babies crying, children wriggling, men standing just outside the church door, spitting tobacco juice. The people sang lustily, tapping their toes as my schoolchildren did when they were singing ballads:

> "Hit's the old ship of Zion, as she comes,
> Hit's the old ship of Zion, the old ship of Zion,
> Hit's the old ship of Zion, as she comes.
> She'll be loaded with bright angels when she comes,
> She'll be loaded with bright angels when she comes. . . ."

How could one worship, David had often said, without at least a semblance of dignity? I could sympathize with his desire to teach the mountain folk a little more of the majesty of worship: the rich tapestry of words from Scripture, prayers mellow with age, pregnant with meaning. *"That our hearts may be unfeignedly thankful. . . ."* *For ye shall go out with joy, and be led forth with peace. . . . Honor and majesty are before him: strength and beauty are in his sanctuary. . . .* But the people had resisted change, and on the whole, Miss Alice sided with them.

When it was time for the sermon, I found myself looking at David with fresh eyes. What did the people see? A tall young man who, dressed as he was now, could have stepped into the pulpit of any city church—striped pants, Prince Albert, white shirt, dark tie. When I first had heard David preach, I had realized that he did not speak the language of the Cove people. He was overly fond of words like exegesis, polemic and anthropomorphism. Obviously, his congregations understood little of this.

But their reaction was not what I would have supposed: His "highfalutin' talk" convinced them that they had snared the most educated preacher in those parts. David had assumed that his ministry was off to a great start—until the Holt working.

It was a sobered David who now began: "I had planned to preach today on The Feeding of the Five Thousand. But things have happened in the Cove which must be brought into the open. So I will just talk to you out of my heart."

The people leaned forward as he went on. "There are those among us who think that Christianity is only for Sundays. They think the preacher should give out a string of high-sounding talk and then should shut his eyes to everything going on outside the church. But friends, what is the church? Not just a building. The church is a fellowship—folks who want Christ to be their Leader.

"Now Jesus dealt in a special way with those who pretended to be good on the Sabbath and then did anything they liked the rest of the week. He had a way of looking them in the eyes, piercing through their double-talk. Some of them—as important in their community as our squires or sheriffs or judges—He called *serpents, vipers, whited sepulchres, full of iniquity.* Those are fighting words anytime, anyplace.

"Now in the last twenty-four hours I've done a lot of thinking about what Jesus' attitude would be about us here in Cutter Gap.

I believe that He would say to us this morning"—David leaned over the pulpit, his eyes sweeping his congregation, as if to talk personally to each of us—" 'Either you do right on Monday and Tuesday and Friday, or you needn't come crying to me on Sunday.' *Take heed,* Jesus warned, *that thy whole body be full of light, having no part dark.* He knew that men who do evil always like to work in the dark. In this Cove there are those who are working in darkness—and they are serving evil."

I felt my throat go dry. The front of the room was still quiet, but among the men near me, I heard whispering and muttering. David was hitting too hard.

"The white lightning being brewed here," he said, "is the devil's own brew. It leads to lust and fights and killings—and now even schoolboys are being used to help sell it. These wrongs must be brought into the light of day. Jesus will pit all His strength against the deviltries in our Cove. And don't underestimate Him! Our God will not lose the fight against evil anywhere in our world." He paused, his face flushed, his eyes glowing. "How many of you want to be on His side? Do you?" He was pointing his finger. "And you? How about you?"

I was caught up in David's emotion. Then just as he was saying, "Let us pray," Dr. MacNeill tapped me on the shoulder.

"Can you come with me?" he whispered urgently.

DR. MACNEILL said nothing more until we were outside the door. "It's Little Burl. A torn abdominal muscle, with a localized abscess. I have to operate right away. Will you help, Christy?"

I said, "I'd do anything to help Little Burl. But I had to dash for air during his father's operation. Suppose I fold up on you?"

"You're the type who never folds while the crisis is going on, only afterward. And there's no one else. Miss Alice is away."

I picked up my skirts and ran for the house to leave a note for David. A few minutes later, as churchgoers began streaming out the door, Dr. MacNeill and I rode side by side from the mission yard, Prince, for once, behaving well. As we rode, I told him how Little Burl had been hurt.

Once we reached the Allens, everything happened quickly. Little Burl's face showed joy. "You'll stay right with me, Teacher? Hit won't hurt?"

"Of course not. I'll hold your hand." He looked so tiny in that big bed with the raccoon, Scalawag, lent by Creed Allen, curled up beside him! Mrs. Allen was more distraught now than she had been at the time of her husband's head operation, and finally the Doctor ordered her taken out of the room.

There was the sickly sweet smell of ether as it dripped into the cone I was holding over Little Burl's face. I said, "I'm going to tell you a story, Burl, about the wicked Hoptoad and the Little Yellow Dragon who lived by the edge of Blackberry Creek. . . ."

The light from the kerosene lamp laid a shadow across the small white face, so still now. At the moment of the first incision, panic rose in me. Then, as I fought it back, the unexpected happened. Words surfaced into my mind with peculiar clarity: You have watched Miss Alice listening and waiting. Get your attention off your problem and look at Me. I am greater than any problem. Had I prayed? No, not consciously. Yet even as I was shrinking from the sight of the blood, I held on to a strong Presence and felt a welling up of joy and gratitude for the skill that was going to save a child's life.

Finally the Doctor said, "Almost finished now. You see how much pus there is. But don't worry—his heartbeat's strong, and you're doing wonderfully."

The child began to come out of the ether and the blue eyes struggled open. There was a weak grin at seeing me. He floated in and out of consciousness, clinging to my fingers. "Can't risk straining the abdominal wall from nausea," Dr. MacNeill said softly. "We've got to watch him every minute."

Finally, Little Burl fell into a deep natural sleep. "He'll be all right now for a while. Let's go out. I'll ask Bob to sit here."

In the yard the Doctor said, "Christy, I need to talk to you. Let's go down to the mill." He led the way down the path to Bob's mill, a picturesque place with its tall waterwheel and the turbulent thunder from the flume. His question was abrupt.

"Was there blockade whiskey where Little Burl was looking?"

I nodded. "Little Burl found the hiding place. Later David poured out the whiskey."

"I thought so." He sighed. "Now I understand why David is on such a rampage against liquor."

This was peculiar. "Why *wouldn't* he be?"

The Doctor held up a restraining hand, half smiling. I had the impression that he was amused at my intensity and would deal with me patiently as with a child, and I felt annoyed. "Let me talk first," he said. "There's a lot that you and David need to know before you judge. Christy, I was the one who warned the blockaders that David was on his way to the federal marshals."

But at that moment Festus Allen appeared. "Burl's wakin' up. Papa said for you to come, Doc."

There was no time for further conversation. Dr. MacNeill decided that he should stay at the Allens' all night, and Mr. Allen courteously rode with me back to the mission house.

DR. MACNEILL, lounging on David's couch-bed three days later, did not seem like a man with anything sinister on his conscience. He looked at me, sitting in David's Morris chair, and then at David, who was sitting on the floor, his back against the wall. "In tipping off the blockaders," the Doctor said, "I was simply choosing the lesser of two evils. The choice was, let this particular still go a little longer—or risk more feuding and killing."

"I don't follow that," David said. "In my book, letting moonshining go on leads to killings."

"Didn't Bob Allen come to you to tip you off about the still?"

"No. All Bob offered was to help find the still."

"The fact remains that Lundy saw him there and now the Taylors are wondering if their old enemies, the Allens, tipped you off. Even if you had Bird's-Eye behind bars, there'd be plenty of others on the Taylor side of this fight. And on the Allen side, there is Bob's brother Ault. He drinks too much, and when he's drinking, he has the quickest trigger finger in the Cove. So we're sitting on a powder keg here, and the solution to the feuding has to come from strategy worked out between us. Believe me, basically I'm on your side."

David sat up straighter, as if some of the pressure was off his chest, but before he could comment, the Doctor hastened on. "David, I have to say that I think you're off on the wrong foot. The type of sermon you preached Sunday isn't the right strategy. When you blast people, a wall goes up, and all they do then is crouch behind the wall to defend themselves.

"Now, about the still: There's another fact for you. The second blockader is Nathan O'Teale—and the third is Tom McHone."

Opal's husband! Poor Opal, with the "liver-growed" baby . . . "Does Opal know?" I asked.

"She suspects, I think, but she doesn't want to face it. Up to now Tom has stayed clear of stilling."

"Then why now?" David's voice was sharp.

"Because since the baby's birth, Opal's had a serious anemia. Tom will let me supply the medicine, but as for money for 'brought-on' food—you've never seen pride until you've met the passion for independence in these folks." The Doctor ran his hand through his hair. "Well, Tom loves Opal, and back in these mountains there's only one real source of money, and that's the sale of good whiskey. Anyway, Cove people don't see anything criminal about home brew—they use whiskey to doctor everything from colds to snakebite. To them, making it is no more morally wrong than making wild strawberry preserves. I just couldn't see a man like Tom turned in." There was silence. The Doctor calmly took out his tobacco pouch and began filling his pipe. "His predicament just dramatizes the whole problem of a cash income in the mountains."

"All right, Doctor"—David sounded a bit rueful—"you've made a valid point, though I can't agree that moonshining is not a moral issue. Now how will we get cash for the mountain men other than moonshine? You thwarted justice last week. What's your alternative plan?" He sounded sarcastic.

The Doctor gave him an enigmatic look. "I don't know. I'm not God. I just live here—and want to help."

Wednesday evening Ruby Mae and I heard a ruckus in the yard. We went out and found Prince banging the sides of his stall and snorting, and the stable door ajar, though David was always careful to latch it. Inside, I found David's saddle lying on the floor. It was slashed and the girths ripped out. I ran to get a look at Prince. His beautiful flowing tail and mane had been sheared off and were lying on the ground. He looked denuded, pathetic. I began a hasty examination of his flanks, searching for any cuts or wounds. So far as I could tell, there were none.

"Oh Lordy, I could bust out cryin'," Ruby Mae said.

Tears were standing in my own eyes. Prince was a caricature. "Ruby Mae," I said, "go get Mr. Grantland."

She ran out, but at once began shrieking, "Holp! Teacher! Quick!"

I dashed to the stable door. In front of the schoolhouse, flames were leaping into the night. I picked up my skirts and ran. David had heard too; he and I reached the spot almost at the same instant. It was the wooden pulpit from the church, carried into the yard, ablaze.

"Can't save it now," David snapped. "But we've got to keep embers from leaping to the church roof."

He called Miss Ida, and soon we got a bucket brigade going. With the fifth pail of water, the fire sizzled down, and the four of us, wet and confounded, stared at the charred pulpit.

Next day the schoolchildren stood in indignant clusters staring at Prince. They had always been fond of David. Now they rallied around him, ready to do battle for Prince and against this "pizen-meanness." That support gave David his idea. He announced in school: "Because you feel as badly about Prince as I do, would you be willing to help me?" Hands eagerly went up. "I've saved the hair from Prince's mane and tail. If you'll help me make that hair into watch fobs, we'll sell them to buy a new saddle and a new pulpit and maybe some hymnbooks too."

The children were enthusiastic. David set up sawhorse tables, and early and late, boys and girls came and went, working on the fobs. Mr. Holcombe, a tinsmith of sorts, made tiny tin necks and rings for them. We wrote a long list of organizations and the response exceeded anything we anticipated. Over three hundred and fifty dollars flowed in—enough to replace the pulpit and Prince's saddle, buy new hymnbooks, and purchase a second horse, a chestnut mare named Buttons.

CHAPTER 12

ONE MORNING I had gone out on the back porch to shake the crumbs out of the breakfast tablecloth when I saw two mounted men riding toward the mission yard. A third in line, a tall, lean man, was walking beside his horse, pointing his gun at the two in front. A man's body was cradled in the saddle. As they got closer I recognized Bird's-Eye Taylor and Nathan O'Teale, their hands manacled to their saddlebows. I ran toward them and saw that the crumpled figure in the saddle was Tom McHone.

"Miss, I'm Gentry Long, United States marshal," the tall man said. "Now don't worry. There's been a raid and there was some shooting, but McHone is only wounded. Can you get a doctor?"

DR. MACNEILL located the bullet quickly, and removed it. It came, he told us, from a .32-caliber Smith and Wesson. But the marshal, Gentry Long, had been carrying a Winchester. Who, then, had shot Tom?

Later, I found Dr. MacNeill sitting by Tom's bed, studying him with a look of intense concentration. "How is he?" I whispered.

"Sleeping now. Barring complications, he should make it. Opal is with Miss Ida, getting a cup of coffee. She is taking it very well."

Indeed, everyone was amazed at Opal's calmness. Apparently she had expected something like this. Now it had happened, and her man was alive; she need worry no more about stillin'.

That afternoon, Ruby Mae—our inveterate scandalmonger— got me off in a corner. "Things is shorely catawampus in this here neck of the woods," she began in her doomsday voice. "Folks say thar was trickery. Tom McHone didn't tote square with the others. They say he informed on Nathan and Bird's-Eye and them North Carolina men they say was in on it."

I said, "Now Ruby Mae, we don't *know* that. Please don't stoke up this gossip-fire by more talk."

Later on that day, going to the kitchen, I heard David and Dr. MacNeill in the parlor. David's voice was harsh. "Doctor, how was the still finally taken—and how was Tom shot? You're hiding something. I remember some high-sounding talk about our working together. When do we start?"

"When do you start minding your own business?"

David's voice rose. "Liquor stored on church property is my business. A wounded man in the mission house is my business. This business was dumped on my doorstep."

As I went past the door, I saw David standing in the center of the parlor, taller than the Doctor, the color in his face making his brown eyes seem even darker. And the Doctor, hair tousled as always, hazel eyes flashing as he lashed out at David, "You're meddling in stuff you know nothing about. Lay off! For heaven's sake, man, lay *off!*" Blindly, never seeing me, he strode down the hall and slammed the front door.

That afternoon the jailer at Lyleton called on our new telephone. Nathan and Bird's-Eye had escaped from jail.

DAVID WENT to Knoxville to talk with the federal agents, get more facts about the raid, and find out whether or not Tom would have to stand trial for blockading.

Tom's wound was healing and he was getting restless. But still he would not talk about the raid. I felt desperate for Tom, though I tried to hide this from him and Opal. What chance did he have against Bird's-Eye? Was it possible that Dr. MacNeill had advised him to pull out of the blockading and that Tom's attempt to do so had miscarried? Was that what Dr. MacNeill was hiding?

When Dr. MacNeill next visited Tom, I caught up with him in the mission yard as he was leaving. "I need to talk to you—and privately," I said.

He looked at me, his eyebrows raised. "A pleasure, Miss Huddleston. How about your schoolroom?"

We went into the empty school. I sat down at my desk, but Dr. MacNeill walked around the room, looking at the children's work on the walls. "You're doing a good job with these children, Christy," he said. "And the children like you. Word gets around." He pulled up a chair and took his pipe out of his pocket. I watched as he filled it. "Would you tell me what those words are on the pipe?"

"It's Gaelic: *Tha mo chos air ceann mo naimhdean*. It means, 'My foot is on the head of my enemies'—a favorite saying of the MacNeills. . . . Now, what's on your mind?"

I took a deep breath. "Doctor, somebody tipped off the revs on the second location of that still. Was it you?"

"No. Though I want this stilling business straightened out as much as you do."

"Maybe. But I think you're holding back information that would help us protect Tom. Why did Tom get shot?"

He met my gaze unflinchingly, and I found myself thinking, either he is a good actor or I have this man wrong. He said, "I could give you five different situations where Tom could have caught a bullet in the back in a gun battle between the revs and blockaders. Christy, I cared about Opal and Tom while you were still in pinafores. I know a lot more about the Cove than you and David do. I suggest that both of you stick to your mission work."

"You don't believe in the mission, do you?"

"I would if you concentrated on the school and the good works and forgot the religious doctrines that just confuse people."

"You don't think religion has anything to offer? Dr. MacNeill, what do *you* believe in?"

He turned his hands outward in an expressive gesture. "I believe in God, in the sense of a starter-force for the universe. And I believe that love is the most creative force in the world. Trouble is, I've seen too much suffering, pain, hatred and dying to go along with Miss Alice's loving God. I suppose the truth must lie somewhere between believing in nothing and the elaborate case the Christians have built up." He waved his pipe airily. "But this is much too serious a discussion for a girl like you."

I ignored that. "You don't consider yourself a Christian?"

"No-o, come to think of it, I don't suppose I do. It never seemed important to me one way or the other. Why is it important to *you*, Christy? What's *your* philosophy of life?"

"Well—I believe that God made us with a free choice. We can choose for Him or against Him, decide to go His way or—"

"And what does that mean? How will it affect Tom's situation?"

"It affects it because evil is real and powerful and some of us live in an ivory tower, and—"

"You're quoting—probably from Miss Alice. Let's stop mouthing platitudes. Why is Christianity important to you?"

I was messing this up and I could have cried at my ineptness. Then my frustration boiled over. "All right, *be* sarcastic, make fun of what we believe. Religion is for frustrated or not-quite-normal people. You're a realist, and religion can't offer any solution compared to some of your medicine in a bottle. That is what you think." Hot tears stung my eyes. I jumped to my feet and turned my back on him.

"Christy, this is the real you talking now, not someone you're trying to be. You have fire in you, and I like fire in a woman!"

His coolness nettled me. I whirled to face him. He was giving me that measured look again—and I wanted to slap his face or pound my fists on his chest because he made me feel like a two-year-old. I hated him. I wanted—I wanted—I didn't know what I wanted. I turned and fled.

That night, Tom quietly left the mission.

DAVID arrived back the next afternoon, upset to find Tom gone. The trip to Knoxville had not been successful. All the prisoners in the jail had escaped, and Gentry Long had given David no clear answers about Tom. He had said, "Don't worry about Tom McHone, Mr. Grantland. There's no problem there." He had laughed a mirthless laugh. Nor would he discuss the raid. So most of our questions were still unanswered.

113

After supper, sitting with David on the porch, I told him of my talk with Dr. MacNeill. "When he questioned me about my beliefs, I—I didn't even make sense," I said. "David, when you tell people why you are a Christian, what do you say?"

David looked reflective. "Well, for one thing, I say that I'm no fundamentalist. I believe there is a scientific explanation for every mysterious happening in the Bible, if we but knew."

"What about Jesus raising Lazarus from the dead?" I asked. "Bethany was only a little village and everybody knew Lazarus."

"That's a tough one, I admit. But there could be any number of explanations. Lazarus may only have been in a coma."

"Then, you don't believe in Jesus' miracles?"

"Christy, you're getting into deep theological waters which will only confuse you more. I don't believe it matters so much what you believe as how you live. Jesus was concerned with ending injustices, with how people lived, whether they forgave one another. Dogma isn't important. It's the results in the community that count."

I felt unsatisfied. "David, why are you here at this mission?"

"Because I was assigned here for a job that needed to be done. Christy, there are almost as many ways to believe as there are Christians, and—"

The screen door banged. It was Miss Ida. "David, you've had a hard two days," she said sharply. "If you give courses in theology to one girl at a time, you'll never get anything done."

David laughed. "All right, Ida. I'll turn in."

He seemed relieved at the interruption.

NEXT DAY, after school, I went to Miss Alice's cabin. She opened the door, and I had scarcely gotten inside before I found myself saying, with no preliminaries, "I have to talk to you. Talking with Dr. MacNeill about my religion, I discovered I really don't know *what* I believe. That's a horrid discovery to make! Something inside me pointed an imperious finger in your direction and commanded, 'Go to Miss Alice!' "

A smile tugged at her mouth. "Christy, child, whatever that is on the inside of thee, it certainly has rare dramatic talent." She was serious again. "Christy, you made a *great* discovery. So many people never pause long enough to make up their minds about basic issues of life and death. They adopt sets of ideas they've picked up some place or other and never come to any conclusion for themselves. But you are facing these issues. That's good."

"But Miss Alice, one religion says this and another religion says that. Maybe one religion *is* as good as another. Who knows?"

"Somebody very wise left us a way we can be sure. It's as specific as a doctor's prescription. Here, I'll write it down." She opened a desk drawer, took out a piece of notepaper, and began to write. As I stood watching her, a faint fragrance—something like dried sweet clover—wafted toward me. It stirred some vague memory.

Then Miss Alice blotted the paper, folded it and handed it to me. "When you take a written prescription from your doctor," she said, "the first step after that is yours. You move on this"—she indicated the paper—"and then God will move. I'll guarantee it."

I stared at her, fascinated by her certainty. "Go on now," she said. "You're dying to see what I wrote. Go—and take that first step." Her eyes sparkling, she waved me off.

I left her and started away from the mission, toward a little, rocky woodland room I knew by a miniature waterfall. As I walked, I lifted the paper to my nose. That same fragrance clung to the paper. Then I remembered the woman's clothes Dr. Mac-Neill had loaned me one afternoon. That was the same sachet.

Sitting on a rock among ferns and laurel, I opened the paper. It read simply:

If any man will do his (the Father's) *will, he shall know of the doctrine, whether it be of God, or whether I speak of myself.*

I read the words over two, three times, feeling let down. What had I expected? Some magic, obviously. I tried to recall Miss Alice's exact words: "Go and take that first step," she had said. The next move would be up to God. But what first step?

I stared at the paper again. *Any man* . . . well, that could be me. If Christy will do His will— But what was the Father's will for me? I tried to reason it out, and faces danced through my mind. David . . . Little Burl . . . Lundy . . . Dr. MacNeill . . . Fairlight . . . Opal . . . *Opal!* My thoughts stood still, like an instrument pointing. Go to Opal. Opal is the key. But the key to what? To the tangled relationships in the Cove? Surely not! . . . But the thought held.

When I rose, the sun was low in the sky. If I hurried, there would be time to get to Opal's before dark. I had not the least idea what I would say or do when I got there.

AT THE boundary of the McHone land, I called loudly, but there was no response. Then, when I was halfway across the yard, a group of men stepped from the woods. I stopped short, my heart thumping. The man in the center was Bird's-Eye Taylor. The men stood rigidly, their hands on their rifles, looking at me, and I realized that I had never before looked into faces as hard as these.

Finally, Bird's-Eye spat into the dirt. "Come traipsin' to do some more pesterin' with other folks' business?" he snarled.

"I've come to see Opal, that's all."

"Go on in, but don't try no dodge. I'm a leetle keerless-like with this here hog rifle."

Heavy wooden shutters had been closed and barred across Opal's window, making the cabin look like a place besieged. Before I could knock, the front door swung open, and as I entered, Opal rushed at me in the darkness, clasping my arms. "Oh, Miz Christy—Tom's hidin' in the woods! I kept wishin'—I needed you so much—how did you know?"

"Opal," I said, "I *didn't* know. I'm here because—well—God told me to come." Immediately the words were out, they sounded slick. But what I had just said, I meant literally. "I got a thought, like an order inside: Go to Opal."

My eyes were adjusting to the gloom, and I could see Opal's face register in turn wonderment, acceptance, then joy. "Then God knows about Tom and me and Bird's-Eye. He *cares!*"

Somewhere in the room a child whimpered. The children were huddled behind Isaak, the twelve-year-old. Now Opal sank into a rocker and held out her arms to them, and the two younger boys came scrambling. As she cuddled Vincent and Toot, she said, "If God knows what's goin' on here, will you ask Him to tell us what to do next?"

I sat down on the cricket stool by the hearth. I had never prayed aloud in my life except for the school prayers, but I plunged in. "God," I said, "we don't have the least idea of the way out for Tom and Opal, but You wouldn't have told me to come here if You didn't have some sort of plan. Would You please tell us what to do about Bird's-Eye?" Sudden self-consciousness all but smothered my words. "And thank You very much."

Gently Opal slid Vincent off her lap, rose, and began stirring the cabbage and side meat cooking over the fire. Finally she said, "Bird's-Eye's daddy didn't treat him good. Whupped him just to be whupping. He learned Bird's-Eye to cotch birds in a trap, bust their legs, make a play-game of rockin' them till they querled over dead. Taught him to be such a good aim that he could drive a rifle ball plumb through the eye of a bird as far away as he could see. That's how he come by his name, Bird's-Eye."

Opal sat down again, wiping her steaming face with her apron. "Bird's-Eye couldn't stomach all that hatefulness, so when he was fourteen he put out for the thick wilderness. Roamed from one settle-ment to another for goin'-on seven years, let his grievin' mother think a varmint had got him. Then sudden-like, Bird's-Eye showed up at his old home one evenin'. Lordamercy, his mother most died dead on the spot. But she welcomed him home.

"After that, Bird's-Eye was stuck on me for a while. Only time I ever seed him nice was one spring afternoon. We had gone traipsin' through the woods. Jumped a deer and Bird's-Eye shot it. It was a doe and in the breshes was its fawn—spotted, wobbly, bright leetle eyes. Bird's-Eye busted one of its legs with a rock. I got fightin' mad, fumped his head. Told him that while I was thar he wasn't a-goin' rock any more animals that couldn't fight back.

"Bird's-Eye he looked at that leetle cryin' fawn like he was

117

seein' it for the first go-round. Took it onto his lap, splinted that pore leetle broke leg. His face was a study as he looked at the leetle thing, like somethin' new was bein' borned inside him. A body could have confidenced that Bird's-Eye—if'n he had stayed that way." Opal's eyes were soft.

"Miz Christy, you said that God sent you an idea that wouldn't go by. Wal, here's *my* idea—that I'm to mosey out to the yard, talk to Bird's-Eye and keep a-seein' him like he was whilst he was docterin' that fawn. See what'n'all happens after that. You stand in the door." She took off her apron and one of her rare smiles broke over her face. "God told you to come—right here—to this here cabin." She hugged me—and was gone.

I stood in the doorway with Vincent and Toot hanging onto my skirts, Isaak standing to one side, trying to act manly. Opal had a fine line to walk, it seemed to me. Since Bird's-Eye had once considered himself her sweetheart, she would have to avoid letting him think that she was turning her back on Tom now. There was far too much "step-husband" business in the Cove— another man stepping in when the husband stepped out. Most of the mountain killings were over women or land.

"You'uns must be hongry," we heard Opal say to the men. "Thar's cabbage and side meat cookin' in thar, and hot corn pone. I could tote some out to you."

It was so unprecedented an offer that the men were at a loss how to react. Opal now tried more female strategy. "Bird's-Eye, if you'd like to leave yer kinsmen guardin', Miz Christy can bring vittles out to them. It would be more fittin' for you, bein' the head of the clan, to eat inside. And I'm sure you're atter Tom yit, but hate won't fill up your stommicks, and my corn pone and huckleberry pre-serves will. And I made me a sweet 'tater pie. Some folks are plumb foolish 'bout my 'tater pie."

"Wal, I reckon—" Bird's-Eye hesitated. "Con-found it. Probably I'm a con-sarned idiot." He followed Opal to the cabin.

I backed away from the door and the children retreated again to the farthest corner of the room. Bird's-Eye nodded to me but did not take off his hat. He removed the cartridges from his gun, placed them on the mantel and stood the gun beside the fire-place. No mountain man would violate hospitality by fighting while "eatin' another's salt." Now Opal would have her chance.

I carried heaping tin plates to the men outside and they fell on the food ravenously. When I got back, I found Bird's-Eye eating just as eagerly. "*That* hits whar ye can hold it!" he said.

In the time-honored way of women, Opal waited until her guest's stomach was full. Then she began, "Bird's-Eye, I memorize how you oncet favored me. Thar was that fawn with the busted leg you splinted up for me. Did ye know I had that thar fawn for a pet till he was full-growed? Aye. So I sez to myself, 'It's my turn to favor Bird's-Eye now.' "

For Opal this was a considerable speech. I saw Bird's-Eye's face relax a little. "What'n ever happened to the fawn?"

"He went boundin' off to the woods one day. Never saw him again." Opal went closer to Bird's-Eye. "Looky here, Bird's-Eye, whilst you was fixin' that fawn's leg, you was a real man. You know that? Killin's easy. Any addlepated fool kin pull a trigger. It's *fixin'* that's hard. It's plumb foolish for you not to let folks in the Cove see more of *that* Bird's-Eye. Lordamercy, if ye'd take a mind to, you could fix up this whole Cove. You was meant to be a clan leader, Bird's-Eye. I've knowed that for a long time."

Opal's words had hit target. Bird's-Eye sat for a time, transfixed by this idea. Then he said, "Wal, Opal, you jest mought have some good notions thar." He stood and reached for his cartridges and gun. "Tell you what. We'uns will lay off here for a spell." He laughed mirthlessly. "But don't expect nothin'. We'uns will be back." And he walked out the door.

CHAPTER 13

I STAYED the night with Opal, sharing Toot's bed. I slept only fit-fully, for the mission would be alarmed about me, yet we dared not send Isaak to tell them where I was.

Later that night, we heard a soft tapping at the door. It was

Tom and Uncle Bogg. The old man had found Tom's hiding place in the woods. We dared not light a lamp lest Bird's-Eye's vigilantes be watching, but by pale moonlight filtering through cracks in the shutters, we huddled for a whispered consultation.

It was obvious that the hours of crouching like a hunted animal had debilitated Tom, who was not altogether recovered from his wound. The shifting shadows drew his cheekbones sharply as with a black crayon, with furrows of pain around his mouth. Opal's solicitude was wrenching to watch. She kept thrusting food at her husband for which he had no appetite. No creature comfort could assuage the hurt in his haunted eyes.

How could Tom contend with the many men determined to kill him? Unless he crossed the state line or went far from home—ideas he rejected—that left only the jail or the mission house as sanctuaries. We agreed that his best course was to try to reach the mission in the dark. He lingered long enough to look down into the face of each sleeping child as if to imprint the images on his mind, and then Opal trailed him to the door. Clumsily, Tom patted his wife's shoulder. "Don't fret, Opal. Hit's bound to be settled soon—one way or t'other."

Next morning the McHone children, Uncle Bogg and I made for the mission through the woods in plenty of time for the opening of school. As we came in sight of the big house, we saw people milling around the yard. Something was wrong.

David ran to me. He looked haggard. "Christy! Where on earth *were* you? I spent half the night searching. Thank God, you're safe!" But then his eyes told me.

"Tom?" My lips formed the word soundlessly.

"Time for school," David said loudly. "Isaak, why don't you go on ahead?"

Isaak looked at David scornfully. "Preacher, you ain't foolin' us none. Have they—got my Paw?"

I had never seen such an agony of compassion on David's face. He looked at the boy, taking his measure. Then he said, "Isaak, you're a man. I can see that. But Toot and Vincent here—"

"They've got *me*." He stood very straight, bracing himself.

"Isaak, we found your father there," David pointed. "He almost—made it to the house. Shot in the back—just once." He put an arm protectingly around Isaak and I sank to the ground and drew Toot and Vincent to me. I wanted to thrust the thought of Opal away. Opal with her dream of reforming Bird's-Eye.

"I want to see my Paw, Rev'end. Take me to my Paw now."

Without another word, David turned and led Isaak to the mission house. I longed to run after them, somehow to stand between Isaak and the moment toward which he was walking so steadily. I remembered his sensitive response to the beauty of "Kubla Khan." Oh, shield him some way! I wanted to cry out to heaven. Don't let this look at his dead father's face send the bitter desire for revenge hurtling down to yet another generation.

That day was a blur of grief. Next morning David and I started for the McHone cabin to make plans for the funeral. At the cemetery on the brow of Persimmon Hill we saw Isaak, with a shovel, digging a grave. As we rode up, I saw that his face was white. He said, "Grandpaw woke me at the crack of dawn. I was frightened, his lips was pulled so tight. Brought me here and says, 'Dig here.' But Preacher, I don't even know how deep to dig hit—" His voice trailed off.

David reached out his hand. "Isaak, give me that spade."

The boy handed it over, hastily brushing away a tear with his sleeve. Then he turned his back on the gravesite to bury his face in Prince's shoulder, talking softly to him as if grateful for the comfort of any living thing.

I thought angrily, Out of what coldness of heart could the squire ask Isaak to dig his father's grave? We tethered both horses and Isaak sat down on the grass close beside me. I said, "Isaak, sometimes when people hurt on the inside, they say or do things they're sorry for afterward. Maybe it's that way with your grandfather." His forlorn eyes gazed at me but he did not respond.

From the energy with which David was wielding the spade, he must be working off some of his anger against Uncle Bogg. At last he straightened up and mopped his face. "That should do it,

Isaak. Why don't you ride to your cabin with us? You can tell your grandfather that it's all finished."

But when we reached the cabin, Uncle Bogg was not there. Opal explained about the grave. "He wanted to hand the hate on to Isaak. He told him to say out loud with every shovelful of dirt, *'They killed my Paw.'*"

OFTEN the men killed in a feud were buried furtively, but Opal wanted "a real funeralizing" for her Tom. David was immediately wary of this. Mountain funerals were usually sentimental orgies, lasting three hours, with wild demonstrations of grief. Such lamentations provided no comfort for a bereaved family in desperate need of consolation and help, and the emotions aroused helped feed the smoldering hates. There would be tears and moanings and then feelings of hate and desire for revenge.

David tried to persuade Opal to have a quiet, comforting, victorious kind of service, but Opal had her own ideas. "Preacher, ye jest can't stop folks from mournin' their loved ones. And I'm a-longin' to hear Miz Henderson preach the Word at the funeralizing."

"Fine, Opal. That's a great idea." David seemed relieved that Miss Alice would share the responsibility at the service.

Most of the Cove was at the funeral. Uncle Bogg was especially pathetic to see. He had withdrawn into himself, refusing even to talk about Tom's death.

According to custom, Tom's coffin was open, placed in the middle of the McHone cabin. Opal had covered the outside with black calico, the inside with white muslin, trying to make it fancy by fringing the edge with scissors. A little American flag and a badge reading GOD IS OUR TRUST AND CONFIDENCE were pinned to Tom's suit, and Opal had tucked an apron in at his feet.

It was the apron that hurt me most. It was a symbol of the heartbreak of women in a man's world where vendettas and wars must always go on—and on—for a man's pride, which he calls honor or integrity, while women are stripped of those whom they most love. Then there is nothing left except to bow the head in grief—and tuck an apron in at the feet.

I searched for anything I might use to cheer Opal in the midst of my own grief. I was determined I was not going to hide behind false piety. God, I thought, if You really are there, why did You let this happen? Why? Opal and Tom were trying to do the right thing. If You're a God of love, why didn't You reward that?

The hymns did not help my skeptical mood: "Come and Lie with Me in the Old Church Yard," and then one that began, *He is gone, our precious darling, They have laid him in the tomb. . . .*

When they were finished, Miss Alice came forward and stood at the foot of the coffin. She looked at Opal, her gray eyes tender, and at each McHone child in turn. Then she began the story of Jesus' friendship with Martha, Mary, and their brother Lazarus. She said that Jesus was sometimes lonely enough to reach out for human friendship. "When He was too weary to go on, He knew that there would always be a welcome awaiting Him in Bethany. There would be a quiet arbor, long shadows and a breeze, and after they had eaten, the four friends would talk until their souls were knitted together.

"One day, when Jesus was several days' journey from Bethany, a runner came with news that Lazarus was dangerously ill. But—Jesus did not rush to Lazarus' bedside. He tarried, while Martha and Mary were almost out of their minds with worry. And then Lazarus died. Why had Jesus failed Martha and Mary? It was hard for them not to be bitter. The body was bound with linen bandages and laid in the family tomb, a cave in the side of a hill.

"Four days later, Jesus came. The sisters spoke words of rebuke: *Lord, if Thou hadst been here, my brother had not died.* But Jesus did not accept the rebuke. Gently, He spoke to Martha one of the greatest promises ever to fall from His lips:

I am the Resurrection, and the Life: He that believeth in Me, though he were dead, yet shall he live: And whosoever liveth and believeth in Me, shall never die.

"Then He said, *Where have ye laid him?* And Mary and all who followed Him down the road, saw tears in His eyes. *Behold how He loved him!* they said with wonderment.

"Friends, when the Master spoke to Martha about seeing the glory of God, He meant that literally. At the door of the cave, He asked that the stone be rolled away. He prayed, and then loudly commanded, *Lazarus, come forth.*

"Suppose I were able now to command Tom to rise up out of his coffin. Wouldn't we all go wild with joy? And so Mary and Martha, close beside Him, watched wide-eyed. Yes, there was a stirring inside the tomb! They dashed in, delirious with joy. Feverishly they unwound the grave clothes. Then they supported Lazarus, weak from lack of food, out of the cave and a mighty shout went up from the townsfolk—hallelujahs and songs.

"Not then, not now. No. The Master doesn't fail His friends, not ever. And He cares still. He cares about Tom and about how unnecessary Tom's death was. He cares about Opal and Uncle Bogg and Vincent and Toot and Isaak. He is weeping with us now—in this cabin in Cutter Gap—just as He did with Mary and Martha and their friends in Bethany long ago."

Now Opal was crying softly, her face hidden. Alice Henderson went on. "But He would be friends with us—on one condition: That *Ye do whatsoever I command you* . . . And, *These things I command you, that ye love one another.* If we had loved one another, Tom would be alive today.

"So I want you to carry two thoughts away. First, the Master cares. He suffers with us. Second, we can have His friendship only if we are willing to let go our hating and feuding and *love one another.*

"Let us talk to our Friend now in prayer."

As she ended, I heard soft weeping—but nothing else. Then a square of white cambric, cut in a curious design, was laid over Tom's face for the trip to the cemetery in the mission wagon, and the lid of the coffin was nailed on, but lightly.

At the cemetery the coffin was set by the grave and there came a sound I shall remember as long as I live—the screeching of the long nails as they were drawn out of the poplar wood. The lid was lifted off and the cambric square removed. To me, the most awful custom was that each member of the family was now supposed to come forward and kiss the lips of the dead person. I could not look at that, so I concentrated on the top of a magnificent hemlock.

Someone started a dirge in a loud wail. I looked back as a woman keeled over in a faint and screams began. Opal threw herself on the coffin. "Tom, Tom darlin'. I can't let them put you in the ground. Tom, this can't be all!" David stepped forward to pick Opal up and support her. He signaled, and the coffin lid was nailed on. Opal turned away, sobbing. A brief prayer by David, shouting above the dirge, and it was over.

I knew that it was this night that Opal would need me most. But I was a coward. I slipped away and fled back to my room at the mission house.

CHAPTER 14

AFTER TOM's murder hot feelings died down and there was a lull in blockading. Perhaps Miss Alice had had an effect; perhaps men were frightened by the result of their own passions. Bird's-Eye and Nathan were still at large. Lundy had crept back to school, but would not speak of his father. Day by day, the boy looked more and more unkempt and wild-eyed.

Opal was still riding a wave of combined numbness and victory that I did not understand at all, but Uncle Bogg was in a deep trough of pain. With a killing in his own family, he saw feuding in a new light—one good result from Tom's death. As for David, he lashed himself for Tom's death. If he had not pressed so relentlessly against moonshining, Tom might be alive.

Miss Alice's view was that the mission had a larger task than finding stills. "Preach the gospel, David, to the hearts of men," she said. "That's your business. Then the fruits, including the reforms, will follow. The question is how to get rid of the evil in men's hearts. Attacking corruption is like cutting weeds. In a fortnight they will grow again. And attacking the men themselves won't work either. We want to *win* people, not war with them."

"Well then, how would *you* deal with evil?"

"By demonstrating to people a way more powerful than evil. Most of us are still talking—in clichés too—a religion we haven't begun living. When your heart is ablaze with the love of God, when you love other people so much that you dare to tell them about Jesus with no apologies—then never fear, the fire will leap from your heart to blaze in the depths of other men's beings. And then reforms will follow as surely as the fruit comes after the blossom on the tree."

"It's too slow a way."

"David, the other is no way at all."

ACTUALLY, though David was not ready to admit it, Miss Alice's remarks made an impression on him. But he and I agreed that we did not yet have the love of God ablaze in our hearts, nor could we manufacture it in ourselves.

David also suspected that he did not yet know how or what to preach to change people's hearts. I wondered how many preachers *did* know? They fell back on creating church organizations, meetings—all of the busy church activities for which Miss Alice had a delightful tag: "Digging worms instead of fishing."

One night when we were out walking, David said, "Christy, I'm not a bit sure that I belong in the ministry."

"David! Surely you're just discouraged."

"No, that isn't it. You see, entering seminary wasn't entirely my choice. Mother was always determined that one of her three sons would be a preacher. I let mother and Ida stampede me."

David had been holding my hand as we walked along. Now his fingers tightened. "But Christy, no matter what I'll be doing, I'll need you. It's only come to me recently how much I need you. I'm asking you to marry me, Christy."

I stood in the road staring at him, too astonished to say anything. In the silence, he kissed me gently. Then he pulled me to him and kissed me harder. "It's all right, Christy. Speech isn't necessary between us. Anyway, I don't want an answer tonight."

Later, I lay awake into the small hours of the morning, excited and yet puzzled about David's proposal. How often I had dreamed of that tender moment in the future! In my mind it had always been in a romantic setting like a summerhouse, and the man was dashing, yet tender. Miss Alice had said to me, "Christy, thee is inclined to think of the poetry side of things, not the prose side." How well she understood me!

David's proposal had been so different from the imagined one. He had asked me to marry him, and yet, it had been a strange half commitment of himself. David was old enough to know what he wanted out of life, but there was something tentative and indefinite about him. He had come to the Cove at the suggestion of his seminary. He had entered the ministry because his mother and sister had expected it. Naturally, he was puzzled about where he belonged.

Perhaps the destiny that had driven me to the Cove was not only for myself but to help David. Was my future bound up with his? That was what I had to find out.

I STILL saw Fairlight once or twice a week. She admired me extravagantly and could not find enough ways to express her gratitude for my friendship. Sometimes it would be a bunch of wild flowers or a homemade basket filled with wild berries left at the mission door; sometimes a laboriously copied poem. My friendship gave Fairlight the courage to let her true self out of prison. If a girl from "yon" singled her out to spend long hours with her, then, perhaps that secret person on the inside, who from shyness and deprivation had kept herself hidden all these years, was a woman worth knowing.

We explored the woods and mountains together, our picnic food packed in one of Fairlight's homemade honeysuckle baskets. It became a game each time to find a picnic spot more delightful than the last one—always beside one of those clear mountain streams where baby trout, playing tag, could be seen as plainly as if they were swimming under glass. Like a couple of children we would toss off our shoes to wade, tying our skirts around our waists, then dry our toes luxuriously on moss and select a flat rock for our table. We added watercress from the stream to our sandwiches, and Fairlight taught me to pick mint, chew it, and then take a drink of the mountain water. The mint made it the most delicious drink of water in the world.

Sometimes the day was so magical that I would dance, and hug Fairlight. Fairlight understood. She always understood. Sometimes we would just lie on the fragrant pine needles, looking up at the sky. I might never have gotten answers to the questions that had driven me to the Cove without those quiet hours in the mountains. Even a small city like Asheville provides artificial distractions which separate us from the roots of our life.

Often I would lie there thinking about David. With the pressures in the Cove, there had been little chance for conversation between us. He reached for my hand whenever we were alone— which was not very often—but he told me so little about himself! He liked to joke and tease, but he was reluctant to discuss serious matters.

EVEN IN the pleasant forest, I hungered for the heights. Upward, upward, my eyes would rove to the necklace of deep blue-green firs near the top of each summit. What was it like to walk up there? I had to know.

When I told Fairlight this, she protested. "That nearest knob, it's more'n four good looks, and a right smart walk." But she humored me and we struck out one day on a trail up the mountain. It followed the knob's contours, but even so I soon found myself reaching for rocks and laurel bushes to hang onto, and often we stopped to rest.

Finally only pride kept me going. We climbed through scrub-woods and, gradually, the belt of hardwood trees—sugar maples, beeches, birches, lindens and chestnuts. And from there we made the final push into the blue-green necklace I had seen from a distance: the fragrant groves of balsam and red cedar—a sylvan, fairy place. From there we crossed a tiny meadow, a tangle of bushes, Queen Anne's lace and a red flower that I did not know.

And then—at last—the top. I lay on my stomach, inching as close as I dared to the edge of the rock shelf. Wave upon wave of green and smoky blue were spread out below in majesty and power.

Fairlight sat behind me, silently. This splendor spoke its own message. It made me aware of a vital connection between me and the Authority behind all this beauty.

Dr. MacNeill had said that he believed in some "starter-force" but he could not credit God with a concern for individuals. Now I knew that this starter-force *was* personal. It insisted that all life was precious—Fairlight and I, every bird and squirrel, every tree reaching through its forest cover for the light. It cried that fear and discouragement were a desecration of this beauty; that hope and effort were always right.

But to the mountain people, Nature was stern. God's lightnings flashed from peak to peak; His hand was in storm and pestilence, in hatred and poverty. Man's only chance was to ally himself to God and desperately hope that in the end this terrible Jehovah would bring the faithful ones to glory.

So fatalism was all too common here. Miss Alice had told me of a sixteen-year-old girl in her school in Cataleechie, dying of tuberculosis. The girl's one request was that Miss Alice make her a shroud, so that she could see it before she died. Indignantly, Miss Alice had refused, suggesting to the girl that instead, she would do better to center her thinking on health.

But death had had more dramatic appeal. The girl persuaded her father to measure her and build her a pine coffin. Then she had had herself photographed lying in the coffin "so that I can see how fancy-fine I'll look." She had died eight months later.

A few days after our climb, Fairlight and I were sitting on her front porch shelling shucky beans. She stared at the pinnacle opposite, with the look I had seen so often. "Christy," she said, "I do think it's witched. Most every day it puts me in mind of the shadder o' death." Her pan of beans slipped off her lap. She reached for my arm. "What is to be, will be. But Christy, I git the trembles when I think about bein' put in a box and a-lyin' thar covered over with dirt."

I started to say, "Fairlight, how silly! You're not going to die—"

But Fairlight's battle with the mountain was a personal battle; it was her life pitted against the shadow. And even as I watched, the sun dipped behind the peak and the gloom slanted across her upturned face. . . .

THE NEXT day Fairlight and I were on our way home from a picnic when we realized that a man was sliding along the far side of a big boulder. Fairlight grabbed my arm—and Bird's-Eye Taylor stepped into our path. Involuntarily I drew back.

"Don't aim to do ye no harm." He was holding out a piece of grubby paper. "I'd be beholden, if'n ye'd give this here to Opal. Thank ye kindly." And he disappeared around the boulder.

I went at once to the McHone cabin and, as Opal's eyes filled with tears, read her the words scrawled on the paper.

"Opal—it was not me kilt Tom. When I can cum back safe I will tell you how it was. A friend writ this for me. X BT"

CHAPTER 15

MISS ALICE, David and I wanted to use the closing exercises at school to try to pull the Cove people closer together, so every pupil was to have some part in the program for the parents. I hoped the program would be a demonstration for some of our victories of the past seven months. If only the boys would behave!

I went to the school early, but found the Becks and the Allens already there. "Miz Christy, this school is a sight to be-hold," Mrs. Beck said, looking at the room we had decorated with rhododendron leaves, ferns, wild lilies and red elderberry branches.

Lundy Taylor sauntered in and handed me a pail of huckleberries. Smirking, he leaned close. "Picked them myself—for you." There was no mistaking the smell of liquor on his breath.

"Thanks, Lundy," I said automatically. I wondered what I should do; but Lundy went to his seat docilely.

Within twenty minutes the room was crowded to the doors with parents standing along the walls. Even Miss Ida was there, dressed in her best black taffeta. David greeted the parents and then called on Mountie O'Teale. The Mountie who came forward was a different child from the defeated girl of last January. She was dressed in clean starched gingham and her eyes sparkled. She spoke slowly. "Fathers and mothers—we hope—you like—our program. We hope—you have—a good time." Not one stutter! It was a proud moment for Mountie and for me.

Then all the children filed to the front of the room to sing "America" (which I had finally taught them), and the ballad they loved best, "Sourwood Mountain."

After that, nine first, second, and third graders stood in a row, each with a large sheet of paper with one letter printed on it. Together, the letters spelled OUR SCHOOL. They recited in turn: Little Burl (well again): "O stands for oblige. We're much obliged for yer comin' today." Joshua Bean: "U stands for united—all together." . . . And so on. At the end, the audience clapped loudly, and the children, very proud of themselves, sat down.

"Now we have Lundy Taylor," I said. There was no response. Lundy was slumped back in his seat, his eyes closed, breathing heavily. David signaled me to go on to the next child. "And next on our program we have Creed Allen."

Creed marched to the front with the raccoon, Scalawag, riding cockily on one shoulder. "Now I'll tell ye about coons," Creed said, as if beginning a naturalist's lecture. "Coons are awful good hands to climb trees. They eat frogs, turtles, berries and crayfish. Corn too, and they wash everything before they—"

His voice was drowned in yipping as Jeb Spencer's two hounds streaked to the front of the room. Scalawag leaped on top of Creed's head, screaming frantically as the dogs clawed Creed's legs, and the children in turn flung themselves on the dogs until Jeb herded them away. It was not the performance that Creed had planned, but everyone enjoyed it.

In spite of such absurdities—each adding to the fun—our program was a success. For the Scripture-memorization prize, the children had picked their own selections. There were some nice ones: the Twenty-fourth Psalm; a portion of Romans Eight; the familiar, *For God so loved the world* . . . Then Festus Allen stood up and began reeling off a whole "begat" chapter from Genesis:

> *"These are the generations of Shem: Shem . . . begat Ar-phax-ad two years after the flood: . . . And Ar-phax-ad lived five and thirty years, and begat Salah: . . . And Salah lived thirty years, and begat Eber: . . . And . . ."*

Festus barreled on right to the end of the chapter. It was the longest selection and Miss Alice gravely bestowed a beautiful new Bible upon Festus of the red hair and the impudent grin.

During refreshments Miss Alice asked for quiet. "Christy Huddleston, up here by me—please." Puzzled, I went to her. "Friends, last January someone who had never taught school before, came to us, with the dream of helping you boys and girls. Already we've seen the longest school term in Cutter Gap so far, and it's been a great term. Much of this we owe to David Grantland— and to Christy Huddleston, whose presence has made it vital. Christy, this is for thee."

Emotion stung my eyes as I opened the package. It was a graceful carved deer. "John Spencer's work," Miss Alice said. "He wanted it to be from all of us. He worked on it three months."

I WAS to spend the month-long harvest vacation with my family. Gradually, during the days since David had asked me to marry him, I had realized that I could not, for some reason that would not come clear to me, rush into a formal engagement. Perhaps I needed to be away from him to get more perspective on the situation. I told him I needed time to think over his proposal, and to my surprise, he made no protest.

The day before I was to leave for my vacation at home, Miss Alice sent for me. She gave me tea, and as I sipped it, she said suddenly: "Long ago, I knew thee would come to the Cove, Christy. I didn't know how or when, but I was expecting thee. I didn't know what thee would be like. Or from what kind of background. But whenever a new insight would come to me, I would jot it down, thinking, What joy it will be to share this with her someday. Whenever I've had a real success with the highlanders, I've thought, I must remember to tell *her* that."

I felt very small and humble. "I don't deserve that."

"Deserve! Child, none of us deserves anything." Abruptly, her mood shifted. "Christy, for some time now, I've been wanting to talk to you, woman to woman. You're so eager to taste life, all of it, to the full." Her eyes sought mine in a level straight gaze. "And Christy, you've been putting me on a pedestal. We human beings weren't meant to sprout wings on this earth. You mustn't go home with such notions about me. So I'm going to tell thee a true story. That's why I asked thee to come here."

She was still looking at me unwaveringly. "Christy, no little girl ever loved her father more than I. I used to sit on his lap by the hour. Touch is important to children. I drew a sort of nourishment from the feel of leaning back against father's black broadcloth cutaway coat. In his Quaker garb he may have looked austere to others, but never to me. He had twinkly eyes, curves of fun around his mouth. I adored my mother too, but in a different way.

"In those days parents were reluctant to talk to their girls at all about sex. In the case of our family, this silence was a tragedy. You wouldn't believe how ignorant I was.

"When I was thirteen, what we called a 'ministering Friend'—a Quaker from England—visited us. When he made much of me, I was ecstatic for many of his ways were like my father's. He had traveled in the South Seas, had engrossing stories to tell. He would spin these stories out endlessly, while I sat on a stool near his knee. Sometimes he would stroke my hair.

"I was still very much a little girl, so my parents saw nothing odd about these story hours. This man came back the next year, and the next. When my parents were not around, he began to tell me of a discovery he had made—that the Spirit of God was a sort of divine electricity that could flow through touch, through laying the hands on the body of another. In the Bible there was passage after passage to show me how Jesus had laid His hands on people to minister. And there was just enough truth mixed in with his

133

false interpretation to make it seem valid to an eagerly questing young girl. For I wanted to make myself worthy of some good and noble destiny in the world."

There was a weight on my chest. "Miss Alice—please, do I have to hear this? I'd rather not."

"When I'm finished, Christy, thee will understand why I had to tell the story." Relentlessly, she went on. "The only thing not understandable is the patience of that seduction. When I was fifteen there was a certain amount of 'the laying on of hands.' Some of it I thought odd; but we had been taught to think of these traveling Friends as divinely chosen oracles of God. And yes, I felt a thrill because I was a normal girl. But because I was so ignorant of sex, I interpreted the thrill in exactly the spiritual way that the man meant me to interpret it. So I looked forward to the man's visit the spring that I was sixteen.

"One afternoon my parents had gone to the country. They trusted him alone with me, for word had not yet reached Pennsylvania that he had been sharply discredited in England. The man told me that he had made even greater discoveries than last year. The words that he whispered to me as his hands moved over my body were blasphemy. I'll draw the curtain there, Christy—but I soon knew that this was wrong, was of evil all the way. I had been duped. I began fighting the man, pummeling him with my fists, but it was too late. When he was finished, I was weeping, crumpled at his feet, no longer a virgin.

"I should have told my parents that night, but the same Victorian reticences that had sealed their lips to sex instruction sealed mine. I took a bath and changed my clothes, and dashed cold water on my eyelids until the tearstains were gone. That night at dinner I was silent, but the visiting Friend declaimed eloquently about the 'indwelling Light,' and my parents listened, fascinated. He left the next day for England.

"By the next month I guessed that I was with child. There are no words to describe the agony of those weeks. Finally, I told my father and mother, and sorrow descended on our house.

"Father was a gentle man, and I had not known that he was

134

capable of such anger. He tried to track down the man, but he had disappeared somewhere in New Zealand.

"The next question was what to do? My parents wanted me to find someone to adopt the baby. But it didn't seem right to me to give away my baby. Nothing could change what had happened, and my life, I felt, was set now in a certain pattern, with no fairy-tale imaginings or running away possible. Probably I would never marry; the kind of man I wanted to marry might not want me now. So why not rear the child I was bearing? In the end, my parents agreed. I did go away to have the baby. She was a beautiful child, a girl. Then I came home to Ardmore.

"Father asked the head of our Quaker Meeting, Sarah Lindsay, to come to our home. She was a tiny woman, but a great one. She listened gravely to my father, hands resting on her lap, praying and listening, as if ready to receive anything heaven might care to give. After a long Quaker silence, she spoke directly to me. 'Thee has made the right choice. Now thee will know, as few humans ever know it, the love of God. Betimes it will mold thee into a great spirit. And thy little girl shall be loved in our Meeting as no child has ever been loved before.'

"At that I started weeping and couldn't stop. Sarah's words began the melting of something hard and bitter in me. I had indeed made the right choice, because in rejecting secrecy, I also rejected the road to cynicism. And Sarah's prophecy about our Meeting came true. When she told them they rallied around me.

"My experience had far-reaching effects on our Quaker community. Courageously, they began sex instruction for the young. And they took a new look at the place of emotion and the inner Light in religion. Several persons, bringing their common sense and intelligence to bear, must agree on new 'insights.'

"To get back to me. I lived at home and taught school. Happiness flowed into our house again, but for me there is a scar and compassion for anyone who has been hurt by life.

"Before his death, my father legally adopted my daughter. She grew up to be a tall, beautiful woman with large expressive eyes like yours, Christy. Except that your hair's darker, you look enough

135

like Margaret to be her twin." I thought back to my first morning in Cutter Gap, when Miss Alice had opened her front door and had been visibly startled at seeing me.

"Margaret died three years ago." For the first time, Miss Alice seemed to be trying to keep her voice matter-of-fact. "Thee must know, Christy. Margaret became Dr. MacNeill's wife."

MISS ALICE had jolted me, but in stepping down from the pedestal on which I had placed her she had, paradoxically, made herself greater—a flesh-and-blood woman who had been through the fires and had emerged a stronger person, with deeper compassion.

Back at home, I thought of all she had taught me. I had believed in gradations of God's acceptance, according to how bad or good we were—or how hard we tried. Miss Alice made me see that God accepted all of us, even when we rejected Him.

Perhaps the most important secret she had taught me so far was how to look at the inner Light for the help needed in dealing with people. I had to recognize evil for what it was, and I had to declare war on that evil—whether it was disease or my own temper. Then I had to ask Someone else to do the fighting for me, and give gratitude to Him for the battle He was waging on my behalf. And the outcome was sure because evil is a coward that slinks away when challenged and faced down.

While I was home, David's letters came regularly—not exactly love letters, but warm and teasing, with tidbits of news. And I realized that my heart was back in the Cove with Fairlight and Little Burl, Opal and Mountie, and many another. My parents agreed that if I did not return to the Cove, I would be leaving an unfinished task. They gave me their blessing on another term of schoolteaching, that fall.

I caught myself thinking often about Miss Alice's daughter, Mrs. Neil MacNeill. What sort of person had she been?

WHILE I was at home, David forwarded to me a letter from our benefactor, Hazen L. Smith, and his wife, in Knoxville. It asked me to visit them, and to talk to some businessmen about more supplies for the mission. And so, in September, I took the train to Knoxville. The Smiths were friendly and hospitable, and Mr. Smith gave me a list of merchants to see.

Everywhere I was received with such openness and so many promises that I was dizzy with elation. One hundred pounds of flour and cases of soap from one merchant. . . . Two hundred pounds of sugar and three cases of pork and beans from another. . . . Three cases of canned milk and a case of Log Cabin syrup. . . . Seeds and tools from a hardware merchant. . . . And best of all, folding cots and blankets! Our boarding school was as good as a fact!

How different my arrival at El Pano from the one eight months before! David was on the platform, anxiously searching the train windows for my face. Then there was his firm hand guiding me to the Harvester wagon. He put both hands around my waist and boosted me in. "Cutter Gap's been a dull place without you." His eyes held mine.

"David, wait till you see all the stuff that's coming. Those people were so generous! We can start the boarding school now."

"Sounds great." But he seemed to be only half listening. He took the reins with his right hand and reached for my hand with his free one. He laced his fingers through mine as he drove. "I've missed you," he said finally. Suddenly he steered the wagon off the road into a little grove of trees and stopped. He moved closer until his breath was on my hair. As his mouth found mine, I wondered how many other girls he'd kissed. I brushed the thought aside, for I liked his arm around me, the way he cradled my head on his shoulder; but again I was surprised that I was so aware of such details. Shouldn't I be feeling more and thinking less?

David chuckled. "Now, this is the kind of conversation I *like*."

I touched his cheek lightly. "We should get to the mission."

"Not yet. We need to talk more about you and me."

I was about to say, "David, I've decided I *will* marry you." But something deep inside held back the words, and I heard myself saying, "I care a lot for you, David. But I need more time to be sure about marriage. You understand, don't you?"

137

Only for an instant did David lose his bouncy mood. The rest of the way to the mission he talked about the last four weeks and how often he had thought of me. I was thinking that surely David and I would find our true way in the months ahead.

CHAPTER 16

WHILE I was away, Ruby Mae had decided suddenly to marry Will Beck. At the wedding, standing on the Morrisons' porch, I wished that I felt easier about the young couple. She was not quite fifteen, Will only sixteen. Girls caught in these child marriages never had a chance. They were worn out by their mid-twenties, grandmothers in their thirties.

Moreover, since they were pretending to be grown up when they were scarcely out of childhood, they could bring little to a marriage. (Granny Barclay commented, "Green apples don't have much flavor.") Besides, all of us had hoped that Ruby Mae would get more schooling. We had succeeded in bringing about a reconciliation between the girl and her stepfather, but that was a mixed blessing. At home Ruby Mae had fallen back into the mountain patterns.

I looked at her standing in the yard, in her white muslin wedding dress, among a knot of admiring relatives and friends. Her hair was piled on top of her head, woman-fashion. It shone like a red flame in the sunshine and her face was aglow.

It felt good to be back among my friends, and the entire Cove was here. As Granny Barclay put it, "Hit's so crowded you couldn't cuss a cat 'thout gettin' fur in yer mouth." Opal stood beside me, her eyes red as she remembered her own wedding, and Dr. MacNeill was talking with Uncle Bogg.

David was standing with Isaak McHone. His father's murder had drawn Isaak and David together. Once David threw back his head and laughed as he playfully rumpled Isaak's hair. But I knew that, underneath, David was not happy about today. He felt that we had failed Ruby Mae.

Uncle Bogg was flourishing a bottle of whiskey with a big white bow tied to it for the traditional horse race, with the "Black Betty" bottle as the prize. David had almost refused to perform the ceremony because of this custom, and the tempers it unlocked. But there was not another preacher within miles, and he could scarcely see the couple start out without benefit of clergy.

There was quiet as everyone listened for the hoofbeats and shouts of Will Beck's friends as they raced for the bottle. They rode dangerously, spurring their horses, streaking over boulders. "They're a-comin'," yelled Uncle Bogg.

The crowd surged forward as John Holcombe's son Arrowood grabbed the bottle. He uncorked it and offered it first to Ruby Mae. She tilted her head to drink, then, sputtering, handed it back. Arrowood took his dram, and then the bottle made the rounds. Before other bottles could be produced, David's voice rang out: "Make way for the bride and bridegroom, folks."

The ceremony took place inside the cabin. Something in David's bearing made conversation cease and the men began removing their hats. And then the ancient and beautiful words rang out: " 'Dearly beloved, we are gathered together here in the sight of God . . .' "

I stood there thinking of the life this girl-bride was assuming. The couple would simply pile a broken-down bedstead, a few quilts, some split-bottomed "settin' chairs" and a minimum of kitchen utensils on a lumber wagon, hitch a cow to the tailboard, and be off to make their way in the world.

Yet the mountain women accomplished so much with so little. I had never known such courageous and hard-working women. Literally and symbolically they never let the fires go out on their hearths.

Now came the exchange of the vows themselves. David's deep voice rang out, " 'Whom God hath joined together, let no man put asunder.' " David had thrown a cloak of love and caring over the unseemly marriage in its shabby setting. The Cove people scarcely knew what to make of the ceremony. I heard, "Best talkinest preacher-person I ever saw." . . . "Lifts my heart." And

Ruby Mae's eyes were "puddling" as she said, "Hit was so beautiful, Rev'rend, didn't know as I could stand it."

The feast of wild turkey, ham, sausage, pie and cake came next. While we were eating, Dr. MacNeill made his way across the room to me. With a start, I realized that I had not seen him since our argument about religion in July. "Do you still think I knew something that would save Tom?" he said. "I'd hate to have you blaming me for his death."

This frontal approach caught me unprepared. Even now the thought that Tom McHone was dead was a stabbing one. I said, "Maybe this isn't the best place to talk about it?"

"Good point." He rumpled the back of his hair with his restless fingers in that characteristic gesture of his. "You've never attended one of our mountain weddings before, have you? *Real* ceremony's coming up. Sometimes the boys shivaree the bride and groom or bell the bride. And there's always putting the bride to bed."

The Doctor was enjoying the look on my face, making no effort to hide his raillery. Well, he was more right about me than he knew. I thought of how little information my mother had given me. She could scarcely bring herself to say the word sex. She half swallowed it so that it came out "sect."

But now Jeb Spencer with his fiddle and Wraight Holt with a banjo started the familiar "Skip to My Lou." The music snaked across the floor, swirled around my ankles, set my toes to tapping. Already the old squire was clapping his hands: "In—a—cir-cle folks! The Tenn'see Wag-on Wheel. Here—we—go!"

Dr. MacNeill said, "Come on, Christy. Into the circle!"

"Cir-cle *left!* . . . Cir-cle *right!* . . . Swing your partner . . . *Now!* . . ." The Doctor was surprisingly nimble. "With a Right Hand Wheel . . . and back—the—other—way. . . . Pick up your partner!" The Doctor's arms lifted me easily off the floor. "Swing your partner!" I spun through the air, blood racing with the music, aware of the Doctor's face close to mine, laughing, drawing me to him. "Right—left. Right—left. . . . Prom-e-nade! . . . Now the Bas-ket . . ." (The step was as complicated as an old quilt pattern.) "And *off* the floor!" And I half collapsed against the wall.

"*You* aren't—even—breathless!" I chided Dr. MacNeill.

"Oh, that was only a middlin'-fast tune."

Music, for singing this time. The Doctor started it:

> "*Cheeks as red as a bloomin' rose,*
> *Eyes of the deepest brown,*
> *You are the darlin' of my heart,*
> *Stay till the sun goes down. . . .*"

Voices picked up the song. An enigmatic look on the Doctor's face. Or was it sad? And why did he keep his eyes on my face? Across the room, David was talking to Miss Alice. Perhaps I should join him.

The fiddle sang again. "We're a-goin' 'Step Charlie,' folks," Uncle Bogg called, dancing a pigeonwing all by himself in the middle of the floor.

> "*Charlie's neat, and Charlie's sweet*
> *And Charlie he's a dan-dy—*"

Dr. MacNeill propelled me again to the center of the floor. He sang as he swung me:

> "*My pretty little pink, I once did think*
> *I never could do without you. . . .*"

Overhead, I heard girlish giggling, laughs and squeals. Dr. MacNeill jerked a thumb at the ceiling. "Ceremony's beginning. They're putting the bride to bed."

"Ladies in! Gents in! Grab, boys, grab!" . . .

"Putting her to bed with all of us still here?" I asked.

"Sure." And I saw the girls begin to troop down from the loft while the men made a dive for Will Beck.

"I'm batchin' it, fellers!" Will yelled. But, held roughly, he was already on his way to the loft, tightly wedged in the group of boys. The whole picture was absurd.

And then Will and the wedding-night scene in the loft receded. The Doctor danced as naturally as a bird flies. His guiding arm was so sure and firm, the rhythm a part of my body.

It ended too soon. My partner spun me around with a final flourish. I met his eyes. They glistened with approval—and something else. His lips brushed my forehead, and for a moment his arm stayed firmly behind my back, pressing me tightly to him.

Now, there were new noises overhead. Inwardly I winced and the Doctor knew it. "Christy, you ought to consider something," he said, never one to lead into a subject delicately. "The mountain attitude toward sex may be more nearly right than your Victorian tradition. It's the way things are meant to be. Here, folks see sex for pleasure *and* for procreation. They're right. Leave out either one, and you're in trouble."

There still is a lot of prudery about sex in Asheville, I was thinking. But why a lecture on sex to me? I was having trouble meeting the Doctor's level gaze. With relief I saw David approaching. "I'm leaving, Christy," he said. "May I take you home?"

I tried not to sound as eager as I felt. "Thanks. I'm ready."

Late that night a strong wind arose. And then it increased in tempo and became a wild wind. And I thought it sounded like a chorus of women crying, sometimes moaning, sometimes chanting in a sweet-sad song:

> *Down in the valley,*
> *valley so low;*
> *Hang your head over,*
> *hear the wind blow. . . .*

THAT WAS A GOLDEN autumn. All the stored-up beauty of summer blazed forth in an avalanche of color—dark red sourwoods, luminous gold hickories, crimson sumac, the scarlet oaks—all with the purple-blue Smokies for a backdrop.

My eyes must be open to this beauty, I thought, because I was in love with David. We were young—and wasn't this what the poets sang about? The trees in their shouting colors were just for us! Even the stars were brighter than before. The Little Bear was laughing, and the Dipper dripping wine, and all for us—for us!

Sometimes David and I would rein in our horses, bedazzled by a single tree, looking, with the sun shining full on it, as if a fire had been lighted at its heart. And David would lean over to plant a kiss on my lips, for kisses were easier now.

His actions told me that he considered that we had a sort of unspoken agreement; but what bothered me was that though David acted as if he loved me, he had never once used the words. Still, in his gay, vital presence my doubts would vanish. Surely, I could not have all this physical feeling for him and not be in love? I must be wrong to insist on his saying certain words. Perhaps his actions were all that was necessary.

We were readying the mission house for boarders now. At dinner one night, I told the others about a book I had found in Knoxville on Danish Folk High Schools. "They are for older youngsters, seventeen and over," I said, "after the crops are in. There are no grades, no degrees. It's called 'Enlightenment for Life' and the idea is not to educate students *away* from the land, so that all the bright students want to live in cities, but rather to send each pupil back to his own community a more enlightened person. They feel that seventeen or eighteen is the time to begin serious education. By then young people *want* answers on what life is all about."

Miss Alice asked, "How about those hard adolescent years?"

"Lessons, sure; but much manual work too, so they will learn respect for it. And a lot of physical activity—deprive adolescents of that, and you get trouble every time."

"Christy, how can you get so worked up over these foreign schools?" David said patronizingly.

"What schools?" It was Dr. MacNeill, standing in the doorway.

"Come in, Doctor." David seemed glad of the interruption. "Set sail with us. We're afloat on a sea of ideas."

The Doctor picked up a straight chair and set it down between Miss Alice and David. "Ideas about what?"

Miss Alice explained, and the Doctor said, "Oh, I heard about Danish Folk High Schools from a visiting professor, the son of a Danish farmer, in medical school. He said going to a Folk School changed his life. Said his teacher gave him a great love for Denmark and her people. He was the happiest man I ever knew, always whistling."

"The Folk School founder, Bishop Grundtvig, had that joy too!" I plunged on. "I think we should do something like it right here. Why couldn't David start classes for the men in the parlor? Not the same classes as for children. We would treat them as adults, as equals."

David was leaning back precariously in his chair. "So a group of mountain men, black felt hats in hand, amble in to go to school. What do I do then?"

"Begin with a ballad or story that takes them into history—what real men and women did; how these mountains were settled. Then you'd have to sell the men on *reasons* for learning to read and write, and for mathematics. Their fathers made handcrafted furniture. You could teach woodworking—let them sell the furniture and keep books. That gives them writing and arithmetic!"

David spoke patiently, as to a child. "Nice theory, Christy. But these men are not capable of it."

"Then why are you here, if you think we're that hopeless?" the Doctor asked. "I'm a mountain man, and if I'm different, it's because of several people who felt as Christy does about the possibilities in some of us."

"Well—that's fine. But Danes are energetic. Most of these men were born lazy and raised tired." David rose to his feet with a look on his face that he meant to be good-humored. "Christy, in four or five years—who knows? But right now we have one small schoolhouse that has just sprung a leak in its new roof. And I've got to fix it. So—if you'll excuse me . . ."

No one said anything for a moment after David left. I felt deflated and tired. What had happened to my golden autumn?

CHAPTER 17

MY RELATIONSHIPS in the Cove were striking deeper levels because of our many shared experiences. More and more often my schoolchildren were opening up to me hidden areas. They would come to school bright-eyed and excited over ghost stories, replete with vivid details: jealous witches forcing someone to eat "witch balls" (pine needles wrapped in human hair); the devil driving a cart black as ink drawn by black oxen down the mountainside. I asked Zady Spencer what Fairlight thought of these stories.

"Mama gets a funny look to her eyes. She heerd a pack of dogs a-howlin' in the night. Said that was a bad sign."

I sighed remembering Fairlight's fear of the "witched" pinnacle. How often we had seen the shadow creep across it! It was like an immense hand raised between the sun and the one who watched. Through the fingers of the giant's hand streaks of light filtered through the trees; but in between eerie dusk lay across the land. And as she watched, Fairlight's eyes would always be frightened.

ONE October day, Fairlight sent Zady to say that she needed me as soon as possible; Zady's eyes were dark with worry. I rode fast up the trail, while Zady bounded back directly up the mountain. The children, solemnly waiting for me in the yard, were so quiet that the place seemed deserted.

Inside, brilliant autumn sunlight spilled across the cabin floor. Fairlight was lying on the bed, her face flushed, her eyes open but dull. I felt her hot forehead.

"Christy—" one hand crept toward me. "My side hurts—*so* bad."

Her breathing was heavy and her lips were twitching strangely. I took her hand. "How long has she been like this?" I said. With so many problems with boarders, I hadn't seen Fairlight lately.

"Mama was ailin', right bad off, all last week," the girl answered. "Yesterday had the trembles. Shook all over like an aspen tree in the wind. But she wouldn't take to her bed."

"Where's your father?"

"Took the hound dogs, went ba-ar huntin'—over Laurel Top somewheres, three days ago. Took John too."

"Christy!" The voice was desperate. "Tell them to take the chairs off'n me. All that house plunder they're a-pilin' on me. Tell them—" She coughed, a deep racking cough, painful to hear.

I pressed her hand reassuringly. "Fairlight, I'm here now. I won't let anybody pile anything on you."

My heart was thumping, but I forced myself to keep panic out of my voice. "Clara," I said, "run to Holcombes' and get one of the men to fetch the Doctor. Say they can use my horse."

As she left, fear became a lump in my throat. I sent Zady and Lulu for cold water and rags and put cold compresses on Fairlight's forehead and wrists. I dared not put them on her chest. She was so hot that in no time at all the compresses were warm.

Clara rushed back to report, "Mr. Holcombe's gone to fotch the Doc. Said he'll search him out."

"Thank you, Clara." I wrung out a rag and gently sponged Fairlight's face. Then I stared as I saw brown fuzz, through her open lips, on her tongue.

Suddenly, her muttering stopped and the fog lifted. She looked directly at me, love and longing in her eyes. "Christy, my time's come. I know it. But Christy, I don't want to die. Don't want to leave my young'uns." Her grasp on my hand was like a vise. "Why do I have to die? Holp me. Christy, will you holp me?"

"Fairlight, you're not going to die." Desperately, I tried to put conviction in my voice. "Dr. MacNeill is on his way to you right now. Everything's going to be all right."

But slow tears coursed down her cheeks. "It's no use. I've knowed this for days. Christy, I don't want to leave Jeb—or the least'un. Why do I have to leave? I'm not old enough to die."

She faded back into delirium. Her eyes were open, but now there was no recognition in them. Zady was standing rigid, the back of one hand pressed to her mouth. My own face was wet with perspiration. I wrung out another compress and put it on Fairlight's forehead, and as we watched, the lines of her face softened and into her voice came the lilt of a young girl's gaiety.

"Race ye to the branch yonder. . . . Oh-h-h, fell in! Scared me fitified! Water's so-o-o cold!" Then she was picking wild strawberries. . . . Making crowns of oak leaves. . . . Running to climb a persimmon tree laden with heavy yellow fruit. . . . At last she slipped into a sleep or a coma, I could not tell which. I sank back into a chair. Little Guy crawled onto my lap and I cuddled him close, cradling his grimy little fingers in mine. Over and over,

Clara went to the door, her eyes searching for the approaching figure of Dr. MacNeill.

Suddenly, there was a violent movement of the bedclothes and Fairlight screamed, *"No!"* Hysteria was in her voice. "The shadder! The shadder's a-comin' for me. Christy, holp me!"

Frantically I put Guy down as she got out of bed. She was right: though the late afternoon sun was still streaming through the open door, as I reached her the slanting shadows of the pinnacle were crawling across the floor toward us. She flung herself at me, grasping my legs. "Christy!" It was a wild shriek, terrible to hear. "The shadder o' death—push hit away. Oh, hide me!"

I tried to take her in my arms, but her body was rigid. My love poured into torrents of words: "Fairlight! *Though I walk through the valley of the shadow of death, I will fear no evil: for thou art with me. . . . For thou art with me. . . .* Oh, Fairlight, do you hear me? He *is* with us, Fairlight. . . ."

Suddenly she relaxed in my arms. Still holding her tightly, I looked up. The giant's hand was upraised now, the light in the cabin all but extinguished. And the blackness of the shadow fell directly across her face.

I stared in disbelief. "Oh, dear God, no!" It could not be—but it was. Her eyes were still staring, but no breath escaped her.

My cry told the children. They rushed to their mother, sobbing, and collapsed beside her on the floor.

We were still there, huddled together, when Dr. MacNeill and Mr. Holcombe entered the cabin. Gently, the Doctor took me by the arm and got me to my feet. He spoke, but I did not hear what he said. Then he and Mr. Holcombe carried Fairlight to the bed.

Dr. MacNeill examined Fairlight slowly, then pulled the quilt over the beautiful face. His eyes sought mine. "She must have had it for a good ten days. When it's not caught, death can come in the second week. Christy, it's typhoid."

A BLESSED numbness, like an anesthetic, carried me through Fairlight's funeral, enabled me to get through the days, to speak words of comfort to the Spencer children, whom we took to

the mission house. Then, about a week after the funeral, the world came back into focus and a wild, searing pain bore into me.

Why? Why had Fairlight been taken? Why were the good and beautiful so ruthlessly plucked? The stem of the flower broken, and no man can mend it; the soaring bird felled so suddenly that the tiny body is warm in death, the unfinished song still in his throat; the heartbeat stilled so easily? Doubts once again gnawed like rats at the fabric of my faith.

Each night sleep came only with exhaustion, and even then I was pursued by nightmares. I turned for help to David. "What do you do, David, when suddenly you can't believe?"

He was putting new screening on the porch door. Now he laid the hammer down. "Believing is never easy, Christy. And you're tired and upset." He drew me into his arms, tilted my head back and kissed my eyelids and then my mouth. "Foolish girl. . . . Words aren't what you need now. You can't solve the philosophic problems of the universe. Just don't think about it." He was using the same tone he took with a very little child. "I'm sorry about Fairlight, Christy. I know what she meant to you. But you will get over this, you know."

"You don't understand. I *have* to know that Fairlight isn't just gone, vanished forever—or I'll go crazy. Can't you understand the need to be sure, David?"

"Of course. I'd like to be sure too. But death is a very great mystery. I can give you good theological answers about it, but knowing you, that wouldn't be enough."

Suddenly, Aunt Polly's face rose before me, the old lady's disbelieving eyes as she was offered seminary answers instead of the reality she needed. I felt a yearning I had not known for a long time—to cry with my head in mother's lap. I said, "I'm sorry, David. Of course, I'll get over this. It's just that I hurt now and I want something to stop the pain."

David's expression cleared. Once again he drew me to him. He said softly, his lips brushing my cheek, "Christy, there isn't anything I wouldn't do for you. You know that."

After a restless night, I got up shortly before dawn one morning, dressed hastily, and tiptoed out of the house. As I reached my well-loved woodland room on Coldsprings Mountain, the sky was rosy. Dewdrops still glistened on the leaves.

My eyes saw the beauty, but I could not respond to it. Anger against God seethed inside me—too much inside me. Sitting there on a rock among the laurel, I remembered the day Fairlight and I climbed the mountain. Then, with an intuitive knowing, I had been sure that God did indeed care. And now I realized that it was wrong not to speak out my rebellion to Him. Speak it out! Yes, and act it out.

My isolation gave me the courage to let all constraint go. I heard myself saying aloud, "Why? Why? I've got to know *why.*" Then on my knees in a bed of dry leaves, I flailed my fists on the earth as I saw in memory Fairlight's lovely face. "Oh God! Oh God—Why are You so hard to find when the need is greatest? . . . I *asked* You for help with Fairlight, God."

Gradually I quieted down. There was no answer immediately, I had not expected there would be. Yet the leafy, soothing quietness enfolded me, and I was aware of a thirst to drink deeply of it. My body was the exterior shell for an inner stillness; the scudding clouds and the tossing trees were the covering for that other stillness without. I wanted to stay there a long time. But Miss Ida would be holding breakfast for me with that tight-lipped smile she reserved for latecomers. I decided that I would return each morning to my mountain sanctuary until some response, some insights were given me. Or else, or else—there was always the stark alternative that I was indeed speaking into nothingness.

My second morning on the mountain, I stopped hurling invectives verbally and began writing my questions in a notebook. Some of what I wrote bordered on blasphemy. Yet if there *was* a God, He would have to be Truth; and candor would be more pleasing to Him than posturing. Gradually the torment of my grief fell away. In its place was left a great wistfulness and a terrible aloneness.

I knew that Miss Alice sensed my isolation, yet she did not intrude. Then one morning I met her saddling her horse.

"You're out early, Christy." It was a half question.

"Good morning. Is it Big Lick or Cataleechie?"

"Big Lick this week." She paused. "Christy, child, thee is in agony." I nodded. She was silent for a time. Then she said with feeling, "Christy, those who've never shaken their fists in the face of heaven have never encountered God at all. Rebellion—and admitting we don't understand—are steps to finding reality."

"But I don't seem to be able to find anything."

She closed the flaps of her saddlebags. "Christy, Job and King David rebelled too. I recommend that you read Job, and the Psalms." She mounted and looked down at me, her eyes luminous. "If I care about thee so much, He does too. More. So much more."

DURING the week that Miss Alice was away, I did read my Bible and there I found astonishing companionship. Other men and women long ago had asked my questions:

> *Therefore I will not refrain my mouth. . . .*
> *I will complain in the bitterness of my soul. . . .*
>
> *All the night. . . . I water my couch with my tears. . . .*
>
> *Why standest thou afar off, O Lord?*

The words were like hands reaching out across the centuries. There was comfort in the knowledge of our common humanity.

Morning after morning I returned to my hillside room to reach out thirstily for the stillness. I had never experienced anything like this silence before. Now I knew that at the heart of the stillness there was food to feed upon, wisdom to accept humbly. Where there was hunger, there would also be bread.

And almost imperceptibly out of the stillness, my answer started coming—only not in any way that I had expected. No effort was made to answer my "Why?" Instead, I began to know, unmistakably, beyond doubting, that I, Christy Huddleston, was loved—tenderly, totally. Love filled me, washed over me, flowed around me. I did not know what to do with love as strong as this. My tears flowed. I could not stop them.

Then the thought came, Wasn't this the confirmation for which I had asked? This love disclosing itself was not Dr. MacNeill's Creator of a mechanistic universe, for the revelation was intimate, personal. Perhaps such an assurance always had to be revealed to the inner person alone, since God insists on seeing us one by one, each a special case, each inestimably beloved.

The world was still full of riddles for which my little mind had not been given answers; David had been right about that. But my fundamental doubt was silenced. I knew now: God *is*. I had found my center; everything else would follow.

That morning the sun came up in a blaze of glory.

CHAPTER 18

TEN DAYS after Fairlight's death, eight more persons had the fever. The mountain people called it "the summer scourge," for many a year when warm weather brought thawing ground and flies the fever began. But fall rains washing human and animal waste into creeks and springs often started the epidemics too.

People remembered those epidemic years: "That September the babe was buried in Verta's arms." . . . "Recollect ye that one day when six folks was lowered into their bury-holes?" Scarcely a family but had lost a child some year or other, before November killed the flies and froze the suppurating ground.

Only recently had the country at large begun to accept the fact that typhoid was a disease of filth, spread by flies, food and linens. Most mountain folk did not understand it.

Dr. MacNeill was hopeful this was not an epidemic, but he was so rushed already that we set up a cot for him in David's quarters where he could stay when he had no time to go home. Frequently he would stop by the parlor, weary and eager to relax and talk. I thought for the hundredth time about the death of his young wife and baby following her typhoid.

Fingers moving restlessly through his hair, the Doctor said, one evening, "What *looks* like sparkling mountain drinking water may contain billions of typhoid bacilli if the water is taken at the bottom of a hill with everything washed into it. Yet every family thinks their water is best." He lit his pipe. "I can hear them now: 'Doc, you're plumb crazy. Our spring bubbles right up out'n the ground.' Or, 'Doc, I raised twelve young'uns on that water.'

"The two keys to the situation are the housefly and the wrong kind of privies—or none at all. Most families haven't tried to deal with either problem. As for nursing typhoid cases, I need separate rooms, continuous nursing, a controlled diet, no visitors. But you've seen it. The sicker the patient, the more folks gather round. Nobody wants to miss a deathbed. There's always the chance that the dying might make a startling confession." He laughed. "Why, I've had patients who so enjoyed being the star of the performance that they surprised everyone and got well!"

Besides the epidemic, we had the problems of our strange assortment of boarders. Little Guy Spencer was staying for a while to let Clara adjust to her role as mistress of the household; Wanda Ann Beck so Dr. MacNeill could treat her trachoma; Mountie O'Teale so she could get away from her terrible home; Izaak McHone because he wanted to be near David; Lundy, at Miss Alice's request, because Bird's-Eye was still missing.

One day, when I was reading aloud to our boarders, Lundy suddenly slumped over in the parlor, blood pouring from his nose. I stopped it somehow, got him to bed, and sent for the Doctor. After examining him, Dr. MacNeill sought me out. "Not much question, Christy. It's typhoid all right—early stage. And it's dangerous for everybody here. You'd better have someone take Little Guy Spencer home. And Christy, we will need medicines and disinfectants. I have calls to make, so would you ride over to my place and get them? I'll give you a list and the key to the room."

I glanced out the window and saw towering storm heads, dark and threatening. "Of course I'll go," I said.

I THREW my body against the door of the Doctor's cabin, a driving rain that had been pursuing me, pelting at my back. The door flew open and the wind almost blew me inside. I slammed the door and leaned against it to catch my breath. There was a growl of thunder, and lightning zigzagged across the sky, flaming at the windowpanes. By its light, I saw the door of the locked room—the secret room the Cove gossiped about—to my right.

I could find no lamp. One hand stretched out to keep from colliding with anything in the murky shadows, I walked over to the door, slid my fingers over the panels to locate the keyhole, and managed to unlock the door with the Doctor's key. Inside there was an odor of chemicals. I felt around. To my right there was a shelf, and—oh, great relief—an oil lamp, with a canister of matches. I took out a match and lit the lamp. Lifting it, I scanned the room eagerly. I was in a laboratory! It had been a bedroom once, for a bed was pushed against one wall. In the middle of the floor stood a stool and table with equipment; against a wall were cabinets with shallow drawers. There was an old wooden trunk by one wall.

Feeling as if the Doctor were looking over my shoulder, I pulled open one drawer after another, all full of slides—hundreds, thousands of them—each one labeled and numbered. How many years of work were contained in these files?

Another wall was covered with charts and pictures of normal and diseased eyes. There were papers covered with notations and, at the far end of the room, shelves full of books and medicines. A covering of dark cloth had been placed over the two windows so that no passerby could look in.

Standing there, new respect for the owner of this room rose in me. David had been right: I had misinterpreted Dr. Mac-Neill's attitude about his work. There was no lack of caring here—quite the opposite.

So the truth about the locked room was more significant than all the rumors I had heard. The Doctor had known that the mountain folk would not understand the type of research he was doing. This room divulged depths in the Doctor which I had glimpsed briefly, at odd moments, and tried to discount.

I wondered about that trunk. Impelled by a curiosity I could not put down, I lifted the lid and held the lamp to peer in. I saw dresses, a furred bonnet, a pair of knitting needles stuck in yarn. Gently, I picked this up. It was a half-finished baby's jacket. I put it back and shut the lid.

I carried the lamp to the shelves of drugs and, with my list, located what was needed. Quickly I went out, blew out the lamp, and shut the door and locked it.

The fury of the storm had abated. It was still raining, but softly, as I rode fast toward the mission. There was much to ponder.

LUNDY WAS an ill-tempered, demanding patient, though his case did not seem serious; even his temperature was moderate. "Maybe I was wrong about him," Dr. MacNeill admitted to us one evening. "Typhoid can wear more guises than almost any disease I know. It can look like colitis, meningitis, malaria, influenza, pneumonia, nephritis or endocarditis. Now, I've some rough typhoid cases across Raven Gap. I'm riding over tomorrow and may have to stay overnight."

WE HOPED fervently that no emergency would arise in his absence. But he had scarcely disappeared down the road when word came that Ruby Mae was "took bad." I insisted on going there with Miss Alice, while Miss Ida took over with Lundy.

Inside the primitive Beck cabin, we found Ruby Mae flushed with fever, her eyes too bright and staring. "I'm so sick," she moaned. "Water, Will. Please—so thirsty—water."

Miss Alice examined her, then said softly to us, "I'm almost sure she has pneumonia. She hasn't coughed at all, has she?"

"No ma'am," Will said.

"Well, her lungs are, as Dr. MacNeill would say, 'consolidated.' Will, how are you fixed for onions?"

Will looked as puzzled as I felt. "Well—considerable onions."

"Then we'll try onion poultices," Miss Alice announced crisply. "Get lots of onions, my boy, and you and Miss Christy will start peeling." She set to work tearing up a sheet into large squares.

Relieved to be told something that he could do, Will chinned himself up into the loft, and soon was back with a piggin heaped with onions. We started peeling and slicing, smiling at one another's ludicrous look as our eyes rained a never-ending supply of tears. When we had a skilletful of onions, Miss Alice heated them, put them into the muslin squares, and gently placed the poultices on Ruby Mae's chest. As fast as the frying pan was emptied, Will and I filled it again. Between each poultice, Will helped Miss Alice turn Ruby Mae, so that the poultices could be applied to both front and back. Miss Alice's hair clung dankly around her flushed face as she kept the heavy quilts tucked around Ruby Mae and applied the poultices.

When I saw that the insides of her hands were blistered, I said, "Let me handle the poultices for a while." She nodded absently, all her attention centered on Ruby Mae. She cares so about these folks, I thought. It's love like Miss Alice's that heals. And suddenly I felt sure that Ruby Mae was going to live through this.

Dawn was not far away when I slipped out the cabin door for a minute, grateful for a few deep breaths of the pure mountain air. Then I heard feet scrambling across the floor. I got to the door to see both Will and Miss Alice rushing toward the bed. With no warning Ruby Mae was sitting up in bed, coughing violently. Miss Alice grabbed a pan and held it under the girl's mouth while I ran to support her head. No wonder she'd been sick with all that stuff in her lungs! I had to look away to keep from gagging. Jubilation was written on Miss Alice's face. "You have succeeded," she said to Will and me, as if her part in it had been negligible. "I've never seen onion poultices do a finer job. I do believe she's going to be all right."

An hour later Will reported that Dr. MacNeill was riding up the trail. I rushed out to meet him. He grinned as he saw me and I blushed. Then Miss Alice appeared and described our vigil. Quickly, he went in and examined Ruby Mae. "I wouldn't dare make a diagnosis quite yet," he said at last. "But the onions did their work." Then he said to Will, "No medicine for now. Total rest and lots of liquids." He turned to Miss Alice and me. "You both need rest. I'll stay here awhile."

Miss Alice shook her head. "No; you need sleep more than I

do, Neil. Why don't you drop Christy off at the mission house?"

The Doctor did not protest. His eyes were bloodshot, with deep hollows beneath them, yet there was still a spring to his step. Clearly, instead of being overwhelmed by the crisis, he seemed in some way fulfilled by its demands.

I started to mount my horse, but there was a ringing in my head and a queer numbness in my legs. Instantly, the Doctor recognized this. "You're going to ride with me," he ordered. He got sacking from Will and threw it over his horse's croup. He mounted and reached down a hand for me, and as his horse moved off through the cool morning air, I began to feel better; no longer exhausted, just comfortably drowsy, as though I could sleep forever, relaxed against the Doctor. But another part of me resisted this vigorously. Why was I always so divided about this man?

"Christy," he said, "every instinct tells me that I should ride on down to the station and put you on a train to Asheville."

"You'd better not try it unless you tie and gag me!"

The Doctor threw back his head and laughed so irrepressibly that I laughed too. "Christy, I've never met a girl as stubborn and know-it-all as you are. If I can't persuade you to go home, can I persuade you to take special precautions?"

"Anything you say, Doctor— Sir."

He reached back and took my hand as though to indicate we were in agreement. When he did not let go, I pulled it away.

Deadly serious now, he said, "When we get back, wash every garment you're wearing in lye soap. Wash your hands in seventy-percent alcohol or bichloride solution. And get lots of sleep."

He said nothing more, and after a while I relaxed, leaning lightly against him until we were back at the mission house.

Then a strange thing happened. I was not tired anymore. Something inside me unknotted, and warmth welled up. I was sure now that I belonged here, helping these mountain people. There was nothing here I wanted for my own self-discovery now; I just wanted to give. Impetuously, I leaned forward and kissed Neil MacNeill gently on the cheek. Before he could say anything, I had vaulted off the horse and dashed into the mission house.

Some neighbor women came in to nurse Ruby Mae, who did have typhoid, and as Lundy's illness dragged on, Miss Alice insisted on assuming much of the burden of his care. One afternoon when we were alone, her eyes searched my face. Then she said abruptly, "You've been wondering about Margaret, haven't you?"

"Yes, but—" I didn't go on.

"*But* how did I know? Christy! How much do you think stays out of those big eyes of yours? You've been aching to ask questions. Would you like to hear more about Margaret from me?"

I tried not to sound as eager as I felt. "Yes. Yes, please."

Miss Alice seemed to be looking over my shoulder at some distant horizon. The room was so quiet that I became aware of a single angry fly buzzing against a windowpane. When she spoke, her voice was soft:

"Margaret was tall, with shining bronze hair. She was a headstrong child. Early, she learned to get her way with my father and me, for I accepted father's philosophy that parents can do nothing greater for their children than give them a joyous childhood. I set out to create 'the habit of happiness' in my daughter. And I overprotected her from our Quakerisms because some of them had always seemed silly to me—like one Friend who longed for scarlet geraniums, but didn't dare to grow them; or another who had false teeth made and then felt 'scruples' about using them—so she deposited them in her bureau and painfully gummed her way through the rest of her days.

"But Christy, what I didn't understand then was that those Friends were training their wills in the only way a will can be trained—by giving up whatever we happen to want at the moment. I simply reinforced my daughter in her selfish ways.

"In her teens, Margaret fell in with a group of young people to whom freedom was a way of life. Not freedom *for* anything, just freedom from responsibilities of any kind. Suddenly she swung into full rebellion against me, and our community of Friends. And it was about that time that Margaret met Neil MacNeill. He liked her fiery, independent beauty. And to Margaret, Neil seemed perfect, since he had no proper background and

159

boasted that he had taken science as his god and needed no other.

"So they ran off and got married. But there was a flaw at the heart of the marriage—a certain feeling of unworthiness in Margaret. She referred to herself as an 'accident conceived in man's lust.' And naturally she had no understanding of God's bringing good out of man's baseness. But her devaluating of herself had been so cloaked behind her happy-go-lucky personality that Neil never saw it until after their marriage. Even worse was his inevitable discovery that Margaret had picked him as a husband because she thought of him as inferior and, therefore, a proper mate for her.

"After a while, it was apparent that they meant to sever every tie with me. I couldn't allow that, so—uninvited—I traveled down to Cutter Gap. Margaret interpreted this as my unwillingness to cut the apron strings—so I moved on to Big Lick Spring. By then I had learned that there's only one way to give advice to the young: give it, and be unconcerned as to whether they take it or not. In time I think our relationship would have been made right, for when Margaret watched Neil's work, she began to see rebellion in its true light: as the easy way, so much easier than commitment. She and Neil began slowly finding their way to a love based on something more enduring than partnership in flight. Sooner or later that love would have dissolved Margaret's feelings of unworthiness."

She paused. "When Margaret died, Neil's rejection of religion—and of me—was complete. In his eyes the Friends and I, in giving Margaret love, had failed. But lately our relationship has improved. Neil has great depths in him. In his laboratory, he is doing research on trachoma. He's published a paper on new techniques of treatment, in the *Southern Medical Journal*."

She rose. "Now I must go back to Lundy."

"Miss Alice, how can I thank you for telling me all this?"

Her eyes were warm as she looked at me. "I see *her* in you, the same vital force: the eagerness to grasp life; the impetuosity; that spice of old Adam in thee. Anyhow," she twinkled at me, "I always toady to the young too much."

Lundy's temperature had been rising for two days. That night he complained of a raging headache, and next morning, Miss Alice told us that he had been delirious.

Neil MacNeill gathered us in the parlor for detailed instructions on sanitation. His face was deeply etched with fatigue and worry lines, and as he held the parlor door open for me, he gave me such an intent look that it made me uneasy. Surely he had not misinterpreted my light heedless kiss? It had been a gesture of admiration and respect, nothing more.

"Situation doesn't look good," he began now. "First off, all water drunk in this house from now on has to be boiled. We'll use formalin for disinfecting Lundy's room. After handling anything from the sickroom, hands have to be washed with seventy-percent alcohol or bichloride solution. All linens used for Lundy are to be soaked two hours in carbolic acid solution, then boiled, then washed in lye soap. All wastes to be buried in a deep trench. Your job, David, I'm afraid. . . . Sorry, Christy," he snapped, "no use turning up your nose. No way to make disease genteel for you."

Soon I began to understand what devoted nursing typhoid required around the clock. There was the endless carrying in and out of pails and water basins and chamber pots; the sponging to try to bring down the fever; the rinsing out of the mouth; and, most continuous and time-consuming of all, the liquid nourishment, spoonfed to Lundy every half hour. "Nothing solid, though," Miss Alice said.

At ten o'clock the next night I took the night watch. The room was full of a dead-mouse smell—the odor of typhoid. Lundy's eyes were open, but I was not sure that he recognized me. His arms and legs were thrashing at the sheet and quilt over him, but since his temperature was 103 degrees, I did not think it a good idea to remove any covers. Finally, he dozed off and I fell asleep on a cot.

I was awakened by a terrible stench: Lundy's diarrhea was still unchecked. Fortunately, Miss Ida, having taken the earlier watch, had put what amounted to a huge diaper on him. Above it his stomach was bloated, with rosy spots on it.

Now began as repugnant a task as I had ever faced. I ran

downstairs, heated buckets of water, and then found a clothespin with a spring on it. I carried the pails upstairs, along with some old newspapers, set the buckets down and pinched the clothespin onto my nose. It might look foolish, but there was nobody to see. In the next few minutes my thoughts moved as fast as my hands. Don't feel sorry for yourself. Lots of people endure worse than this. . . . Put your mind on Grandmother Rudd's rose garden—the old-fashioned white roses with the delicate fragrance. . . .

Finally it was finished and I stuffed the soiled things into the chamber pot, put the lid on, and set it out in the hall. In a corner of the sickroom, I found some outsize diapers neatly folded—and blessed Miss Ida as I fastened them on Lundy.

"Sick. . . . Sick. . . . Paw? Where's Paw?" he whimpered. Then he slept, and as I began scrubbing myself in the kitchen, I saw that Miss Ida's alarm clock read only ten past twelve. I couldn't believe it! My vigil had scarcely begun.

I returned to the bedroom and gratefully lay down on the cot—but not for long. After a while, I lost track of how many times I was up and down. The night seemed interminable, but sometime toward dawn it began to rain and the rhythm on the roof lulled both Lundy and me to sleep.

I was awakened by the sound of a knocking on the back door. Whoever it was, was knocking softly, hesitantly, and yet would not give up. I dragged myself off the cot and downstairs. Cautiously I opened the door partway to have a look. Then I drew back, startled. Bird's-Eye was standing there.

He said, "I come back because I heerd 'bout Lundy. Besides, ain't got no stummick for hidin' out no more."

MISS ALICE stayed around the mission house almost continuously the first day Bird's-Eye was back, and I noticed that she was studying him closely.

In the sickroom Bird's-Eye had no idea how to express his concern except with his usual gruff insults. "Bein' as leather-headed as ever, son? Ought to box yer jaws so ye'll know hit's me." As Lundy blinked in delight Bird's-Eye added, "Why, ye be grinnin' like a possum!" Then, ill at ease, he backed out of the room, twisting his hat between his hands. In the hallway, he appealed, "With Lundy fast to his bed, I'd like to holp here for a span."

It was Miss Alice who answered. "Bird's-Eye, we could use help. But we can't hide you from the law."

"I knowed that when I snuck back. I've mommicked things up good, and ain't no use a-runnin'."

To our surprise, Bird's-Eye followed his words with deeds. Without complaint, he helped with the menial chores, even with the task David found most repugnant of all, burying wastes in a trench four feet deep.

But although David was glad for the help, he appeared to find this new Bird's-Eye even harder to bear than the old one. One morning I heard him remonstrating with Dr. MacNeill. "Why should we be taken in by a murderer and his no-good son? Lots of other people are down with typhoid and none of them are getting the nursing Lundy is."

But the Doctor said only, "I have to do my utmost to save any life, all lives. Unfortunately, we can't nurse them all. Three more deaths this week. . . ."

By the end of that week, a total of fifty-four typhoid cases had been reported. Scarcely a family was left untouched. One week Dr. MacNeill brought in, on his saddle, the pathetic surviving children of a mother who had died soon after her husband. A soup kitchen was set up at Miss Alice's, with pails of soup sent to cabins where there was no one left to cook. We never got a full night's sleep and our nerves were raw, our tempers snappish.

Now, new stills were set up and all began producing at capacity. The mountain people had a fixed idea that drinking liquor killed germs and kept up strength. To David this was one more frustration to bear.

Perhaps the most amazing thing of all was that everywhere in the Cove folks who had seemed lackadaisical rose under the crisis to unbelievable heights of performance. I found myself wondering wistfully what had been the missing factor in the mission's presentation of religion that the motivation of disaster now provided. Was not our faith meant to build a fire under people? Did people always have to wait for tragedy to be shocked into forgetting about themselves?

It was a black day when David reported that Zady had typhoid. "David," I urged, "bring her here at once."

"Christy, you can't take on any more. You should go home. This is no place for you. Neil says you're pushing yourself too hard."

"You mean to tell me I shouldn't think about anything but my own skin? David, when I volunteered to come to the mountains, I thought it was from lofty motives. But now I know I came for *me*. I can't turn around and leave now for the same reason."

Silence fell between us. Then David said carefully, "Your parents are frantic about you. I had a letter from them."

"I understand how they feel, but, David, I owe it to Fairlight to take care of her child."

We stared at each other. We're too tired to be arguing like this, I thought. When you're exhausted, quarreling is so easy. . . .

"Do what you want to do then." He shrugged and left.

So we brought Zady to the mission, and with her coming our big back room began to look like a hospital ward.

By the third week, Lundy's temperature was dropping and he was ravenous. Dr. MacNeill warned us that Lundy must stick with soft foods until ten days after his temperature dropped to normal. The walls of the intestinal tract of a typhoid patient, he said, were thin and ulcerous. Solid foods could perforate them, sometimes with hemorrhaging. Lundy clamored for solid food, whining about "mincy lady vittles" and being "starved to death."

One evening thoughts about David tumbled over themselves in my tired mind. All his plans had been set aside in favor of trying to get the people to clean up barnyards and build privies. It was dirty work and poor David hated it. He hated illness too, and was having it harder than the Doctor really, for MacNeill was only doing what he had been trained to do.

I hadn't been much comfort or help to David lately. Moved by a sudden compulsion, I slipped away from the mission house to his bunkhouse. David opened the door, obviously surprised. "Why, Christy! Anything wrong?"

"I need to talk to you, that's all. May I come in?" He stepped aside for me to enter. Then, obviously embarrassed at the messy room, he began straightening things up. I sat down.

"David, don't look so startled. I only came down here to tell you that I realize there has to be both give and take in real love. And so far I've been mostly a taker."

A light came into the brown eyes. He moved closer to me. "Christy, I never know what to expect from you." He kissed me and then drew me to him with such urgency that I pulled away. David looked at me in surprise. "You're not sure *what* it is you want to give, are you, Christy?"

"That's what I came to tell you—just what I want to give. But you never want to talk. I need to know what you're thinking."

"If you really want to know what I'm thinking," he said lightly, "it's how soft your hair is against my cheek."

The banter silenced me for a moment, but my questions were still there between us. "David, please . . . can't we talk for just a minute?" I drew a deep breath. "David, when you asked me to marry you, it was so unexpected that I told you I needed time to think it over. But I was—well, flattered. Any girl would be."

After a pause David said, "Well, there've been times when I wasn't sure *how* you felt about me."

"But, David, you've never asked me how I felt."

There was an awkward silence. David seemed to be struggling within himself. All at once I was aware again of the half-made couch-bed, the litter of clothes scattered around the bunkhouse. I said, "David, do you think it's all right for me to be here?"

"Why not?" he said. The words came out abruptly. "You certainly didn't hesitate to go by yourself to Neil MacNeill's cabin."

I felt unreal. Surely David knew that my visit to Dr. MacNeill's cabin had been only to get medicine? I started to say this, but no words came. I walked out the door.

Next morning David asked me to forgive him. "Of course, I

forgive you," I said. But inside something was crying out, Oh, David, what's wrong? I'm afraid to admit it, even to myself, but you don't really want me to marry you. Oh, David! Somehow you can't give love, you only want to *make* love.

But how could I say such things to David? So aloud I said lamely, "It's all right, David. We're all worn out, and not ourselves at all."

It was true. Total weariness was in our bones, behind the eyes, befogging the brain. Nor was there any respite. East Tennessee was having a mild late autumn. Here it was, into November and still no freezing ground. The plague spread and spread.

At night in my room, I would look into the darkness and see faces with eyes glazed with fever, the freshly dug graves on the hillsides, and that vacant desolation on the faces of the children left, and the look of the women with empty arms.

CHAPTER 19

ZADY was better. We permitted Clara to stay with her sister, while I took some broth to a patient in the hills. On the way back home I was aware of a throbbing head, an odd tic in my face. Tiredness, I supposed.

Crisis met me at the mission-house door. "It's Lundy. Awful sick," Opal told me. I could hear people running around.

With dread in my heart I climbed upstairs. Miss Alice was in Lundy's room, her eyes wide with apprehension. "He sneaked two hard-boiled eggs from the kitchen. His temperature's 103.6 degrees and he's in pain. If Neil were here and diagnosed perforation, he'd operate immediately." "Where is he?" a voice said.

"Across the river. We can't expect him back under three hours."

"OO-oo-law!" Lundy cried from the bed. "Can't you give me no easing powder?" With a look of desperation on her face, Miss Alice went back to attending him.

For the next two hours Lundy's temperature mounted steadily. Bird's-Eye took over the nursing, and Miss Alice went to her cabin to see what her medical books had to say on typhoid perforation. She came back more troubled than ever. "In perforation the pain is likely to be on the right side. The only suggestion is to turn the patient on the left side. If that doesn't relieve the pain—operate.... If only Neil would come!"

Soon after we got Lundy onto his left side, hiccups set in and his temperature began dropping—which made Miss Alice look more distressed than ever. Soon the pallor of his face was suffused by a dusky pink color. He began breathing rapidly and shallowly. Hearing someone at the front door, I ran to the top of the stairs. It was Dr. MacNeill! One look at my face and he came bounding up the stairs. But it was now too late to operate. Lundy was in deep shock, his body turning blue, his heart action erratic.

Surely, after all these weeks of effort, it can't end like this, I thought. Bird's-Eye, standing against the wall watching, now had a tremor around his mouth. But Dr. MacNeill's face was grim. I heard him say, almost in a whisper, "Saying a prayer, Alice?"

"Yes, Neil, I was."

"Prayer, Alice, won't change the course of typhoid." He leaned over Lundy some moments. Then he straightened up. "It's all over." He turned to speak to Bird's-Eye.

But Bird's-Eye had slipped from the room.

To MY relief, Bird's-Eye showed up again after supper. All of us except Dr. MacNeill were sitting in the parlor, too weary to start the next round of chores, reluctant to leave the comfort of one another's company, when he appeared suddenly in the doorway.

"Bin a-trompin' and a-trompin'," he said to Miss Alice. "I'm needin' to talk to you. To Opal too."

Miss Alice drew him into the room. "We're glad you came back, Bird's-Eye. Dr. MacNeill is out searching for you. We're grieving along with you. You know that."

"Oh, I ain't faultin' none of ye, ma'am. Couldn't nobody do nothin' for that Lundy, so stiff-necked he was, and raspy." Bird's-Eye's bravado was gone, but his eyes held no cravenness. "No need to let no grass grow under my feet." He looked directly at

Opal. "My give-out is about Tom. Like I writ ye, wasn't me kilt Tom, Opal. Bin a-wantin' to tell you this, but with Lundy sick to his bed 'n' all—" His voice trailed off.

Opal reached for Isaak's hand as if to hang on to him.

"That day you fed me, Opal, you said ony addlepated fool could pull a trigger, but hit took a *man* to fix things. Wal, studied on hit, and knowed you was right. Had my craw full of killin' onyway. Took my men, cloomb back up to my place.

"Nobody was thar. Then Lundy come in, a-packin' his rifle an' braggin' that he'd done hisself proud—he'd kilt Tom. Said now he'd holped me, so he was a man-person."

Opal sucked in her breath and Isaak clenched his free hand.

David's voice boomed out, "Just a minute, Bird's-Eye. If this story's true why did you let so many weeks go by without mentioning it to anyone? Your son is dead now and can't defend himself. What *proof* can you show that it was he who shot Tom?"

Bird's-Eye looked nonplused. "Don't reckon," he said slowly, "I've got no ev-i-dence to show. Oncet my passel of men heerd 'bout Tom being shot, said they warn't takin' no chances of ruination with the Big Law. They lit out back home into North Carolina, so they ain't here to back me up." He shrugged. "Ony-way, druther be clomped in jail my own self than Lundy. Couldn't turn in my own flesh 'n' blood."

Miss Alice leaned forward in her chair. "There *is* proof, Bird's-Eye. I've known for a month now that Lundy shot Tom."

Amazement gripped us all as she went on. "After Lundy got sick, Bob Allen came to see me. He said he was concerned about our nursing Lundy here. Said he knew something that was weighing on him. Bird's-Eye, the night you were at the McHones' Bob went to see David. Going home, at the edge of the mission woods, he heard the shot that killed Tom and saw Lundy fleeing."

"Saw him for shore?" Excitement crackled from Bird's-Eye.

"Yes. For sure."

Excitement died. "But he wouldn't holp me. I'm a Taylor. He's an Allen."

"If Bob didn't mean to help, he would have kept quiet. Bob

and I have talked often. He hasn't found hatred good food either."

This was too much for Bird's-Eye. Conflicting reactions struggled with his flintlike features, like a sledgehammer smashing a boulder to bits. And for the first time, real emotion showed.

This is one of those moments, one of those great moments, I thought. I looked at Opal. Obviously she had found it agony to relive Tom's murder, but there was triumph on her face. Something important was vindicated for her. When she had fed Tom's enemies that day, she had stepped out in faith—and her words had gone like an arrow to their mark.

And Miss Alice—all the time she was nursing Lundy, she knew!

There was that swimming feeling in my head again. The others left, and Miss Alice and David and I were alone. David was sitting in a chair, hunched over, stark misery on his face. "Miss Alice, Christy—" he said. "I have something to tell you both. I've made a decision. As soon as the epidemic is under control, I'm resigning. This experience in the mountains has shown me what I needed to know: I do not belong in the ministry."

I felt sick for him. "David, please—"

Miss Alice said calmly, "The Friends say that every one of us belongs in some kind of ministry. Ministry isn't just a profession of the church, David. Thee has been ministering in a hundred ways, doing God's work here."

"But there's such a thing as doing His work and yet not feeling a *part* of His work. You know God in a way that I don't, Miss Alice. You have an inner sureness I envy."

"Could it be, David, that deep down thee has never really wanted it—or Him?"

"Yes—you could be right. I think I've been running away from— a lot of things in my life."

"Not things. Persons. And now you want to run again."

"But I don't want to stay anyplace where I'm doing more harm than good."

"Your work here has been good, but that's beside the point. All your life you've had people at home telling you what to do. You've resisted and resented that—quite rightly—because it was a

169

threat to your manhood. You lay at your mother's door your de-cision to enter the ministry, but perhaps there was another reason: that thee saw in the ministry the chance to tell others what to do, for a change. But it doesn't quite work out that way, does it?"

David was silent, obviously struggling with her questions. And as so often happened when I was with Miss Alice, a new, luminous idea fell into my mind: Perhaps David can't truly love anyone until he can give himself and his love away to God.

Miss Alice rose. "Whether or not thee belongs in the church professionally isn't for me to know. If not, thee will find another avenue of service, equally fine. But David"—her voice grew warm—"there's a chance that this moment of facing thyself could be the sign that thee *does* belong."

There was pain in David's eyes as he stood up. I was agonizing for him. "You've both made me look at myself and see things I haven't wanted to see. I have some tough thinking to do. I'd better get on with it."

I got to my feet too, only to find the room whirling around me. I reached out for the table to steady myself. Dizzy! But the oil lamp is on that table. I must—I— As I pitched forward, I heard, as from a great distance, David's voice.

THE BLANKETS were heavy, so heavy. They were crushing me. Why were they keeping me pinned down with all this weight? And my tongue felt dry and swollen. Water would taste good. Pick a sprig of mint first. I would get some for myself.

But first I must open my eyes. I was in my room and Miss Alice was bending over me. I looked up at her. "Am I sick?"

"You've a little fever, but you're going to be fine."

My eyelids were so weighted that they shut themselves. Duti-fully, I opened my mouth when I felt a spoon touch my lips. The liquid trickled down my throat, but my throat and tongue were sore.

Day melted into night. . . . Night into day. . . . People came and went. Why would they not leave me alone? Someone was always changing my covers. Why did they wash me so much? They should know that it did not matter. . . . Nothing mattered at all.

Dr. MacNeill's face was over me. He must be talking to me, but I was not sure what he was saying. I would ask him to repeat that. No, I could not; it was too hard.

Light . . . darkness . . . starlight . . . moonrise . . . dawning . . . hours . . . days . . . eons, melded into one.

The voices of those men were angry. It was Bird's-Eye Taylor shouting at David. "Preacher, I'm a-warnin' ye. Keep yer religion inside the church-house." He was raising his shotgun. David had a gun too. They're going to shoot it out! Maybe if I stand between them. "David, that's not the way! Put the gun down!"

I put my fingers in my ears to shut out the sound of the explosion. "Oh David, you killed Bird's-Eye! . . ." Miss Alice kept telling me that David had not killed anyone. But she was so good and kind. . . . "Miss Alice, please don't leave. Stay with me. Miss Alice . . . . What will you do with my dresses?"

Days and nights. . . . David's voice: "Christy, Bird's-Eye and I haven't been shooting it out. He and I are friends now."

Sights and sounds and words. . . . Perhaps later on I would understand what the words meant. . . . "Christy, I'm not going to quit. Got a letter from my seminary asking me to talk about a new opportunity. I sure was tempted to leave the Cove. But I can't run again. I have to stand my ground and find myself right here. Understand me, Christy?" His voice had that old jocular ring. David was himself again. I was glad that David was happy. . . . Then the deep voice retreated.

There was something strange about it all. I was letting something go. What was it that I was letting go? Well, whatever it was, it was all right. David was happy. Wearily, I turned over.

Now Little Burl was there! "Teacher, Teacher, I come to swap howdys with you." I took him in my arms and hugged him. "You're *cold,* Little Burl." I was dancing up and down the hillside to warm him up, both of us laughing hilariously.

Hear the wind blow, love. . . . Bend with the wind and let yourself go. . . . The gusts were stronger and wilder. They were going to blow the postman and me right off that cliff. But Mr. Pentland was a nice man, a friendly man; I was safe with him. . . .

My body felt weightless. Light was drawing me irresistibly, dazzling light. I was running in shimmering splendor. The grass was dotted with buttercups and pinks and mountain bluets, like patches of sky fallen into the grass. The light—I must get to the light!

But I came to some sort of barrier. Not a wall because I could see through it. Not glass because when I put out my hand I felt—nothing. But I was stopped there nonetheless. Some sort of decision seemed to be required of me. I could go on—or stay on this side of the barrier: I had been stopped to make certain that I would consider my choice.

Over there was the light. . . . The air was crystal, as if a sun of suns was glinting off numberless prisms, reflecting the light rays so dazzlingly that I had to put my hand up to shield my eyes. I was *seeing* in a manner I had never seen before. The light appeared to come from inside the leaves, the blossoms, the blades of grass. Each leaf, each petal stood apart from all others, poised in motion, energy in balance. Never had there been such colors or such light, never in all the world. *In all the world* . . . . For now we see through a glass, darkly; but then face-to-face . . .

Now into the scene trooped a group of children. They were beautiful children. They were like spirited colts out for a frolic. I could feel the love that surrounded them, and out of the love flowed harmony. And there, amongst them, was the happiness that all men seek and so few find. . . . I want the joy of those children. Yes, I will go on. Yes, I must. . . .

At that instant I saw Fairlight. . . . She was barefoot, wearing a blue plaid dress I knew well, carrying a honeysuckle basket and swinging along like a highland princess. Why, she looked *happy*—serene, confident. She had not seen me. I wanted her to see me. "Fairlight!" I started to call out—but something held me back.

Children surrounded her, and she was kneeling now, planting lady's slippers on the bank of a stream. The light danced on her fingers, splintering into diamonds in the water, tossed back into the air, caught in her hair. She was singing a haunting ballad:

> *"O come you home, dear Johnny,*
> *O come you home from sea?*
> *Last night my daughter Polly*
> *Was dreaming of thee. . . ."*

"Fairlight! Oh, Fairlight . . ."

But from a great distance someone was calling my name, pulling me away from the light. I would ignore it. I had to go on. . . .

Over and over the voice called my name. Why could I not go on? There was something in the voice that pulled me back. And it was like the love I had seen among the playing children.

Then I knew. I *had* to go back. Someone loved me, needed me. . . . That light was not for me yet. But sometime. Oh, *sometime!*

I WAS HEAVY, so heavy. My eyelids would not open. The familiar voice, a man's voice, very soft. He was talking to me, calling me. "Christy, Christy, come back to me. Christy, wherever you are, listen to me. . . . Christy, I love you, love you, *love you.* Christy, can you hear me? *I love you!* You cannot leave me without knowing this. Christy—"

And then the tone of the words changed. "God, I have fought against You. Not only fought, God, but cursed You when You let Margaret die—and our son. I did not understand anything about You. I still don't understand anything—except that somehow I know *You are love:* for in my heart has been born so great a love for Christy as I did not know could exist on this earth. You, God, must have put it there. So what do I do with it now?" The voice broke, and I tried to lift my hand—but it was too heavy.

"Lord God of heaven and of earth, I am not worthy of—of anything. There is nothing more that I can do for Christy. Nothing at all. So I offer back to You this love You gave. It's all I have to give You. Here are our lives—hers and mine. I hold them out to You. Do with us—as You please." The voice fell silent.

So it was Neil's voice that had called me back. He needed me. He *loved* me.

Warmth came into me, starting at the top of my head and flowing steadily downward. My eyelids fluttered open. Neil was still sitting there by my bed, his head sunk on the covers, one hand stretched out, with the bowl of that old pipe of his clutched in it; but the stem of the pipe was broken and lay on the rumpled covers of the bed.

I could move my fingers now. I felt across the counterpane until my hand reached his, the big hand with the blond-red hairs on top. My fingers closed over his hand and gripped it. His head came up. *"Christy!"*

The joy of the children was in his voice.

Catherine Marshall

Catherine Marshall flashed to the top of best-seller lists eighteen years ago with *Mr. Jones, Meet the Master,* her blank verse edition of sermons by her late husband, the brilliant young Senate chaplain, Peter Marshall. She followed this with *A Man Called Peter,* a biography of her husband, another runaway best seller. To date, her ten books—all inspirational nonfiction—have sold more than two-and-one-half million copies in hardcover editions. Yet to Mrs. Marshall, they were all merely preparation for years of work that went into *Christy.* "As a teen-ager," she says, "I used to sit on a hillside, high above an Appalachian valley and dream of writing a novel. With *Christy,* I am connected with my original dream."

The story was born in 1958 when Catherine Marshall suggested that her parents revisit the Tennessee mountain community where they had met in 1909. Her mother, young Leonora Whitaker, from Hendersonville, North Carolina, had been a teacher in a one-room mission school; her father, the Reverend John Wood, was the Presbyterian minister. Mrs. Marshall went with them on several nostalgic returns, talked with her mother's former pupils, listened to outpourings of memories, and read copies of *The Soul Winner,* published by the American Inland Mission. In one issue Leonora wrote: "I sometimes shudder when I look into the faces of my students, and note their intelligence, and realize the responsibility that rests upon me as their teacher. . . ."

Although already familiar with Appalachian ways—she was born in Johnson City, Tennessee, and spent some years in New Creek Valley, West Virginia—Mrs. Marshall next plunged into intensive background research in the Library of Congress, studying Appalachian geography, folklore, ballads, tall tales, clothes and speech. She put the book aside in 1959, the year she married Leonard LeSourd, executive editor of *Guideposts* magazine, acquiring two sons and a daughter, in addition to her own son, the Reverend Peter John Marshall. Family responsibilities then kept her busy, and she also took time out to write two nonfiction books. In 1965 she began intensive writing on her novel.

Although *Christy* is firmly based on her mother's experiences, Mrs. Marshall says the fictional story quickly took over. But many of the most surprising episodes are true—among others, the seven-mile walk in the snow with the postman and the piano hauled over the mountains. But the typhoid epidemic is fictional and cost the author much time and trouble finding someone who could describe in vivid detail this fast-vanishing disease. The onion poultice remedy came from a retired nurse, and Christy's delirium from the memories of a Tennessee doctor's daughter who had had typhoid as a child. There was no murder near the mission when Leonora taught there, but Mrs. Marshall studied many old Tennessee murder trial transcripts to make her discussion of feuding authentic.

Since John Wood's death, Leonora Whitaker Wood, now seventy-four, has wintered with her daughter near Palm Beach, Florida. Mrs. Marshall says, "Mother has followed the writing of the book with delight; it has been the fulfillment of a dream for her too."

The same sure faith which has illuminated all of Mrs. Marshall's books runs through *Christy* like a bright thread. "Faith is a challenge," she says. "It was faith that took my mother into the mountains on a wild adventure. It is my inheritance from her and from my father. I couldn't have done anything I have done without it."

EIGHT YEARS ON BROADWAY

"Both profound and amusing; a little gem"
NEW YORK HERALD TRIBUNE

"A lasting work of art"
SATURDAY REVIEW OF LITERATURE

"You won't find a truer or more beguiling book"
NEW YORK TIMES

"An authentic part of our American folklore"
NEW YORK TIMES

"One of the most chuckling books of our time"
ATLANTIC MONTHLY

"A delightful book alive with energy and
collisions and the running water of happiness"
NEW REPUBLIC

"A well of wisdom concerning the secrets of all hearts"
NEW YORK HERALD TRIBUNE

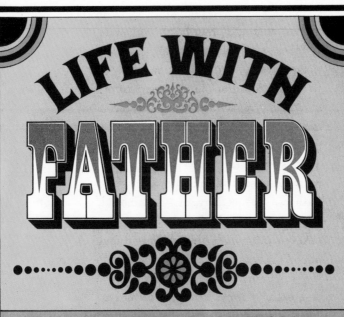

LIFE WITH FATHER

⋙ A CONDENSATION FROM ⋘

GOD AND MY FATHER
LIFE WITH FATHER & LIFE WITH MOTHER

BY CLARENCE DAY

TITLE PAGE BY JOHN ALCORN

ILLUSTRATIONS BY ERIK BLEGVAD

Clarence Day's series of stories about his fiery and astounding Father has become one of America's most beloved small classics. Such a rich and rounded character, so warm, so wayward, so furious in his sweep through the maddening vagaries of family life, has rarely been seen in print; and he is twice as delightful because he *is* fact, not fiction. Thanks to the amused yet loving reminiscences of his oldest son, Father—Clarence Day, Sr.—is immortal.

What one generation takes for granted, the next one often finds absurd; but although nobody now is invincible or embattled in exactly the way Father was in the 1880s, there is something of every father's foibles and of every family's crises in the Day family's entertaining adventures.

"A meaning that sinks deep into you while you are laughing."—*Yale Review*

"A sizable addition to the understanding and the amusement of the world . . . Imbued all through with a sympathetic understanding of human nature."—*The New York Times*

"A wholly delightful book, to be recommended unreservedly to anyone who ever had a father or a mother."
—Isabel Paterson in the New York *Herald Tribune*

‑‑ Father and I ‑‑

THERE WAS A TIME in my boyhood when I felt that Father had handicapped me severely in life by naming me after him. Clarence! History, so far as I could see, was thronged with objectionable persons with the fancy name Clarence and as for the Clarences in the fiction I read, they were horrible. In one story, for instance, there were two brothers, Clarence and Frank. Clarence was a "vain, disagreeable little fellow," who was proud of his curly hair and fine clothes, while Frank was a "rollicking boy, ready to play games with anybody." Clarence didn't like to play games, of course. He just minced around looking on. This wasn't an exceptionally mean Clarence, either. He was just run-of-the-mill.

Father, however, had never even dreamed of there being anything objectionable in his name. Quite the contrary. And he had lived a good rough-and-tumble boy's life. He had played and fought on the city streets, and in the summer, at the farm where Grandpa was born, had gone barefoot and driven the cows home just as though he had been named Tom or Bill.

Father was too independent to care if people thought his name was fancy. He had plenty of prejudices himself, but they were his own. He paid no attention to the prejudices of others, except

179

to disapprove of them. If any boy had tried to make fun of his being named Clarence, Father would simply have told him he didn't know what he was talking about. In fact, Father would often try to impress on me my responsibilities as the son to whom he had given his name. A great deal was expected, it seemed, of a boy who was named after his father. I used to envy my brothers, who didn't have such things expected of them.

I envied them still more after I was old enough to begin getting letters. I then discovered that when Father gave me his name he had also, not unnaturally, retained it himself. He was too accustomed to opening all Clarence Day letters to remember to look for a "Jr." So far as mail went, I had no name of my own.

When I was a small boy I heard mostly from firms whose advertisements I had read in the *Youth's Companion* and whose circulars I had requested. The circulars described remarkable bargains in magicians' outfits, pocket knives, trick spiders and imitation fried eggs, and they seemed interesting and valuable to me—when I got them. The trouble was that Father usually got them and at once tore them up. I then had to write for another circular, and if Father got the second one too, he would explode with annoyance. He became particularly indignant one year, I remember, when he was repeatedly urged to take advantage of a bargain sale of false whiskers. During this period I got more of my mail out of Father's wastebasket than I did from the postman.

At the age of twelve or so, I stopped writing for imitation fried eggs and turned to a new field. A cousin of mine lent me some books by Horatio Alger, and they opened my eyes to a brand-new attraction—the ways a boy could earn money. Father began to receive letters beginning:

DEAR FRIEND DAY:

In reply to your valued request for one of our Mammoth Agents' Outfits, kindly forward postoffice order for $1.49 to cover cost of postage and packing, and we will put you in a position to earn a large income in your spare time with absolutely no labor on your part, by getting subscribers for *The Secret Handbook of Mesmerism*.

One spring, as the result of what I had intended to be a secret application on my part, Father was assigned "the exclusive rights for Staten Island and Hoboken of selling the Gem Home Popper for Pop Corn. Housewives buy it at sight."

After Father had stormily endured these afflictions for a while, he and I began to get letters from girls. Fortunately these were rare, for they were ordeals for both of us. Father had forgotten, if he ever knew, how silly young girls can sound. When he opened these letters, he read them all the way through, sometimes twice, muttering to himself over and over: "This is very peculiar. Here's a letter to me from some person I never heard of. I can't see what it's about." By the time it had occurred to him that possibly the letter might be for me, I was red and embarrassed and even angrier at the girl than at Father. And on days when he had read some of the phrases aloud to the family, it nearly killed me to claim it.

This sort of thing went on even after I grew up. Some fifteen years after the telephone had been invented, Father, in spite of misgivings, got one. It was put on a wall on the second floor, where everybody could hear its loud bell. From the first it made trouble. It rang seldom but it always chose a moment when there was nobody on the second floor. Mother would pick up her skirts and run upstairs, calling to it loudly, "I'm coming! I'm coming!" but the fretful thing kept right on ringing. Father couldn't regard it as inanimate either. He scolded and cursed it, and when somebody telephoned him and he couldn't make out at once who it was, he would shake his fist and shout at it, getting red in the face. "Speak up, speak up! I can't hear a word, I tell you!"

He always assumed when the bell rang that it was for him. One day a new friend of mine, a girl who lived in a settlement house in the slums, telephoned to invite me to lunch with some visiting Russians. Father answered the telephone. "Yes, this is Mr. Day. Speak up, hang it! Don't mumble at me. *What?* Come to lunch? I've had lunch. . . . Next Friday? Why, I don't want to lunch with you next Friday. . . . Yes, my name is Clarence Day, I told you that before. . . . Lunch with you in Rivington Street?

I never heard of such a thing in my life! . . . Russians? I don't know any Russians. . . . No, I don't want to, either. . . . No, I haven't changed. I never change. . . . What? . . . *Good-by*, madam."

"I think that was a friend of mine, Father," I said.

"A friend of yours!" he exclaimed. "Arguing with me about lunching somewhere in the slums. I can't stand it, that's all I have to say. I'll have the confounded thing taken out."

Father was in Wall Street, and one time I had asked his opinion about a low-priced stock I'd been watching. "Not worth a hang," he told me. But I still wanted to buy it, so I placed the order with another firm instead of with his own brokerage office. At the end of the month this other firm sent me a statement, and of course they forgot the "Jr." When I came in, I found Father excitedly telling Mother that this firm had opened an account for him without being asked, and that he'd like to wring their necks.

"That must be for me, Father," I said. We looked at each other.

"*You* bought this stuff? After all I said about it?" He handed over the statement and walked out of the room.

Both he and I felt offended and angry. But in a few days we made it up. Nobody could stay angry with Father—he was too utterly guiltless of having meant to offend.

The good part of all these experiences was that in the end they drew Father and me closer together. My brothers had only chance battles with him. I had a war. Neither he nor I relished its clashes, but they made us surprisingly intimate.

If Father never got over owning his name, that was natural enough; for *everything* Father had ever owned seemed to be permanently part of him, no matter what happened to it. This was true even of his old clothes. When he gave me an old necktie or a discarded pair of trousers, they still seemed to him to be his. Not only did he feel that way about it, but he made me feel that way, too. He explained to me that he gave things he didn't care about to the Salvation Army, but that when he had a particularly handsome tie which had plenty of wear in it yet, or a pair of trousers he had been fond of, he saved them for me.

A pair of striped trousers which he had worn to church for

years went up to Yale with me one term. As I was short of clothes, they came in very handy. I had to be careful not to take off my coat while I was wearing them, though. They looked oddly baggy in the seat when exposed to full view—on nights when I was playing billiards in a poolroom, for instance, or climbing a college gate quickly. In fact, to get over a gate at all in Father's trousers was quite a feat. On nights like these, as I was undressing in my bedroom, I sometimes had moral qualms over the kind of life I was making Father's trousers lead.

One week I lent them to a classmate of mine to wear in a play. When I saw Father's Sunday trousers running across the stage pursued by a comic bartender yelling "Stop thief!" I felt distinctly uncomfortable. Even worse was the night when a girl whom Father would have by no means approved of sat on what was my lap but his trousers. Father was eighty miles away, but I became so ill at ease that I got up and left.

There had always been a special sort of rightness about Father's things in our eyes: his watch chain, his studs and cuff links, handsome and simple, not ornate like those in fashion in those days. We regarded all these objects with reverence.

Once in a long while, when I was small, Father would take me down to his office. If it wasn't raining he wore his tailcoat and his silk hat and carried a cane. When he passed a friend on the street, they would raise their canes and touch the brims of their hats with them in formal salute. I admired this rich and formal gesture.

These trips with Father were a great treat. Mother and my three little brothers saw us off from the stoop of our house, and I hopped along at Father's side through long rows of comfortable brownstone houses from Madison Avenue west to Sixth. We climbed the Elevated stairs and waited until a stubby little steam engine, with an open coal car, puffed in, pulling three or four cars. *Too-oot, too-too-toot!* it whistled. We got on board and walked leisurely through the cars till Father found a seat he liked.

During the journey downtown, except when the smoke from the engine was too thick for me to see out, I stared fascinatedly into the windows of tenements, or at the even more interesting second-floor rooms of lodging houses for tramps. I envied the tramps. They looked so easygoing. If I were a tramp, I wouldn't have to put on tight white kid gloves and pull some unwieldy little girl around a waxed floor at dancing school. It wouldn't cost much, either. The lodging-house sign said "Ten Cents a Night."

Father's office at 38 Wall Street was always busy in what seemed to me a mysterious way. The cashier sat on a stool, in a cage, with a cash drawer, a safe full of records, another safe for securities, and a tin box full of postage stamps, which he doled out as needed. Bookkeepers in black alpaca coats made entries in enormous leather-bound ledgers. Office boys ran about, and Western Union messengers rushed in with telegrams. In one room four or five whiskery men sat around a table full of company reports, watched the ticker and wrote mysterious things on a blackboard.

Father went into his private office, where a little coal fire was burning, and while he opened his mail, I proudly cleaned and filled his inkwells, and put fresh pens in his penholders. He had quills at home, but he used only steel pens here because he wrote a good share of the firm's letters in longhand, himself.

Once, afterward, we lunched at Delmonico's. I didn't appreciate the French cooking there. It tasted all right, but it was dainty and there wasn't much of it. However, dessert was a large chocolate éclair. The richness of its soft, thick yellow interior and the meltingness of its chocolate outside were so delicious that time stood still as I happily ate it.

After lunch, we took the ferry to Staten Island and saw Buffalo Bill in a Wild West show. He made me want to be a cowboy. I told Father this on the way home. He said I might as well be a tramp. I wondered if I'd better tell him that this idea, too, had occurred to me, but I decided not to mention it. "Put your cap on straight," Father added. "I am trying to bring you up to be a civilized man."

I adjusted my cap and walked on. The more I thought about it, the less I wanted to be a civilized man. What with "improving" books and dancing school and sermons on Sundays, the few chocolate éclairs that a civilized man got to eat were not worth it.

THE FIRST THING I wrote about Father and Mother was merely a
filler in a column I was writing for the New York *Evening Post*. It
went like this:

> My father is fond of dogs. Likes to train them. His method is
> this: He says to the new dog, "Good Jackie." The dog wags his
> tail. "Come here. Come here, boy." The dog looks at him doubt-
> fully. My father, who hasn't a great deal of patience, raises his
> voice: "Come! Come here, sir!" The dog grows alarmed and tries
> to get out. My father advances upon him, repeating, "Come
> here!" with increasing annoyance and sternness.
>
> "I wish you'd let Jackie alone," says my mother. "He doesn't
> know what you want of him."
>
> "Pooh! Of course he does," declares my father. "Come *here*,
> sir!" And he drags the new dog from under the sofa.
>
> "Sit up," he instructs him. The dog is utterly limp. "Sit up.
> Come! Sit up." He shakes his finger at him. "Sit up, sir!"
>
> "Please," says my mother. "How *can* you expect the poor thing
> to sit up when he doesn't know a word you're saying!"
>
> "Will you let me alone?" shouts my father. "Sit *up*, sir!"
>
> My mother goes to the door. "I'll not stay here and see that dog
> frightened to death."
>
> "Frightened!" my father says, testily. "Nonsense! I know dogs."
>
> The dog sees the door being opened and suddenly bolts.
>
> My father grabs fiercely at him. In vain. "Confound it!" he
> says, in a passion. "You've spoiled my whole plan." He stamps.
>
> "You could never—" my mother begins.
>
> "I COULD!" roars my father. "But I can't do a thing if I'm inter-
> fered with. JACKIE! Here, Jackie! Come here, sir! *Jackie!*"

I showed the column to Mother.

"That's the way he *always* treats dogs," she said. She hurried
off with the clipping to Father. "Here, Clare," she said triumphantly, "read this!"

Father read it in his careful way, and looked up at Mother with a smile of satisfaction. "I hope you'll behave yourself after this," he chuckled, "that's *just* how you kept interfering."

Each incident I wrote about after that became a subject of debate between Father and Mother. Because they were without self-consciousness, the publicity seemed to be of no concern to them, so long as each felt I had presented his or her side so clearly that the other should blush. Neither of them ever did blush. However, they got so provoked at each other once or twice that they went back and refought the whole battle.

FATHER, although spirited and jolly, was a clear-eyed and careful young man. He did things one at a time, and until he got married he continued to live with his parents.

He was self-reliant however. He had made his own way from the start. In 1866, when he was twenty-one, he had already had nearly seven years' business experience. He then asked his first favor of Grandpa: the loan of three thousand dollars—at six per-cent—to buy a seat on the Stock Exchange. When he began to make money, he started in to arrange the other sides of his life.

One of the first things he did was to buy new furniture for his bedroom—a solid brown walnut set that he used for the next forty years. His next step was to buy a little clavier keyboard and learn finger exercises. When he had exercised his fingers enough, he bought a piano and hired an old German musician to teach him how to play. What with Father's criticisms of old family ways, and his determined pounding on his piano, Grandpa began to get restive. He tried to be patient, however, in the hope that his son would soon marry.

In 1869 Father treated himself to a trip abroad. He had several things to attend to. He went to the best watchmaker in Switzerland and selected a watch that he wore for the rest of his life. After that he went to London, where he ordered clothes enough for his immediate needs, and left the tailor his measurements. From that time on, Father ordered his suits and overcoats from London. He never had many clothes at once, but they had to be right.

The next year, 1870, he went over again. He wanted to see more of Europe. He also wanted some shirts from Paris. As Father made his way on board the French Line's *St. Laurent* in New York, he saw Alden B. Stockwell, a dignified, older man he had met on the Stock Exchange. Stockwell was saying good-by to his brother, Levi, and to their little sister, who was seventeen but still wore her red hair in a braid. Girls were children then until they suddenly "came out" in society as young ladies. Father was introduced to Levi and this schoolgirl, his future wife, and the *St. Laurent* sailed.

Levi got seats for the three of them together at table. This was exceedingly agreeable for a sociable young man like Father, but Mother seemed far less sure. One day Father called to the waiter: "Here, bring that back, I want some more—that is *good*." Mother told him, "There are other people here besides you!" "He makes me so mad," she wrote her mother.

Young Mr. Day didn't mind if he did. He found this schoolgirl great fun. He promenaded the deck with her on breezy days, with her veils flying and her skirts billowing out. And when the weather grew rough and she was too ill to stir, he and Levi took turns carrying her up on deck for a breath of fresh air.

They went to Paris, and while Levi attended to his brother Alden's business, their little redheaded sister visited the galleries and cathedrals with young Mr. Day. Young Mr. Day began to discover that he had fallen in love.

But it took him three years to propose. Mother, who lived with her brother Alden, was still a pupil at Miss Haines' School in Gramercy Park. He couldn't marry a schoolgirl. The other difficulty was that she was the sister of one of the richest men on Wall Street. Father was afraid Mother would expect him to provide for her more luxuriously than he had any intention whatever of doing.

Meanwhile, Mother had proposals from six beaux before she was twenty. With none of these was she in love, but she wasn't in love with Father, either, she thought. He didn't behave right. Her other beaux sent her flowers and presents, some too beautiful to accept. Father didn't even pay her compliments. She didn't know

Father said he wouldn't leave until Mother promised to marry him.

what to make of him. Yet somehow he had a kind of realness for her that the others lacked.

In 1873, Alden got into a financial contest with Mr. Jay Gould, and found himself outflanked and then ruined. Mother was sent home to Painesville, Ohio, leaving behind her a brother who no longer smiled but still would not acknowledge defeat.

It was then that Father asked Mother to marry him. Mother wasn't sure whether she was in love or not. She invited him to Painesville. Seeing her in her old family home was a test she had imposed on each of her suitors.

Painesville had been settled by New Englanders late in the seventeen-hundreds. Its shady streets, its brick sidewalks, its Colonial houses surrounded by trees, made it one of the loveliest towns in the Western Reserve. But its standards of comfort were simple. Its one hotel had dismayed the fashionable beaux from New York.

When Father arrived there he behaved very differently from

his predecessors. Whatever their private opinions of Painesville, they had been too guarded to express them. Father expressed his at once. He told Mother and her parents just what he thought of it. He said it was "a blasted hole."

Father's frankness amused Painesville. He seemed to be a clean, energetic, likable young fellow and all the time that he was in Painesville he did not "touch a drop." He told Mother that this was merely because there was nothing in the place fit to drink, but Painesville didn't know this, and his sobriety impressed them. It even impressed Grandma. She and Father didn't get on well—then or later—but she had nothing against him, she said.

Father said he wouldn't leave until Mother promised to marry him, and he urged her to hurry. Although part of this was ardor, the rest was impatience—he wanted to get out of Painesville. He said he should think that she'd want to get out of there too.

They were married in New York in June, quietly, in Alden's house. Immediately after the ceremony the young bride and groom sailed for France.

It had all been so sudden, just at the last, that Mother felt shaken up. The weather was rough. She took to her berth and she stayed there. When Father offered to bring her anything to eat she moaned. Father had an excellent appetite himself and he found the weather exhilarating. He urged Mother to "make an effort" to get up on deck. She'd be all right then, he assured her. When this had no effect, he went off and filled his lungs with sea air and ate three hearty meals a day and felt sorry for Mother. He kept trying to think of something that he could do for her to make her well again. One afternoon, ruddy and glowing, he opened their cabin door. "Vinnie?" he said. "Are you feeling better? I wish you'd been with me at lunch." No answer.

"I had two helpings of salmon," he added, to tempt her, "and the *sauce tartare* was delicious."

A vivid, unwelcome picture sprang up in Mother's mind. Faintly, she begged him, "Don't talk to me, darling, just now."

It was nearly a year, she told me, before she could bear to eat salmon, with or without sauce tartare.

189

From Father's point of view, Mother never did know how to handle an ailment. He thought there was nobody like her, but he always seemed to disapprove of her when she was ill.

Mother would keep going as long as she could when she felt ill, but sometimes she had to give up and crawl into bed. Yet she didn't make noises there, so Father was sure she wasn't suffering. When people thought they were ill, he declared, it was merely a sign of weak character. But every time he tried to strengthen Mother's character in this respect, she seemed to resent it. When she was ill, Father felt lost, and said so.

When he came home from his office, the first thing he did was to look for Mother. One night about six o'clock he opened the door of her bedroom. There was no light except for a flickering little fire in the grate. A smell of witch hazel was in the air, mixed with spirits of camphor. On the bed, huddled under an afghan, Mother lay still.

"Are you there, Vinnie?" Father said, in a voice even louder than usual because of his not being sure.

Mother moaned, "Go away."

"What?" he asked, in astonishment.

"Go away. Oh, *go 'way.*"

"Damnation!" he said, marching out.

He told himself Mother was perfectly healthy and would be all right in the morning. He ate a good dinner. Being lonely, he added an extra glass of claret and some cheese. He had such a long and dull evening that he smoked two extra cigars.

After breakfast the next morning, he went to her bedroom again. He stood at the foot of Mother's bed, looking disconsolate because she wasn't well yet. His features were lumpy with gloom.

"For mercy's sake, Clare, don't come in here looking like that," Mother begged.

"What do you mean? Looking like what?"

"Oh, go away!" Mother shrieked. "I never will get well if you stand there and stare at me that way! And let me alone."

Outside her door, when I asked him how Mother was, he said with a chuckle: "She sounds *much* better this morning."

It was only when she did begin to get well that Father realized at last how feeble she had become. He kept patting her hand and saying, "Dear Vinnie," and telling her he couldn't stand it.

Mother was pleased by this. When she saw other women being fussed over by their husbands, she often wished she got more attention. But she was not really the kind of woman to linger much over endearments. She liked things of that sort to be electric, and to come in quick flashes, and pass. So after Father, who wasn't very inventive, had patted her hand twenty times one afternoon, she snatched it away in annoyance and said: "Stop, Clare! That's enough! It's time you were starting."

Mother had coerced Father, much against his will, into saying he'd go to a tea that Mrs. Nichols was giving. He looked handsome in his cutaway. Mother felt she was being generous to Mrs. Nichols to send such a distinguished-looking man to her tea, while Mother sat in bed with nothing to look forward to but chicken broth. Things tasted so good at a tea.

"Anything I can do for you while I'm out?" Father asked.

"Yes, Clare," she said suddenly, "there *is* something I'd like. Do bring me some of those little sandwiches Mrs. Nichols has—they'd be so nice with chicken broth."

"Sandwiches and *broth?*" Father said in dismay.

"No! Just sandwiches," Mother said. "Those little thin sandwiches. Bring some in your pocket."

"Oh, some sandwiches, eh?" Father put on his high hat, took his stick and gloves from the table, and left.

He enjoyed himself more than he had expected to at the tea. He picked out a good corner to sit in with his cup and plate, and then as he talked and munched appreciatively, he remembered that he was to get some sandwiches for Mother. A table across the room was piled high with them, but how could he possibly march up there publicly and juggle the sticky things into his coattail pocket? It would be such an *odd* thing to do. He was sure that Mother would understand how impossible it was.

When he got home, Mother's broth was sitting beside her on the table, waiting for the sandwiches. She heard Father put away his things in the coat closet. At last, he came to her room, beamed cheerfully, and started to sit down.

"Don't sit on my sandwiches," she warned him.

He half put his hand to his coattails, then frowned.

"Oh, Clare!" Mother cried disappointedly. "You *forgot* them!"

"No! I didn't forget them!" Father said crossly.

"Why didn't you bring them, then? Did you eat any yourself?"

"Yes," said Father, recollecting the taste with pleasure. "Several. They were very nice."

"Oh Clare!"

"I wanted to bring you some, Vinnie, but the table was over there—and they—" Suddenly he didn't understand, himself, why he hadn't brought those sandwiches home. He looked helplessly at her.

"You never will do *anything* that you think isn't 'suitable,' " Mother said irritatedly.

"Why of course I won't," he said frowning. "Why should I?"

Father and Health

FATHER had been putting on weight and he didn't like it. He was a solidly built man, but trim and erect, and his extra pounds made him uncomfortable.

So Father joined the Riding Club, in East Fifty-eighth Street, and after practicing in the tanbark ring, rode out in Central Park. The Park suited Father. He liked landscapes to be orderly, and suitably arranged for his own use.

His first horse was a powerful bay by the name of Rob Roy. This horse didn't like Father, and Father had still less affection for him, but this was not considered important. Father had bought Rob Roy because he was spirited, sound and handsome. He had paid three hundred dollars for him, and expected him to do what he was told. Rob Roy, however, never looked upon the transaction in this way. He had an independent and self-absorbed nature. Even if he had been devoted to Father, which he never was, this would have made trouble.

One typical scene between them occurred near the Park entrance. Rob Roy and Father made a fine sight as they trotted out of the club into the Park. Each healthy and strong, and each intent on his own thoughts, they went up the bridle path. So far their plans had coincided. But then a difference between them arose. Father wished to keep on. Rob Roy didn't, I don't know why. Father gave him a cut with his whip. Rob Roy whirled around. Father reined him up sharply. Rob Roy reared. Father in his anger struck him again, and Rob Roy violently pawed the ground and tore it all up. Neither would give in; but Rob Roy had the whole day before him, and Father had to go to his office. He returned with Rob Roy to the club.

Such combats awed our family. We had never dreamed that anyone, man or beast, would resist Father's will. This rashness of Rob Roy's was like Satan's rebelling against God.

In spite of Rob Roy, Father grew so enthusiastic about riding that he bought a second horse for the rest of us when we went to the country for the summer. Father liked to have his family—particularly Mother—do things with him. But Mother distrusted horses, so we boys took turns riding with him.

One morning, when Father and I were out in farm country, he turned into a new road. Just over a crest, hidden from sight, was a washout—which my horse, ahead of Father's, jumped. A little farther on I reined him in and looked back for Father.

He was lying face down in the road. Rob Roy, who had fallen beside him, scrambled up just as I turned, and I saw him step over Father. I galloped back, dismounted, and managed to roll Father over. He was senseless. I began shouting for help.

Off in a hollow was a farmhouse. At last I saw a man come out of it and walk up the hill toward us. He got Father to his feet, and we went slowly along to his house, Father stumbling between us. We put him in a chair, on the grass, and washed his face. He didn't seem to understand questions, so the farmer and I anxiously decided I'd better hitch my horse to the farmer's buggy, put Father in, and drive him home.

Father was so groggy he could hardly sit up, but he absolutely refused to have anything to do with the buggy. "Take that thing away," he said, and added imperiously that he wanted his horse.

The farmer and I were taken aback: we had naturally supposed that we were in charge. But, shaken up though he was, Father was still somehow the master of the situation. With great misgivings the farmer and I hoisted him up on his mount.

On the way to Dr. Coudert's place, Father wobbled about in the saddle, but his knees held on. When I rang Dr. Coudert's bell, he looked down out of his bedroom window. "Good morning, Day," he called. "What's the matter?"

"Accident," Father said thickly. "Come my house. Fix it."

He trotted away, lurching in the saddle. I hurried after him. At our doorway, Mother came running out as he tried to dismount. "Dear Vinnie," he muttered, and toppled into our arms. We got him to bed. It was weeks before he got up again. I suppose he had had a concussion, but we boys weren't told any details.

After he got well, he seemed to want to forget the whole thing. He didn't even seem appreciative of all Mother had done, until one day, as a surprise, he gratefully bought her a beautiful ring with three rubies. When Dr. Coudert heard about this, he strongly approved. He told Father that he owed his life to Mother, she had been such a good nurse; and when Mother heard him say it, she nodded her head violently and said that was true.

FATHER'S experiences in the sickroom were few. Aside from his rare colds, his only foes were headaches.

When he had a cold, his method of dealing with it was to try to clear it out by main force, preferably by sneezing. Mother didn't like him to sneeze; he did it with such a roar; and she was sure it was catching. Father said all this talk of germs was newfangled nonsense. He said his sneezes were healthy. And presently we'd hear a hearty, triumphant blast as he sneezed again.

When a headache started, Father lay down, shut his eyes and

yelled. The severity of a headache could be judged by the volume of sound he put forth. His idea seemed to be to show the headache that he was just as strong as it was, and stronger. When a headache and he went to bed together, they were a noisy pair.

After he had yelled long enough, Mother would go in and rub his back. Father loved that. It was attention, and sometimes it was soothing, even though her method was to make rather quick, short dashes up and down the spine. However, just as Father began to relax and close his eyes, Mother's own back would commence to ache, bending over him, and she would straighten up, with one last brisk rub which destroyed whatever small rhythm she had achieved before.

"Damnation!" Father would cry. "You've only just begun."

"Heavens, Clare! Nobody has their back rubbed all day long," Mother would reply briskly as she tucked in the sheet.

One evening Father found Mother worrying because her sister was ill with some disease that was then epidemic.

"Oh, pooh!" Father said. "People always imagine they have any ailment that's fashionable. Then they go to bed, and send for the doctor. Poppycock. Cheer 'em up, that's the way to cure 'em."

"How would you cheer them up?" Mother asked doubtfully.

"I? I'd tell 'em, '*Bah!*'"

When, at seventy-four, Father came down with pneumonia, he insisted it was only a cold. When the doctor warned him that it really *was* pneumonia, Father glowered at him. "I didn't send for you, sir," he said. "Doctors think they know a lot. But they don't. There's no need to continue this discussion. Good-by, sir."

But the discussion kept on, and Father at last became convinced he was ill. The doctor, leaving him alone to digest this fact, came out in the hall to have a few words with Mother. As they whispered quietly outside Father's door, they heard his voice from within. Apparently, now that he knew he was in trouble, his thoughts had turned to his God. "Have mercy!" they heard him shouting indignantly. "I say have mercy, damn it!"

Father never thought for a moment that God could *mean* him to suffer. He couldn't imagine God's wishing to punish him either,

195

for his conscience was clear. His explanation seemed to be that the heavenly powers were muddle-headed. However, in spite of them—and the doctor—Father got over pneumonia.

EVERY respectable New York citizen in the seventies owned his own decent three- or four-story house, unencumbered by mortgages, and situated within one or two blocks of Fifth Avenue. Ours was a sunny house at 420 Madison Avenue, just below Forty-ninth Street. St. Patrick's Cathedral, at Fiftieth Street, had been recently dedicated, and Columbia College occupied the block from Forty-ninth to Fiftieth, and from Madison to what is Park Avenue now, but was then an open cut full of trains.

Our house had all the modern conveniences. It had gas lights in every room, even the cook's. We used kerosene lamps in the parlor, but that was only because the gas chandelier was too high to light without climbing up on a stepladder. There was a hot-air furnace that roared and rattled, and most of the rooms had fireplaces too. The waitress was always lugging a coal scuttle or an armful of logs up the stairs. On every floor except the fourth, the children's, we had running water, and there were two shining tin bathtubs. The maids didn't have a tub, but there was a china water pitcher and bowl in their bedroom, the same as in mine.

All the plumbing was completely boxed in, of course. When we opened the stately door of Father's bathroom and looked in there, in awe, we saw a long dark mahogany case in which his tin bathtub shone, and a forbidding mahogany structure, three feet square, with a solid closed cover. It wasn't the custom to have a washstand in the bathroom, but there was one in a box at each end of the second-floor hall. The one window in Father's bathroom opened into an airshaft above the ceiling. The whole place had a brooding tone, like a church crypt.

In nearly every room there was a bellpull which jerked at one of eight dangling bells that hung in a row in the kitchen. In each of the three upper hallways was a speaking tube too, and as these also connected with the kitchen, Margaret, our cook, had her hands full. The way to use a tube was to blow into it vigorously, until one worked the whistle on the mouthpiece below. On hearing this whistle Margaret was supposed to spring to the appropriate tube and shout loudly up it. But Margaret was so short that she had to climb up on a chair before she could do this, and then, if it was the wrong tube, get down again, move the chair and haul up all her petticoats once more to make another climb. By that time Father or Mother had lost patience and begun pulling a bell, and Margaret would clump upstairs to answer it.

On the sidewalk, below our nursery windows, was a gas lamppost. A small German band used to come of an evening and toot away under its flickering light. We were thirsty for music—there were no phonographs or radios then—and we huddled in the window, squirming ecstatically. Sometimes Father would come out and tell them to go away, but as soon as he retreated we'd toss down pennies, and they'd play one more tune.

Down a murderously dark, steep flight of stairs was the front basement, where we boys had our supper. Daylight filtered in through a barred window, and sitting on a window seat, we could see the legs and feet of passersby on the sidewalk above.

On one wall was an engraving of Landseer's *Stag at Bay* looking tragic and male and magnificent. On the other side of the room from the stag was Father's desk, where he made entries in his ledgers. His mood while he did this was cheerful, if he and the country were prosperous. In bad times he flung up his head in defiance, and looked at bay, like the stag.

⇒⟫ God and My Father ⟪⇐

WHEN WE BOYS were little, we used to go to Mother's room Sunday evenings, and sit in a circle around her, while she told us a story from the Bible or talked to us about how much we ought to love God. She loved God herself, and she deeply loved us. She was especially tender and dear on those Sunday evenings. One of my brothers told me years afterward how much they had meant to him, and how he had cherished the memory of them all his life.

I was a little older than my brothers, though, and my feelings were mixed. I wish now that I could have listened uncritically and have thought only of the look in Mother's eyes. What difference need it have made to me whether we had the same ideas about God? But there I sat, staring uncomfortably at the carpet and trying to avoid answering questions.

One night Mother repeated the Twenty-third Psalm to us and asked us to learn it by heart. *"The Lord is my shepherd . . ."* she whispered softly. *"He maketh me to lie down in green pastures: he leadeth me beside the still waters. . . ."* She raised her eyes and went on bravely, although with a quiver of fear: *"Thy rod and thy staff they comfort me."* She had often thought she felt the Lord's rod.

Father, going by in the hall, looked in and smiled affectionately at us. When he went off, I found myself speculating on Father's opinion of the Twenty-third Psalm. I couldn't imagine Father allowing anybody whatever to lead him to a pasture and get him to lie down somewhere in it. I could see him in his tailed coat and top hat, refusing point-blank even to enter a pasture. But in spite of my admiring him for this attitude, I also felt resentful about it. It would have been so much easier for me to be properly reverent if he had not been around.

FATHER'S IDEAS on religion were straightforward and simple. He had noticed when he was a boy that there were buildings called churches, and he accepted them as he accepted banks. They were both respectable and venerable, and frequented by the right sort of people.

But Father never allowed churches—or banks—to dictate to him. As a respectable New Yorker, he belonged in the Episcopal Church. He felt that Religion should not try to stir up men's feelings; and the Golden Rule struck Father as claptrap. Whatever he did unto others was all right, but that didn't mean that others could do the same things to him. He saw other men as disorderly troops, and himself as a general; if my father had been asked to return good for evil, his response would have been a full-throated "Bah!"

Both Mother and Father insisted strongly on our going to church, though they differed in their reasons. Father simply said, "Men who neglect going to church are a lazy, disreputable lot."

My mother put it differently. Church was a place where you worshiped and learned to be good.

Father's moral instructions dwelt on integrity. We must be upright, fearless and honorable; and brush our clothes properly; and in general always do the right thing in every department of life. To Mother's annoyance, he never had a moment of feeling unworthy. Other people went to church to be made better, she told Father. Why didn't he? He replied in astonishment that he was all right as he was.

When hymns were sung, Father usually stood as silent as an eagle among canaries, for most of the hymns inculcated meekness and submission:

> *Hide me, O my Saviour, hide,*
> *Till the storm of life be past;*
>
> . . . .
>
> *Cover my defenseless head*
> *With the shadow of thy wing.*

Father would have scorned to ask shelter. As he stood there, high-spirited, resolute, I could imagine him marching with that same independence through space—a tiny speck masterfully dealing with death and infinity.

The Episcopal service he didn't criticize; it was stately and quiet; but the sermon, being different every Sunday, he found a very bad gamble. And once in a while there would be an impromptu prayer at which he would take great offense. I remember seeing him so restive during a prayer of that kind that—although the entire congregation was kneeling in reverence—he suddenly gave a loud snort and sat up straight in his pew, glaring at the minister.

I glanced over at Mother. She had been sailing along devoutly, in the full tide of prayer, with the lovely rapt look that would come at such times on her face; but she had also begun to watch Father out of one eye—and now here he was sitting up. "Put your head down," she whispered fiercely; and then, when he wouldn't, she felt so torn between her yearning to sink back again into the sweet peace of prayer and her hot determination to make the bad boy in him behave, that, as hurt as a child, she sent him a look like a flash of lightning, shooting out through quick tears. This sank into him, and with a deep angry growl he bent stiffly down again.

Father never doubted the existence of God, but his God had small use for emotionalism and prized strength and dignity. How did Father think God felt toward my mother? Why, about the way he did. God probably knew she had faults, but He saw she was lovely and good; and—in spite of some mistaken ideas that she had about household accounts—He doubtless looked on her most affectionately. Father didn't expect God to regard *him* affectionately, but naturally God loved my mother, as everyone must. At the gate of heaven, if there was any misunderstanding about his own ticket, Father counted on Mother to get him in. In short, Father and God, Father felt, usually saw eye to eye, though it was hard to see why He had made so many damned fools and Democrats.

The world's stupidities weighed on Father's spirit at times. He was always trying to bring this or that good thing to pass, and when he found obstacles in the way, he would call God's attention to them. These obstacles should not have been there. When he prayed about these things, Father's tone was loud and angry.

He usually talked with God lying in bed. On those rare nights when he failed to sleep well, the sound of damns would float up through the floor—at first deep and tragic and low, then loud and exasperated. Fragments of thoughts and strong feelings came next. At the peak of these, God would be summoned. I would hear him call "Oh God?" over and over, with a rising inflection, as though he were demanding that God should present Himself instantly.

Then when Father seemed sure that God was listening, he would begin to expostulate: "Oh God, it's too much. Amen . . . I say it's too much . . . No, no, I can't stand it. Amen." After a pause, if he didn't feel better, he would seem to suspect that God might be trying to sneak back to heaven without doing anything, and I would hear him shout warningly: "Oh God! I *won't* stand it! Amen."

But his wrath didn't last—he was genial at heart. The next Sunday after an outburst he would be back in church, not perhaps as a devotee, but at least as a patron.

Father finally found a minister or two whose sermons he liked. One was the Reverend Mr. Henshaw of Rye, New York, near our house in the country. Mr. Henshaw wasn't "one of these pious fellows," Father said, with approval—though why piety was so unsuited to the clergy he never explained. Another was the rector of St. Bartholomew's in the city. Father liked going to St. Bartholomew's. The congregation were all the right sort, and the sermon was like a strong editorial in a conservative newspaper. It gave all wrong-headed persons a sound trouncing, just the way Father would have.

BEFORE OUR St. Bartholomew period started, we went to the Church of the Peace Everlasting near our home at Forty-eighth Street and Madison. Its name, so far as Father was concerned, was a mockery, for he suffered most cruelly there. Yet he went there for years, for he disliked change more than he did suffering.

The clergyman there was a plump, bustling good-hearted man, the Reverend Dr. Owen Lloyd Garden. He was of Welsh descent and very emotional, and he used to plead with us at times in his sermons, in a sort of high mellow howl. At such moments Father would testily stir in his seat. "There he goes sniveling again," Father would mutter.

Mother, from her end of the pew, would signal to him to stop. If he didn't notice, she would tell my small brothers to pass word along to me that I must make Father keep still. The most I felt up to was to get him to see Mother's signals, and that meant that I had to poke him. This was nervous work. It was like poking a stallion. When he became aware that he was being prodded, by my small, timid finger, he would turn fiercely upon me and I would hastily gesture toward Mother. "Clare! You mustn't!" she would whisper. "Bah!" he would reply.

"Oh, Clare!"

"I know, Vinnie; but I can't stand that damned—"

"Sh—sh! Oh, hush!"

Another thing he detested was the picture Dr. Garden drew, sometimes, of a businessman sitting in his office. Dr. Garden would describe how this hardheaded man sat there, studying his ledgers closely and harshly for hours. Then he would chance to look out of his window at the light in God's sky, and it would come to him that money and ledgers were dross. Whereat he would bow his head, and with streaming eyes resolve to devote his life to Higher Things.

"Oh damn," Father would burst out, so explosively that the man across the aisle jumped. Aside from the wild untruth of such pictures of business, these sermons, from Father's point of view, showed both ignorance of and disrespect for finance.

It was Father's custom to put one dollar in the contribution plate weekly, no more and no less. When the plate was brought to our pew, Father would pass it on to us, and we boys would each thump in a nickel, trying to produce a loud ringing sound, as though it were a quarter. Mother would quietly slip in her offering in a tight little roll; more than she could afford to give, probably, and saved up God knows how. Then Father would hand the plate back to the usher, who would patiently wait while Father took out a crisp new dollar bill, drew it through his fingers so as to make a little crease in it, lengthwise, and laid it out flat on top of everything else, large or small.

This dollar became the subject of debate at home. Mother felt there were Sundays, after a sermon had described some great need, when such a sum was not enough. After a while she made him feel that it was beneath his own dignity not to put in more, sometimes. So Father compromised: before starting for church, he put his usual dollar in his right-hand waistcoat pocket, but in the left-hand pocket he put a new five-dollar bill. Let Garden preach a decent sermon for once and he would give him the five.

This made every sermon a sporting event to us. When Dr. Garden entered the pulpit we boys watched with a thrill, as though he were a racehorse at the barrier. It was kind of awe-inspiring to see him go down every time to defeat.

One Sunday in Lent, Dr. Garden was ill, and the substitute clergyman spoke on the needs of some lumber country in the northwest. He had worked there; he knew the business. My brother George nudged me and pointed at Father. His face was keen and set; he was taking in every word. But we couldn't tell whether he liked it. Suddenly, before we thought the sermon was half through, the man finished.

The organist began playing the offertory. It seemed to take the usher hours to get up the aisle, but at last he stood at our pew. Father reached automatically into his one-dollar pocket. Then, as we let out our breaths in disappointment, he put the one-dollar bill back, and decisively took out the five.

We could barely help cheering aloud at that clergyman's triumph. Yet he never knew what he had done. Only the Recording Angel and the four little Day boys knew of his victory.

FATHER never stayed for Communion as Mother did, always. He walked home with us boys. When Mother thought I was old enough, she explained this. She said nobody could go to Communion who had not been confirmed. Everybody was baptized, as a baby, of course, to make him a Christian; but to be a full member of the church, one had to be confirmed.

Mother had liked Father's parents so much that it hadn't even occurred to her to question them about Father's religious upbringing. Nobody had purposely hidden the worst of Father's story from Mother—least of all poor Father himself. He was far too unguarded to have any secrets.

I remember, for instance, when he had his pocket picked on the streetcar, coming home. When he came in the front door, he was swearing in loud whispers. Mother, from her room, heard him talking to himself in the front hall. "Damned rascals! If I ever catch them—

"Not a word. I shan't say a *word* about it." He stamped up the stairs. "Well, Vinnie," he said to Mother, and sat down by the fire, in what he evidently meant to be an impenetrable silence.

"Clare!" Mother said sharply. "What has happened?"

"Damnation!" Father said. "How do you know it's happened? There's entirely too much talk in this house. A man can't have any privacy in his own home, that's what it comes down to. I had my pocketbook stolen, that's what's happened."

"Oh, *Clare* dear! Did you have the cook's wages in it?"

Father sprang from his chair in a fury. "I knew you'd ask that."

I heard him say later, in honest bewilderment, "She finds out every damn thing I ever do."

A man who was so unselfconscious would have betrayed his religious shortcomings promptly, if he had known them. But it wasn't until Mother asked Grandpa one day where Father had been baptized that Grandpa said Father had never been baptized at all. I doubt if I can even imagine what a shock this was to Mother, a sheltered lady in the conventional eighteen-eighties. She had never known of anyone who had not been baptized. It was simply unheard of.

Mother hurried home to Father with her terrible news, supposing that as soon as he heard it he would be baptized at once. She had her second great shock when he flatly refused. He was surprised and displeased to hear he hadn't been christened, but he declared that nothing could be done about it now.

Mother cried. "Clare dear," she said, "aren't you a Christian?"

"Confound it, of course I am a Christian," Father declared. "A lot better Christian than those psalm-singing donkeys at church."

"Oh hush, Clare!" Mother always was terrified when he bordered on blasphemy.

Now to say "hush" to Father was like pouring kerosene on a fire, yet I repeatedly saw Mother try to quench his flames in this way. Neither she nor Father studied the other's nature. They invariably charged at each other full tilt, and learned unwillingly—

if at all—by collisions. So Mother said "hush," and conflagration was on.

In desperation Mother went to Dr. Garden and told him the whole horrible story. Dr. Garden was agitated. If you died unbaptized, you would land in hellfire. Even the Apostles had been baptized. If Mr. Day was going to set himself above the Holy Apostles... Mother felt more frightened than ever. That was exactly what Father *would* do.

Mother at once began a campaign to break Father down. Pitched battles were fought whenever she suddenly felt like it, and Father hadn't the patience to explain clearly what he was thinking—that baptism should come only when one was young. Since it hadn't been attended to in his own case, it would be ridiculous to baptize him now. Baptism seemed a mere technicality to him anyway. If he ever came to be tried by his God, he could easily establish the fact that his position was sound.

Eventually Mother's tactics improved. She had handicapped herself by attacking Father on religious grounds. He became more vulnerable when she begged him to do something for *her*. They were in love with each other, and he would have done a good deal for Mother—"Anything in reason," he said. Exactly what sort of rigmarole would he have to go through, anyway?

Mother showed him the baptismal service in the prayer book for those of riper years. Reading it, Father said the thing was even more impracticable than he had supposed: the book said a congregation would have to be present. Father declared that ended it. He certainly wasn't going around to the Peace Everlasting to be made a fool of in that way.

The way it actually ended was simple. One day Mother heard that an acquaintance, the Reverend Mr. Morley, had taken the Church of the Epiphany, a mile or two north of where in later years they erected Grant's Tomb. This part of New York was like a remote suburb then. No one Father knew would be there, and young Mr. Morley agreed to make everything as easy for Father as possible. At last, Father agreed. Perhaps he had got to the point of wishing to get the thing over with.

When the day of the baptism came, the only person who had to be reminded of it was Father himself. He had come down in a good temper that morning, and the bacon and eggs had suited him for once. Mother gave him a happy, tender look, and the dining room seemed full of sunshine. But when Mother said it was nearly eight o'clock and the cab was here, Father demanded what cab. He listed to her answer in horror, and sprang up with a roar.

It was all to do over again. Father was back at his original starting point, that this thing was all folderol. A woman of less determination would have given up. But Mother, though frightened and tearful, was angry, and she had a weapon: the waiting cab.

There were some things that were unheard of in our family. One was wasting money on keeping a cab. The thought of the waiting cab seemed to hypnotize Father. He went down the steps and entered the cab with us blackly. The horse and the coachman both jumped as he slammed the door shut. We bumped along over the cobblestones on ironshod wheels. It was soothing to see the landscape slide by at five or six miles an hour. Milkmen ladling milk out of tall cans. Chambermaids polishing doorbells. Horses straining at streetcars. But Father was glaring about, looking like a caged lion. A woman's demands on her husband, he said, were simply beyond human reckoning. Mother pointed out that he wasn't doing it for her but for God, but Father said he had never had any trouble with God till Mother appeared on the scene.

The church was cold and bare and smelled of varnish. Mr. Morley approached our little group trustingly, to shake Father's hand, but he got such a look that he turned to me instead and patted me on the head several times. Then he led us to the front of the church and the service began, with Mother, a sexton and me as congregation.

As the service went on, Father grew restive. "O Merciful God," said Mr. Morley, when the questions were finished, "grant that the old Adam in this person may be so buried, that the new man may be raised up in him. Amen." He had to say this, because it was in the prayer book; but Father's eyes were on fire. There was a great deal of the old Adam in him, and it didn't look buried.

As we drove off afterward, Mother sank back, quite worn out. "I hope you're satisfied." Father was still seething. If he could only have known it, long quiet days were ahead, when he could go back to his comfortable old ways in church. He got out at the nearest Elevated station, to take a train for the office, with the air of a man who has thoroughly wasted his morning.

Father and the Servant Problem

ONE AFTERNOON, years before this, Father came home to find that our cook had walked out and left us. I was four, George was two, and there was a new baby besides. Mother was ill and hadn't been able to go to an agency, and as she had never been taught to cook herself, the outlook for dinner was poor.

This state of affairs was unprecedented in all Father's experience. In his father's home, they never changed their servants suddenly; they seldom changed them at all; and as his mother was a past mistress of cooking, he had always been doubly protected. He asked Mother, who was in bed, what she was going to do about it. There were no telephones then, so she said she hoped she would be able to go to an agency in the morning. "In the *morning?*" Father said. "Where *is* this place?" And he clapped on his hat and strode over to Sixth Avenue.

It was late when he got there, and he bounded up the stoop three steps at a time, and went quickly into the office, where gas lights were burning. He had never been in such a place before, and to his surprise it was empty, except for one severe-looking woman at a desk. "Where do you keep 'em?" he demanded, his mind on dinner.

"I will take your name and address," she informed him, "and then the details as to what kind of person you require."

Father had no time, he told her, for any such folderol. She was standing in the way of his dinner. "I am asking you where you keep them!" he roared.

"Why, the girls are in there," the lady said calmly, "but clients are not allowed in that room. If you will tell me—"

But Father had already thrown open the door and gone in. There sat the girls, young and old, all shapes and sizes: ladies' maids, waitresses, washerwomen and cooks. The manager was by now at Father's elbow, but Father, glancing around, paid no attention to her. He noticed a little woman in the corner, with honest gray eyes, shrewd-looking and quiet. He pointed with his cane. "I'll take that one."

The manager protested she didn't yet know the position. . . .

"Cook," Father said, "cook."

"But Margaret doesn't wish to be a cook. She wants—"

"You can cook, can't you?" Father demanded.

Margaret's plain little face was pink with excitement at being chosen above all the others by this masterful gentleman. Well, she said, she *had* cooked for one family— "Of course she can cook," Father said. "I knew at once she could cook."

The manager didn't like the way the discipline of the office was being spoiled. "What day would you wish her to come?" she said. "And will you please give me your name?"

"Yes, yes," Father said, without giving it. "Come on, Margaret." And he planked down the fee and walked out.

Margaret trotted home at his heels. He sent her down to the kitchen immediately, while he went upstairs to change.

"I don't know why you make such a fuss about engaging new servants. It's simple enough," he said comfortably to Mother that evening, after Margaret's first dinner.

It was the first of a long series, for she stayed with us twenty-six years.

At first, when we went to Harrison, in Westchester County, for the summer, we hired a temporary cook so that Margaret could stay in town. We hated to leave her, but somebody had to take care of our house at 420 Madison. Little Margaret made a pretty small watchman, for she was no size at all, but she had an indomitable spirit.

But Father had no patience with the substitutes. One was a nice woman, Delia, who got on well with Mother but whose cooking didn't suit Father at all. Mother didn't share Father's concern with food; her great interest was babies. She wanted to keep Father pleased, of course, but if it was too difficult, she didn't always care even about that. Delia cooked well enough, and Mother hated to risk getting someone else who'd be temperamental.

Our dining room became a battleground. At breakfast, Father would put down his coffee cup and roar: "Slops! Damn it, slops! Take it away, I tell you!" he would bellow. And while Delia frantically hurried to make a fresh pot, he would savagely devour his omelet and bacon, and declare that his breakfast was ruined.

He ate Delia's meals heartily, as Mother kept pointing out, but he said he didn't feel nourished; he felt all gone inside. One night after a four-course dinner, he fretfully got up from the table, went into the library with his cigar, and moaned that he was starved. His moans were, as always, full-throated. Every now and then, when his miserable condition seemed to strike him afresh, he laid down his book and shouted "Starved! Starved!" in a grief-stricken roar.

Our next cook was Japanese. Father was appeased for the moment by the disappearance of Delia, but then he found that the new cook's first dish was Oriental. After eating the rest of his dinner, he went up to his bedroom, declaring vehemently that he was poisoned. He lay down on his sofa, and filled the air with groans. From time to time he stopped and listened to what he could hear of our talk. His feeling was that we ought to be sitting in silence until he recovered. "Poisoned!" he occasionally boomed, to remind us. "Dear God! I am poisoned!"

The next day old Margaret was sent for to come at once and the house in town was left to take care of itself.

When she arrived, she looked strangely swollen and bulky, and as she crowded through the back door, she bruised me with her hard, bony hip. Only it wasn't her hip, it turned out; it was her favorite saucepan, which was tied to her waist under her skirt. Several large spoons, a dipper, a skillet and two pair of shoes were made fast under the skirt elsewhere. In her arms she had some bundles wrapped in newspapers, which Mother thought at first held her clothes; but we found they contained cheeses, melons, lamb and other provisions. Margaret had no faith in being able to buy supplies in the country.

"But didn't you bring any clothes with you?" asked Mother.

Little Margaret pursed her lips closely together, and then she said unwillingly, "I have me other clothes on me."

Under her street dress she was wearing two other dresses, a collection of stiffly starched petticoats, three aprons and two nightgowns.

MOST OF Margaret's dishes were delicious, but even she sometimes miscalculated. A large, royal-looking steak would be set before Father, which, upon being cut into, would turn out to be too underdone. Father's face would darken with disappointment. He would raise his foot, under the table, and stamp heavily three times on the rug. *Thud; thud; thud.* At this solemn signal, we would hear Margaret leave the kitchen below us and come clumping up the steps to the dining room.

"Margaret, look at that steak."

Margaret would peer at it with a shocked look. "The Lord bless us and save us," she would say in a low voice, and then make off with the platter, to better it as best she could.

But sometimes Margaret's cooking was so superb that Father's face would crinkle with pleasure, and with a wink at us he'd summon Margaret with his measured thumps. She would appear, clutching her skirts with both hands. "What's wanting?" she'd ask.

"Margaret," Father would tell her affectionately, "that fricasseed chicken is *good.*"

Margaret would turn her wrinkled face aside, and look down, and push the flat of her hand out toward Father. It was her "Get along with you" gesture.

Long after Margaret died, Father was speaking one night of how good her things always had tasted. "I wish she could hear you," said Mother. She smiled tenderly at the thought of that gallant and dear little figure. "If anybody ever was sure of going to heaven," she added, "I know it was Margaret."

This struck Father as a recommendation of the place. He said casually, "I'll look her up when I get there." Mother started to say something but checked herself. "What's the matter?" he asked.

"Well, Clare dear," said Mother, "Margaret must be in some special part of heaven, she was so good. You'd be very fortunate, Clare, to get to the same part as Margaret."

"Hah!" Father said, suddenly scowling. "I'll make a devil of a row if I don't."

⮞•๑ Father and His Boys ๑•⮜

MOTHER WAS sure that her four boys were the best little boys in New York. Other people didn't always agree with her, but her firm belief was that we never meant to be rough, and that if we *were* rough we were privileged characters because we were boys. Males, Mother felt, owed certain duties to women and girls, but they also had certain rights.

Father's attitude was different. His standards of behavior for children were as high as Mother's, and he was only too ready to believe that we hadn't lived up to them. "Of course it was 'by accident,'" he would roar, "but it's your business to see to it that accidents don't happen. And a spanking will probably assist you to bear that in mind."

"Oh, not this time, Clare," Mother begged him one Saturday when he was saying this to me. "Clarence didn't know he would knock off the cabman's hat with his little snowball." I fully agreed with her. I had *hoped* to do it, but when I succeeded I had been immensely surprised—so surprised that I hadn't made good my retreat. Also I hadn't known that Father was inside the cab. Father proceeded to give me the spanking.

It must be a terrible thing for modern children when a caller arrives and they are supposed to sit down in the sitting room and be social while the visitor tries to make conversation. In the eighties, children were children and grown-ups grown-ups. We liked our uncles and aunts and a few old family friends, but other grown-ups were foreigners.

But Mother wanted her friends to have a look at us sometimes, to let them see what we were like. When we were sent for, we generally had to speak pieces. What the feeling of the visitors was about this I do not know, but it somehow solved the problem of how to get children in and out again, and it was then the conventional thing to do.

My piece came first, all about death and battles. Then George would do the Charge of the Light Brigade. I forget what Julian did—the Battle of Blenheim, I think. Everybody brightened up a little when Harold's turn came. He was last, he was chubby, and, as Mother explained, he was too small yet to say a whole poem. Mother smiled lovingly at him as he knitted his brows and began:

> *"Fowever float zat standard sheet*
> *Where bweezy fo-bit—"*

"Where breathes the foe but falls, darling," Mother said softly.

Harold reddened with embarrassment at being called "darling" in public, and set his fat little jaws with an obstinate look. *"Where bweezy fo-bit falls afore us,"* he repeated. A few more lines and he bowed with a jerk. We tried not to run as we left, but in the hall there was always a rush for the stairs and the playroom above.

To us BOYS, our hall had a solemnly dramatic atmosphere about it. That was where the impressive black hat rack stood, and it was usually there that we got spanked. The hat rack consisted of a long black walnut chest, in which were hidden all the family's galoshes and rubbers. Mounted on this was a mirror, seven feet high, in a fluted black walnut frame, with a carved overhanging canopy. At each side were brass hat pegs; under these were two umbrella racks with deep brass pans.

Opening off the hall on one side was the dining room with its vast black walnut sideboard, and its great round black walnut table. Dark red curtains hung in the windows, and gory battle scenes and a crayon portrait hung on the walls. Under the huge mantelpiece was a little brass grate, small, but the cheeriest thing in the room.

Every evening from six to seven, while Father and Mother were having their dinner, this dining room became as sacred, in my eyes, as a high court or shrine—although owing to the imperfections of the service and Father's temper it was considerably noisier. I sometimes leaned over the banisters in the narrow hall outside, looking down in through the doorway. After seven, when the table had been cleared away and covered with a Turkish cloth of soft reds and gold, we boys went trooping in. The dining room became a sitting room then. Nobody ever went into the parlor, except to play the piano, or when visitors called.

When I turned seven, Father said that I was old enough to join him and Mother at dinner, but I found almost at once that the honor I had won was a hollow one. I had to keep still, and say Yes sir and No sir, and submit to being taught what seemed to me superfluous manners. On one of my first stately nights in the dining room, we had turnips for dinner. Father noticed that I didn't take any. "Have some turnip," he said.

I was happily stowing away some flaky boiled potatoes with bits of green parsley on them, and a chunk of hot juicy steak. "No, thank you," I said, foolishly. "I don't like turnip."

"I'll tell you what you like and what you don't like," he said, and although his tone was peremptory his look wasn't unkind. "Turnip's good." He deposited on my plate two generous spoonfuls of mashed turnip. "Eat that. At once."

The sadness of an exile on some foreign shore flooded my heart. I thought of how gay it had been with my brothers. "I don't

want to eat it!" I wailed. "I'd rather go without dinner, Father!"
I stood up, suddenly ablaze with rebellion.

Father roared, "Sit down, sir!" I wouldn't. Mother gave a frightened cry and begged us to stop, but the next instant Father led me off by the ear into the hall.

After he had given me a spanking we returned to the dining room, and I ate my turnip. But I was boiling with rage. I could see no sense in being made to eat turnip, and Father didn't explain. He never explained anything. The fact that Father loved me and cherished me and worked and planned for my welfare meant nothing to me as I choked down those turnips.

As a small boy, I remember thinking that when Father was in an expansive, jolly mood, a boy could trust him—but not when he felt thoughtful. At such times he would think of some brand-new ambition. Not for himself, but for me.

One such ambition was that in addition to French I should learn German. One of the hopeful pictures in his mind of my future was that of my traveling widely in Europe, conversing in an affable, condescending way with all nations. When I protested that I didn't want to converse with them, he laughed at my spluttering. "I decline to have any son of mine grow up to be a blockhead, and blunder around the Continent in a helpless and ridiculous manner." And I was more exasperated than ever when I found that Father had never studied German. He said that was why he wanted me to, so that I wouldn't miss it, as he had all his life. He then proceeded at odd moments to try and teach German to me himself. He began with the word *Ich* for "I." I could not or would not lend myself to saying such a word right. I was willing to call it either Ick or Itch, but that was as far as I'd go. We had many heated sessions before he resigned me to what he called my "barbarous fate."

One day, soon after this—I was about ten and George eight—Father suddenly remembered an ambition of his to have us taught music. He enjoyed music; to play Mozart or Chopin on the piano gave him a sense of well-being, so he held that all children should be taught to play some instrument, and sing. But there are children and children. I had no ear for music.

Father was the last man to take this into consideration. He looked upon children as raw material that a father should mold. When I said I couldn't sing, he said nonsense. He played a scale, cleared his throat, and sang "*Do, re, mi.*" Then he called to me, in a firm, kindly voice, to sing it, too. I planted myself respectfully before him. He played the first note. I had only the dimmest understanding of what he wished me to do, but I struck out, haphazard, and chanted loudly: "*Do, re, mi.*"

"No, no, no!" said Father, disgustedly. We tried it again. "No, no, no!" He struck the notes louder. I gradually saw that I was supposed to match the piano with my voice, but that didn't help any. I could make my voice deep, shrill or medium, but that was the best I could do.

It was a nightmare. He abandoned the other outlandish words and reduced his demands to my singing one single note: *Do.* I opened my mouth wide, as instructed, and shouted the word *Do* at random, hoping it might match the piano.

George sat on the sofa watching me with sympathy. George was a good brother, but I used to get tired of being his pathbreaker in encounters with Father. As I was the eldest boy, the new projects were always tried out on me.

One day when Father had been away, reorganizing some upstate railroad, he returned in an executive mood and summoned us before him. We were informed that in spite of my failure as a singer we older boys must at once learn to play on something. "You, Clarence, will learn the violin. George, you the piano."

I was appalled. The days were already too short; and now here was a chunk to come out of playtime three days every week for lessons, and a chunk every day for practice.

George sat at the piano, and faithfully pounded out his exercises. He had some ear for music, and also the advantage of playing on an instrument which he didn't have to be careful not to drop.

But I had to go down into our dark little basement for my lessons, and the violin was a queer cigar-boxy thing that a fellow was liable to crack, just putting it into its case. And then my teacher seemed queer to me, because he was different from the people I generally met. Herr M. was probably worth a dozen of some of them, but I didn't know it. He was one of the violins in the Philharmonic; a grave, middle-aged little man, who was obliged to earn extra money by giving lessons.

The violin is intended for persons with a passion for music. I wasn't that kind of person, but Herr M. greeted me as a possible genius. He taught me how to hold the contraption, how to move my fingers on its stem, how to draw the bow across the strings. As a mother recalls the first cry of her baby, I remember the first, unearthly cry at birth of my new, cheap violin. Herr M. looked as though he had suddenly taken a large glass of vinegar. He snatched the violin from me, readjusted its pegs, and comforted it gently by drawing his own bow across it.

He handed the instrument back to me with careful directions. I tucked it under my chin again, held my bow as ordered. "Now," he said, nervously. This time there were *two* dreadful cries: one from my new violin and one from the heart of Herr M.

When he presently came to, he smiled, and said if I wanted to rest a moment he would permit it. He seemed to think I might wish to lie down. I didn't feel any need for that; all I wanted was to get through. But Herr M. was by no means ready to let me proceed. He desperately seized the music book, and began to point out the notes and tell me their names. After a bit he took up his own violin, and instructed me to watch how he handled the strings. At last, he nerved himself to let me try again. "Softly, my child, softly," he begged.

That was Wednesday. What struggles he had with himself before Friday I can only dimly imagine. When he came back for my second lesson, he was not unkind but remote. He did little sums on bits of paper and gloomily tore them up.

During my third lesson I saw tears in his eyes. He went up to Father and said he felt sure I'd never be able to play.

Father didn't like this at all. He said he felt sure I would. Herr M. came stumbling back down. He had gone upstairs gallantly, resolved upon sacrificing his earnings for the sake of telling the truth. He returned with his future earnings, but with the look of a lost soul. He no longer struggled. He accepted this as a hellish experience, but one he must bear.

He was not alone in his sufferings. One day I was slaughtering a scale in the front basement room, when Mother came down and stood in the kitchen door across the hall. She whispered to our good Margaret, "What *shall* we do?"

"The poor little feller," Margaret whispered back. "He can't make the thing go."

I was indignant. I began to feel a determination to master this thing. Such misplaced determinations are one of the darkest aspects of human life, they spread so much needless pain; but a boy will put in enormous amounts of his time trying to prove he isn't as ridiculous as he thinks people think him.

All during the long winter I worked away at scales. I gave no thought to the family—but they did to me. Our house was heated by a warm-air furnace, with outlets in each room, and sound traveled ringingly through these tin passages. No one, anywhere, could settle down to anything while I was practicing. If visitors came they soon left. It was a hard winter for Mother, but when she said to Father that it was plain I had no ear, he replied only that the violin was the noblest instrument invented by man. Learning to play it required persistence. The motto was, Never give up.

I kept begging Herr M. to let me learn a tune, and at last he chose as simple a thing as he could find for me and the neighbors. It was spring now, and windows were open. That tune became famous. I engraved it on the neighbors' hearts, in my own eerie versions; because the horrors I produced were never twice the same.

So the unhappy melody writhed in the air, and things began to be said to Mother. The end, she said to Father, had come. Father was outraged. His final argument was that the violin had cost twenty-five dollars. But it was put to him that my younger brother Julian could use it later on.

Then summer came, and we went to the country; and in the autumn little Julian was led down to the basement in my place. He had an ear, however, and I believe he learned to play fairly well. This would have made a happy ending for Herr M. after all; but it was some other teacher who was engaged to teach Julian. Father said Herr M. was obviously a failure as a teacher.

→»Father and the Family Accounts €«–

FATHER was always trying to make Mother keep track of the household expenses. Before he got married, he had kept a full set of account books which showed exactly how much a month his clothes or his cigar bills amounted to. These books gave him great satisfaction.

But they were never the same after his marriage. He still knew what his personal expenses were, but they were microscopic compared to his household expenses and of these he knew only the horrible total. His money was flowing away in all directions and he had no record of it. Mother didn't feel that women should have anything to do with accounts, any more than men should have to see that the parlor was dusted. She had been head of her class at school and spoke beautiful French, but she was unsympathetic about ledgers.

Figures were so absorbing to Father that he couldn't believe Mother really disliked them. He said confidently that she would soon learn to keep books. Meanwhile, she could tell him what she spent, and he would enter it himself until he could trust her to do it. That day never arrived. So although the household bills gave Father plenty of data which he could stare at, in horror, most of the details were not clear to him, and most of the rest were incredible.

Every month when the bills came in there was trouble. Father asked Mother to explain items he did not understand, but now and then there were items she didn't understand, either. She behaved as though the bill were a total stranger to her.

When the bills were larger than Mother expected, she felt guilty and hardly dared to let Father see them. When some of them seemed small to her, she felt happy, but not for long, because they never seemed small to Father.

One constant mystery to Father was the way the monthly outgo jumped up and down. "Anyone would suppose there would be some regularity after a while which would let a man try to make plans, but I never know from one month to another what to expect."

Mother said things just seemed to go that way.

"But they have no business to go that way," Father said.

Mother said she didn't see what she could do about it. All she knew was that she hadn't been extravagant. She didn't, in fact, have any great extravagances, but she was one of those people for whom charge accounts were invented. When she charged something, the first of the month seemed far away. She never had much cash, and when she did she couldn't bear to part with it, but shopping on a charge account was fun.

Father did his level best to take the fun out of it, but Mother was obstinate. She could sometimes, though not often, be managed by praise, but criticism made her rebellious. She was a woman of great spirit who would have flown at and pecked any tyrant. But Father had the best of her there because he didn't know that he was a tyrant. He regarded himself as a long-suffering man who asked little of anybody and showed the greatest moderation in his encounters with unreasonable beings like Mother. Mother's one advantage was that she was quick, and elusive. She did the best she could to keep down expenses, she said firmly to Father, and besides, the Ward cousins spent twice as much.

Father said, "The Wards don't have to work for it. I don't wish to be told how they throw money around."

219

Mother said, "Oh, Clare, how can you! They just live comfortably, and I thought you were so fond of Cousin Mary."

Father declared that he wouldn't have Cousin Mary or anyone else dictating to him how to run things.

"Oh, Clare, please! I can't bear to have you talk so harshly of Cousin Mary when she admires you so."

At that moment, one of the children would cry and Mother would have to go off to see what was wrong, or she would have to run down to leave word for Mrs. Tobin, the washerwoman, to do Father's shirts differently. Something like this happened to almost every financial conversation.

Sometimes, when the household expenses shot up very high, Father got frightened. He always did some yelling, on general principles, but when his alarm was genuine he roared in such real anguish that Mother felt sorry and tried hard for a while to keep count of things for him. The expenses, to his utter amazement, would take a sharp drop. Father always told Mother this good news, because he couldn't keep things to himself, but he did it in as disciplinary a manner as possible. "I've told you again and again that you could keep the expenses down if you tried. This shows I was right."

Mother didn't lose her presence of mind at these attacks. She said this was all due to her good management, and Father ought to give her the difference. At this point Father suddenly found himself on the defensive, for the more they talked, the clearer it seemed to Mother that he owed her the money she had saved. Rarely could he get out of her room without paying it. He said that this was one of the things about Mother that was enough to drive a man mad.

The other thing was her total lack of system. Whenever she did keep accounts, they were on backs of envelopes or little bits of paper with much scratching out and many mystifying omissions. Father would pore over these for hours, calling out to Mother to tell him what this was, in a vain attempt to bring order out of chaos. At last he invented what seemed a perfect method of recording expenses. Every time he gave any money to Mother, he would ask her what it was for and would make a note of it in his own pocket notebook. His idea was that these items, plus the bills, would show him where his money had gone.

But they didn't. "I gave you six dollars in cash on the twenty-fifth of last month," he might say, "to buy a new coffeepot."

"Yes," Mother said, "because you broke your old one. You threw it right on the floor."

Father frowned. "I'm not talking about that," he answered. "I am simply endeavoring to find out from you, if I can—"

"But it's so silly to break a nice coffeepot, Clare, and there was nothing the matter with the coffee that morning; it was made just the same as it always is. And I couldn't get another pot like it, because that little French shop has stopped selling them."

"I gave you six dollars to buy a new pot," Father repeated, "and now I find that you charged one at Lewis and Conger's. The bill says: 'One coffeepot, five dollars.' "

"So I saved you a dollar," Mother triumphantly said, "and you can hand it right over to me."

"But what did you do with the six dollars?" Father cried.

"Why, I can't remember now! Why didn't you ask at the time?" Father groaned. "Wait a moment," said Mother, "I spent four dollars and a half for that new umbrella you said I didn't need."

Father wrote in his notebook: *New Umbrella for V.*

"And that must have been the week," Mother went on, "that I paid Mrs. Tobin for two extra days' washing, two dollars more makes six-fifty. There's another fifty cents that you owe me."

"I don't owe you *anything*," Father said. "You have turned a coffeepot for me into a new umbrella for you. You seem to think I only have to put my hand in my pocket to get you more money." Mother not only thought this, she knew it. His wallet was always full, and it was provoking to have to argue money out of him.

ONE WINTER, when most of her boys were away at school, Mother was invited to go up the Nile in a houseboat with a Mrs. Tytus. Mother loved travel and explained to Father what a wonderful chance this was. He was not impressed. Most women were glad to have a home, he said, but the only thing Mother seemed to want was to be on the go. He went on to say that he himself would no more think of going to Egypt than to the North Pole. Never in any circumstances whatever would *he* take Mother there.

"But that's just why I want to go, Clare, dear. I thought it would please you."

"You thought it would *please* me?"

"Oh Clare, don't you see, if Mrs. Tytus takes me to Egypt, you won't have to." She then told Father how much her letter of credit should be. She was saving him money, she added, because it would be nearly twice as much if he took her himself.

When Father said violently that he wished her to remain at his side, she said Dr. Markoe had told her to go. And to clinch the matter, she brought Mrs. Tytus to see him. Mrs. Tytus was tactful and beautiful. Mother was pertinacious. Between them, they bore Father down, and on the appointed day Mother got aboard the ship, letter of credit and all. Father kissed her, and marched stiffly off the ship. Then he turned back at the foot of the gangplank, calling loudly, "Dear Vinnie!" Mother waved, the whistles blew hoarsely, and the crowds jostled, hiding them from each other as the ship slid away.

Father began looking for letters the very next morning, and when none came he cursed the postman. But a letter did arrive in a few days, mailed by the harbor pilot, and after the first three or four weeks we heard from Mother often. At every port, Mother met people she knew. "There isn't a city in Europe," Father said, "where your mother wouldn't spot a friend in five minutes." Upon his soul, he had never known anyone like her. Some letters abused the bad habits of foreigners, and Father relished her complaints. But when the letters began coming from queer-sounding Egyptian cities in the interior, he got nervous. This was entirely needless, he said. New York was full of obelisks and mummies. He spent a great deal of time staring in deep disapproval at the snapshots they contained, one in particular of Mother looking very roguish and chic in her voluminous dress, sitting way up on top of a tall and insolent camel, with two big dark men in turbans at

Mother looked very roguish and chic.

one side, and no other member of the party in sight. Father looked at that and groaned about "the ends of the earth."

The nearer the day came for her return the more indignant and impatient he got. He forgot this mood, however, the minute he hugged her at the pier. He instantly took charge and ordered customs inspectors around and got her through in a jiffy, and found a man to shoulder her trunk and picked out the best hackman, and as the carriage rattled off over the cobblestones, Mother said she was glad to be back.

Father had taken particular pains to have everything in the house in its place, so that when Mother came in the door, she would say that home was just the way she had left it. Instead, what she said was "Oh, this poor room!" and she put down her handbag and began setting the chairs at different angles and moving her favorite ornaments affectionately. "Poor things," she said, as she patted them, "didn't anybody know enough to turn you around the way you belong?" But when she saw Father's face fall, she smiled and said, "You did the best you could, darling."

Her letter of credit had been very much on Father's mind. It had been a generous letter of credit, and he thought he had a right to expect that Mother still had a substantial balance which he could now restore to his bank account. His real expectation was that she had spent every cent and had even had to borrow from Mrs. Tytus. The fact that she avoided the subject pointed to this latter outcome.

One night she went upstairs and came back down with some papers. "You might go over these, Clare," she said. "I couldn't keep track of *every*thing, but I did save the bills." And she went off to bed. Father checked the bills carefully: there were still several hundred dollars unaccounted for, and he waited for Mother to confess what she had done with the balance. Day after day went by without her saying one word, and Father became alarmed.

Mother did have a confession to make: she hadn't spent all her letter of credit but she meant to keep the balance herself. It was wicked of her to feel that way, she supposed, but she had had a taste of independence, and she was reluctant to drop back into her Victorian role. When at last she nerved herself to tell Father about the balance, he said she was home now, thank God, and as he always paid her bills she had no use for this money.

"Yes I have, too," Mother said.

"Well, what will you use it for, then?" Father asked.

Mother wouldn't explain. "Oh, lots of things, Clare. Things I'd like to get when I need them, without so much talk."

This seemed unconvincing to Father. The only safe place for it was in *his* bank account, as Mother, of course, didn't have one. But Mother insisted on keeping it in her own bureau drawer, and Father could do nothing with her: she was always much harder to manage after that sail up the Nile.

MOTHER's Egyptian hoard lasted for years, though it was only a few hundred dollars. As it dwindled Mother grew restless. She didn't clearly realize that she was groping toward a life of her own. Younger women told her that it was childish to have to struggle with Father over every dollar. "Just estimate what you need for the house and yourself," they said, "and have Mr. Day hand you a monthly check with no talk about it."

It was a tempting idea. The only thing was that she couldn't figure how much to ask for. She knew that Father wouldn't give her any large sum, yet she knew that any allowance that wasn't large might sometimes be too little, there were so many unexpected emergencies. She felt that an allowance wasn't safe.

She talked it over with Father, however, just to see what he'd say. Father said a great deal. He said that of all the damned nonsense he had ever heard this was the damnedest. Mother was a lovely woman and he was very fond of her, but neither she nor any of her family knew the first thing about money.

Mother immediately told him she knew as much about money as he did. But she secretly realized that she was not good at figures, so she played with the allowance notion for years without really pushing it. When Father made a row about some bill, she counterattacked by declaring that he wouldn't have any such troubles if he gave her an allowance. In the excitement of denouncing allowances, Father would lose sight of the bill.

The custom of the times made Mother's talk of an allowance seem preposterous to Father. Much later than Father's day, a lady was not supposed to have any occasion for cash. Two or three dollars for carfares and candy was plenty. Ladies wore trailing skirts, which they had to hold up with one hand when they walked in the street. With the other hand they carried an umbrella or parasol, or on cold days a muff. In the side seam of their skirts was a pocket which held a tiny purse, a handkerchief, and a vial of smelling salts. But this pocket was not easy to get at, and it was embarrassing to feel around for it, so when they were to take a streetcar they tucked a nickel inside a glove.

When I was little, Mother wore bonnets, tied under her chin. Later on, she had a hard time with the fashionable stiff hats. They perched on top of ladies' hair, pinned on with long jeweled pins, and were insecure in a wind. No matter how thoroughly ladies were buttoned up, they were always coming apart. Their escorts protected them however, swelling with whiskers and grandeur.

Women were not fitted to deal with the world; and a man's manner in supplying a woman with money was supposed to be tender—but firm. As years went on however, Father lost all hope of molding Mother into his pattern and began to admit that the allowance plan might not be so bad. And so many other women now had allowances that Mother began to feel that she could do it if they could.

What finally did it was a bill from Mlle. Mimi. Father came to Mother holding the repulsive thing between his thumb and one finger. "I will not send this person a check," he said.

Mother flamed up at him. "Clare, it's the only hat I've bought since November, and it was reduced from forty dollars!"

"I do not object to your buying a hat if you need one," he answered, "but the person from whom you bought it isn't fit to be in the hat business, or in any other kind either."

"Poor Mimi! She does sell her things very cheap."

"Her bill gives no such evidence," said Father. "But that is not what I'm talking about. If this confounded person wants to be paid, she can put her name on her bills."

"But Clare, she did. Her name is Mimi!"

"Mimi what? Mimi O'Brien? Mimi Weinstein? I will not write a check that says 'Pay to the order of Mimi.' It's impertinent of her to expect it."

The final outcome of the conversation was that Father agreed to the allowance, though he was still in doubt about what it would cover. "I hope to God it will work," he said pessimistically.

What happened was that Mother, despite many secret charities, began hoarding. She had a nest egg now and was determined to add to it. She had got too accustomed to Father's paying the regular bills for her to pay them herself. As this began to dawn on Father his surprise and grief were acute.

"It doesn't cover a blasted thing," he told me.

However, the matter was settled in Mother's mind. It was not an easy allowance to get; it didn't just come. But eventually Father would glumly bring it home, and Mother would receive it, exhausted but triumphant.

ONE OF THE WAYS in which Father and Mother were as alike as two peas was in their love of a good time. They both had immense energy, and when they went to a dance or a dinner where they enjoyed themselves, they came home refreshed.

But there was this great difference: Mother always wanted to go; Father never. He said he hated parties. So Mother accepted all invitations and didn't tell him until the time came to go. Every time Father got into the carriage and drove off to their friends', he felt imposed upon and indignant, and Mother was almost worn out.

The surprising thing was that both of them then had a good time. Mother would alight from the carriage half-crying, but determined to enjoy herself; and Father, who never stayed cross for long, cheered up as soon as he went in the doorway.

When he sat next to some pretty woman at table, he would be gallant. He had charm. Women liked him. It never did them any good to like him if the wine and the cooking weren't good; that made him morose. But when the host knew his business, Father was gay and expansive, without ever a thought of the raps Mother would give him on the head going home.

"Clare, you were so silly with that Miss Remsen!"

He would chuckle, trying to remember which was Miss Remsen. Pretty women were much the same to him. He was courtly to them by instinct, but he was completely wrapped up in Mother. He liked a pretty woman as he liked a cigar or a flower; if either a flower or a cigar had made demands on him, he would have been most disturbed.

It thrilled Mother, at parties, to have some distinguished man make himself agreeable to her, for she greatly admired fine males. If there were none of this high type to fascinate her, she liked men who were jolly. Only they mustn't flirt with her. A husband belonged to his wife. So did a widower.

Father had every intention of outliving Mother and she knew it. He said she couldn't get on without him, and he must stay alive to take care of her. Mother snorted and said she could get on perfectly well, but of course she'd die long before he did. What worried her was how he'd behave himself when she was gone.

On a trip abroad, Mother and Father visited an ancient chapel in England. They were shown a tomb where a noble crusader was buried, with his effigy on top. Mother was much impressed till the verger pointed to the figure of his third wife beside him. Mother immediately struck the tomb with her parasol, demanding, "Where's your first, you old thing?" She told the verger he ought to be ashamed for exhibiting a wretch like that, and she left the chapel at once, feeling that it was no place for Father.

ALTHOUGH Father enjoyed himself when Mother and he went to parties, the idea of giving a party in his own home seemed monstrous. The most he would consent to was to have a few old friends in to dinner.

But Mother got tired of dining with nobody but his old friends all the time; and she knew that the surest way to get invitations was to give them. To forestall opposition, her method was to invite one couple whom Father knew, so that if questioned by him as to who'd be there, she could say, "Why, the Bakers and a few others." This reassured him till the night of the dinner arrived. When he came home and found rented palms in the hall, it was too late to stop her.

She had, by that time, gone through the most elaborate preparations. She had arranged for a professional waiter, old John, to act as butler, and for an excitable young chef to take charge of the kitchen. Old John and Mother got out arsenals of table silver, piles of plates from a top shelf, embroidered table linens from a cupboard. They put leaves in the table, filled vases with flowers, and arranged little plates of salted nuts and chocolates.

Then after Mother had laid out her dress and slippers, and done things to her hair, she desperately tackled the worst job of all—putting her bedroom in order. This room, in spite of Mother's random efforts, was always getting into a comfortable, higgledy-piggledy state. When Mother entertained, everything had to be put away out of sight, and so neatly that any drawer a prying guest might open would be in beautiful order. Letters and pieces of string were hurried off the dressing table, medicines and change off the mantel, stray bits of lace, pencils and old macaroons off the bureau; all were jammed into cabinets or on closet shelves. When some article was urgently needed the next week, Mother couldn't remember where on earth she had put it.

On Thursday afternoons in the winter, Mother was always "at home." She served tea and cakes, and quite a few people dropped in to see her. When her favorite niece, Cousin Julie, came to live with us, bringing a great gilded harp, Mother at once made room for this beautiful object in our crowded parlor, and Julie had to play for the Thursday-afternoon visitors. Performing frightened Julie, but Mother said she must get over that. Then, thinking one day about all her social debts, Mother suddenly decided to give a musicale. Julie would play, and her teacher, Miss Kregman, would bring her own harp, while a friend of Julie's, Sally Brown, would play the piano.

Mother could have had a grander musicale if Father had provided the money for paid musicians, but he said he washed his hands of the whole affair. Still, getting up a party was fun anyway. The flowers would be pretty, Mother had a special kind of little cakes in mind, and everybody would enjoy it thoroughly.

Mother knew, however, that even her homemade artists would take some managing. Julie was devoted to her, and so was the other victim, Sally Brown. But Sally would rather have done anything than play in public, and the whole idea sent chills down Julie's back. The one Mother worried about most, however, was Miss Kregman. She was angular and plain and Mother didn't feel she was decorative.

Father didn't feel she was decorative either. He said, "I'll be hanged if I come." Musicales were all poppycock anyway. "Nothing but tinkle and twitter."

"Nobody's invited you," Mother said, secretly relieved.

Everybody was fascinated by all they could see of Miss Kregman.

ON THE MORNING OF THE MUSICALE, it began to snow. Father had forgotten what day it was, of course; his mind was on a waistcoat which needed fixing. To his astonishment, he found Mother up on a stepladder, arranging some ivy. "What on earth are you doing up on that ladder, Vinnie?" he said. "Here's my waistcoat, it's got to go to the tailor at once." Mother gave a loud wail of self-pity at this new infliction, but Father simply handed it up to her and went out.

That afternoon the snow turned to rain. When we boys came in and put our sleds away, the parlor was full of folding chairs and the rubber tree had been strategically placed by Miss Kregman's harp, in such a way that the harp would be in full view but Miss Kregman would not. We went up to the playroom as Julie was coming downstairs. She was pale. Looking over the banister, we saw Miss Kregman arrive in her galoshes. Sally Brown, who was usually gay, entered silently just behind her. Mother's excited voice floated up to us. There was not a sound from the others.

At the hour appointed for this human sacrifice, the parlor was packed. Mother clapped her hands for the ladies' chatter to halt, and we could hear the first hesitating strains. Then someone slid the doors shut. I thought of Sally, too numb to feel the piano keys, and of Julie's icy fingers plucking her strings.

When we boys went down to dinner we heard that the ladies had admired the girls' playing, applauded, and eaten up all the cakes. But there had been two catastrophes. One was that everybody had been fascinated by all they could see of Miss Kregman, her feet, working away by themselves, as it were, at the pedals. She had forgotten to take off her galoshes. The other was that Father had come home during a sweet little lullaby, and the ladies had distinctly heard him say "Damn" as he went up to his room.

In the summer Father, who was a sociable man, permitted guests to stay with us in the country, where he sometimes felt lonely. But in town he felt that he must be stern with would-be house guests or he'd be overrun with them.

It was usually Mother's relatives who stayed with us. Father's relatives were well-regulated New Yorkers who stayed in their own homes, and he often told Mother that the sooner hers learned to, the better.

When Father got home for dinner and Mother was obliged to confess that some of her relatives were concealed in the spare room, up on the third floor, those relatives were likely to wonder about the indignant roars they heard downstairs.

Most of them had been led to suppose Father loved them; and as they were hospitable persons, they didn't suspect that the muffled outcries were occasioned by themselves. Mother simply said that Father was worried about something and they must pretend not to notice. When Father glared speechlessly around the table at dinner, they felt sorrier for him than ever.

Our guest room, although its black mahogany furniture and marble mantel were somewhat somber, had an air of dignified welcome. But this was misleading. Every drawer in the bureau was filled to bursting with the overflow of other rooms. One of the two big closets was locked. In the other were ball dresses, an umbrella stand, piles of magazines, and a job lot of discarded bonnets. After taking a good look at all this, a guest generally gave up all hope of unpacking. He had little opportunity, however, to dwell on small inconveniences, for he soon became engrossed by the drama of our family life. Our disconcerting inability to conceal any of our emotions absorbed him.

I never supposed that our daily lives were different from anyone else's until I went off on visits myself. When I saw a friend's dignified parents being formally polite to each other, I thought they were holding themselves in, and wondered which would blow up first. I was depressed when they didn't. They seemed to me lifeless.

On another visit, I was shocked to discover that a family could be mean to each other. Even the children made sarcastic remarks, as though they were trying to hurt one another. All of us got hurt often enough, but our collisions were impulsive. We all had red hair and got angry in a second; but in a minute or two it was over.

In another family the father, when he was annoyed, wouldn't speak. Around the first of the month, when the bills came in, he would sit without saying a word all through dinner, looking down at his plate. After we boys left the room, we heard his wife beg him to tell her what to do: she was willing to live in a tent and spend nothing if he would only be pleasant. Her husband listened in silence and then went off to his study.

This seemed to me gruesome. Our own homelife was stormy but spirited. It had tang. When Father was unhappy, he poured out his grief with such vigor that it cleared the air. He was a thoroughly good-hearted, warm-blooded man with no meannesses he needed to repress, so he saw no reason for hiding his feelings.

As I grew up and saw more of Father, I realized that with his friends he was one of the jolliest and most companionable of men. Toward people not of his own sort, though, he was imperious. When they annoyed him, he snorted like a bull and had no compunctions about any wounds he inflicted. In fact, he felt they should be grateful to him for teaching them better.

It seemed natural to me that any father should snort about the behavior of his wife and his children. It seemed natural, too, in those days, for a man to make his employes live exactly as he decreed. But Father expected *everyone* to conform, even people he read about in the newspapers, or passed in the street. He'd look around at his fellow passengers in a horsecar like a colonel distastefully reviewing a slatternly regiment. They didn't have to be bankers or lawyers, but they did have to be neat and decent. And self-respecting. Like him.

When politicians didn't behave as he would, Father ringingly denounced them to his family. That the rest of us never joined in these political monologues suited him exactly. He didn't wish to be hindered when he was letting off steam.

But a time came when Mother began attending a class in current events, conducted by a Miss Edna Gulick. Miss Gulick darted about on the surface of political or industrial problems, but in so sprightly a way that the most baffling issues began to seem childishly simple to Mother.

One day, when Father was bombarding President Benjamin Harrison and somebody named William McKinley for trying to ruin the country with a new tariff, Mother boldly said she was sure that the President's idea was all right; he had only been unfortunate in the way he had put it. "Miss Gulick," Mother declared firmly, "says the President prays to God for guidance. He is a very good-hearted man."

"The President," said Father, "is a nincompoop, and I wish you wouldn't talk on matters you don't know a thing about."

"I do too know about them," Mother exclaimed. "Miss Gulick says every intelligent woman should have some opinion about them."

"And who, may I ask, is Miss Gulick?"

"Why, she's that current-events person I told you about."

"All you need to do is listen to *me* if you want to know about current events," Father said.

"But you get so excited, Clare dear. Miss Gulick says kindness is much more important than arguments. It makes her feel very sad when she reads about strikes, because capital and labor could easily learn to be nice to each other."

At this, Father burst out of the house, banging the door, and finished buttoning his coat on the top of our stoop. "I don't know what the world is coming to anyhow," I heard him exclaim to a few surprised passersby on Madison Avenue.

BUT MOTHER still had more feminine things to worry about. There was, for instance, the mending. Four boys had to be kept in repair besides Father, and her workbasket was always piled high. There was more talk about Father's socks and shirts than anyone else's. Father didn't like things to disappear for long periods; he wanted them brought promptly back and put in his bureau drawer where they belonged. This was particularly true of the colored socks supplied to him by a haberdasher in Paris.

These colored socks were the one outlet of something in Father which ran contrary to his religion of propriety. That was a day of somber suits, quiet neckties and dark socks; but Father's, hidden by his trousers and high buttoned shoes, had an astonishing range of color and fancy.

Father got holes in his socks even oftener than we boys did. He had long athletic toes, and when he lay stretched out on his sofa talking to me, these toes would begin wiggling in a curious way by themselves, as though they were living a life of their own. Soon one and then the other slipper would fall off, always to Father's surprise, but without interrupting his instructions to me; and a little later his busy great toe would peer out at me through a new hole in his sock.

Mother felt that it was a woman's duty to mend things, but she hated it. She rather liked to embroider, but her darning of Father's socks was an impatient and not-too-skillful performance. She said there were so many of them that they made the back of her neck ache.

Father's heavily starched shirts, too, were a problem. When he put one on, he pulled it down over his head, and thrust his arms out blindly right and left in a hunt for the sleeves. A new shirt was strong enough to survive these strains without splitting, but life with Father rapidly weakened it, and the first thing he knew he would hear it tear. That disgusted him. He hated any evidence of weakness, either in people or things.

Buttons were Father's worst trial, however. Ripped shirts and socks with holes in them could still be worn, but garments with buttons off couldn't. Furthermore, buttons always deserted Father's service suddenly, and at the wrong moment. At such times he wanted help and he wanted it promptly. He would appear at Mother's door with a waistcoat in one hand and a disloyal button in the other, demanding that it be sewn on at once. If she said she couldn't just then, Father would sound as if he were drowning and a lifeguard had informed him that he would save him tomorrow.

One night before dinner, he said angrily, "Not a thing is done for a man in this house. I even have to sew on my own buttons. Where is your needle and thread?"

Mother reluctantly gave these implements to him. He marched off and sat on the edge of the sofa in his bedroom. The gaslight was better by his chair, but he needed extra room. He laid scissors, thread and waistcoat down beside him, wet his fingers, held the needle high up, and began poking the thread at the eye.

Like every commander, Father wished to deal with trained troops. The contrariness of the needle and the limp obstinacy of the thread made him swear. He stuck the needle in the sofa while he wet his fingers and stiffened the thread again. When he came to take up his needle, it had disappeared. He felt around everywhere for it. He got up, holding fast to his thread, and turned around, facing the sofa to see where it was hiding. This jerked the spool off onto the floor, where it rolled away and unwound.

The husbands of two of Mother's friends had had fits of apoplexy and died. It frightened her horribly when this seemed about to happen to Father. At the sound of his roars, she and I rushed in. There he was on the floor, his face dark red, as she had feared. He was trying to get his head under the sofa and he was yelling at something. Pleading with him to stop only made

There he was on the floor, his head under the sofa.

him more apoplectic. Finally, he stood up, tousled but triumphant, the spool in his hand. Mother ran to get a new needle. She threaded it for him and he at last started sewing.

Father sewed on the button in a violent manner, with vicious haulings and jabs. Mother said she couldn't bear to see him—but she couldn't bear to leave the room, either. She stood watching, appalled, itching to sew it on herself, and they talked at each other with vehemence.

Then the inevitable happened: the needle struck forcibly on the button, Father pushed at it harder, and it burst through the hole and stuck Father's finger.

He sprang up with a howl. To be impaled in this way was an affront. He turned to me, as he strode about on the rug, holding his finger, and said wrathfully, "It was your mother."

"Why, Clare!" Mother cried.

"Talking every minute," Father shouted at her, "and distracting a man! How the devil can I sew on a button with this gibbering and buzz in my ears?"

FATHER WASN'T bored in his old age. He kept up his billiards, tried to beat himself at solitaire, and enjoyed his drives until automobiles crowded the roads. He also enjoyed having a go at the morning paper, in a thoroughly combative spirit. Every time the President did anything, Father either commended him—in surprise—for having some backbone for once, or else said he ought to be kicked out of office. "And I'd like to go down there and kick him out myself," he'd add fiercely. This was especially the case during Woodrow Wilson's two terms. There was something about Wilson that made Father boil.

His dentist made a bridge for him to replace some lost teeth in front. Father soon took it back. "What's wrong, Mr. Day?" Dr. Wyant said. "Is the occlusion imperfect?"

"Your thing won't stay in; that's what's wrong with it."

Dr. Wyant was puzzled. "You mean that the denture seems to work loose when you are at table?"

"It stays in when I eat," said Father, "but when I say what I think of that man Wilson, it pops right out."

FOR ALL the years of our childhood, we lived at 420 Madison, and Father was sure we were there permanently. We were fond of 420. Endless household events had taken place there. It had become a part of ourselves.

But business began invading upper Fifth Avenue and spreading to Madison. More and more of the old houses around us were made into stores. After 1900 the whole district began sliding downhill, and finally, a group of gigantic buildings sprang up into the air around us and most of the brownstone houses disappeared. What drove Father away at last was the noise of the new streetcars. The old horsecars had had something human about them; the strident and unnatural din of the new cars wrecked Father's sleep. We moved finally to 43 East 68th Street, a largish house and modern compared to 420 Madison.

It was years after we left 420 before I went back there. Then one day I had an appointment in an office on the twelfth floor of the skyscraper which had been put up on that site. My brain must have been unconsciously full of old memories, for when I stepped out of my taxi, I somehow expected to find two rows of houses, set well back from the sidewalks, with the cheerful rattle of a cab going by. Instead, I found myself under immense ramparts that rose high into the air.

I went into the new 420 and got into an elevator. Up we shot, past the floor where Father's four-poster and bureau had been, past the level of the nursery and my bedroom, up and up; and there, suspended high above our old life, was the office where I had an appointment. I felt dizzy, though I had been up in hundreds of skyscrapers higher than this. I pushed the button on the office door and in a moment the man inside opened it, as casually as though everything were perfectly natural and he were living on solid earth.

Our Sixty-eighth Street house was home to us for some time, but Mother often talked about the advantages of an apartment. That was nonsense, Father said in disgust. A respectable man owned his own home and didn't live in a "damned hole in the air."

One evening I was in the library with Mother and Father when a nurse came in to take Mother's blood pressure, as the doctor had ordered. This was a new thing for Mother. It alarmed her. She turned—as she always did when she was in trouble—to Father. "Clare," she said urgently, "you must have yours taken too."

Father scowled. He was seventy, and when he and his friends met at the funerals that came often now, he had seen some of them shaking their heads and whispering things about "blood pressure." What angered Father was that it seemed able to kill healthy men—men he had felt sure would last for the next twenty years. Like himself. Father said we all had to die, he supposed. But he didn't know what the matter was nowadays. Somebody died every month. And it was always some sound, healthy man.

He said he was beginning to hate all these funerals.

"But when somebody dies, the people who loved them want to say good-by," Mother said. "You didn't use to mind going, Clare."

"Well, Vinnie," Father replied, "I was younger then. What bothers me now is that every time I go to a funeral they read all that business about the years of a man being threescore and ten. I know I'm seventy but I'm as well as I ever was, hang it."

The trained nurse still stood there waiting. Father glared. "I won't have anything to do with this blood pressure."

"Everybody has blood pressure, Mr. Day," the nurse said.

"A lot of them have," Father replied, "but I haven't."

Mother said: "*Please*, Clare!"

"Oh pshaw," said Father, "if it will gratify you, go ahead."

The nurse adjusted the strap and looked at the indicator. The pressure was abnormally high.

"Pooh! What of it?" said Father. "All poppycock."

"Mr. Day, really," the nurse said, "that condition is dangerous."

Father's face stiffened. He rose, walked away, and said with unwilling concern that he didn't believe a word of it. His need seemed to be to put it out of his mind. I took out of my pocket some brokerage accounts I had been attending to for him. "May I ask you about these, Father?" He usually hated to bother with them, but now he thankfully sat down and examined them. When we had finished he seemed to have sponged off the slate.

There were lots of things about him beside his arteries that wouldn't have suited the doctors at that time. But he continued to make his machinery serve by expecting much of it. He gave it no doubts to deal with, and perhaps that kept him hearty.

Mother's attitude was exactly the opposite. She tried every "health food," and took to heart all the ominous warnings of advertisers. But she came of a long-lived family, and both Father and Mother lived to a ripe and hardy old age. In spite of his sureness that he would outlive her, Father went first, in his eighties, and not from "a hole in the air," but properly, from his own house at 43 East 68th Street.

FOR YEARS MOTHER HAD GONE to the family plot in Woodlawn cemetery with her arms full of flowers, to lay the pretty things by some family headstone, as a sign of remembrance. One Sunday when she was past seventy, and Father was nearly eighty, she asked him to drive there with her. Father refused. He winked at me and said to Mother, "I'll be going there soon enough, Vinnie."

Mother said please, one of the headstones had settled and she wanted him to tell her whether it needed attention.

Father asked whose headstone it was, and when Mother told him he said, "I don't care how much it's settled. I don't want to be buried with any of that infernal crowd anyhow."

Mother said she knew how he felt about some of the family, but he wouldn't mind when it was all over. Father said yes he would. He became so incensed, thinking of it, that he declared he was going to buy a new plot in the cemetery, a plot all for himself. "And I'll buy one on a corner," he added triumphantly, "where I can get out!"

Mother looked at him, startled but admiring, and whispered to me, "I almost believe he could do it."

SOME TIME after Father's death Mother bought an apartment at 1170 Fifth Avenue, with a magnificent view of Central Park. Her homes had always been of absorbing interest to her, and the apartment was a kind of new toy. A friend, calling there for the first time, would no sooner get into the living room and start to make herself comfortable than she would be hustled right back to the elevator landing so that Mother could show everything straight from the beginning: the living room papered in green; the dining room with its crimson damask paper; the inevitable blue room, for guests; and Mother's own bright bedroom from which she could look out on the Reservoir while she ate her breakfast.

In all her homes Mother had had a reception room. Its formality helped her and her friends through awkward situations, and through pleasant, although formal, visits as well. So Mother had her pink and gold reception room at 1170. She loved to sit in one of the pink satin and gilt chairs by the window, her feet on a little mahogany footstool, a book of poems in her lap, and her lavender wool scarf over her shoulders, watching the changing light over the Reservoir.

However, Mother was usually active, and she soon sent out word that she was again at home on Thursdays. Then every week saw a group sitting around the dining-room table, with its lace cloth and the tea service, while Mother poured and laughed, and got indignant, and told stories.

A time came when Mother had a new, young daughter-in-law. She decided to give, as she hadn't for years, a big reception. All day long, on the great day, boxes of flowers came every few moments until the apartment was crowded with them. Mother got more and more excited. Extra maids got under one another's feet as they cleaned silver, and a little after four commenced a stream of ladies in black or purple satin, with husbands, when there were any, in morning coats and striped trousers. Mother sat enthroned in the living room wearing a new royal purple velvet gown and carrying orchids in her left hand. By her side stood the new daughter-in-law in pale beige lace carrying an old-fashioned bouquet of tea roses and forget-me-nots.

Mother was in high feather, her voice carrying above the chatter as she sat there completely in her element, until by seven thirty, triumphant if exhausted, she had greeted, introduced and poked up more than a hundred persons.

This was the beginning of a gay and busy winter for Mother until one of her Thursdays, late in January 1929. On that day there were fourteen people around the dining-room table, and Mother was gayer than ever. But afterward, she felt a queer pain in her left side. On Friday she lay quiet and unlike herself in her room. Saturday, however, still in bed, she joked with her doctor while telling him a mischievous story. Ten minutes later, without ever having known she had the dreaded angina pectoris, she died.

THE FOLLOWING Monday, dressed again in her new purple velvet gown and surrounded by orchids, Mother seemed to receive for the last time the friends who crowded in to bid her farewell.

Clarence Day

I was Clarence Day, Jr., in 1945, in Chicago. I had to get my hair dyed red. So did the dozens of other boys who acted the roles of the four carrot-topped Day sons. We were in the dramatic version of *Life With Father*, which delighted audiences for eight years, in New York and on tours—the long-run champion of Broadway history. I was in the Chicago company, and it was my fate to report every month at Marshall Field's beauty salon. "I have an appointment with Miss Lillian," I used to gulp to the receptionist, while the ladies under the hair dryers stared.

However, that was the only unpleasant chore connected with the play. I am willing to wager that right this minute a group of actors are rehearsing *Life With Father* somewhere, just as someone else is opening the pages of the book of stories on which the play was based. To many of us, the author of that book is far from a stranger. Nor is the scene of the stories, the house at 420 Madison Avenue, a place we have not visited.

An exact reproduction of the morning room of that house was the setting for the play—a lovely Victorian room, with lace curtains, rose-sprigged carpet, Vinnie Day's rubber plant, and, on a cushion at the fireplace, the china pug dog which she sent back to McCreery's Department Store so that her eldest son, Clarence, could have a new suit of clothes. "Why, your suit won't cost Father anything," Mother exclaimed in the play—a line which always received the biggest laugh of the evening. But laughter was tucked into every line of the play. It nestles in every page of the

242

book, too, together with the tender, touching quality of life itself, as families everywhere have lived it.

Clarence Day, Jr., whose pen wove that magic fabric, died in 1935, a few months after *Life With Father* was published. It was an instant best seller, as it has continued to be: twenty-six printings, fourteen foreign-language editions (including Arabic, Icelandic and Lebanese).

Such fantastic success would have astonished the mild, unassuming author. Born in 1874, he led a quiet, unspectacular, and courageous life. He attended St. Paul's School and Yale, after which he joined his father's brokerage firm. While serving in the Spanish-American War, he contracted the arthritis which, slowly and cruelly, made him a bed-ridden cripple.

But not an idle one. That was not in the Day family tradition. Impish, witty, despite the constant pain, Clarence Day, Jr., conducted business ventures from his bed, and became the author of magazine articles and books. He was also a talented cartoonist, in the style of James Thurber. But it was not until the publication of *Life With Father* that he became internationally famous.

When the play opened, he had been dead for almost four years. It used to sadden me that he never lived to see the warm happy glow on the faces of the audiences leaving the theater. When I left the Chicago company and returned to New York—my hair no longer a flaming sunset—one of the first things I did was to go to Madison Avenue and stand across from where the Days' brownstone had once been. The block was lined with modern buildings. Along with its author, the house that had become so real to me existed no more.

But then it struck me: Clarence Day, Jr., and the brownstone he wrote about were not gone at all. They existed, bright, fresh and undimmed, in that best and safest of regions, the human mind. Tomorrow, some reader would turn the first page of *Life With Father* for the first time, and he, too, would come to know the author, the brownstone, and the family who once lived in it.

—Arthur W. Cavanaugh

a condensation of

the fox and the hound

Neither had an enemy as dangerous as man

by Daniel P. Mannix

Paintings by Nita Engle
Woodcuts by Walter Ferro

The fierce contest between fox and hound
is as ancient as the wide fields and
woodland over which it ranges. From birth,
each has instincts and resources
that will be decisive in the ultimate trial
for survival. But rarely do *both* contestants
know at first hand the
kindness and cruelty of man.

Tod, the fox, was raised for the first year of
his life by a farmer. But while the man fed
and played with him, the young
fox's heart remained wild and it was
freedom that finally won him.
Copper, the hound, lived all his life with
single-minded devotion to his Master
and to the hunt.

The story of the long ingenious combat
between Tod and Copper is a remarkable
insight into the world of two animals.
Unsentimental but affectionate, it is full of
poignant feeling for the passing of the
world both fox and hound inhabit: for
man, the first friend, is the final adversary.

No one who has ever loved animals—
or the land—can fail to be deeply touched
by this remarkable book.

CHAPTER 1

THE BIG half-bred bloodhound lay in his barrel kennel and dreamed he was deer hunting. Deer was his favorite quarry, but trailing it was usually strictly forbidden. He had been whipped, beaten, even hit in the flanks by bird shot for this crime; yet once, after a journey to a faraway place, he had been allowed to track a deer. Now he smelled again that warm, rich odor as he toiled after the quarry. Again he heard the *toot—toot— toot* of his Master's horn blowing the "gone away" and the notes made him yelp with excitement. He was not running now, but flying over the ground, and the scent was growing stronger. The hound kicked convulsively and whined with eagerness.

Now he was vaguely aware of a shrill *yip-yurr!* repeated over and over. The splendor of the deer hunt faded, driven away by that infuriating yipping. With a cry the hound came awake. He smelled the pungent scent of fox very close. At the same moment the taunting yipping came again. With a roar of fury, the hound burst from his barrel into the early dawn. A few yards away, a fox sat grinning at him. Crazed with rage, the hound flung himself at the intruder. The fox did not move. As the hound's jaws were about to close over the interloper, he was flung on his side and lay groveling on the earth. He had come to the end of his chain.

By now all the hounds in the pack, as well as the fierce mongrel catch dogs, had awakened and were raging at the ends of their chains. The fox cocked his head and grinned at them, knowing he was safe, then turned to the hound and barked again teasingly, setting the hound screaming with frustration.

The headlights of a car swept the hill, briefly illuminating the coat of the fox so that it glowed as if with an internal light. Instantly the fox's grin vanished; he crouched and turned to look at the lane leading up to the isolated cabin below him. As the lights of a second car glided over him, the fox skulked away. He began to run as soon as he was clear of the light, and vanished into the scrub-oak thickets.

The hound recognized the distinctive sound of his Master's car. A moment later he identified the second vehicle. When this particular car came, he was always called on to track a man. The hound didn't like tracking men especially—the scent was always poor and there was no killing at the end of the trail. Although not bloodthirsty like the catch dogs, he did enjoy those last exciting moments of the chase, the crack of the rifle, and then smelling the dead quarry.

Still, anything that got him off the chain was a relief. So he stood hopefully, his tail wagging, as three men started up the hill. Soon the shortsighted hound could see that the figure in front was his Master. He recognized him by his walk rather than by his appearance. He began to wiggle with excitement.

The Master came up to him and the hound saw that he was putting on a heavy leather belt and that he carried the long leash that meant man tracking. He was to go and the rest would be left behind. Frantic with pride and delight, he groveled on the ground, turning his head sideways to expose the jugular vein as a sign of utter abjection. The Master patted him and spoke his name, "Copper." The hound sprang up and, putting his forepaws on his Master's chest, tried to lick his face. He was good-naturedly repulsed. His kennel chain was released and the tracking leash fastened to his collar. Copper at once hurried the Master toward the cars.

There was a young Trigg* hound named Chief, an excellent tracker and brave fighter who was the Master's favorite. Copper hated Chief with a hatred surpassing the hatred of a jealous woman. He was mortally afraid the Master might take the Trigg too and wanted to get him away as quickly as possible.

When they reached the cars, the Master spoke to the other two men, whom Copper recognized primarily by the smell of their leather leggings. He had gone out with them before. The Master unclipped the lead and opened the door of his car and ordered the hound to get in. Copper sprang in promptly, jumping up to his special seat on a rack behind the driver. He lay down, thumping the boards enthusiastically with his tail.

When they reached the highway, the second car passed them. A flashing light appeared on its top and it gave a moaning wail. They speeded up. The motion soothed Copper, and he dozed.

He was awakened by the car jolting over a dirt track. It was broad daylight. The cars stopped and the Master opened the door and allowed him to jump down. Copper ran around investigating new smells and paused to eat a little saw grass, for he felt slightly carsick.

The Master was speaking to a man who had come from a cabin with something in his hand. The Master took the object and held it out toward Copper. It was a scent guide, a cloth object that would give Copper the scent of the man he was to track. He smelled it carefully. There were several human scents, including those of the men who had just handled it.

When Copper heard the familiar clicks as the tracking leash was again snapped to his collar and to the Master's belt, he started off. One of the leather-smelling men followed as the Master took Copper on a long swing around the cabin. The hound worked slowly, sorting out the different scents that came to him. Animal scents he ignored. Occasionally he skirted patches of wild mustard or mint, which gave off an odor that tended to mask other

* Many special types of hounds have been bred by dedicated hunters for greater strength, more bell-like voice, etc. These hounds are known by the names of the men who developed the breeds.

scents. Twice he crossed clearings where the sun had burned off most of the scent. He worked these carefully to make sure of not missing a faint trail.

At last he hit a clear man track. Copper stopped instantly, sniffing long and loudly. Then he went back for the scent guide. The Master held it out. Yes, one of the odors, and by far the strongest, was the same as that of the track. Without hesitation Copper went to the trail and started out.

It was damp and cool under the trees and the scent held well. Copper forged ahead, at times dragging the Master after him. By working from one wisp of scent to the next he was able to unravel the "line"—the scent trail left by the quarry. In one especially bad spot he had to dig to find the scent where it had soaked into the ground. In another place, the scent had been blown away, but Copper found a suggestion of it beneath a fallen tree.

The line came out on a dirt road. The quarry had rested—the scent was quite strong—and smoked. But here the trail ended. Copper circled the spot to make sure. Then he lifted one leg and left his sign; this was a signal that the quarry had vanished.

The Master talked to the leather-smelling màn while Copper rested. He was tired and thirsty. The Master poured water from a canteen into the rim of his hat, and Copper drank eagerly. Then he washed out Copper's nose and massaged his feet. Finally he shook the leash and said, "Go on, boy. Go find 'em."

Copper looked up reproachfully. He had indicated that the trail stopped here. Yet the Master was insistent. Although there was no scent of the quarry, there was the scent of an automobile. As he had to track something, he began tracking the car.

Following the car was fairly simple, although the hot road hurt his pads. Copper soon found that enough scent had clung to the damp grass along the edge for him to follow it there. Even better, the sun was making the scent rise so it floated a few inches above the ground and the hound did not have to drop his head. Then, after a time, he came on clear though not fresh man scent running off the side of the road. Copper turned and started after it eagerly.

Working along the side of a hill, they came on a rockslide lying in the full glare of the sun. Here Copper could not find a trace of the trail. The Master pulled him off the rocks and unsnapped the leash from his collar as a signal he was to stop tracking. Copper lay down thankfully, licking his bleeding pads.

The men left him and climbed the rockslide, stopping to pick up something, while Copper watched in agony. He could not understand how they could smell the line when he could not. At the top of the slope, the Master called him. To avoid the rocks, Copper loped around the slide and joined the men. The tracking leash was snapped onto his collar, and the Master repeated, "Go on, boy. Go find 'em."

Copper cast around and, sure enough, there was the scent again. How the Master had found it he could not imagine. Trained never to give tongue while following a man, he could not suppress an eager whine. Then they were off, the big hound pulling excitedly on the leash until the Master cursed him.

The scent was growing stronger. The eager hound forced his way through laurel and greenbrier so thick the men could hardly follow. Suddenly he stopped dead and tested the air. There it was. The man was so close the hound could air-scent him, and the sweet-sick smell of death was strong. There was also blood.

The hound plunged down into a gully, the men sliding after him. He splashed through the water and up the opposite bank, took one strong sniff and then sat down. The quarry was here.

The Master unsnapped the leash and the men moved toward the body. A droning mass of blowflies rose above the corpse. Then Copper smelled something that sent shivers of fear and excitement through his body. Bear!

He began feverishly to cast around. It was bear, all right. The bear had blood on his paws and he had been in a frenzy of rage; Copper could tell by the special quality of the scent. As he was no longer tracking a man, Copper felt justified in giving tongue, and his deep bay rolled out, first in a long howl and then in short, gasping cries. Instantly the Master was by his side. Copper showed him where the line was, but the Master walked back and forth until he found something to look at on the soft earth. The Master's inability to scent a perfectly clear line, as well as his tendency to stand for a long time staring at pointless marks on the ground, always irritated Copper. Finally the tracking leash was snapped on and he was told to go ahead.

It was no use. The bear had traveled much faster than the man. Copper could barely own the line. After a short time, the Master pulled him off. The bear was gone.

FOR THE NEXT few days nothing happened. Copper amused himself by lying in front of his barrel and checking various odors the breeze brought him. He could see the cabin at the foot of the little rise where the kennels were, but beyond that the world fuzzied into a black-and-white haze. Everything looked black and white to Copper, as to all dogs. He did not depend much on his eyes, which had often caused him to make shameful errors. If the Master changed his clothes, Copper would often bark at him until the Master spoke so he could recognize the voice.

Yet lying on the hill, Copper could tell what was going on in the world about him fairly well. Dozens of distinct odors poured into his nostrils. Flowers, grass, trees, the other dogs, activities in the cabin—these he ignored. But a distant herd of deer passing through the woods, a stray dog, a human stranger, a rabbit or a raccoon caused his nostrils to twitch as he separated the important scent from the mass of other odors. He could also tell when it was going to rain by the moisture in the wind.

A few mornings later, Copper was awakened by the ringing of the telephone in the cabin. It was still pitch-black, but he could smell the dawn not too far away. The phone stopped ringing. Then the lights went on. All the dogs knew what that meant, and their chains rattled as they shook themselves and came out of their kennels to stretch. Copper was sure there was a job on.

The cabin door opened, emitting a flood of light, and the Master came out. The pack began to scream with excitement. The Master shouted, "You, Chief! Strike! Ranger! Hold that noise!" The dogs subsided.

With swift efficiency, the Master hitched up the dogs' trailer to his battered car while the pack watched anxiously. Then he came up the hill. The dogs groveled, barked, whined, and stood on their hind legs in an agony of anticipation while he made his choice. To Copper's inexpressible delight, he was selected. The Master also took Red, a young heavy-coated July hound, and Ranger, a buckskin Plott known as a fighter.

But then the Master took the favorite Copper so hated, young Chief. Chief was a big hound, black and tan with a white-tipped tail. He was faster and more belligerent than Copper. He not infrequently hit by chance on some line that Copper was patiently working out, gave tongue, and took the pack away.

Last, the Master selected Buck, a long-legged Airedale type, and Scrapper, whose ancestry was uncertain. The inclusion of these two catch dogs meant they were going after dangerous game. Like all the other hounds, Copper feared and disliked the catch dogs. He had discovered from painful experience that when excited they were more likely to attack the hounds than the quarry. The hounds were put together in the trailer, but the catch dogs were kept in separate compartments.

The ride was not long. At sunrise they reached a small town, and the car slowed down. Another car was parked in the silent street, and the Master pulled up alongside. Copper knew the man in the other car. He smelled of a special grease he used on his gun and appeared only before dangerous hunts.

The two men finished talking. When the cars started off, Copper dozed. When he awoke, the cars were climbing a steep grade. Scenting conditions were so good that even in the trailer Copper could smell pines and deer. The cold mountain air made him feel better, and he stood up, swaying in rhythm with the motion of the car.

The cars pulled off on grass and stopped, and the Master came around to let out the excited hounds and catch dogs. Sheltered beneath a great cliff stood a small farmhouse, flanked by an apple orchard and a sheepfold.

A man came from the house and took them to the sheepfold.

The sheep were bleating and smelled heavily of the special odor of fear all animals quickly recognize. The smell made the pack prick up their hackles and move toward the fold stiff-legged. Even Copper, well broken to all domestic stock, felt a charge of cruelty surge through him. The Master ordered them off, and when the catch dogs ignored him he took a stick to them.

The farmer was pointing to the ground; the Master and the grease-smelling man bent over to examine it. Then the Master called Copper over. As the hound leaped forward, the others tried to follow but were ordered back, to Copper's great satisfaction. The instant he applied his trained nose to the spot where the Master was pointing, Copper burst into a long, sobbing cry. It was the same bear he had scented beside the dead man.

His tail wagging frantically, he began to work out the line. It was strong and fresh. Copper broke into his deep bay. Now the rest of the pack were allowed to run over. They sniffed, and then simultaneously broke into the steady cry of hounds on a scent.

"Go get 'em, boys. Woo-whoop!" shouted the Master. The pack went streaming across the orchard, swept along by the sound of their own music. The catch dogs were at the end, only occasionally getting wisps of scent that made them yelp with eagerness.

The scent held well in the forest beyond the orchard, and the pack pressed on with a reassuring rhythmic baying. When at times the scent failed, the pack stopped baying and anxiously fanned out to find the line. Copper usually found it. He knew the best places to check: the hollow formed by two roots at the base of a tree; a damp spot where the scent might cling; or a protected hollow where the scent might have drifted and could not rise again. Often scent particles clung to the surfaces of leaves that had touched the bear's sides. When Copper was sure, he would speak and the rest would run over and cast out ahead of him. Occasionally one of the other hounds would strike something and speak of it doubtfully. Copper would check the spot and the rest would wait until they heard his affirmative deep bay.

Once, when the whole pack had been at fault for several minutes, Red, the young July hound, shouted eagerly. No one paid any attention to him, for Red had never opened on a line before. But the puppy kept pleading until finally Copper investigated. Red stood back while Copper applied his expert nose. To his surprise, there was the scent. A lesser hound would have gone on and opened on the line farther ahead, as though he had discovered it himself, but Copper would not stoop to such an act. He instantly confirmed the pup's yelps. The pack rushed over and soon were in full cry. After that, whenever Red spoke he was awarded respectful attention.

They came to a blowdown where wind had knocked over a stand of sharply scented hemlocks. The pack slithered over the trunks to the other side. Here they checked. Somewhere in the blowdown they had lost the scent. The pack started casting—working out in ever increasing circles trying to pick up the trail again. Copper crawled back to the last spot where he could positively identify the scent and then came slowly back to the blowdown. It was noticeably warm in the blowdown and this gave Copper an idea. He stood up on his hind legs. Ah, there it was! The scent was floating, just above his head when he reared up. With nose still strained upward he started across the blowdown. His feet slipped between the trunks, but he was higher now and his straining nose could touch the floating line. When he reached the hard ground on the other side, he had to stand up again to reach the odor, but he kept on.

Now the other hounds followed Copper's example. They worked their way into a pine forest. Under the trees, the scent dropped to the ground again. Here the hounds were able to follow it easily, and burst into full cry.

They quickly outdistanced the men. The other hounds had moved into the lead, for Copper, with his heavy bloodhound build, was never a fast dog. Red was in front, then Ranger and then Chief, with the catch dogs in the rear behind Copper. The scent was getting stronger. The bear was close. Copper dropped back more and more. His legs were stiff, his lungs burned, and in addition he had no desire to come up with an infuriated bear. Copper was no fighter.

Suddenly, among the blackberry bushes, Red, Ranger and Chief broke into the viewing cry, and there came the sound of smashing brush. In spite of himself, Copper caught the excitement and put on an extra burst of speed. The catch dogs tore past him, Scrapper snarling at him to get out of the way.

Then through the hysterical yells came a deep-throated bellowing. The bear had turned at bay and charged. The dogs fell over each other trying to avoid him. Copper, mad with excitement, broke through the last cover and saw the bear. The great animal had backed against a fallen tree, so the dogs could not take him from behind. He swung his head back and forth, champing his jaws as the dogs rushed him. The catch dogs had taken up their places one on either side of him while the hounds ran around behind them. First Buck and then Scrapper would leap forward, and the bear would swing his head to face the adversary. Then the other dog would spring in, tear out a mouthful of fur, and jump back to avoid the bear's return blow. They were making no real attempt to attack—only to hold him there.

Twice the bear started to leave the tree and run. He could easily outrun the pack in this heavy cover, so the hounds rushed in to help the catch dogs snap at him and force him back.

The sound of the Master's horn signaled the pack that help was on the way. At the call, the catch dogs moved into position. When both were ready, Buck gave a quick, sharp bark. Instantly Scrapper rushed in, making a feint at the bear's side that drew him out slightly from the protection of the tree. Buck leaped in and grabbed the bear's ear. Scrapper bounced forward, snapping to keep the bear from turning on his friend, and Buck managed to fling his body over the bear's neck, still hanging to the ear.

The bear stood up on his hind legs, reaching behind him for the Airedale. He seized Buck in both paws and flung him away into the bushes. Then he turned on the rest of the pack. Copper saw the Master and the grease-smelling man come tearing through a mass of honeysuckle with their guns. Seeing them, the bear whirled and charged the Master.

The Master tried to jump back, but his foot caught in the

honeysuckle and he fell. The bear was on top of him. Even at this terrible moment Copper could not bring himself to close with the bear, but Chief charged in from behind. Closing his forefeet under him, he slid under the bear and seized the raging animal in a tender spot. The pain was too terrible for the bear to take. He whirled around. Chief hung on, although he was lifted off his feet. The Master rose on his elbow and fired into the bear's side and the grease-smelling man also fired. The bear went down, gushing blood, and the dogs poured over him.

The Master rose and limped toward the dogs. Copper went to him, wagging his tail in self-esteem for having done a good job of trailing. The Master paid no attention to him. He went over to Chief and, taking the dog's head between his hands, spoke to him in the love talk that once he had used only to Copper. Watching them with savage jealousy, Copper knew that his day was done and that soon there would be a new leader of the pack.

CHAPTER 2

THE FOX PUP'S first memory was that of hearing an eager scratching at the mouth of the den, followed by excited whines. The pup was merely curious, for the noises were not unlike fox noises and he knew of no reason to fear them. Yet in a moment his mother was on her feet, hissing and snarling. She gave off the terrible scent of fear.

His brothers and sisters were whimpering with terror, but the pup kept his wits. He had always looked to his mother for guidance and now he gave a plaintive yip meaning "What do you want us to do?" At once his mother picked him up by the scruff of his neck. She ran down one of the long passageways of the huge den. It had been used by generations of foxes, and some of the passageways were fifty feet long. There were ten bolt-holes besides the main entrance, and the vixen ran toward one of these.

She stopped just short of a bolt-hole. The ground trembled with the stamping of men's feet, and their voices and the yelping of dogs came clearly through the hole. The vixen backed down the burrow, dropped the pup and ran back for another.

The pup lay cowering as he listened to the terrifying sounds and smelled the new odors that seeped along the tunnel. He heard a dog forcing its way into the main entrance, and then heard it scream. The vixen had grabbed it by the nose. He listened to the gurgling noise of combat as the dog tried to tear himself free. Above, the men were shouting and stamping on the ground. He heard a second dog yell in the main den, then the screams of the vixen. She was running through the den with the dogs after her, trying to lead them away from the pups. Then came the most awful sounds the fox pup had ever heard: the death cries of his brothers and sisters. A third terrier had been sent down the main entrance, and found them.

His mother suddenly appeared beside him and dropped, panting. They lay with their noses touching while the roar of the dogs tearing through the passageways looking for them echoed through the earth. His mother rose and, writhing around in the narrow passage, began to dig desperately at the roof. The earth fell in showers around her, blocking the tunnel. She lay down again.

They heard the footsteps of one of the terriers coming down the burrow, separated from them only by the thin earth barrier. The foxes lay motionless, not daring to breathe. The dog scratched at the fallen earth but it had cut off the scent, and he backed out of the passage. The foxes resumed breathing.

By lying perfectly still the foxes had largely cut off their scent, as the odor was spread by the heat of their bodies; but with the two animals crowded together the passage grew warm, and the scent began to rise out of the bolt-hole and catch in the tangle of honeysuckle that covered it.

The dogs had come out of the den now, and the pup could tell by the slower breathing of his mother that she was no longer so frightened as she had been. The men had tramped over the entrance of the bolt-hole several times without noticing it; they would soon leave. Then one of the terriers scrambled over the honeysuckle tangle. The foxes heard him stop suddenly and begin to sniff. He broke into an eager yelping, and the foxes heard the other dogs racing to him. The vixen pushed the pup behind her with her nose and crawled up toward the entrance.

The men ripped away the honeysuckle and a dog managed to worm his way down the hole. There was a narrow shelf along the side of the hole and the vixen crawled onto it. She let the little dog pass below her and then suddenly seized him across the loins with her long, pointed jaws. She clamped down with all her strength and had the satisfaction of hearing the backbone snap. The dog screamed in agony and lay paralyzed.

Above them came the furious yelling of men and dogs, then a *thump! thump! thump!* The men were digging down to them. At once the vixen slipped off the shelf and began digging desperately, but before she could break through the blocked passage another terrier came down the pipe and managed to wriggle over his mortally wounded comrade. The vixen was forced to turn to face him and he began the chop bark that meant "Here she is! I'm holding her at bay!"

The men began digging in earnest. There was nothing the vixen could do. When she attacked the terrier he retreated, meeting her attacks with open jaws. She could not get past him, and if she had the men and the other dogs were waiting for her. As the top of the tunnel caved in the vixen made one last frantic effort to escape. She leaped toward the light, and as she bounded out a terrier seized her.

The pup, trembling in the now open passageway, heard the hissing screams of his mother, the yells of the men, and the guttural sounds of worrying as the terriers made their kill. He knew his best chance of safety was to remain absolutely still. He lay in the pipe, a little ball of wool, with only his eyes—just changing from baby blue to yellow—showing he was alive.

Then one of the men gave a cry and reached down for him. The pup did not move until the man's hand actually closed over him. Then he gave a bansheelike screech and buried his little milk teeth in the man's thumb. The man started, and grabbed the pup by the back of the neck.

He was put in a bag and carried to a car. Throughout the long drive the pup lay quietly. Unlike a human being, he was incapable of speculating about the future, and so did not suffer any agonies of apprehension. At last the car stopped, and he heard voices. He was carried away from the car, and then was gently shaken out on a floor.

The pup looked up at the man bending over him, conscious of the terrifying smell of the man, the strange smell of the room, and the smell of a dog not much bigger than himself who came over and sniffed him. The pup snarled, but was not really frightened. The dog's tail was wagging; there was no scent of anger; his friendly actions were sufficiently foxlike for the pup to recognize.

The man spoke to the dog, who hastily retreated. Then the man tried to touch the pup, but he brought his hand down from above in an action recognized by dogs and foxes as an aggressive attempt to get a neck hold. The pup twisted himself around with bared teeth. The man withdrew his hand and then extended it again, this time moving it along the floor. The pup snarled again, but after a few seconds allowed the man to rub him under the chin and scratch back of his ears. In spite of his fear, a delicious sense of well-being flooded through the pup and he lay almost hypnotized.

After that, the pup tamed rapidly. He quickly learned his name—the humans called him "Tod"—but he would almost never come when called. If the calling became insistent, he would sneak quietly through the house until he could see if the person calling had some sinister motive. If the person had a toy, food, or was even lying on the floor patting the rug, he would joyfully bound in; but if the person had no obvious reason for wanting him, Tod would watch for several minutes and then cautiously withdraw.

At first Tod was given the run of the house, but later he was locked up after supper in a bare room. He hated to be confined and deeply resented this treatment, so as soon as the dishes were put in the sink he would quietly steal away. At first he hid in a dark hallway, but he found that when both the man and his wife were looking for him they could block both ends of the hall and he was sure to be caught. He tried hiding in various rooms, only to find that when the humans saw him they could simply shut the door. Finally he learned to keep moving, making it almost impossible to trap him. He followed this pattern rigidly from then on, always going along the same course because the first time he followed that particular route he had escaped. Tod made no attempt to understand why a certain device succeeded or failed. If it failed he abandoned it, but if it succeeded he would, unlike the dog, meticulously duplicate the pattern in every detail.

As Tod grew bigger, the man did a number of things that puzzled and somewhat annoyed him. He would throw some object on the floor, and the dog would bring it to him. Then he would throw it out for Tod. Tod would pick up the object; but as he could see no reason to bring it to the man, he would carry it off. The man would catch him and take the object from his mouth. Tod hated this and fought so furiously that the man gave up.

The man began to take Tod out for walks, at first keeping him on a long lead. Tod loved these walks—there was so much to see and smell outside. After one walk, the man had only to approach the drawer where the lead was kept and Tod was wiggling and whining with anticipation, holding up his head for the lead. As soon as Tod saw they were headed back again to the house, he would lie down or brace himself with all four feet against the lead.

At last the man let him run free. Perfectly happy, Tod ran around checking new scents and enjoying the sights. He was fascinated by the farm animals, especially the sheep. Their heavy odor attracted Tod, and the first time he encountered the flock he ran eagerly toward them. The sheep scattered in all directions, with Tod bounding joyfully in pursuit. Then Tod began to herd them. Delighted at his power, he drove them from one end of the pasture to the other. When the sheep grew panicky, Tod would stand still until they had quieted, often dropping his long nose between his forepaws, with his hindquarters elevated in the same playful attitude he used with the man or dog.

When autumn came, Tod was delighted to find that he could see vast distances from the top of a hill, unhampered by tall grass or bushes. Walking in this open country was a real pleasure; Tod had trouble making his way through dense cover. He loved the dry leaves, and batted them around with his nimble forefeet, or sprang up to catch them in the air with snapping jaws, or rolled over and over in them. It became harder and harder for the man to entice him back to the house. Food had no particular attraction for him; he was well fed, and could quite easily go for forty-eight hours without eating. Also, he was growing bigger, stronger, and more self-confident. Tod often spent several nights out, turning up eventually for his bowl of milk.

It began to grow colder. Tod rather enjoyed the cold, but it upset him not to be able to smell in the early morning when the ground was coated with hoarfrost. He ran around sniffing desperately, afraid something had gone wrong with him or with the world. He did not relax until the sun started a thaw and scenting conditions were better.

One evening when Tod refused to return to the house it was because the atmosphere was oppressive. The air seemed thick, somewhat like the heavy, moisture-charged air before a rain, yet more dense and confining. He ran around whimpering until finally the man went in. Then Tod got lonely and went to the back door. He could smell the people and food inside and hesitatingly lifted one paw to scratch; then thought better of it. He ran around the farm for a while and finally slept in the woodpile.

When he awakened, the world had turned white. Tod sat up, astonished. He poked at it and was charmed when his nose plunged into the stuff. Thoroughly excited, he bounded out, knocking snowdrifts about by quick sideways motions with his nose. When the man came out, Tod was still rollicking so happily that he allowed himself to be picked up and carried inside for breakfast. As soon as he was through eating, he anxiously scratched at the door to be let out again. This time the man and dog went with him, Tod running on the surface of the snow while his two companions floundered helplessly in the drifts. This was exactly Tod's idea of a joke, and he made the most of it.

But as the winter continued, Tod grew restless and then irritable, snapping at the dog and biting the man when picked up. He stayed away more and more, returning to the farm mainly to pick up food at the garbage dump in the far pasture. Sometimes, however, he still craved companionship and would scratch and bark at the back door until he was let in. Then he would run ardently from the man to the dog, to show how glad he was to be home. For a day or so he might stay at the farm, following the man everywhere and even going contentedly to his once hated room at night. Then a throbbing would start in him and he would grow restless again. Finally Tod stayed away completely. He did not want to be confined, and his wild life was making him increasingly distrustful of any human.

Tod's coat, which had been lackluster and shabby, was now thick. His back became a burnished red with golden tints, his chest and belly a creamy white, while his ear tips and the lower parts of his long legs were a rich black. His brush was nearly half his own size now, and a snowy tassel appeared on the tip. Around his neck a slight but noticeable ruff stood out when he was excited, and accentuated his ears and his nose. During the summer he might have been mistaken for a small yellow dog or even a large cat. Now he was unmistakably a fox.

Slowly Tod gained a knowledge of his territory. His short height was always a major problem, and he liked to go from rise to rise, stopping to look around each time. He often ran along the top of a post-and-rail fence, where he could see a considerable distance. When he jumped down again he could no longer keep his faraway landmarks in view, so he traveled from marker to marker—a special gateway, a stump, a knoll or a large stone—passing close to the marker yet not touching it. In the woods he never passed a fallen tree without running along it or a stump without jumping on top. He did this partly so he could look around, but also for the fun of it. When he found a trail, he followed that for convenience. As time went on, his route became routine. His range was about a square mile, and although when hunting was poor he was forced to extend it, he always left his known territory with reluctance.

Mice were his staple. Even with snow on the ground he could scent a mouse tunnel, and would plunge his long nose into the snow to check. He could hear mice running through the tunnels several feet away, and would give a great bound, land with his forefeet pressing down the tunnel on either side of the quarry, and bite between his paws blindly. Sometimes he got only a mouthful of leaves or snow; often he got a mouse. But rabbits were his favorite quarry. He liked the flesh better than that of mice, and one rabbit would last him two or three days, but he hunted them for sport as much as for food.

One of his favorite rabbit grounds was an orchard where the rabbits came to strip the young trees when snow covered their herbage. On a straightaway the rabbits could outrun him; however, they usually tried to dodge around the trees, and Tod could turn faster than they could. Also, when a rabbit went down a hole he had to hesitate for a split second at the mouth to clear away the snow, and in this second Tod could often grab him. It was safer for a rabbit to plunge into a brier patch, for he could hit the brambles at any angle.

One spring afternoon when Tod was loping along his route, he stopped short to investigate some cattle in a field. They had been in the barn most of the winter, and this was the first time he had seen them. The cows raised their heads to look at him. Tod ran from side to side, trying to make them panic as he had done the sheep. Instead, two heifers charged him. Their attack was so unexpected that only by rapid dodging was Tod able to escape. However, he soon found that cattle always charged in a straight line and could be easily avoided. He also found that by moving slowly and keeping close to the ground he could pass right through the herd. From then on, Tod frequently turned aside from his regular route to torment the cattle, his mouth open in his distinctive foxy grin of triumph.

That spring Tod also encountered farm dogs. They liked hunting but had not good enough noses for it. The first time Tod heard one of them on his trail he followed his standard route automatically, even running along two sections of a fence at his usual spot before dropping down to continue his wild flight. Then he realized the dog was no longer giving tongue. He cautiously swung around to study his back trail and found the bewildered dog running up and down the fence trying to pick up the trail. When the dog finally gave up, Tod trotted off thoughtfully. He knew now that by fence running he could throw a dog off. From then on, whenever he was chased by a dog he would follow his usual route to the fence, run along on the top rail and drop off.

It did not immediately occur to Tod that any fence would do as well. It was slowly and mostly by chance he picked up a whole repertoire of tricks to throw off dogs. Whenever a dog was at a loss, Tod memorized that particular spot and what he had done. Once he threw off two dogs by running across a newly plowed field, and from then on he always cut across that field when chased. But when wheat started to come up in the field the trick no longer worked, since the scent no longer evaporated quickly from warm, bare earth. He could not understand this.

However, Tod was not entirely incapable of associating ideas. Once when a dog was after him Tod saw the cattle in the field and turned off his usual route and ran across the field toward them. When he drew close, he dropped and wormed his way into the middle of the herd. In a few minutes the dog, intent on the trail, charged blindly toward the cattle. The cows bawled and charged him. As the startled dog sprang aside a cow caught him and rushed him against the fence. Tod, sitting up to see better, watched the dog go flying into the air, yelping with pain and fright. Tod danced with delight. He was so proud of this trick that he deliberately went looking for dogs thereafter to lure them into the field. Finally, to Tod's great disappointment, every farm dog in the neighborhood learned to avoid the herd.

Tod followed his beat with such regularity a man could almost have set a watch by him. Part of his run was along an embankment where a train ran twice a day. Tod had originally climbed the embankment because it gave him a better view. He soon learned to trot along one of the rails—for the cinders hurt his pads—before turning off to take a footpath through a juniper tangle that, in turn, led him to a culvert under a highway and thence up a hill to the fallen pine under which he usually denned for the day.

Tod usually reached the embankment an hour before dawn, but one morning he was late, having been delayed by an encounter with an opossum. As he trotted along the rail shortly after sunup, he heard the whistle of an oncoming train. Tod felt the rail vibrating under his pads, and stopped to stare down at it in wonder. Then he heard the train and, looking over his shoulder, saw the monster racing down on him.

Tod ran for his life along the rail, but the train was faster. It never occurred to him to leave the rail until he came to his familiar turning-off place at the juniper thicket. The cowcatcher was almost touching his brush when he reached the place and made a hysterical bound off the embankment. Hitting the ground with all four feet, he continued racing along the path, positive that the train was after him. Gradually he realized the monster was still rushing by on the embankment. Tod stopped and stood watching it, gasping for breath.

A week or so later, he was again delayed, and again heard the whistle and felt the vibration while running the rail. This time he started running instantly and reached the jump-off spot in plenty of time. After a few more such experiences, he learned that the monster always continued in a straight line, not unlike the cattle, and therefore could be easily dodged. He even made a game of this, and would deliberately jump on a rail and race the engine, jumping off when it got dangerously close.

One morning in autumn Tod, who was bored, for hunting was easy in the autumn, left his usual range and roamed afield. On one of these trips he passed a cabin on the slope of a hill, and

smelled dogs. He gave an experimental bark to see what would happen, and instantly dogs burst from their barrel kennels, screaming with rage. Tod turned to run and then saw they were chained, as he had once been. He loped off, grinning.

A few nights later Tod came by and went to the nearest barrel, stopping just outside the circle of hard-packed earth that showed the limits of the captive's chain. When he began barking, he was rewarded by seeing a big hound burst out and rage at him. Other dogs erupted from their kennels, and Tod sat in the midst of his hereditary enemies, enjoying their futile fury until car headlights swept the hill, and he hurried away.

Two months after this Tod again happened to pass the hill shortly before daylight. He stopped in front of another kennel and barked tauntingly. The hound burst out, standing on his hind legs as he forced himself against his collar, and within seconds the whole hillside was a madhouse of raging, thwarted dogs.

The cabin door was thrown open, and a man new to Tod came out. Tod ran. He had almost reached cover when he heard the cry of the hound he had been goading take on a note of triumph and sound nearer. Tod glanced back. To his horror, the hound had broken his collar and was after him.

Tod sped for the woods, confident he could outdistance the hound as he had the farm dogs. But the eager baying got rapidly closer. He turned loose his top burst of speed. The man was shouting, "Chief! Come back here!" The hound paid no attention, and as Tod dived into the woods the hound was right behind.

Tod headed for the embankment. The sun was coming up, and he heard the whistle of the train at a distant crossing. The scent was poor on the rail, so he slowed down. The hound finally picked up the scent and loped along between the rails, checking at intervals to make sure his quarry had not jumped off. Then Tod felt the tingling of the rail under his pads. The train was coming.

The hound now saw Tod running ahead. He burst into the cry that meant "In sight! In sight!" There was the insistent bleat of a hunting horn, but the hound disregarded it. He tore along the ties, and Tod had to stretch himself to keep ahead.

The pulsation of the rail increased. Tod waited as long as he dared, and then flung himself down the embankment. He heard another desperate call of the horn, the frenzied whistle of the train, and then a single scream of agony from the hound. The train swept past and Tod made his way to the juniper tangle, where he watched a man come along the tracks. The man stopped and stood looking at the dead hound a long time. Then he knelt and gently lifted the body. Tod heard him make an unfamiliar sobbing noise, and cocked his ears to listen.

The man looked out over the juniper cover while Tod froze. Then the man, holding the dead hound, shouted at the top of his voice in a tone filled with hatred. Slowly the man turned away, still carrying the dead hound. When they were gone, Tod rose stiffly and walked along his usual footpath through the junipers, crawled through the culvert, and went up the hill to his pine-tree den. For once in his energetic life he had had enough.

CHAPTER 3

FOR THE NEXT few days, Copper was supremely happy. His hated rival was dead, and every day now the Master came up the hill and picked him—and him alone—to go out.

True, he could have wished that the Master would do some real hunting rather than the boring preparatory work required of him. The same day that Chief was killed, the Master had driven Copper back to the railroad tracks where the fox had jumped off. Although the scent was cold, Copper had no trouble following it through the junipers and the culvert to the hill where Tod had his den. Copper threw his deep voice and strained at the lead, but the Master held him back, studied the hill carefully, and then dragged the reluctant Copper back to the car.

From then on, the Master and Copper drove for hours over the rough back roads every morning. From time to time the Master would get out of the car and stare at marks in the dust that apparently told him something. Sometimes after such a study he would take Copper over the fields to a point where two fence lines crossed or there was a fallen log over a stream, or a gap in the hedgerow. If the ground was hard, or if there was grass, the Master would call on Copper, and he would apply his marvelous nose to the place indicated. If a fox had passed that way in the last day, he would throw his tongue. In such cases, the Master would let him follow the line to a soft place where there were marks. Then the Master, after examining them, would pull him off, saying, "No!"

For a long time, Copper could not understand the difficulty. Then one morning he hit the scent of the fox who had run the rails. He followed the line to the banks of a creek where the fox had trotted across fresh mud to drink. The Master examined the mud, and Copper sensed the excitement in his voice as he ordered, "Go get 'em, boy!" Copper waited to have the lead unsnapped, but the Master repeated the order and the astonished hound realized he was to track while on lead. Disappointed but obedient, he set off. He was still tracking when night came, and although the scent grew no warmer the Master seemed pleased at having discovered the fox's run.

For days after that Copper tracked the fox until he knew the animal's regular route almost perfectly. When he learned that the Master was interested only in this especial animal, he ignored other fox trails. Never before had the Master been so determined to trace the entire run of a fox, and Copper grew eager for the climax that he knew was coming.

There had been a cold spell and every morning the ground was covered with frost, so scenting had been difficult until well after the sun rose. Then came a warm night. Copper was still sleeping when he heard his name spoken. At once he wormed his way out of the barrel and jumped delightedly on the Master. He knew this must be the day, for the Master had no lead and was carrying a shotgun. They started off, stopping to pick up two other men at different farmhouses, both with guns. Copper recognized them by their odor as old hunting friends of the Master's.

The sun was up now and rags of mist lifted like steam from the warm earth. When the car stopped and the Master dropped off one of the men, Copper recognized the spot: it was the crossing where a multiflora-rose hedge and a wire fence covered with honeysuckle intersected. The man took up his position in a sassafras thicket fifty feet downwind from this crossing on the fox's usual route. A few miles later they dropped the second hunter at the log over the stream, another fox crossing.

Next, the car stopped near the railroad tracks. Copper jumped out as soon as the door was open. He hit the trail through the junipers, checked the culvert briefly and crossed the road. The wind was against him but Copper did not worry. The fox would surely be lying up on the hill ahead, as he had a week ago.

They started up the hill. The breeze was blowing from behind them and told Copper nothing. When they were close to the crest the Master gave a yell. "Here, boy, here!" He pointed downhill. Copper tore down, baying at the top of his great voice. The scent was breast high as he saw the fox cross the road ahead of him, a brief flicker of dark gray. As he ran, Copper heard the Master's car pull away. He knew from past experience that the Master would speed to the next crossing and wait there.

Copper knew that the fox was now on his regular route and would stick to it, as he could make better speed along the familiar path than across country. He ran the route upwind so he could smell anything ahead of him. There was a damp, strong north wind blowing and occasionally Copper got whiffs of scent from the fox himself as well as from his tracks.

Now the fox was running easily, not far ahead. Copper charged on recklessly, and the scent grew gratifyingly stronger, as it does when a quarry puts forth its full efforts. There was even a wonderful trace of the fear odor which caused Copper to redouble his efforts. In spite of his heavy build, the half-bloodhound was capable of putting on a surprising burst of speed for short distances.

They were approaching the next fox crossing now, a windbreak of evergreens beside the road. The Master would be behind the evergreens, waiting, so Copper's baying took on a triumphal note as he anticipated the boom of the shotgun. But then he heard a sound that filled him with shame—the noise of the Master's car coming up the road. In his excitement Copper had committed the unforgivable crime of pressing the fox too hard and not giving the Master a chance to get to his stand. He fell into a trot, but it was too late. The fox was still running strong. Copper followed the line through the evergreens. Then, safe from possible punishment, he resumed baying. He heard the Master's car go on.

Beyond the trees, the fox had left his usual run to cut across a pasture. The trail was distinct: he had zigzagged, as though looking for something. Copper cut straight across, following the fox's general drift rather than the zigzags. At one place the fox had stopped to roll in some half-dry manure before going on. This neutralized his body odor, but in the short-clipped field Copper could still smell the scent from his pads.

By ignoring his regular run the fox missed the next road crossing where the Master would have driven his car to wait. There was nothing to do but bay as loudly as possible so the Master could tell what had happened. The fox was now running in an almost perfectly straight line, clearly headed for some definite objective. Copper knew from the smell that the fox was a young animal, and young ones were most apt to go down holes.

The trail led into another field of short grass. Here the fox had made a number of spy hops—leaping high in the air to see about him. This left a series of puzzling breaks in the trail. Then the fox had turned off at a sharp angle, dropped down and started to crawl on his belly. Here the scent was so strong Copper burst into full cry, lifting his head as he ran in hopes of seeing his quarry. Instead, a flock of sheep exploded in front of him. A belligerent ram stood threatening, head down. As the trail led right under him, Copper grabbed the stupid beast by the wool around his neck, dragged him to one side and continued on. But the panicky animals had virtually obliterated the line with their pungent odor.

In disgust Copper made a long cast around the fence. He finally picked up the line again where the fox had gone under the fence. He had crawled in among the sheep and watched Copper come up. Then when Copper started to make his cast, he had back-tracked and headed toward his regular run.

Copper began to bay again, in indignation at the trick as much as in satisfaction at hitting the line. He came to a place where the fox had run up a half-fallen tree. Copper jumped clumsily on the trunk and followed the scent until he came to the end, five feet above the ground. Here the fox had apparently jumped off. But Copper knew this trick. He turned and retraced his steps. Just as he had suspected, the fox had run to the end of the log, turned and backtracked. Copper followed the double line to a point where there was only a single trail and started off.

Soon he came to a place where the fox had obviously run around in circles, hoping to leave such a tangle of trails that the hound would be hours unraveling them. But Copper simply made a long cast around the place, knowing the fox would have to come out somewhere. He soon struck the fresh, straight trail and burst into a little clearing. There was a crackling in the frozen ferns ahead, and the smell of fox hit him like a blow. The fox had been lying in the ferns, confident that the hound could never read the riddle of the log and the tangle.

The fox burst from cover and ran along the slash below a high-tension line. He went through a hole in an overgrown fence and suddenly put on speed, Copper close behind. The hound knew they were coming to a crossing; he recognized the multiflora hedge where one of the gunners had been stationed.

At once, Copper put forth his utmost speed, at the same time changing his rather perfunctory baying to a loud cry in order to alert the man ahead. It was crucially important for the fox to be pressed as hard as possible coming into the crossing, as otherwise he would have time to detect the presence of the waiting man.

The thorny stems of the hedge hung down in a veil, and under them the fox had made a run that was almost a tunnel. Copper was too big to follow him there; so he ran paralleling the hedge.

Two farm dogs rushed out of a barnyard and ran barking toward Copper. Thinking he was running from them, they closed in, snapping and snarling, and to his annoyance Copper found himself involved in a dogfight with the ignorant curs. The three furious animals spun in a circle, rearing up as each dog tried to get higher than the other for the back-of-the-neck grip, and then falling, to roll together on the grass. Copper did his best, but he was outmatched. Disengaging himself, he ran, the curs chasing him victoriously across a field and under a barbed-wire fence. This was the limit of the farm, so they stopped, barking loudly and threatening all sorts of punishments if he ever dared return. Finally they trotted back to the barn, shoulder to shoulder, feeling proud of themselves.

Stiff and shaken, Copper returned to the fox's line. As he approached the crossing, he winded the gunner. That meant that the fox had done the same, and Copper followed the trail with a sinking heart. Yes, the fox had avoided the crossing and gone over the road a quarter of a mile farther down. There was nothing for it but to keep on and hope for the best. After all, there were two more crossings, and at one the Master was sure to be waiting.

Copper knew from experience that from now on the fox would be doubly cautious at all crossings. But when Copper sensed a weakening of the scent, he felt a thrill of exultation. Scent fades with a weakening fox. Copper's baying increased in tempo, pitch and volume.

The fox tried backtracking again, and then headed for the log crossing over the stream where the second gunner had been posted. Copper had almost reached it when he saw the man stand up from his ambush. Copper's nose told him the fox had already passed. After his long vigil, the man had taken his eyes off the log for a moment, and of course it was in that instant that the fox had slipped by. Raging, the hound crossed the log. There was still the Master. He would not relax for a second with a fox running, and he never missed.

The fox took advantage of his lead to make for a swamp, where he left another maze of trails. The swamp was too big for Copper to circle it and pick up the trail; he had to work it out. But the job was not hard, for the sun had melted the frozen mud and there were puddles that held the scent beautifully. The fox had doubled in and out, but Copper could tell the difference between a trail a minute old and one two minutes old, and he was never confused. Copper even got a glimpse of the gray shape as he emerged from the rushes, and for a few wonderful seconds the hound was running across a meadow by sight, telling the whole world of his triumph.

Now the fox tried what were obviously his last tricks. He ran along the bank of a stream and then down into the water. Copper was sure he had not gone downstream, for he would have had to cross a dam of driftwood and there was no scent on the dam. Copper waded up the stream, smelling each rock and water-soaked log, but found nothing. Then he tried the banks. Still nothing. He returned to the last place he had a sure scent: the spot where the fox had gone down into the stream. There was something peculiar about the scent. It was double! The fox had run down to the stream and then backtracked.

The hound backtracked some distance before the double trail stopped, but the fox had not jumped to either side. Ah, the stream! He could jump back into that. For the second time Copper waded into the stream, but now below the dam, and began checking. Mulberries overhung the water, and from their trailing limbs Copper was able to pick up the scent he sought. He followed to the place where the fox had left the stream and resumed his run.

But this had been a long check and the scent was growing cold. Copper hurried on to where the fox had run a hard-topped road. The scent from the pads would not spread on the hard asphalt, but remained in little patches that made tracking difficult. Several times Copper was nearly hit by passing cars, but he remained indifferent to them in his concentration.

The fox had cut into some woods and down a slope. Copper remembered this place. They were coming to another road crossing. There was a sumac tangle here, an ambush, from which the Master would have a perfect shot at the fox as he crossed the rutted dirt road. Once before in this place the Master had shot a fox running before Copper just as this one was doing. Baying with the full force of his great lungs, Copper threw all his powers into catching up and preventing the quarry from hesitating.

Suddenly Copper saw ahead of him the lithe form of the fox speeding toward the road. He broke into the "quarry in sight" cry for the waiting Master. The fox could not turn or stop now with the hound only yards from his brush.

The fox had almost reached the road when down it came an ancient, rattling farm truck, its driver indifferent to the baying hound or the fleeing scud of the fox. Copper saw the fox hesitate. For an instant he thought the animal would dodge in front of the truck, but he swung off to one side.

Bang! A charge of shot struck under the white-tipped brush. The fox leaped convulsively, his hindquarters twisting at right angles, his brush shooting out sideways to act as a counterbalance. Then the brush spun around and around, as though giving him momentum, and the slim form seemed to shoot over the ground without touching it. In seconds he was out of sight.

Copper plunged after him. Had the fox been hit? Copper smelled the odor of the shot mingled with the scent of fear, but no blood. It was useless. The sudden fright had temporarily paralyzed the scent glands. Copper turned sadly back to where he could hear the Master yelling at the truck driver.

CHAPTER 4

ToD LEARNED three lessons from that terrible day which had climaxed with a sting of shot in his hide that itched long afterward. First, he never again used the same lying-up place twice in succession. Second, he detoured around crossings. Last, he learned a number of alternate runs he could use when hunted.

Tod went down a hole to escape only as a last resort. He was always afraid of being bottled up, and perhaps there was even a certain feeling of pride in shaking hounds off fair and square.

Gray foxes had no such pride and when hunted nearly always climbed the first tree, leaving the hounds raging hopelessly below. Once Tod had even seen a gray go up a telephone pole.

Tod was now a full-grown fox, with all his physical powers and enough know-how never to worry where his next meal was coming from. He had reached his adult weight of twelve pounds and was three and a half feet long, including his fifteen-inch brush. He had no natural enemies, for man had exterminated the wolves, lynxes and eagles in his district long ago. So far, he had actually benefited from man's presence. Man had cleared the fields, making ideal country for field mice, rabbits, woodchucks and pheasants—all excellent fox food. The pastures and hedgerows grew an abundance of grasses, berries, wild grapes and other edibles foxes ate almost as often as meat. The farmers also thoughtfully stocked fat, helpless chickens, ducks and geese. Although he seldom bothered the farmers' livestock, Tod was virtually a parasite on men.

Tod usually slept during the day, selecting a high hillside as a lookout. Even when he was fast asleep, he was instantly alert at the first hint of an alien scent. His hearing was incredible— he could detect the squeak of a mouse at three hundred yards, and he could hear a car a mile away. He liked to lie with his long, thin nose resting on his forepaws and his brush straight out behind him. He dozed in quick catnaps, constantly awakening to check the terrain.

At dusk, Tod came fully awake. He stretched, then yawned until his pink tongue curled between his long white canine teeth. Then he stood up and cocked his head on one side with a typical foxy look as he gazed across the valley. Unlike Copper, Tod had excellent vision, but until something moved he could not interpret the details he saw. He depended on his nose and keen ears more than on his eyes.

One evening Tod trotted down the hill to where he had cached a woodchuck killed by a hunter. He had eaten part of the animal and had covered the rest with loose dirt and dead leaves. To his disgust, Tod found that crows had eaten most of his cache. The remainder was not really gamy enough for him; he liked his meat so decayed it would fall apart easily. But he was hungry, and he lay full length, his eyes half closed with bliss, chewing through the tough hide and feeling the bones crunch between his jaws.

Then he played with the carcass, tossing it up, catching it, pretending it was alive so he could worry it, and rolling it about with his long forepaws, which he used almost like hands. Finally he dug a large hole, his forefeet going like pistons, and pushed the carcass in with his long muzzle. Using the side of his muzzle, he swept the loose dirt in place, and afterward tamped it in with forceful blows of his nose. Last, he left his sign, wetting it to mark it as his personal cache.

He continued on his regular route. In the orchard, he found several windfall apples. He patted them to make them roll, and amused himself for nearly half an hour with these delightful toys, making graceful, curving bounds as he came down on them. Tiring of the sport, he grazed a bit and then dived through a rabbit hole under the fence and picked up his route. Customarily his route ran along the edges of fields, partly because Tod felt exposed in the open, partly because by keeping close to the hedgerows he could often cut off rabbits feeding in the open fields.

Several times Tod left his route to visit scent posts. A scent post could be an isolated tuft of grass, a piece of dead wood, a large stone, a tree or a fencepost. It had to be near a run, and never more than three feet in diameter—if it were larger, something might be hiding behind it. Tod approached these scent posts with anticipation. Generally there was no new scent there, and after smelling carefully Tod would leave his sign on the post, to establish the boundaries of his range and also so passing foxes would know about him and would leave their own scents. When another fox *had* been to one of the posts, Tod would sniff the significant odor long and critically.

Tod did not welcome other foxes, male or female, on his range, but he did not violently object to them either. There was plenty of food, and he did not begrudge a stray rabbit or a few mice to visitors. Of course, if another dog fox deliberately took over his territory, using his runs, hunting on his special preserves and scaring away the quarry every night, that was a different matter.

As winter set in, Tod extended his range greatly. He went where the food was, and on bad nights depended on caches placed up and down his runs. During the golden autumn days he had often killed a dozen rabbits a night, and as he never ate more than one he buried the rest. True, Tod was careless about burying his quarry, and the caches were frequently found by raccoons, opossums, skunks, and even crows; but enough were left to give him an almost endless supply when hunting failed.

Tod did some scavenging himself. He investigated garbage dumps, checked roads for animals hit by cars, and knew where the carcasses of three deer lay that had been shot during the season and escaped to die later of their wounds. He also went to barns and outbuildings looking for rats. He was always cautious when near human habitation, for when raiding chicken houses he had learned that humans, too, resented poaching.

Back in late November, Tod had begun to take an increasing interest in the scent of vixens at his posts, often following their trails. During the winter nights he would mount to the top of a rise and give a call in four notes, repeated over and over. Sometimes he would stand with his muzzle up, like a dog baying at the moon; more often he would drop his head almost between his forelegs as he called. The call was sometimes answered by other dog foxes; rarely by the sharp double yap of a vixen. But by January the vixens began to answer more frequently, and their cries took on a squalling note. Tod now had a driving urge that made him call more than ever; the night was full of other dog foxes anxiously calling. The vixens' squalling became tortured and urgent; the males yowled like tomcats.

One night as Tod lay among some frozen weeds, his magnificent brush covering his delicate nose—the only part of him not warmly covered by his thick pelt—he heard a vixen call again and again. Tod pricked his ears, then rose and, trembling with excitement, raced toward the cry.

He found the vixen trotting down the side of a little stream, closely followed by two dog foxes. He ignored them and ran eagerly toward the vixen. She looked him over and then darted away. Tod raced after her and the other two males furiously followed. He caught up with her in a dead-end gully, and she ran to him, crouched, and, squealing hysterically, presented her throat. Tod could tell by her scent that she was considerably older than he was, but only the intoxicating odor mattered.

The other two foxes rushed forward, jostling Tod to one side. But the vixen sprang up, hissed and snapped at them, and then tore away through the woods with all three males after her. Then she ran to Tod again, cringing and crying.

This process was repeated until all four foxes were exhausted. At last one of the rival males remained lying on the ground when the vixen started running. Again she ran to Tod, cringing and screaming. Having only the vaguest idea of the part he was to play, Tod reared and drummed on her with stiff forelegs. The vixen lay motionless, but when the other male tried to approach she rushed at him and bit him savagely. This male, too, disappeared.

Still giving her piercing cries, the vixen returned to Tod and flung herself on her side. The tired, puzzled and somewhat frightened male had no idea what she wanted. Suddenly she charged him with bared fangs. In self-defense Tod bared his own, and at once she submitted; then, seeing he would do nothing else, sprang up and again attacked. By now, Tod was frantic with anger, bewilderment, and some urge he could not understand. He threw himself on the vixen, grabbing her by the back of the neck and shaking her as he would have shaken a rabbit. Then at last instinct asserted itself and they mated.

Afterward, the foxes lay side by side. Half in play, half in affection, Tod threw a long leg over her back, and the vixen turned to lick it. Tod felt a strange sense of proprietary affection toward this half-crazy, puppylike creature. Vaguely he sensed that she was putting herself under his protection and he would have to defend her, much as he had to defend his range. The realization worried him, and he rose and began to trot away.

The vixen promptly sprang up and trotted at his side. Tod had no idea what to do. In a way, he liked her companionship, yet his native desire to be alone was strong. Obviously the vixen had no such doubts; when he quickened his stride she loped along beside him, as though this was her predestined place.

They left the woods and started across the open fields toward Tod's home range. Now the vixen showed signs of nervousness. She whimpered and tried to turn him back by snapping at him. Swinging his muzzle from one side to the other, Tod avoided her bites and kept on. When she persisted, he broke into a run. She soon spun around and headed back to the safety of the woods she knew. Glad to be rid of her, Tod kept on, slowing to a walk. He had gone nearly a mile when he realized the vixen, having found he would not yield, was following him. Far from being flattered, Tod was distinctly annoyed. He thought he'd gotten rid of her.

The stars were taking on a washed-out look, and Tod could smell the coming dawn in the breeze. He was now ravenously hungry. He wanted rich bird meat—not the stringy flesh of rabbits. He remembered a stand of pines where pheasants roosted.

The sun had risen by the time they reached the pines, and to Tod's disappointment the pheasants were awake. He and the vixen dropped flat on their bellies and lay motionless as they watched the pheasants mantle—stretch one leg and one wing together as they prepared to fly down. Wistfully, Tod thought of every trick he knew. None would work with wide-awake pheasants.

Then to his amazement Tod saw the vixen rise and deliberately trot past the pines. A chorus of cackles went up, interspersed with the warning cry of the cocks. The vixen paid no attention and continued on her way. As she passed behind a rise several of the pheasants flew to higher limbs to keep sight of her. She reentered the pines a few yards from the roosting place. The pheasants still watched suspiciously. One young hen flew from one pine to another, crying constantly, afraid to let the predator out of her sight. To follow the vixen among the thick trees, she had to fly lower and lower.

Now Tod slunk forward, watching the hen pheasant, who

still had all her attention on the vixen. When she was only a few feet above the ground, Tod made his rush. As he sprang, the rest of the flock saw him, and from a dozen throats went the shrill danger scream. The hen looked stupidly around for the threat; as she did so, Tod had her by the leg. The vixen hurled herself at the thrashing bird and with one nip broke its neck.

To Tod's outrage, when the pheasant ceased struggling the vixen dragged it away. When Tod tried to assert his rights, the vixen attacked him with such frenzy he gave way. Not until she had eaten her fill was he allowed to approach the bird.

THE VIXEN turned out to be a most useful hunting companion. She would leave him to make a swing around likely territory and drive rabbits to him, and she was amazingly dexterous in herding a flock of pheasants toward him as he crouched in ambush. She would lie by the hole in the fence while Tod went into the orchard. When a rabbit dashed for the hole, she was ready.

With this mutual assistance, a bond grew up between them that slowly ripened into deep affection. The vixen had deliberately selected Tod over the two more sophisticated older males, although it would never have occurred to Tod that the whining, abject female was actually dominating the affair. The vixen's previous mate had died a month before in a trap. Even though they had been faithfully mated for three years, she had at once set out to find a new mate.

CHAPTER 5

THAT spring was raw and wet. The vixen, used, unlike Tod, to the protection of the woods, sought the shelter of overhanging rocks, and during heavy storms even went down holes. Tod regarded this conduct as dangerous. Under the overshoot of a rock, you couldn't see what was coming up behind you, and heavy rain killed scent. Going down a burrow was worse—

you might, as Tod vividly remembered, be trapped there by terriers. But the vixen had been brought up in a district where men were scarce and dogs nonexistent.

At the scent posts, Tod discovered that the vixen violently resented trespassers, so he tried to keep them off his range. His anger, however, was directed toward other males; when he came upon a visiting vixen he was polite. He soon discovered that his mate resented this chivalrous attitude. Once she came upon him with a cowering, squalling vixen, and attacked the husband stealer with an insane frenzy. Tod watched aghast while the two vixens tore at each other, screaming.

The strange vixen went down and Tod expected to see her give the formal token of fox surrender by presenting her jugular. Instead, his mate got the foreigner by the back of the neck and worried her until she lay limp. Finally his mate dropped the corpse on the bloody snow and limped stiffly away, followed by an awestruck Tod. Tod could not know that she was not fighting for prestige or sport, as did the males, but because life would soon be stirring within her. She needed Tod to hold the range and provide food for her pups.

As March came on, the vixen's belligerency increased. There would be plenty of food on the range for the pups, but she savagely begrudged every mouse taken by other foxes. Tod had never hated his quarry, any more than he hated the apples he ate, or the hounds and men who chased him. He only feared them as he might fear lightning. Now, encouraged by the vixen, he began to hate other foxes with a fanatic, unknowing intensity that would last until autumn, when the pups would be on their own.

The vixen wanted him to maintain a range some five miles square; but there were several other dog foxes in the district who were mated to vixens with similar expansive ideas. Fighting broke out along the boundary lines, and by unspoken agreement the dog foxes reduced the ranges to about a square mile. The vixens did not approve, but they were forced to accept the compromise.

So far, Tod's mate was slender and as active as ever, although she no longer liked to play. Tag had been their favorite game, and they would chase each other over the fields and through the woods. Now she began to grow quick-tempered, for the growing pups were draining calcium from her system and the loss made her weak and irritable. After enlarging—and abandoning—many burrows, she at last settled on an empty woodchuck hole in a cover of scrub oaks. The burrow was small, even after she dug it out. The main room was two feet square; there was one entrance, and the passageway was little more than ten feet.

This cramped den struck Tod as a deathtrap. His parents' den had had a network of long passages, and the main room had been twenty by thirty feet. Also, it had been located on the side of a hill, as proper fox dens should be, so the occupants could see for miles around. However, there was no arguing with a female.

The vixen spent a great deal of time remodeling the den and even allowed Tod to help. Both had begun to shed their winter coats; but the thick undercoat matted and clung to them in gray tangles that could not be bitten free. The itching did nothing to steady their volatile tempers.

The vixen was now so swollen that she had trouble getting in and out of the entrance. She made it clear to Tod that his presence was unnecessary, but Tod was too curious to leave the area, so he would lie up nearby during the day. Before going out on his nightly rounds, he would sniff at the hole and cock his head to listen; but neither scent nor sound told him anything except that a very irritable vixen was within.

One evening as Tod walked toward the den, he stopped suddenly. A series of whining yelps was coming from the opening. Tod trotted closer. Yes, there were strange new smells there. Neither the sounds nor scents were foxy; Tod was saved from infanticide only by the vixen, who thrust her nose out of the burrow, hissing and snarling. Tod leaped back and hastily withdrew.

Hunting was good that night, and, knowing the vixen must be hungry, Tod carried a rabbit back to the den as a peace offering. She snatched it without the usual friendly byplay both indulged in with food and dragged it into the den.

Even though he brought her food every night, it was not until two weeks later that the vixen allowed him to inspect her treasures in the den. There were five of them, blind, squirming and helpless. They were not much bigger than mice, but it was obvious the vixen considered them the most remarkable creatures on earth. She nudged them with her nose (an act that produced a storm of excited yelps), and then lay on her side so they could nurse, moving them against her with swipes of her long nose. She watched them nurse with an expression of utter delight.

Tod was again forbidden the den, but he had seen enough to make him wildly proud and excited. He wore himself out bringing food, often far more than the vixen could eat. Feathers began to accumulate in front of the den's entrance, together with woodchuck hides, neatly turned inside out, and rabbit legs.

In spring, game was so plentiful that Tod's only problem was transportation. He carried his kills in his mouth, and when the result of a night's hunting was, perhaps, ten mice, a pigeon, a starling and a muskrat, it would require several trips to get it all to the den. Once, when he was returning with a mouthful of four mice, Tod came on two cock pheasants fighting. Dropping the mice, he got one bird. Then, after some thought, he neatly tucked two mice under each pheasant wing and triumphantly carried the whole load to the den.

It was nearly a month before the pups' eyes opened, which was lucky, for they were such restless little things they would have crawled out of the den in spite of the vixen's best efforts. Their eyes were blue-gray instead of the adult yellow-amber. Their noses were flesh-colored, and they still had their baby teeth. They were clumsy at first, and fell over themselves trying to walk; but at the end of five weeks they could scamper around. The vixen had to become more of a disciplinarian. She began weaning them, and when the most aggressive of the pups rushed at her to demand his right to nurse, she whirled on him with a snarl that made him fall over on his back in astonishment.

The vixen fed the pups by regurgitating food from her stomach. At first she gave them well-digested food, then partly digested, and then almost raw food. Finally she brought them freshly killed prey, carefully ripped open, for the pups' milk teeth could not bite through tough hide.

When the pups were strong enough to scramble about outside, they were delighted, if a little alarmed, by the world beyond the den opening. They nudged stones with their noses, then leaped back terrified when the strange objects rolled. Feathers were safer. They batted them around with their paws, grabbed them as they fluttered down, rolled on them and stole them from each other. The strange smell of the woodchuck hide and rabbit legs—quite different from the odor of the fresh meat their mother had fed them—at first made the pups suspicious, but as they grew older they staged ferocious tugs-of-war with them. The vixen would lie on the earth mound above the den, watching her pups with pride and love.

Tod was nearly as delighted with the pups as his mate, but she was still suspicious and somewhat jealous. By degrees she relented and let Tod play with the pups, but if any of them seemed too pleased with the game, she would grab the offender by the neck and carry him squawling and kicking back to the den.

Mostly the pups played with each other, learned how to use their teeth, how to jump forward and backward in mock fights, and how to employ their long forelegs. They also learned how to grab a moving object, get the best purchase on it and hold it steady for a bite. One of the pups was bigger and more aggressive than the others. As the pups grew older and their playful fights became more serious, he was able to dominate the others. Since foxes are not pack animals, the leadership was not so serious as it would have been among dogs or wolves, and everyone was glad when the problem was solved and they could relax.

The biggest pup was the first to make a "kill." While turning over a rabbit skin, he uncovered a burying beetle. He regarded the scurrying creature, his nose between his forepaws, then knocked it over with one deft pat. The beetle lay kicking while the pup regarded it sideways, not sure what to do next. Ultimately he summoned enough courage to dispatch it with a nip. Then he ate his first quarry proudly and went looking for more. Soon

287

all the pups were beetle hunting among the oaks, knocking dead leaves about and pulling pieces of bark off trees when their noses told them something was underneath. One day a little vixen found the first warm-blooded quarry—a white-footed mouse with squirming young clinging to her, hampering her escape. The scent drove the litter wild, but the vixen managed to keep her quarry and make the kill.

The biggest pup was a bully. Whenever the parents brought in food, dead or alive, he would grab it, and then, if he was not especially hungry, sit on it to keep the others away. But he was his mother's favorite and she indulged his antics. Then one day, when she was not around, Tod brought in a live muskrat. The big pup rushed in, only to receive a bite that sent him away screaming. After that, he was much more cautious.

The pups seldom came out in the daytime. When the sun dropped a head would appear at the den's mouth, with huge ears pricked for the slightest noise and big baby eyes eager and curious. After a careful check, the pup would emerge, followed by the others, and they would start foraging. Sometimes the whole family would race through the woods, Tod leading, followed by the biggest pup, then the vixen, and then the rest of the family in a long line, each stepping conscientiously in the paw marks ahead of him, so that to a casual observer only one fox would seem to have passed. They seemed held together by an invisible string, and no matter how Tod dodged and ducked through the cover, the rest followed him, nose to brush, until all were tired. Then the parents hid dead mice, birds and rabbits in the cover and watched the pups find them.

From the adults the pups learned which creatures were dangerous and which were not. A screaming mother robin diving at your head was not dangerous, for instance, but a great horned owl drifting by on silent wings was. The scent of cattle meant nothing, but the scent of a passing dog did. The pups were highly imitative, and their reflexes were lightning quick.

The parents always approached the den from downwind to detect the presence of any enemy, and checked the cover to see

if humans had found their home. If so, the vixen was prepared to move the pups instantly to another burrow already selected for emergencies. They did not like to call attention to the den by hunting near it, and the farmer's roosters, who could be heard crowing from a nearby farm, were quite safe. On the other hand, with surprising stupidity, the foxes made no attempt to conceal the den entrance, and as the pups grew older they left a series of hunting trails all pointing toward the entrance, like spokes. Refuse also marked the entrance as an occupied den.

The pups learned to catch May beetles and June bugs, making graceful, sinuous observation leaps to clear high grass while watching the progress of their prey. They learned to eat fresh grass, new buds and berries. They discovered that a skunk was not easy prey—although the biggest cub required a demonstration before he was convinced and had to roll in a mud wallow afterward—and that a nest of yellow jackets could not be dug up as casually as an ants' nest. The pups were content to live on easily obtained food, and were so reluctant to hunt big game that at this stage few could have survived the winter, when neither insects nor plants would be available.

The pups' irresponsible behavior often drove Tod and the vixen half mad with exasperation. They insisted on regarding rabbits as animated toys rather than as quarry to be killed as fast as possible. The older foxes knew there was no use spending half a night tracking down a rabbit, for the amount of strength you used up would not equal the amount of strength you obtained from eating the rabbit. Yet there was no way they could pass this knowledge on. Perhaps this was just as well; otherwise the countryside would have been thick with foxes, whereas even if a pair of foxes lived for fifteen years and had an average litter of five cubs a year, probably only two of the pups would survive—enough to take the places of their parents.

So Tod and the vixen had to watch the half-grown idiot pups gaily chasing rabbits they could not hope to catch, and refusing to learn to stalk. It did no good to refuse to feed them—the parents tried that early in the game—for the pups existed nicely on insects, grass and an occasional mouse. As far as the pups were concerned, it would always be summer, and their parents were stupid old codgers to work so hard catching difficult prey.

Finally, however, the biggest pup killed a large quarry. When the nearby farmer planted corn, he left a strip of plowed but unplanted land running parallel to the tall green rows. His guinea hens liked to scratch and take dust baths in the soft soil. The biggest pup discovered that these birds could not fly and began chasing them wildly around the barn. Their frantic squawks brought the small farm dog racing to the scene and the fox pup had to run for his life. After he had recovered from his fright, however, the overconfident pup was still determined to get a hen, although both parents tried to lure him away from the farm.

Through what he considered great cunning, the pup learned to wait in ambush at the edge of the corn rows in early morning, when the hens were released from the chicken house. Before long they would make their way to the plowed land. Gathering himself, the pup would make a lightning rush. One crunch of his long, thin jaws and the hen died instantly, both lungs crushed. The pup would be on his way to the den before the rest of the flock had recovered sufficiently from shock to start cackling. Since the farm dog had not been able to trail him on the plowed earth, the pup paid no attention to the anxiety of his parents.

One morning Tod and the vixen were lying in front of the den with the other cubs when they heard the frenzied cackling of guinea hens in the valley below them. They rose with one accord and sniffed the morning breeze. It brought them the information that the pup was running and the farm dog was trailing him at last. This was a day when scent held well, for it had rained during the night and the moisture still lay on the ground.

The vixen gave a bark that sent the rest of the litter running for the den, and then she and Tod hurried toward the farm. They ducked under a fence and galloped to the top of a hill. A fearful sight met their eyes. The pup, still holding the chicken in his mouth, was running wildly only a few yards ahead of the dog.

Together the foxes charged down the slope and went for the

dog. Fast as Tod was, for once the vixen was faster. She hit the cur so hard she rolled him over. He sprang to his feet and turned on her but now Tod was on him. The fight raged up and down the pasture while the guinea hens went mad from their posts on the barn roof. The pup fled, dropping the chicken at long last.

The vixen and the dog were rolling together on the ground, and Tod had sprung back for a fresh hold when a movement by the barnyard caught his eye. There stood the farmer with a gun. Regardless of the vixen or the pup, Tod turned and bolted for the fence—a flicker over the close-cropped grass. He heard the report of the gun and instinctively flinched, but the shot hit ahead of him. As he flung himself under the fence, he heard the second barrel go off. The farmer had fired at the vixen. Afraid of hitting the dog, he had again aimed too high and she also escaped.

Tod took care to tangle his trail before heading for the cover. When he got there he found the exhausted pup and vixen already in the den. He and the vixen licked each other's wounds, but Tod refused to stay long. He hated being underground, and ran through the cover, constantly testing the wind and listening for distant sounds.

Two hours later, he heard the noise he feared more than anything else in the world except the crack of a gun—the deep, bell-like voice of Copper. Tod stopped, frozen, one foot upraised. Then he ran to a hill where he could overlook the valley. He saw that Copper was following the pup's trail. With him was the farmer and Copper's Master—even at that distance Tod recognized him by his movements. Both had guns.

Tod waited until the hound was hidden from the hunters by a line of wild cherries overgrown with grapevines, and then ran toward him. He deliberately crossed upwind of the hound, and Copper got the full scent and sight of the accursed fox he and the Master had been after so long. He burst into the "view cry" and rushed after the fleeting form. The clumsy hound could not possibly overtake Tod, so the fox ran just ahead of Copper, luring him away from the den.

They had gone only a few hundred yards when Copper heard

a commanding call. The Master had broken open his shotgun and was blowing across one of the barrels, producing a deep note with great carrying power. The call was repeated insistently, and Copper reluctantly turned back. Frustrated, Tod ran for the den. He tried to show the vixen by his actions that their only safety lay in flight, but she ignored him. She had never been hunted by hounds and she had no confidence in her young mate. Instead, she sent the pups into the den.

The cry of the hound drew nearer. Now came the terrible man scent and the stench of the hound. Tod knew it was too late to save the litter; he and the vixen would have to save themselves. He tried to entice her away, but she was utterly bewildered. She ran into the den to the pups and then burst out again to listen. Finally, ignoring Tod, she dashed off recklessly to lure the hound away. Tod made a last effort to get the pups out of the den and start them running. Then he made a circle through the oak cover, keeping downwind of the dog.

He heard Copper lead the men to the den, sniff at the mouth, and give the bark that meant the quarry had been brought to bay. Copper's Master stayed there but the farmer left. Tod heard the vixen running back and forth among the oaks, trying to decoy Copper away. At last not even the Master's discipline could control the hound and he took out after her. His voice faded in the distance.

Now came the sound of a farm truck toiling up the hill. The farmer drove it as far into the oaks as he could. The two men ran a long hose from the truck's exhaust to the burrow, thrust the end into the hole and padded it with old clothing. The truck engine was allowed to run. Soon the stink of the car fumes seeped up through the ground.

Tod went to find the vixen. He barked from several hilltops, but there was no answer. At last he heard the faraway baying of the hound. Tod was able to cut ahead of the dog, and found his mate crouching in a ditch, absolutely exhausted and covered with mud. He licked her face, but she was too beaten to respond. Tod ran back, easily taking the hound off her line, for she was so tired her scent was very faint. He baffled Copper by running a wall and leaping into a tree that overhung it, leaving Copper no scent clue of any kind.

After nightfall, when the hound had given up, Tod went back to the den. The vixen had dug up the bodies of the cubs and laid them out in a row. Their coats were damp where she had licked and licked, trying to restore them to life. Beside the biggest pup was a fresh-killed chicken she had gotten from the barnyard, hoping the odor of his favorite quarry might revive him. All night she worked over them. It was not until morning, when the blow-flies came, that she gave up; and even then, for days afterward she returned to the den, vainly hoping the cubs would once again run out to greet her.

CHAPTER 6

WINTER struck early and hard that year. The frozen ground hurt the foxes' pads, and at night the intense cold "froze" scent so the foxes were forced to hunt in the warmer daylight. The scent world had changed. The habits of their quarry also changed. Rabbits crouched in brush piles or even in drainpipes. Game birds roosted deep in honeysuckle tangles. The foxes might not have survived had it not been for their teamwork. If they passed a drainpipe under a road, for instance, one fox would stand at one end of the pipe while the other ran through to chase out any rabbits. The intense cold gave both foxes magnificent deep pelts of orange, lemon, ebony and ivory, but on the very worst days even Tod had to take refuge in a burrow.

One morning, while Tod was running along a high ridge, he saw the Man and Copper following his route along a fence line. The Man had a pack basket on his back, but no gun. After waiting until the Man was out of sight, Tod trotted down the hill and began to trail him, stepping in his tracks, a game Tod enjoyed. Then Tod stopped suddenly. He had recognized the strong odor of fish oil—Tod had caught an occasional sunfish during summer droughts when pools were low.

Still following the Man's trail, he caught two more odors—the scent of fox urine and the delicious smell of decayed woodchuck. Such strong smells fascinate a fox. Looking up, Tod saw ahead of him the unmistakable cache of another fox. He was outraged. This was his own hunting ground. Fearful that the intruder might still be about, he approached cautiously. He could see where the other fox had scratched the ground in front of the cache with his hind feet after leaving his scent marker, for there was a V of torn earth, the apex at a thistle and the sides stretching away from it toward Tod's trail. He would teach this interloper a lesson by stealing his cache.

Ordinarily, Tod would have scented the fish-oil lure from his usual route and would have approached the V through the open end. But because he had been following the Man, he came in from behind. With no trouble, he dug up the piece of woodchuck and bolted it. Although most of the fish-oil scent was concentrated in the cache, a few drops had fallen in the open V. Thinking there might be another cache, Tod began to dig.

Suddenly there was an explosion. Something leaped up through the loose dirt ahead of him and two jaws flashed together with a terrible snap. Tod went straight up in the air, landed on all four feet, and fled like a flicker of light. Then, seeing he was not pursued, he made a long swing and came slowly back.

The thing was lying motionless on the ground. Tod inched in. The thing smelled of butternut wood and smoke, with a faint scent of iron. Tod had no fear of iron. He had often run across horseshoes, crawled under manure spreaders, and used iron fences as scent posts. Very carefully, he extended one paw and poked the thing. By now he was convinced that it was lifeless in spite of the way it had moved. A chain was attached to it, and fastened to a stake. After failing to pull the stake up, Tod contemptuously left his mark on the whole affair.

Curious rather than alarmed, he continued to track the Man. Half a mile farther on, he smelled the fish oil again and came on another of the curious caches. Profiting from his previous experience, Tod swung around to unearth the cache. Then curiosity prompted him to see if there was another of the iron things here. With a careful paw, he dug in from the side of the V and, sure enough, touched a hard edge. With fantastic delicacy of touch, he reached under the object and gave it the flip he occasionally used to toss a mouse out of its tunnel. He got his explosion. Feeling proud of himself, he left his mark again.

Tod had now acquired two pieces of delicious woodchuck, well seasoned, and was beginning to enjoy this business. Hurrying on, he found several more caches, each with a buried iron object. He conscientiously sprang them all.

Then Tod found a mink caught by one foot in one of the traps. The tortured animal was rolling on the ground, his teeth scratching on the iron and then tearing at his own foot. Tod ran back and forth, approaching the mink as closely as he dared and then leaping back, half hysterical with excitement. He stayed by the gasping, snarling mink until it was time to return to his lying-up place. Somehow, he understood now, these iron things, though not alive, grasped and held anything they caught.

From then on, Tod made a circuit of the trapline every night. He gained no advantage from springing the traps after eating the bait; he simply enjoyed the excitement, for Tod had an active mind. He delighted in experimenting with unusual objects to see what would happen, and now he grew cocky and overconfident.

Occasionally Tod would find another fox caught, for the trapline was not confined to his range, and because it was winter Tod did not hesitate to trespass on other territories. The sight of a trapped fox invariably drove Tod half mad with anxiety. He would run around crying, and then dig up a cache of food and bring it to the victim. Tod did not precisely feel sorry for the doomed fox, yet the fact that he would bring the fox food showed he was not entirely indifferent to the captive's fate. He was especially attentive to pups, and would often stay with them until his nose told him the Man was coming.

One morning, while Tod was lying up in the lee of a stand of hemlocks, he heard a jay screaming in the valley. There was a special note of insistency in this bird's voice that made Tod suspect he saw a man. Tod swung downwind to investigate.

The Man was making one of the caches. When he finally left, Tod went over to investigate. He could smell the fish-oil lure and the bait—it was muskrat this time. At last he edged in cautiously, checking with eyes and nose and occasionally patting the ground lightly with one extended forepaw before putting his weight on the spot. He reached the edge of the V. He could smell the iron thing under the loose soil. Delicately he scooped out earth to one side of it until he could insert one paw underneath. Then he gave his flip.

Instead of leaping up, the trap went off under the ground and seized his paw: it had been set upside down. But even as the jaws closed, Tod threw himself backward and his foot tore free. Tod stood staring at the partly exposed trap. Then in a blind fury he tore it up by the chain and shook it like a rabbit.

Tod left the trapline alone for a couple of days because his foot was sore; but the temptation to outwit the Man proved so strong that on the third morning he went back to the line. So sensitive was his touch that he could tell by feeling the edges of the traps how they were set. If they were set in the normal way, he flipped them up from below. If they were set upside down, he dug down until he reached the release catch and jarred it loose. For two nights he systematically sprang all the traps on the line, confident now that he understood the whole system.

The next night Tod found a cache freshly baited, and located the trap without trouble. He dug under it. It was upside down, so Tod began to dig in from above. A trap jumped to meet him and the jaws flew shut on his paw. There was another explosion under the trap. Two traps had been set, one above the other. The top one, right side up, had caught him.

The traps were now chained to a drag that moved with the trap, so Tod could not free himself by a quick jerk, as he had done before. In his fear and agony, Tod ran blindly, the drag bumping behind him. Going at top speed, he tore between two rocks and the drag caught. There was a jerk that flung Tod down, but when he got up the trap had been torn from his paw.

Tod limped for many days. Yet, incredibly, he returned to springing traps, for he needed excitement almost as much as he did food. When Tod was playing with a trap, little spasms of ecstasy trembled through him as the threat of imminent danger sent adrenaline through his veins. It was to those pulsing shots of adrenaline that Tod owed his quicksilver reflexes, and his whole being revolved around them. He was prepared to run great risks to obtain that thrill.

Tod now worked out a new trap-springing technique. Using the side of his paw and employing delicate surface strokes, he would brush away the loose dirt covering the pan that would spring the trap. Once the trap was uncovered, Tod could see how best to deal with it. He began to notice a new odor, the acrid scent of metal where the rough edges of the pin and release catch had been filed away to give the trap a hair-trigger set. But he had developed so fine a touch at uncovering the pan that no matter how lightly the trap might be set he did not spring it accidentally. Now Tod was sure man had nothing more to show him.

One evening, as Tod lay brushing the loose earth from a trap chained to a stake, he felt something prick his paw. When he jerked his paw away, the thing's curved tip clung to his fur and set off the trap. A fishhook had been soldered to the pan. This time Tod was caught.

He spun around and ran, but when he came to the end of the chain he was thrown down with a force that sent spasms of torture up his leg. Now it was Tod's turn to tear at the iron jaws, to bite at his own leg, to tear up the ground in a circle around the immovable stake, and finally to fall exhausted and panting on the snow. Time and again he rushed the full length of the chain, only to be brought down; but each abrupt yank jerked his foot a fraction of an inch clear. No sound escaped him in spite of his almost unbearable pain. Finally the chain did not yank him back, and he went on, falling, recovering, still making wild rushes, unable to realize that at last he was free.

He felt himself falling, and hit ice-cold water. The shock brought him to his senses. Too weak to struggle, he let the current carry him downstream. A bridge of ice had formed across the stream, and here he dragged himself on the shore. Whenever he tried to stand, his leg buckled. Foot by foot he wormed his way through a pine watershed, found an old woodchuck hole he knew and crawled down. There he lay for two days.

The vixen, casting about through the woods, hit his trail and followed it to the burrow. She seemed more annoyed than sympathetic, snarling and hissing at the burrow's mouth, although when she wriggled down the hole she licked his injured foot. Then she went hunting for herself. She brought him no food that night, but the next evening she arrived with a rabbit. Tod was now furiously hungry, and when the vixen crouched down by the burrow and started to eat the rabbit Tod pulled himself out and attacked her. After a hissing, snapping, screaming session the vixen retreated while Tod bolted the food. From then on she fed him regularly, and gradually Tod recovered. No bones had been broken, although he would always favor that foot, especially after a hard run. At last Tod had learned his lesson. He stopped playing with traps, avoided the caches of other foxes, not knowing for sure if they were genuine or a trapset, and was alarmed by the mere scent of old iron.

In midwinter there came a severe blizzard, and for once the foxes were hard pressed for food. Territorial boundary lines were forgotten as all foxes roamed the countryside. They found corn-cobs and a few forgotten windfall apples, and even chewed the bark of branches; but the craving for meat grew intense. Even a mouse became a valuable catch, and every morning there were fresh tracks around the farmers' chicken houses, which were seldom bothered in better times.

Then one evening Tod and the vixen found a dead sheep. Scavengers had already been feeding on it but hungry as they were, the foxes circled the carcass, testing every wisp of breeze, not daring to approach within fifty yards. They returned the second night, and came within twenty yards. A dog had been feeding on the sheep, tramping down the snow and leaving his heavy scent. Obviously nothing had happened to him. Even so, the foxes were not yet convinced. On the third night the foxes could resist the remaining meat no longer. Yet they did not go straight in to it. Characteristically, they headed for a little mound that overlooked the carcass to study the situation.

As they bounded up the slope, Tod abruptly checked. There was no man scent, yet there was a certain quality about a bare patch at the top of the mound that reminded him of the deadly Vs. He hung back. Unhesitatingly, the vixen ran to the top. The earth leaped up. The vixen rose in the air, fell, and tried to run, but the trap had her. Frantically she rushed to and fro; the stake chain was short, and she could not get up enough momentum to jerk free. She tore at the steel jaws. It was useless. Tod ran about helplessly near her all night. He stayed with the gasping, doomed vixen until, at dawn, he saw the distant figure of the Man with Copper at his heels. Then he slipped away. He returned that night, but the vixen was gone and the smell of death was heavy on the mound.

TOD ONCE again began to listen for the sound of a vixen, but although he spent hours barking from hilltops, no female answered. Trapping had decimated the fox population and the remaining dog foxes were desperate. Several drifted away to search for mates elsewhere, but Tod hated to abandon his beloved range.

One night, trotting down a well-padded trail by a laurel thicket, Tod found a vixen. She was young, and so starved her coat seemed to hang on her in folds. Her brush was ragged; her pads were worn, her flanks hollow, her eyes hot. She lay on the ground with hardly energy enough to snarl, and showed no interest in Tod. Tod went off and brought back a squirrel he had cached. After a long time the vixen ate it, snarling at him as she did so.

They did not mate until the next night, although Tod never left her side and had to drive off two other males during the long wait. Afterward, she followed him docilely enough, treading in his exact tracks and humbly accepting anything he offered her.

He showed her his regular routes and the boundaries of his range, and by spring they were an old, established married couple.

Traps were still laid for him, but Tod avoided them all, for the Man had to leave some traces of scent. He even took to wearing rubber boots, but Tod came to associate the smell of rubber with the human, and avoided it.

When spring came and his new vixen showed an interest in burrows, Tod decided this time to select the location of the den himself. He was bent on raising this litter, though he no longer felt confident of being able to outwit the Man.

CHAPTER 7

For several days, Copper had been aware of a growing sense of excitement. Men had been coming to the cabin who smelled of dogs and horses. Whenever the Master brought them up to meet him, Copper sniffed the strangers' trouser legs with interest. The men did not smell of sweat and manure, and he had never smelled dog or horse odors like these. The animals must be kept on a different diet.

The strangers spoke in shrill, fast voices, unlike the drawls Copper knew, and when the Master spoke to them he sounded nervous and respectful. Copper knew these strangers wanted something that would involve his services, for they showed great interest in him. When they left, Copper would jump frantically on the Master and try to lick his face to show that he would do his best for the Master, and the Master would pat him and speak comfortingly. As long as the Master loved and had confidence in him, Copper did not care about anything else.

One morning, while he and the Master were returning from the trapline, he heard the sound of a new kind of horn. There was a crackling in some half-frozen sumac bushes and hounds began to appear out of the cover, followed by men on horseback, talking and laughing.

Several of the hounds ran over to him, wagging their tails, the skin on their foreheads pulled taut by their open, grinning jaws. Copper stood stiff-legged, his tail rigid, scowling, his massive forehead ridged with wrinkles. These strange hounds were too friendly: there were certain formalities to be observed when dogs met. Also, Copper had never seen so many dogs together in his life. From the way they exchanged signals by motion of heads, tails and bodies, Copper knew they were used to working as a pack—they even smelled as though they all slept together. They seemed to have no individuality. Copper was relieved when, to a blast from the horn, horsemen and pack moved off.

Several mornings after this chance meeting Copper and the Master got in the car and started off before sunrise. The Master stopped the car at a crossroads, and Copper smelled the odor of horses, people, hounds, and the exhausts of cars. When the Master opened the door, Copper jumped out somewhat doubtfully.

There were three buildings at the crossroads: a country store, a shipping shed, and a farmer's house under a stand of elms with the farmer and his family sitting on the steps. The children knew Copper and shouted to him. Copper indulgently waved his tail, but he was concentrated on the pack, assembled behind a rider and guarded on the sides by two more riders with long whips in their hands. There seemed to be cars and horses everywhere.

The Master went over to talk to the rider in front of the pack, and Copper followed. He knew at once that these hounds were going hunting; they were intent on the huntsman and yawning with nervousness. At long last the huntsman sounded his horn and rode away, the pack following him in a compact mass, picking their way among water-filled ruts. The men with whips came next, and then the field trailed along behind. Many of the cars followed down the road.

The Master spoke to him and cut across country headed for a ridge, his boots crunching through the frozen snow that streaked the hillside. Copper followed, thankful to be alone, stepping in the man's footmarks to save breaking through the crust. On top of the hill was a dogwood grove. Copper dropped his nose to sniff briefly at a rabbit track, and then hit the line of a fox. He almost broke into a bay, but an instant's check told him the scent was really a couple of hours old.

They reached the grove and halted. The riders and hounds were mounting the hill below them, upwind of the cover. The huntsman shouted to the pack and waved his arm, and they broke their tight formation and bounded into the cover, spreading out as they did so. Copper trembled with excitement. He longed to go in too, but the Master had said nothing.

Crows had begun screaming somewhere over the field beyond the dogwood grove. At the sound, the Master gripped Copper by the neck and ordered him to stay. The Master began calling urgently, yet without daring to shout, to someone. A gust of wind swept up the hill and hit Copper full in the face. There it was! The fox he and the Master had sought so long was somewhere around! And he was running. The burst of energy had thrown his scent into the wind, and he was scudding across the field, doubtless with the crows wheeling and diving around him.

The Master dragged Copper across the field and, pointing to a spot in a furrow, said, "Here, boy, here!" Copper applied his nose and instantly smelled where the fox had been lying. He must have stolen out of the cover, run a few yards into the field and then, seeing riders ahead of him, hidden in the furrow.

Copper promptly gave tongue; but once he left the spot where the fox had crouched, the scent vanished. The fox must have run along one of the ridges left by the plow, and the turned earth held no scent. But Copper checked, and found the wind had blown the scent into the furrow beside the ridge. Here he could just barely follow it. Behind him, he could hear the huntsman laying on the pack.

The fox had next crossed to a cutting and run down it. Copper was nearly trampled by the riders, who belted down the cutting at full gallop and paid no attention to him or the Master. They went on to cross a stream that was a brown torrent from the melting snows. Here were several riderless horses tearing along wild-eyed, and men who were remounting, the backs of their coats plastered with mud. As far as Copper was concerned, this was the last time he was going hunting where horsemen were involved.

There was a good run next over open fields, and the foxhounds streamed away with the riders after them. They must have gone half a mile when several riders shouted. The pack raised their heads at the yells, as did Copper. Then he saw the fox, moving ahead of them with small, neat strides unlike the leaping drive of the hounds, who now broke into the viewing cry. The fox's tongue was lolling, but at the sound of the bloodthirsty cry he put on a fresh burst of speed and flashed away out of sight in seconds.

Mad with excitement, Copper extended himself to his utmost. Now was the time to force the exhausted fox to the limit. Gasping and forcing his tired legs forward, he crossed a road, made a wide swing and picked up the line where the fox had gone on. He was about to speak on it when another scent hit him. The fox had made a swing and doubled back. He was making short, tired turns now. Ignoring the line entirely, Copper cut across country, following the airborne scent, and giving tongue. The huntsman instantly sent the pack to him. They were only seconds behind the fox now and nothing could save him.

The cry of the hounds took on a shrill, angry note and Copper lifted his head. There was the fox. His brush hung low; his back was arched; his head was down; his jaws dripped white slime. Forced out of his usual range, he was running blindly through a new housing development. As the pack hurled themselves forward people ran out of doors, children screamed, and dozens of pet dogs barked hysterically. None of the people seemed to notice the shadowy form of the fox as he glided through hedges and around trees.

As the horsemen and the pack tore through the development, screaming women clutched their children, and men shouted at the riders and kicked at the hounds. Utterly bewildered, Copper swerved, made a detour and tried to come up with the fox again, but now there were people everywhere; and, judging from the sound, the pack had gotten into a fight with the local dogs.

A car with a siren and flashing light on top came roaring up the street, and Copper decided to get out of there fast.

It took him two hours to lick himself clean. When the Master finally returned and Copper heard the tone of his voice, the hound hid trembling in his barrel kennel. As the Master did not call him, Copper knew his fury was directed elsewhere, but even so the wise Copper decided to keep out of his way.

CHAPTER 8

It was spring and Tod was feeling content with himself because after a long and diligent search he had found a large patch of saw-toothed grass and grazed it down like a sheep. He had been increasingly troubled by worms as the winter progressed, and the grass cleaned them out, so he now experienced a feeling of well-being he had not known for weeks.

Tod had good reason, in any case, to feel relaxed. At this time of year there were no traps set, no one was hunting him, there was plenty of food, and the vixen had recently given birth to a fine litter of pups in a den Tod had selected himself. The den, used by generations of foxes, was among a heap of boulders that could not be dug out and had eight well-hidden escape tunnels. The vixen had meekly accepted Tod's choice.

One morning early, Tod trotted to the top of a hogback ridge where there was always a cross-current of air, to get the scent picture. He sat down with his brush curled around his feet to look out over the valley. Roosters were crowing in a distant farmyard, and a red squirrel raved at him from an oak, his tail and hind legs jerking convulsively. Tod rose and continued on his way. He checked a few scent posts, heard the thump of a rabbit and, just for sport, chased the flickering white tail until the rabbit went down a hole. There was a commotion underground; a woodchuck was in the hole and was blocking the rabbit. Tod started to dig, his forefeet flying. He forced himself down the hole and, by making a long stretch, was just able to grab the rabbit. He headed for his den with it, galloping up the hillside stained with flowers. After listening at the mouth of the burrow, he dropped the rabbit inside.

This was the vixen's first litter, and she was so worried over her offspring that she never came outside. Tod heard her come up the pipe and drag the rabbit down into the main den. He listened with his head cocked on one side until he heard the pups mewling, and then trotted off contentedly to lie up some fifty yards from the den, where he could keep an eye and nose on things.

At dusk he rose and stretched, shooting out his claws, and then went over to sniff at the den. He heard nothing, but because the smells were right he went hunting in a cheerful frame of mind.

By a pond, he came upon a Canada goose grazing on the tender new grass. Tod pretended elaborate unconcern while all the time approaching the goose by a circuitous course, until finally he sprang for her neck. She threw herself backward, honking loudly, and the gander rushed up the bank from the pond and went for Tod. An infuriated gander was more than Tod was prepared to handle, and he fled across the meadow. The gander retreated with dignity to the pond, where his mate was already afloat.

Swinging around, Tod stole back toward the pond, crept to the top of a little rise and, in the fast-gathering darkness, watched the birds. His ears were up, his lips pulled back in a foxy grin.

Motionless as a stone, he saw the goose swim to the bank and climb to her nest. She carefully removed the gray down with which she had covered the eggs and, after elaborate wriggling, sat down to brood. Tod glided off the hill and crept toward her. It was almost completely dark now and he inched along by means of gentle pushes with his elbows. By imperceptible degrees he reached the nest and gently inserted one exquisite paw under the goose. He found an egg and worked it out until he could slide his nose in and grab it. The goose gargled to herself, but did not realize what was going on. As soon as he had the egg in his mouth, Tod hastily backed away, turned and ran.

He went to one of his favorite eating places and, chewing open one end of the egg, licked out the contents. Then he gamboled around the empty shell in triumph. The whole adventure had contained just enough danger to give it spice. Hugely content with himself, he continued his rounds.

It was only when the stars began to wash out and the dawn breeze stirred the aspens that he remembered that he had a family to feed. He headed for one of several housing developments that had mushroomed in the neighborhood over the past year or so. Tod at first had been suspicious of these places, but his curiosity caused him to investigate them and he found that they were an excellent source of food. In the nearest development, he made a cursory check of several yards that had once had pens containing rabbits, chicks or ducklings. Tod had cleared them all out and they had still not been restocked. He went to several doorsteps where milk bottles had been left. With quick blows of his long nose, he drove in the cardboard lids and lapped up the milk as far as his thin muzzle could reach.

He then made a tour of the garbage cans. By standing on his hind legs and bracing his forefeet against the side of a can, he could pry the lid off with his all-purpose nose. In one can Tod found a real prize, a chicken carcass with plenty of meat on it. Tod stuffed several tidbits inside the carcass. Then he took it home, stopping to slash at a house dog that had come tearing out of its kennel, screaming its stupid head off. He dropped the chicken at the mouth of the den and waited until he saw the vixen appear, sniff at it, and then pull it in. Satisfied that she had accepted his offering, he headed for his lying-up spot.

Peaceful day now followed peaceful day until the time came when the pups were able to make short excursions from the den. When the long shadows stretched out at twilight they would tumble out of the den and frolic while the vixen watched them with a devoted, happy expression that was as clearly defined as Tod's mischievous grin.

The only bad days for the litter were rainy ones. Then the active pups, cooped up in the den, were miserable. One pup would crawl up the entrance burrow and sit with the raindrops pelting off the end of his nose, dolefully regarding the weather. Before long, one of his litter mates would drag him away by his brush and take his place, hoping to detect some change. When the sun did finally break through, the whole litter would come bobbing out to cavort in the open.

Tod was an excellent provider. He brought in far more food than the family could eat, and the den area became littered with putrefying carcasses surrounded by haloes of buzzing bluebottle flies. Although the foxes enjoyed the smell of carrion, ultimately the den became too odoriferous even for them and they moved to another burrow. By now the pups were half grown, and old enough to travel on their own. They followed their parents to the new quarters in single file.

Now came the training period. The pups learned to distinguish between taste and smell—no easy task, for these two senses are coordinated. At first, they handled everything with their teeth and tongues to get the taste. Later, one quick sniff told them all they needed to know. They watched their parents, duplicated their actions, and were able to communicate an astonishing amount of information by their brushes, facial expressions, body movements, angle of ears, and even by their fur—when raised, it meant danger.

When the time came for more formal lessons in hunting, either Tod or the vixen took them out one at a time, as foxes never hunt in packs, only in pairs. It had been a warm, dry spring, and many little truck gardens had been planted near the housing developments, so there were plenty of rabbits about. As a result, hawks and owls began to move into the area in great numbers. Often, the foxes would hear the agonized scream of a rabbit in the grip of great talons. Assured of an easy meal, they would drive off the winged predator and appropriate the catch.

Before long, the pups were hunting mainly on their own, although the family still used the den area as a rallying ground. Tod paid no attention to the truants. When winter came he would have to drive the male pups, at least, off the range, so the sooner they left of their own volition the better.

Tod was trotting along a timbering slash when he heard the distant squeal of a rabbit repeated over and over again. He loped off to investigate. But somehow the squealing of this rabbit did not sound exactly right. Tod circled the spot carefully, and as he came downwind of the noise he tasted the taint of man in the air.

However, Tod's curiosity was stronger than his fear. He sneaked through the cover toward the sound. A slight motion caught his eye. The Man was sitting behind a small bush, and kept almost as motionless as Tod, but at intervals he raised something to his lips. When he did, there came the scream of a rabbit. After a few calls, the Man lowered the object and waited.

There came a rustling in the undergrowth, and one of Tod's half-grown pups burst out, looking around eagerly for the rabbit. With one swift, easy motion the Man raised his gun and fired. The pup leaped into the air, dragged himself a few feet and then collapsed. Tod had seen enough. He glided away through the cover. Not until winter set in with full force and made hunting difficult did he pay any attention to rabbit screams.

A few weeks later there was only one pup left. Tod knew now what was happening to them, but there was no way he could tell the vixen. She was frantic, and spent long hours following the trails of the missing pups. Tod knew it was useless, yet only by ignoring the calls himself could he attempt to transmit his own knowledge of the Man. One evening while Tod was investigating one of his scent posts he heard the agonized scream of a fox pup. He raced toward the sound, his mane standing up with rage and his teeth bared. He struck a game trail through the forest and flashed along it, reckless of possible danger. The sound grew louder and he had almost reached the spot when the vixen cut in front of him. She, too, was racing to the rescue.

Ahead were a clearing and the remains of a lumberman's cabin. It was from this clearing the cry was coming. The vixen exploded out of the cover and paused for a moment to look around, standing with one forepaw upraised and her ears cocked. Instantly there came the stinging crack of a rifle. The vixen dropped where she stood, dead before she hit the ground.

Tod turned just in time. The plaintive cry of the pup still continued, and in spite of his terror Tod circled the clearing. Now, together with the scent of the gunpowder, he could smell the Man. Tod saw him go over and pick up the vixen. Then he went to a square box and lifted some sticklike object. At once the noise of the pup's crying ceased. The Man removed a flat disc, put it carefully in an envelope, disconnected the amplifier and carried it and the phonograph to a car. Taking the vixen's body with him, he drove away. In the following weeks Tod heard the pup's crying repeated several times in different parts of his range, but, hearing the surface noises of the record, he was never fooled again.

When winter came Tod was chased several times by small packs of dogs from the new housing developments. He would perform some simple trick to give himself a brief lead and then lay down a perfect cat's cradle of tracks, only to jump clear at the end and canter off to the top of a little hill where he would watch the fun, grinning broadly as the baffled dogs ran in futile circles. When they showed signs of giving up in discouragement, Tod would run a few paces down the hill and give his short, sharp bark to attract their attention. Then, as the pack took after him in full cry, he would whisk away to repeat the trick elsewhere. The dogs usually grew tired of the game before Tod did.

THE FIRST snowfall came early that year. Tod was lying up on the hogback ridge under the black oaks fast asleep, and did not even take the trouble to move as the flakes came drifting down except to bury his nose deeper in his fur. A squirrel ran along a dead pine, his claws scratching loudly on the bark, but Tod slept on. A buck and two does trotted past. Tod never moved a muscle. Human noises came: men shouting to each other on a farm, the swish and roar of cars on a highway. Tod was dead to the world.

Then came a faint—oh, so faint—grinding sound of snow packing under the gentle tread of a man's boots. Tod was awake and gone in a wink. In seconds, not worrying about heading into the wind, he was over the nearest ridge.

Once he was protected by the ridge, he slowed and circled downwind to test his back track with nose and eyes. It was possible that the human meant no harm and would not follow him. But a fleck of snow leaped up beside him, and with it came the report of a gun. The shot came from Tod's side of the ridge, so it could not have been fired by the man he had heard. He did not know from where it had been fired, so, at random, he shied to the left. As he did so, he caught the unmistakable scent of man right ahead. He turned again and ran back. There was a man with a gun on the ridge now.

So there were three men, one on either side and one tracking. Tod turned and ran in his original direction, going all out. Another shot, and a hole appeared in the snow almost under his nose. He could smell the stench of powder. He ran as he had never run before. Another shot sounded far behind him.

Tod ran for nearly a mile before slowing down. He jumped on a stump to watch his back track. When nothing moved after half an hour, he decided the men had given up. He quartered the area for a good lying-up place, and picked the base of a choke-cherry where the wind had left a spot fairly free of snow.

An hour passed and Tod dozed off. Then he heard the angry scolding of a jay, and was instantly alert. He saw the figures of men moving on both his left and his right. Then he saw, farther away, the third man following his track in the snow. Tod had a wide range of vision, so he could watch all three men at the same time without moving his head. The tracker waved his hand to the others and pointed down. They waved back and started forward while the tracker waited until they were well advanced.

Tod saw the man on his left suddenly stop, stare at him, and then start to raise his gun. Tod waited for no more. He ducked around the tree and started running again. There was no shot, but he went nearly three miles before lying up. He hid in the heart of a hazel thicket heavily overgrown with wild rose. For a long time he remained awake and listening, but finally, deciding the chase was surely over, he fell asleep.

Here there was no jay to scream a warning. Instead, he heard the crackle of the bushes on either side of him. Tod waited only long enough to make certain of the men's positions and that the tracker was with them before slipping away. This time he kept right on going; and when he did finally lie up, he stayed awake until it was almost dark and the men had given up.

Tod now added the humans' technique of still-hunting to his list of dangers. It was not the tracker who was the menace but the men on the flanks. From now on, when he was disturbed, Tod ran with an eye out to both the right and left.

CHAPTER 9

As the years passed, the countryside contin- ued to change. Tod hated the changes. His was basically a world of sound and scent; and when the sounds and scents altered he felt lost and bewildered. Now he found his familiar trails cut by highways, new buildings and other strange objects.

Every year, scenting grew more difficult. Huge, stinking bull- dozers tore the guts out of the land and when they were finished they left great rivers of concrete over which poured a constant flow of traffic, filling the air with fumes that polluted all other odors. Most of the trees had been cut down, and the air became dry, hot and lifeless. Nearly all the farms were gone, their places taken by the housing developments or by gigantic factories that added their quota of pollution to the atmosphere.

The people who were moving in were unlike the people Tod had known. They came in great hordes as though fleeing some terrible natural catastrophe, like animals running before a forest fire. As with all fugitives, there was an air of panic about them. Instead of going about standard tasks like the farmers, they rushed around in pointless activities, always in automobiles. They raised no food, they kept no animals—except countless dogs— and as the houses increased the groundwater level sank until the earth was hard under Tod's feet. There was an unpleasant taste to the streams; the fish were dead; and the wild plants that had once been a staple part of Tod's diet grew difficult to find.

Yet Tod lingered. This was his beloved home, the range for which he had fought, the place where he had known so much happiness and so many triumphs. There were still a few trees, a few bushes and a few rocks he could remember ever since he was a pup. He was too old to start life over.

Although most of the other animals, and all the foxes of Tod's generation, were dead or gone, there were foxes of new generations in plenty. They were not like the foxes of the old days; they were mangy, rickety and stupid, and complete scavengers. They looted garbage pails, hung around the dumps looking for scraps. Not one of them could have stalked a field mouse. Yet they proliferated at an amazing rate, often building their dens under garages or in the junkyards that now littered the landscape. Garbage was plentiful, the new people had no guns, and the packs of hounds had long since disappeared.

Tod avoided these scrawny foxes, with their odor of slops and their skulking ways. Although he bred the vixens he took little interest in them or their progeny. The old thrilling courtship through the deep woods and the brave battles with worthy opponents were gone; these vixens were openly promiscuous. As there was now no need for a pair of foxes to hunt together as a team or for the male to catch game for the vixen and their pups—food being provided by a benevolent society—there was no bond between the two except momentary sexual gratification.

Of the human beings Tod had once known by sight or smell, there was left only the old trapper who had tried to catch him ever since the death of the Trigg hound on the railway line, so many years ago. The trapper had only one hound left, old Copper. Copper lived in the shack with the Man, for the hillside where the barrel kennels had been was covered with new houses. The trapper had nothing but a tiny patch of land left around his cabin; on every side the new developments pressed in on him. The trapper, Copper and Tod were the last three living creatures in the district who still remembered the old days.

When winter came, the old Man and his old hound would still set out after Tod through what little open land was left. They usually started out after a night snowfall, and Tod had gotten to expect them. When he awoke in the morning to find a sprinkling of fine, powdered snow on the ground, he would run to the nearest hogback to look for the two. If they did not come, he would go looking for them. He recognized them as dangers, but they were part of his life, and besides he enjoyed a little danger.

When spring came that year, the rains did not come with it. Tod went to all the places where the first spring buds and grasses had always grown, but was hard put to find even the tough, cleansing saw grass. At least he did not have to share his finds with the other foxes. They ate garbage winter and summer.

By July Tod had trouble finding water for the first time in his life. The streams were now run through culverts and used as sewers, and the ponds had been drained to make room for the houses. Tod had to dig to find moist earth he could chew. He licked stones damp with early morning dew and ate the bulblike roots of May apple and snakeroot for moisture. There were still mice and a few rabbits and squirrels around; and now when Tod made a kill, he eagerly lapped the blood of his quarry. So, in spite of the drought, he was able to maintain himself.

One night, while making his rounds, Tod heard the barking of a fox. For a fox to bark at this time of year was strange enough, but Tod had never heard a bark like this. The voice was hoarse and choked, sent out no message, and ended in a series of long howls. Driven by curiosity, Tod loped toward the cry.

He found the fox in the center of a little clearing. It was a wretched-looking animal, one of the scavengers, standing with arched back and head down, barking. Then came the awful howls. Suddenly the fox began to snap at the air, as though catching invisible flies. The moon struck a bit of quartz, making it glimmer, and the strange fox rushed to the stone, biting it. Lured by this remarkable performance, Tod took a few steps closer.

The fox saw him now and ran forward, crouching and whimpering. This was female procedure, but Tod was quite sure the

stranger was a male. Slowly Tod realized the stranger was begging for help. Tod could not imagine what was wrong.

Now the stranger fell on his side and clawed at his throat with
his forepaws. Tod could hear him gasping. Out of sheer confusion,
Tod reared up and struck at the stranger with his stiff forelegs.
The stranger continued to roll on the ground, choking. Then
suddenly he leaped to his feet and ran. He passed so close to Tod
that his brush touched, but paid no attention to him and vanished
among the trees, crashing through underbrush as recklessly as
one of the stupid dogs. When the sounds ceased, Tod went over
and smelled the stranger's trail. It told him nothing.

A FEW mornings later, Tod was cutting across the lawn of one
of the new houses when a fox exploded out of a hedge and rushed
across the lawn. The fox's lower jaw hung down, coated with
saliva; his eyes were glassy and he seemed to run blindly, swaying
as though unsure of his balance. Tod snarled and turned sideways, guarding with his brush. As he was much the bigger animal,
he took for granted the other fox would avoid him.

To Tod's astonishment the other fox charged. Tod gave him
a blow with his rump that set his adversary reeling. Instead of
putting himself on guard, the other fox again attacked blindly
and with a silent fury that was terrifying.

Tod was now raging. He reared up, striking stiff-legged at his
opponent and looking for a good hold. But before he could close,
the door of the house was thrown open and a man came out
shouting. Instantly Tod headed for the hedge, slipped through
and ran along the other side. He looked through the hedge,
and to his astonishment saw the strange fox turn and charge the
man. The man kicked him away and dodged back into the
house, slamming the door behind him. The raving animal charged
again and again into the door in a frenzy of pointless rage.

A week later, Tod saw another of these uncanny animals. A
flock of pigeons came down in the early morning to feed in a
small field that had not yet known the bulldozer's blade; and by
hiding in a sassafras patch, Tod could occasionally catch one.

Below the field a new concrete sidewalk ran to a corrugated shack where children were picked up each morning by the school bus. Lying in his sassafras ambush, Tod was watching the pigeons feeding. A group of children walked along the sidewalk, shouting and talking. Suddenly Tod heard them scream.

At the shrill sound, the pigeons took to the air with a hard rustle of wings and Tod looked in annoyance at the children. Most of them were running away, giving ear-piercing shrieks of terror. A few were dancing backward, the girls with their skirts wrapped around their knees and the boys kicking wildly. Tod smelled an odor of such abject fear that he sprang to his feet.

A fox was darting among the children, biting right and left. At each flicker of his head, a horrible screech went up from the bitten child. Tod could see that the fox was slashing with his canines rather than biting. He was doing terrible damage.

A little girl tripped and fell. At once the fox turned from the other children and sprang at her. There was no slashing here—he tore at the child's arms and legs in a delirium of fury. Paralyzed by terror, the girl lay helpless, squealing like a rabbit.

Adults were coming now, mostly women who, as soon as they saw what was happening, screamed louder than the child. Several of them rushed at the fox, who promptly turned on them. When one woman found a stick and lashed at the fox wildly, the insane creature locked his teeth in her ankle. The woman fell with a fearful cry.

A siren wailed, and a car tore up with a flashing, rotating light on top. Two men sprang out and ran to the women. The fox turned on them, but they wore boots. There was a succession of revolver shots and the fox was knocked lifeless onto the ground. Tod slid away. He was both curious and frightened.

Almost nightly Tod in his wanderings smelled the odor of other foxes. Formerly he would have ignored them or even driven them away, but now he fled from them. Once he saw a fox appear out of nowhere and attack some laundry waving in the wind on a line. A woman rushed out of the house yelling, and the fox went for her. Tod heard the woman scream as he galloped away. When he went back to the pigeon field, he saw that the children waiting for the bus were surrounded by armed men.

In spite of his precautions, Tod was once attacked by one of these mad foxes. Confident of his great speed, Tod ran from the animal at an easy lope, but to his astonishment the fox sped after him at such a terrific pace that Tod had to exert his best powers to escape. When Tod finally stopped to look around, he saw the fox spinning in circles, slashing at himself until he dropped, his head twisted to one side, his legs kicking wildly.

Other animals were also affected. Tod was attacked by squirrels and rats; even by a rabbit. He killed these mad creatures with a swift, expert nip before they could bite him. The dogs affected he avoided easily.

An atmosphere of terror hung over the housing developments, and Tod stayed as deep as he could in the remaining woods, living largely on mice. Soon traps were everywhere. They no longer bothered Tod, for he knew them too well; but often he passed foxes caught in them. Then he began to come across something new—dead foxes and other animals lying in open fields or along the hedges. They were rigid, their lips curled into a snarl, and when he sniffed at them there was an acid odor from their mouths that he soon came to associate with their deaths.

Game was scarce, and Tod was delighted to run across some small balls of lard lying along one of his routes. He was not especially hungry at the moment, so he picked up one and, instead of swallowing it at once, carried it in his mouth, looking for a good place to bury it. He chased a rabbit, dropping the pill in his excitement and, when the rabbit escaped down a hole, went back for the ball. The ball had broken open, and Tod smelled the same acid odor he had detected on the dead foxes. Tod rolled it over with one foot thoughtfully. He might have swallowed it after all if he had not heard the angry squeaking of two mice fighting, some ten yards away. In three bounds Tod reached the spot and by a quick bite managed to get both of the contestants. Delighted with himself, he trotted on, forgetting the ball.

The next night his hunting was unsuccessful, and he went

back to look for it. The ball was gone. Sniffing about, Tod picked up the line of a cat. The cat must have eaten his ball; so Tod, feeling that he had been robbed, followed the trail. He did not have far to go. Halfway through a wire fence was the cat, cold dead.

The cat had been almost entirely eaten by crows during the day, and it reeked heavily of the acid odor so Tod left it alone. As he walked on through the darkness, his nose near the ground to pick up any useful scents, a shadow flickered over him. He crouched automatically, but the shadow was a barn owl, a harmless bird as far as Tod was concerned. He heard a terrified squeak and sprinted forward, hoping to rob the bird of his mouse kill, but the owl was already back in the air when he arrived. There was a dead crow there, partly eaten by mice. It must have been one of these mice the owl had caught. Tod did not care for crow; and besides, the bird also had the acid odor, although now quite faint.

Just at dawn he managed to catch one of the few remaining rabbits, and started for his lying-up place. On the way, he shied abruptly from a dark mass at the foot of a cottonwood. The barn owl lay there dead, and a skunk was eating it. Tod was far too wise to risk being blinded by the skunk's musk, so he went on.

The next night he returned to the spot and found the remains of the dead skunk beside the owl. Both animals had been almost completely devoured by scavengers. A few feet away was a dead blue jay, quite untouched, so Tod made a meal of that. He had gone only a few hundred yards before paroxysms of pain gripped him. He vomited, tasting a faint suggestion of the acid. Spasms returned at regular intervals, and each time Tod writhed on the ground, biting at his own stomach in agony. By dawn he was so weak he could hardly move. He managed to crawl under some bushes and lay there, semiconscious, until nightfall. It was two days before he had recovered enough to hunt again.

By now the woods and fields were full of dead or dying animals, but Tod left them severely alone. Finally he killed a muskrat he found badly wounded from a fight and, after carefully smelling the animal all over, dared to eat it. He suffered no ill effects, so he caught a rabbit. That was all right too, so he resumed his hunting; but never again would he eat any dead animal, no matter how hungry he might be.

Wild animals were not the only victims of the poison pellets. Tod now found pet dogs whose horribly distorted bodies showed they had died in torture. The wholesale destruction was incredible, but the rabbits, gray squirrels, muskrats, and most songbirds remained. There were even some foxes left. They took refuge in the few remaining patches of cover, and lived as best they could.

Meanwhile, after the deaths of the dogs, Tod saw men driving around in cars and collecting the poisoned lard balls. He had seen no rabid animals of any kind for a long time now; perhaps the time of terror was over.

Shortly after sunup, while Tod was lying on his oak ridge, he saw a long procession of cars driving slowly down a back road that had been newly hard-surfaced. Tod had never seen so many cars before, and he lay watching them with both ears cocked. This seemed to be something new. The cars stopped and many of the people got out, lining up along the road. They all carried sticks, and several had guns.

Tod waited to see no more. He slipped over the ridge and cantered away at a long swinging lope. He ran to the next ridge, stopped and looked back. There was no sign of the people, so Tod, his mind now at ease, continued at a walk. He reached the top of the next ridge and froze to a stop. Coming toward him was another long line of people also carrying sticks and guns.

This was alarming, but Tod had learned long ago not to give way to panic. Instead of running he stood poised and watching. The people were coming slowly, stopping to examine every ditch and furrow, bending over patches of soft earth, and sometimes shouting excitedly and pointing with their sticks at the ground. Tod could not imagine what they were doing, but he did not like it.

Above him came a loud drone, but Tod did not bother to look up. He knew it was one of the huge, noisy things that passed by in the sky occasionally but never did any harm. This time the flying thing did not pass on but circled and came back over the ridge, its shadow sweeping over Tod and making him wince.

A man in the crowd stopped and lifted a device, holding it to his ear and to his mouth. He seemed to be listening, then talking, then listening again, while all the time the flying creature circled the ridge above Tod. Tod ducked over the hill and ran. There was no use going back toward the other line of men, so he turned left, the flying thing following him until he reached the shelter of a patch of woods. Here he stopped to get his breath.

Two foxes dashed past him from the woods, going all out. Tod hesitated a moment and then headed for a wild-rose and grapevine tangle that was one of his favorite hideaway spots, but before he could reach it he heard shots and yells ahead of him. Now he knew why the foxes had been running—men were coming from that direction too.

Tod whirled around and ran. There were men on both sides of him and behind him, but straight ahead might still be clear. As he broke out of the woods he saw long lines of men coming down both ridges, and they shouted as he appeared. He sped for the end of the valley before he could be trapped.

As he ran he heard shots. A fox, wild with fear, cut in front of Tod and flung himself toward one of the lines of people. Terror-smitten, the fox ran up and down the line until a shot paralyzed his hindquarters, and a boy rushed forward and beat him to death with a stick. Tod put forth his best speed and reached the ends of the encircling lines before they could close. Here was a vast, broad field without cover enough to hide a rabbit. For a fraction of a second Tod hesitated, but he had no choice. He dashed into the open, entirely exposed, tensing himself for the shots he knew would come.

There were no shots, only yells, and Tod felt himself to be in the clear. There were no humans ahead of him, only a single car stopped on a rise of ground. Out of the tail of his eye he saw the car start to move in a wide arc to head him off. Tod altered his course slightly and made for a distant fence beyond which showed a patch of woodland. The car put on speed, reached a plowed stretch and came to an abrupt halt.

The door flew open and two tall, thin dogs leaped out and raced toward him. A brown one was in the lead; a white one followed, as though tied to the first by an invisible leash. Tod was so sure of his ability to outrun any dog that he slowed down to watch the curious sight. They ran at an undulating pace, almost like weasels, at first making a few spy jumps to see over the rough terrain, and then flattening out with ears laid back as they got their positions.

Suddenly Tod realized that these animals were covering the ground at an alarming speed. He ran, and to his unbelieving horror he saw that the long, skinny creatures were fast over-hauling him. He could never reach the fence now. The white dog had pulled up even with the brown and they were racing in competition, each trying to reach him first. Coming in from an angle, the brown dog put on a final burst of speed and was on him with wide-stretched jaws. But the greyhound was going too fast to stop, and ran right over Tod, rolling him on the grass. Tod came up on his feet and was off again, but he was now forced to run parallel to the fence instead of toward it.

Tod managed to duck around a thistle, and the tan hound went by, going almost over on his side as he tried to turn. Then the white hound swung in from the side. Tod dropped flat and she went over him. This gave him a few instants' start, and he dashed for the fence. Their backs bent like snakes, the greyhounds were after him. He was too tired to dodge. His whiskers were touching the poison ivy covering the locust fence posts when the white hound grabbed him.

She was going too fast to pin him down, so she tossed him. Tod felt himself go up in the air, and writhed desperately so he would land on his feet. As he hit the ground, he saw the tan dog lying on one side. He had made too close a turn, and fallen. The white hound was doubling to grab him, but Tod had a moment's respite. He wormed through the poison ivy and made a break across the next field.

He got a good distance before he heard a shout that meant he was seen. Tod knew he could never make it to the woods. He heard the greyhounds coming and nerved himself for the death fight as they closed in. Ahead was a barbed-wire fence. Tod slipped under the lower strand, ran a few feet, and turned at bay with bent back and jaws open for the finish.

The tan greyhound was going all out, intent on Tod. Astonished, Tod saw him hit the almost invisible wires, rebound from them, and fall helpless with a broken back. The white hound saw the danger at the last instant and tried to turn, her whiplike tail thrashing as she twisted. Tod saw her slide on the wet grass and hit the barbs sideways. The barbs tore through her hide and she screeched in pain. She limped off to her crippled partner. The men were coming up, but they stayed with the wounded hounds. Tod made it to the woods at little more than a trot, crawled into the deepest cover he could find and then collapsed, utterly and completely beaten.

No matter how hard a run had been, Tod had always been able to snap back the next day; but this time he could not. Even when he could hunt again, he had to rest going up a steep hill; and, after a fast, hard spurt, a burning pain often shot through his chest and he was forced to stop, gasping for breath. He began to live more and more on mice and whatever plants he could find in the receding woodlots.

CHAPTER 10

COPPER no longer dreamed of deer hunting. His dreams now were disordered nightmares that made the hound twist and moan until the Master shook him awake. He spent most of his time dozing in a corner of the Master's cabin on a heap of sacks.

One by one Copper had seen the other hounds go. Even though he had never been especially friendly with the other dogs, he missed them. Now the kennel hill was gone and the old familiar dogwoods, buttonwoods and elms had been cut down.

Copper knew why these strange, unnatural dreams came to torture him. The air brought no delightful, intriguing messages, for it was poisoned with the stench of exhaust fumes. Perhaps even worse was the constant noise—the continual droning whine of traffic on the highways, the drumming beat of the turbines of a new pumping station that ran night and day. Often this station filled the air with a sickening stench of gas, while the factories gave off a fine soot that covered the ground like a poisonous black hoarfrost. He missed the pleasant smell of the trees, the pure quality of the air under their leaves, and the damp, clean earth that lay under their shelter.

It was many months since he and the Master had gone hunting, though the Master often carried a gun. When the Master took Copper out it was on a lead, and the Master would weave oddly or even stumble. The Master often stood in the doorway looking over the once lovely valley and sighed. He never shouted or laughed or played with Copper anymore; and there was a smell of alcohol in the little cabin. It frightened Copper to see the Master stagger and sometimes fall. The old hound cowered in his corner, and was always relieved when the Master finally collapsed across the bed and after a few minutes began to snore loudly. But no matter how bad things might be, as long as he had the Master, Copper could not be really miserable.

The new people who had moved in did not like the Master. They seldom spoke to him, and when they did there was a contemptuous note in their voices that Copper felt. Then something had happened which, although he could not understand its import, Copper sensed meant ultimate disaster.

One day a group of these new people came to the cabin with two leather-smelling men. Copper cheerfully wagged his tail when he smelled their leggings. But these were not the interested, admiring leather-smelling men of old; they liked him no more than they liked the Master.

With the crowd was a lean, nasty-voiced man who smelled of

antiseptic. He had intoned what had seemed to Copper like an endless speech while looking at a piece of paper. The Master protested, but the nasty-voiced man appealed to the leather-smelling men, who seemed to support him.

At last the Master and Copper got into a car and were driven many miles to a place Copper disliked at first smell. It was composed of big, barren buildings inhabited by men and women reeking with the sour odor of old age. A man pointed at Copper and ordered him to stay in the car, and Copper realized dogs were not allowed here. Then the Master yelled and shouted until even the leather-smelling men gave off a faint whiff of fear. Finally they were driven back to the cabin and allowed to stay there, to Copper's great relief. In the most terrible of his nightmares, Copper dreamed of that dark, gloomy place where no dogs were allowed and he would be separated from the Master.

Everyone avoided them after that, to Copper's relief. Then, inexplicably, the Master suddenly came into great demand. The leather-smelling men had brought in a dead fox, still smelling of powder where it had been shot and of some new, frightening scent Copper could not identify. They and the Master had talked a long time. Then dozens of people arrived to plead with the Master, all talking at once.

That evening, the Master took down his old traps and boiled them in hemlock chips over the fire, whistling to himself. Copper was sorry to see the traps, for it meant he could be of use only as a trap dog, but he was happy to see the Master happy. They ran a trapline, and in the morning Copper tracked the captured animals to where the drags brought them to a halt.

Copper had been allowed to go on the great drive where hundreds of people had beaten the countryside so that no fox would be left alive. Copper's work had been to check drains, holes and thick clumps of greenbrier to make sure there were no fugitives lurking inside. As always he had done a conscientious job, and when the day was over he was sure he had not missed a fox.

During the next few days the Master and Copper were happy. Then people came in at all hours of the day and night to talk seriously. The Master listened to them. It was nice to be liked, and Copper dreamed no more of the dark cluster of buildings where dogs were not allowed.

One evening—oh, glories of glories!—the Master got down his old shotgun. Copper went mad with joy and the Master fondled him just as he had in the good old days. They slept together that night on the bed, the Master's arm around the old hound and Copper's head resting on his shoulder. Even so, when the Master rose as the first scent of morning came into the air, took the gun and whistled to Copper to follow him, the hound could hardly believe the wonderful truth. Once again they were going fox hunting.

THEY WALKED until they were out of the poisonous miasma that overhung the district and into the good clean air of open country. Copper had almost forgotten there was live air like this. It was a perfect scenting day, moist but not wet, with a light breeze. The ground felt warm under Copper's pads, but the air in his nostrils was deliciously cool. Joyfully he plunged into the white mist that rolled toward them as they entered the hollows, zigzagging to pick up the grand odors that told of rabbit, pheasant, mouse and woodchuck. Copper felt young again, going hunting with the Master, and all he needed was the trace of a fox to make him completely happy. But the foxes were gone, he could not find a single trail.

Then the Master called him and together they went along the railroad tracks, turned off by the juniper tangle and started up the hill where they had first tracked The Fox—the one who had killed Chief so many years ago. Suddenly the Master shouted, his voice shrill with excitement. Copper dashed forward and, under an old fallen pine, hit the well-known scent. It was The Fox—the last fox left in the whole area.

Copper's great voice boomed out, and they were off. The scent leaped from the ground. There was no need to lower his head as he ran shouting for the Master to follow. Ahead he could just make out the white tip of the brush drifting over the fields. He pressed hard, for the sun was rising fast and would burn out the scent.

Soon Copper stopped baying to save his breath. The fox followed a line of bluffs to a river, turned, and ran along the bank. Then he made a sharp turn into a cornfield. Copper was forced to drop his head, and as he worked out the line he heard the raging cries of crows. Copper knew they were screaming at the fox and he raced ahead, picking an occasional wisp of scent from the cornstalks as he passed.

Outside the field, the fox doubled and ran back on his own trail. As Copper followed, he heard the blast of the Master's shotgun. Wild with hope, Copper dashed on. He found the Master staring into some woods. He pointed and cheered Copper on. Copper swerved and hit the scent almost immediately; it was stained with the odor of panic, but there was no blood. The Master had missed.

Beyond the woods was a little field entirely surrounded by a stone wall. Copper knew the place well. Inside were a number of flat stones standing erect, each with a small mound before it. Copper's nose told him the fox had jumped on the wall and run along it. A common trick. Copper sprang heavily to the top of the wall and followed. He was back at his original starting point before he realized what he was doing.

Annoyed, Copper jumped off and tried the ground both inside and outside the graveyard. The Master came up, took him to where the fox had first come to the wall, and ordered him to backtrack the animal. Copper looked up reproachfully—all his training was against running heel, but he reluctantly obeyed. He had gone only a few feet along the old trail when he realized that there was a fresh trail laid over the old—and the fresh trail was not going to the wall but away from it. The fox had jumped on the wall, run back and forth a few times, and then jumped off onto his old line and backtracked it. Furious, Copper gave tongue in indignation. Another few feet and he found where the fox had turned off from his old line. They were off again.

The fox had swum a pond, but Copper was able to pick up his

scent along the edge where it had been blown in from the surface of the water by the fresh breeze. He followed it around the pond to the place where the dripping fox had emerged. The shock of the cold water kept the scent glands in the fox's pads from functioning for a while, so Copper followed the wet trail across the grass, guided by the dampness until the glands began giving off scent again. The sun was high now, cooking out the scent in the open, but among dead leaves and damp grass it was holding well. Copper's lips sucked it up from the earth as if tasting it.

Only twice that afternoon was Copper at fault. Once was when the fox crossed a burned field where no scent would lie and the ashes got into Copper's nose, making him sneeze and gag. Even so the hound was able to follow by catching traces of scent from tufts of dried grass that the fox had touched. The second was in a fire lane where the trees had been felled. There the fox had jumped from one trunk to another as lightly as a cat, while the heavy hound had to blunder through them.

When night came, Copper was still on the trail. During the day, Copper knew from the scent that the fox was suffering more than he from the heat of the sun. Now that it was cool, the quarry's odor did not have the hot, thick quality of an overheated, exhausted animal. On the other hand, in the cool of the night the scent was stronger and easier to follow.

Several times the fox vainly tried to double back toward his old range. Copper came to one place where the fox had tried four times to cross a highway, each time being turned back by the traffic. Another time he had found himself in a new development and been chased by dogs. The shock killed his scent, and it was more by sheer luck than skill that Copper was able to pick up the trail again. At last the fox gave up trying to return to his home range and cut straight across country.

Copper could soon tell that the fox was now running aimlessly, plunging blindly ahead through brambles, across streams, over walls, and forcing his way through fields of tall grass. When dawn came Copper was still following, while the fox was noticeably weakening every hour. But the old hound was near the point of exhaustion himself. His pads left dabs of blood and his hind-quarters wavered as he ran. But now the hound could smell the spots where the fox's breath had caught among the vines and bushes as he gasped for air. He could not be far ahead.

Distantly, he heard the sound of the Master blowing across the opened barrels of the shotgun. Copper bayed in reply, tired as he was. The call was repeated, closer this time. Again Copper summoned up enough breath for a feeble call that was more howl than bay, for not only his feet but his lungs were torturing him.

The trail led through a mass of briers and Copper could hear the fox ahead of him. He struggled on. Again came the call on the shotgun barrels, and Copper managed to give a weak and faltering reply. Then he broke out of the briers and saw the fox.

The fox's head was down. He was panting and his swollen tongue hung out. His brush was covered with mud. Ahead of him was a fallen tree trunk. The dying animal made an effort to climb over it, and fell back. At the sight, Copper gave a clear, long-drawn-out cry of triumph and staggered toward him. The fox made a last effort to mount the log, and then fell to the ground, limp and motionless. Copper reeled forward, fell, got up, and managed to reach the fox. He gave the body a feeble shake and then collapsed on top of the corpse.

COPPER WAS scarcely conscious of hearing the Master's call or of being lifted and carried to the car. Back in the cabin, he felt a sting of alcohol on his lips that made him choke. He struggled feebly. Vaguely he knew that people were crowding into the tiny room, shouting and laughing. He felt the Master massaging his legs and chest. At long last, he was able to lift his head, although his vision was blurred.

He was shown the dead fox, but he was too tired even to sniff at it. While the Master held the fox, men pointed boxes at him and lights flashed again and again. When they finally left him in peace, Copper sank back and slept as though he were dead.

Slowly the Master nursed him back to health. The fox was skinned and the pelt hung with a skinning board in it, just as in the old days. Gradually Copper regained his strength until he could walk with the Master. He was blissfully happy now. Everyone liked him and liked the Master. The Master's voice was always cheerful, and when he was cheerful, Copper was cheerful.

But Copper was again conscious of a change. Fewer and fewer people came. The cabin sagged and the Master grew increasingly silent and began to drink more heavily than ever. He seldom took Copper for walks now, and the old hound lay on his pile of sacks, puzzled and disappointed. He tried his best to make the Master happy again, clumsily trying to play, licking his hand, running to the door to show he was all ready to go hunting—if there was anything left to hunt. Nothing he did won even a smile or a caress from the Master.

Then one day the nasty-voiced man from the great, somber place where dogs were not allowed came back. With him again were the leather-smelling men. There were some other people too, people who had patted him when he and the Master had come back with the last fox. Now their voices were angry as they pointed at the old cabin and the outhouse, at the bottles on the floor and at the gun. They talked and talked to the Master, while Copper listened in dumb misery.

He heard a sound he had never heard before. The Master was crying. He sat on the edge of the bed, sobbing, and tears came through his fingers. Copper forced his way through the people and anxiously licked the Master's hands, asking to help. The Master stroked his head just as he had in the old days, and Copper wriggled joyfully.

The Master went to the wall, took down the gun and loaded it. Copper barked and cavorted happily. They were going hunting again, and surely the Master would take him? Yes, the Master called to him and, leaving the people, they went outside.

The Master led him a little way from the cabin and, sitting down beside him, stroked his head. Copper licked his face and whined. They had killed the great fox, the fox that had eluded them for so many years. Now they were together again, and happy, for nothing could separate them.

The Master made him lie down, and then held one hand over his eyes. Copper lay trustingly. The Master knew best. Did he recall the many good times they had had together and this last great run—a day and a night and part of another day? Of course he did. Copper gave the Master's hand one last lick. He did not care what happened as long as he would never be separated from the Master, for he had killed the great fox, and in this miserable, fouled land there was no longer any place for fox, hound, or human being.

Dan Mannix

Twenty years ago the southern Pennsylvania countryside was spectacularly inviting. Many of the houses were built by seventeenth-century farmers who were careful in their stewardship of the land. Even two hundred years later the life in that countryside remained pleasant indeed.

Dan Mannix and his wife, Jule, bought a house and twenty-five acres of land near Malvern, Pennsylvania, in 1947. The house had character and grace; it had been built by one of George Washington's generals in 1789. Close by were woods which were home to many animals Mannix would come to know intimately. On his own acres he housed, besides a pair of foxes, a hawk, a raven, a crow, an ocelot, a rattlesnake, horses, sheep, ducks, geese, a peacock, chickens, rabbits, skunks, and two eagles who would figure in a Reader's Digest Condensed Books selection— Mannix's *The Way of the Eagle* (Winter 1966).

But in these two decades the land has been transformed. A highway was cut through nearby Downingtown. (A colonial barn, an inn and an old forge were destroyed to

332

let it pass.) Three cloverleafs now feed traffic onto that road. Their cost: an old mill and several hundred acres of land. This year another highway is planned. It would cut through land where underprivileged Pennsylvania boys are taught farm skills, and multiply the number of cars moving in and out of nearby Philadelphia fifteen times. Already the fouled air from city traffic hazes the sky in Malvern and burns the lungs of all living creatures. Local people have made a dedicated attempt to stop the further mutilation of the land. The response to their petitions has been simply, "We must have progress." Mannix now wonders what that word "progress" means.

Much of Dan Mannix's writing has been the result of his lifetime love affair with wildlife and nature. Born in Philadelphia in 1911, he was only six when he persuaded his family to let him keep pet skunks. (Later, they even tolerated a ten-foot alligator in the family swimming pool.) After graduating from college Mannix traveled all over the world doing articles, books and movies about wild animals. Fortunately, Jule Mannix, a former radio actress, and the Mannix children are animal lovers, too. At the Malvern farm, the pet skunks, raven, crow and peacock wander about as they please. A closer watch is kept on the ocelot, eagles and hawks, as well as on the foxes, who hungrily eye the chickens.

When Nita Engle, the gifted artist who did the illustrations for *The Fox and the Hound,* visited the Mannix farm, one of the foxes took a liking to her and jumped up on her lap. "I've never seen anything so beautiful as that animal," she said, "or anything so sad as what's happening to the land there. You should see what will be lost. It would break your heart."

The Fox and the Hound reminds us of what we all stand to lose by our perhaps mistaken idea of progress. It continues to lead to the relentless mauling of the land upon which men and animals alike—whether we are willing to admit it or not—still depend. "I don't know where we'll move if this new highway comes through," Mannix says. "It's getting so there soon will be no place to go."

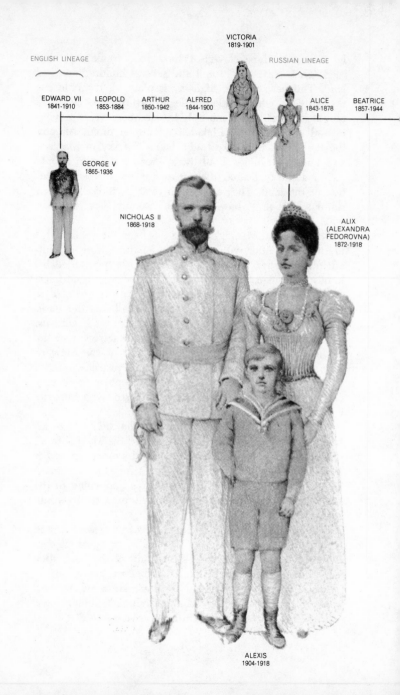

VICTORIA
1819-1901

ENGLISH LINEAGE

RUSSIAN LINEAGE

EDWARD VII
1841-1910

LEOPOLD
1853-1884

ARTHUR
1850-1942

ALFRED
1844-1900

ALICE
1843-1878

BEATRICE
1857-1944

GEORGE V
1865-1936

NICHOLAS II
1868-1918

ALIX
(ALEXANDRA
FEDOROVNA)
1872-1918

ALEXIS
1904-1918

VICTORIA
1840-1901

HELENA
1846-1923

KAISER WILHELM
1859-1941

NICHOLAS
AND
ALEXANDRA

A CONDENSATION OF THE BOOK BY

ROBERT K. MASSIE

ILLUSTRATED BY
GABRIEL PASQUALINI

They called each other "lovy," "my sunshine," "my angel"—and together they ruled one sixth of the globe. They were Nicholas and Alexandra, the reluctant autocrats of Imperial Russia, who preferred the simple joys of family life to all the jewel-encrusted glitter and pomp of the world's last great autocracy.

Theirs was a lifetime love affair in which happiness was shattered when Alexis, their fifth child and only son, Russia's heir, was born with the terrible defect of hemophilia. Guarding this tragic secret from the world, the parents turned hopefully to doctors—and found that they could do nothing to relieve the small boy's agonies. Finally, in despair, Alexandra placed her son's fate, and the fate of her husband and his empire, in the hands of Gregory Rasputin, an evil but gifted faith healer who had an amazing power to help Alexis. And it was Rasputin who persuaded Alexandra and, through her, Nicholas to resist the Russian people's clamor for reform; and thus helped make the Bolshevik revolution inevitable.

Nicholas and Alexandra is the first intimate account of a family whose private tragedy was to have momentous consequences for the entire world.

PART ONE

Imperial Russia

So IMMENSE were the dominions of Tsar Alexander III, father of Nicholas, that as night began to fall along their western borders day was breaking on their Pacific coast. Between these frontiers lay one sixth of the land surface of the globe. Rivers, wide and flat, flowed peacefully through the grassy plains of European Russia toward a limitless southern horizon. Eastward, in Siberia, even mightier rivers rolled north to the Arctic, sweeping through forests where no human had ever been, and across desolate marshes of frozen tundra.

Thinly scattered across this broad land lived the Tsar's 130 million subjects: Slavs, Balts, Germans, Georgians, Armenians, Uzbeks, Tartars and others. Some were clustered in provincial cities and towns, dominated by onion-shaped church domes rising above white-walled houses. Many lived in straggling villages of unpainted log huts, where pigs wandered freely down the muddy street.

For six interminable months of winter, the countryside became a wasteland of freezing whiteness. Inside their huts, in an atmosphere thick with the aroma of steaming clothes and boiling tea, the *moujiks* (peasants) sat around their huge clay stoves and argued and pondered the dark mysteries of nature and God.

Three fourths of the Russians were peasants, freed from serf-dom a generation before by the Tsar-Liberator Alexander II. But freedom did not produce food when famine came. Then the moujiks tore the thatch from their roofs to feed their livestock, and, wrapped in ragged cloaks, stood all day in silence along the snowy roads. Noble ladies drove their *troikas* through the stricken countryside, delivering with handsome gestures of their slender arms a spray of silver coins. But soon the tax collector came to gather up these coins and ask for others.

When the hungry moujiks grumbled, squadrons of Cossacks would ride into the villages, knouts to flog troublemakers swing-ing from their saddles. Bitterness flowed with the blood, and landowners and government functionaries were roundly cursed by the peasants.

But never the Tsar. The Tsar, far away in a place nearer heaven than earth, did no wrong. He was the *Batiushka-Tsar*, the Father of the Russian people. He did not know what suffering they had to endure. "It is very high up to God! It is very far to the Tsar!" said the Russian proverb. "If only we could get to the Tsar and tell him, our troubles would be at an end!" said the moujiks.

Moscow was the real hub of Russia, the center of railroads and commerce, but the capital of Alexander III's empire was St. Petersburg—today's Leningrad. At a cost of 200,000 lives, Peter the Great had built this strange, artificial city, the "Venice of the North," on nineteen river islands, chained by arching bridges, laced by winding canals. To the northeast lay Lake Ladoga; to the west the Gulf of Finland; between them rolled the cold, swift flood of the river Neva, its northern shore dominated by the grim Fortress of Peter and Paul, and the fortress cathedral. For three miles along the southern bank ran a solid granite quay, lined by official buildings, the foreign embassies, and the huge Italian-style palaces of the nobility.

St. Petersburg's architecture, fashions, morals and thought were Western, even Mediterranean, not Russian. The city was the center of all that was advanced and smart and much that was cynical in Russian life. Society spoke French; their furniture and clothing came from Paris. The noblemen vacationed on the Riviera, rather than going back to the huge country estates which financed their pleasures.

St. Petersburg was a northern city. In the winter, icy winds and snowstorms froze the Neva hard as steel. Tsar, government ministers, priests and factory workers alike layered themselves in clothing and, upon coming in from the street, headed straight to the bubbling *samovar* for a glass of hot tea. Yet summers could be hot, and then open windows brought the salt air of the Gulf of Finland, the aromas of spice and tar, and the sound of church bells and carriage wheels.

St. Petersburg's Winter Palace had a row of gigantic galleries, each as wide and tall as a cathedral. Great marble columns supported high gilded ceilings, hung with immense crystal and gold chandeliers. Guests ascended a white marble staircase between baskets of orchids and potted palms framing huge mirrors. Along the corridors, Chevaliers Gardes in white uniforms with eagle-crested helmets, and Cossack Life Guards in scarlet tunics stood at attention.

Here, at Imperial balls, Tsar Alexander III appeared with the Empress Marie, wearing jeweled gowns and her famous diamond tiara. There were quadrilles, waltzes, mazurkas, polonaises. At midnight, supper was served. Through the long windows the merrymakers could see the wind blowing gusts of fine powdered snow along the icebound Neva.

The Tsar stopped here and there to chat with the guests, but soon withdrew, for he abhorred society. He felt that a true Russian should be simple in manners and dress; he wore his peasant trousers and boots until they were threadbare. He was a blunt, narrow and suspicious man, but with a strong mind and will, and an enormous capacity for work. He had awesome physical strength. Once at dinner, when there was trouble in the Balkans, the Austrian Ambassador hinted that Austria might mobilize two or three army corps there. Alexander picked up a silver fork, twisted it into a knot and tossed it onto the plate of the Austrian

Ambassador. "That," he said, "is what I will do to your two or three army corps."

Alexander *was* the government. No parliament existed. Even Imperial grand dukes, serving as provincial governors or high-ranking officers, served only at the Tsar's pleasure. A snap of his fingers, and they stepped aside. Hundreds of his political enemies made the long journey to Siberia. But Alexander made autocracy work: already he was being compared to Peter the Great.

It was Russia's good fortune that Alexander married the charming Princess Dagmar of Denmark, who took the Russian name of Marie Fedorovna. Russians loved this small, gay, witty woman, and the Empress gloried in the parties and balls of the Russian Court. "I danced and danced. I let myself be carried away," she wrote at the age of forty-four. Delightedly, she passed tidbits of gossip along. "They danced the mazurka for half an hour," she wrote a friend. "One poor lady lost her petticoat which remained at our feet until a general hid it behind a pot of flowers. The unfortunate one managed to hide herself in the crowd before anyone discovered who she was."

By the time Marie was thirty, she had met the requirements of royal motherhood by producing six children: Alexander, who died in infancy, Nicholas, George, Xenia, Michael and Olga. She acted as a buffer between her brood and their strong, gruff father, who dominated them, and she instilled in them unquestioning filial loyalty and respect for family life.

Running his vast empire required all of Alexander III's great energy. So he could work undisturbed, the family lived in his country palace at Gatchina. It had nine hundred rooms, but the children were brought up with spartan simplicity. They slept on army cots, took cold baths, and ate porridge for breakfast. At lunch they joined their parents; but as they were served after all the guests, and had to leave the table when their father rose, they often went hungry.

Everything about Alexander inspired awe in his shy eldest son, Nicholas. In October 1888, the Imperial train was derailed as the

Tsar and his family were in the dining car. The roof caved in, but, with his great strength, Alexander lifted a beam and held it long enough for his wife and children to crawl free, unhurt. The thought that one day he would have to succeed this Herculean father all but overwhelmed the shy young Nicholas.

The future Tsar was educated by tutors. The most important of these was Constantine Pobedonostsev, a brilliant philosopher of reaction, later called "The High Priest of Social Stagnation." The Russia he described to Nicholas had nothing to do with the restless giant stirring outside the palace windows. It was God, he explained, who had chosen the Tsar. A Tsar who was not an autocrat was failing his duty to God. "Among the falsest of political principles," he added, "is the principle of the sovereignty of the people."

For young Nicholas, the dramatic proof of these teachings against liberalism was the brutal assassination of his grandfather, Alexander II. For his historic freeing of the serfs, he was known as the Tsar-Liberator, and he had just approved the establishment of the first representative body to advise on legislation. As his carriage rolled through the streets of St. Petersburg, a bomb exploded under it, wounding his equerries and one of his Cossack escorts. The Tsar was unhurt. Stepping from the splintered carriage, he spoke to the wounded men and asked gently about the bomb thrower, who had been arrested.

At once a second assassin ran up and threw a bomb at the Tsar's feet. In the sheet of flame and metal Alexander II's legs were torn away, his stomach ripped open, his face mutilated. Still conscious, he whispered, "To the palace, to die there." What remained of him was carried into the Winter Palace and up the marble stairs. He was laid on a couch, unconscious now, one eye closed, the other open but vacant. Horrified, the Imperial family crowded into the room. Thirteen-year-old Nicholas, deathly pale, watched from the end of the bed. At the window stood the future Alexander III, his fists clenching and unclenching, until the surgeon announced, "The Emperor is dead."

At this the new Tsar nodded grimly and motioned to his wife.

Together they walked out of the palace, now surrounded by guardsmen with bayonets fixed. They drove away "accompanied by a whole regiment of Don Cossacks, in attack formation, their red lances shining brightly in the last rays of a crimson March sunset." Later, Alexander III proclaimed that he would rule "with faith in the power and the right of autocracy."

TSAR NICHOLAS II

NICHOLAS at twenty-one was a slender youth of five feet seven inches, gentle, kind and friendly. In many respects his education was excellent. He had an unusual memory and had done well in history. He spoke French and German, and his English was so good that he could have been mistaken for an Englishman. He rode beautifully and was an excellent shot.

"Nicky smiled his usual tender, shy, slightly sad smile," his young cousin and intimate companion Grand Duke Alexander—"Sandro"—once wrote. Himself prepared to like everybody, Nicholas hoped that people liked him. As best he could tell through the thickets of flattery and etiquette, they did.

Nicholas's essential function was to wait discreetly until it came his turn to be Tsar. Alexander III was only forty-five years old. Expecting that he would continue to occupy the throne for another twenty or thirty years, he dawdled about giving his son the experience to succeed him, and Nicholas happily accepted the playboy role to which he was assigned. Though he appeared at meetings of the Imperial Council, he bolted at the first opportunity. He went to operas, theater and ballet, to soirées and balls.

But Nicholas was never happier than when he was sitting on a white horse outside the Winter Palace, his arm frozen in salute as squadrons of Cossacks trotted past, pennants fluttering from their lances. The army's pageantry and history fascinated him. No title meant more to him than the rank of colonel awarded him by his father. At nineteen, he was given command of a squadron of Horse Guards and, in a great military camp outside St. Petersburg, lived the pleasant, mindless existence of any wealthy, aristocratic young Russian officer. His modesty made him popular, and the Empress was afraid that he would forget he was the Tsarevich. "Never forget that everyone's eyes are on you," she wrote.

Nicholas wrote back, "I will always try to follow your advice, my dearest darling Mama. One has to be cautious." But to his diary he confided: "We tasted six sorts of Port and got a bit soused."

It was as a young officer that Nicholas first met a small, vivacious seventeen-year-old, Mathilde Kschessinska, a dancer in the Imperial Ballet. She had been rigorously schooled in ballet for ten years and was the best dancer in her class. By chance, that year, the Imperial family attended the school's graduation performance and supper, where the Tsar himself sat next to Mathilde. When he moved on, his place was taken by the Tsarevich.

That summer Kschessinska was selected to join the troupe which danced for the officers at camp. The Tsarevich came every day to watch her performance and talk to her. As they were never alone, the romance that summer did not go beyond flirting. In October, Nicholas set out with his brother George on a cruise which took them from the Mediterranean Sea to India and Japan. This royal tour was intended to educate Nicholas in diplomatic niceties—and to help him forget the dancer.

In any case, Nicholas's feelings for a tall, golden-haired German princess, Alix of Hesse, were more serious. She was a younger sister of Grand Duchess Elizabeth—Ella—the wife of Nicholas's uncle, Grand Duke Serge. Nicholas often visited this young aunt, and when Alix came there his visits became even more frequent. Serious and shy, Alix burned with inner fires, and when she set her blue-gray eyes on Nicholas, he was overwhelmed. But his parents saw little to recommend a minor German princess as a match for a future Tsar, and Nicholas left St. Petersburg for his grand tour in a gloomy mood.

UPON HIS RETURN to St. Petersburg, Nicholas again began to see Mathilde Kschessinska. At first, they rendezvoused secretly in carriages on the bank of the Neva. Later he began to call on her at her father's house. Usually, he brought with him three youthful cousins, Serge, George and Alexander—Sandro. Kschessinska served them champagne and listened while they sang folk songs. As his affection for Mathilde grew, Nicholas gave her a diamond-studded bracelet. After her performances, he would come for her, driving his own troika, and they would gallop off on starlit rides across the plain outside St. Petersburg.

Kschessinska's father was shattered when she announced, at the end of the summer of 1892, that she wished a home of her own. He asked whether she understood that Nicholas could never marry her. Mathilde replied that she wished only to seize whatever brief happiness Fate was offering her. She rented Rimsky-Korsakov's house, and Nicholas celebrated the house-warming by giving her a vodka service of eight gold glasses inlaid with jewels. They led there, Mathilde said later, a quiet, delightful life.

In 1893, Nicholas went to London for the wedding of his cousin George—later King George V—to Mary of Teck. He and George looked so much alike that even people who knew them well confused them, and a gentleman of the court begged Nicholas not to be late for his wedding ceremony.

In St. Petersburg, meanwhile, Mathilde's career was gathering momentum; in later years she would rank with Pavlova and Karsavina as a ballerina. But the flame between Nicholas and herself began to flicker. He had never hidden his interest in Alix. Now he told Mathilde that he hoped to make the Princess his fiancée. Nicholas and Mathilde said good-by at a highway rendezvous, she seated in her carriage, he astride a horse. When he rode away, she wept. But she soon consoled herself with Grand Duke Serge, and later with another of Nicholas's cousins, Grand Duke Andrei, whom she finally married, in exile, in 1921.

Like Nicholas's parents, Russian society did not share his love for Alix. She had made a bad impression during her visits in St. Petersburg. Badly dressed, an awkward dancer, with an atrocious

French accent, she was also too arrogant, unkind society said.

In any case, the Tsar was angling for a bigger catch for his son: tall, dark-haired Princess Hélène, daughter of the Pretender to the throne of France. But Hélène did not please Nicholas; and she was not willing to give up her Roman Catholicism. The Tsar then sent emissaries to Princess Margaret of Prussia. Nicholas declared that he would rather become a monk than marry the plain, bony Margaret. She spared him by announcing that she too was unwilling to adopt the Russian Orthodox faith.

If Alix was denied him, Nicholas said, he would never marry. As long as he was well, Alexander III ignored his son's demands to see Alix and propose. But in the winter of 1894 the Tsar developed kidney trouble. As his vitality ebbed alarmingly, he began to consider how Russia would manage without him. Nothing could be done about the Tsarevich's lack of experience, but he could at least provide his heir with the stabilizing effect of marriage. Reluctantly he permitted Nicholas to propose to Alix.

TSARITSA ALEXANDRA

ALIX Victoria Helena Louise Beatrice, Princess of Hesse-Darmstadt, was born in 1872, and named after her mother, who was the youngest of Queen Victoria's nine children. Alix was the nearest rendering of Alice in German.

Her mother called her "Sunny," and wrote Queen Victoria that Alix was "a sweet, merry little person, always laughing and a dimple in one cheek."

When she was six, Alix's four-year-old sister and her mother died of diphtheria. The deaths had a shattering effect on Alix. She sat quiet and withdrawn; a hard shell of aloofness formed over the warm, generous and sensitive, if obstinate, little girl. Only in cozy family gatherings could she become once again the sweet, merry Sunny of her early childhood.

She was still Queen Victoria's favorite grandchild, and Mrs. Orchard, her governess in Hesse-Darmstadt, received a steady flow of instructions from the Queen. Alix's standards became thoroughly English, Victorian and strict. Years later, she had the Russian Imperial family eat on the stroke of the hour, and divided its mornings and afternoons into rigid little blocks of time, as Mrs. Orchard had taught.

Alix made her first visit to St. Petersburg at the age of twelve for the marriage of her sister Ella to Grand Duke Serge. Nicholas presented her with a small brooch. Overwhelmed, she accepted, then shyly pressed it back into his hand. Nicholas was offended.

They met again five years later when she visited Ella. Nicholas took her skating and tobogganing in the afternoons, and persuaded his parents to give her a special tea dance, followed by a supper of *blinis* and fresh caviar.

Alix liked Nicholas's wistful charm and his appealing blue eyes, and gradually became sure that she loved him. The insuperable obstacle to marrying him was religion, Alix being a fervent Lutheran. The fact that Nicholas would one day be one of the mightiest rulers in Europe influenced her not at all. She had already rejected the proposal of the heir to the British throne.

In the spring of 1894, Nicholas again helped represent Russia at a wedding—that of Alix's brother Ernest, Grand Duke of Hesse-Darmstadt.

"What a day!" Nicholas wrote in his diary the day after his arrival. "About ten, I went to Alix, and then began between us the talk which I had long ago strongly wanted and at the same time very much feared. We talked till twelve, but with no result; she looked particularly pretty, but sad. She still objects to changing her religion. Poor girl, she cried a lot. . . ." It was Grand Duchess Ella who calmed Alix's fears. She herself had accepted Orthodoxy and she insisted that a change of faith was not really so enormous or unusual a problem.

During Ernest's wedding ceremony, Nicholas watched Alix closely. He wrote, "How much I would have liked to have been able to look into the depths of Alix's soul!"

346

The very next day Alix capitulated. Nicholas wrote in his diary: "Today is the day of my engagement to my darling, adorable Alix. O God, what a mountain has rolled from my shoulders! . . . After lunch we went to Church and had a thanksgiving service."

Once it was made, Marie and the Tsar responded gallantly to the match. "Your dear Alix is quite like a daughter to me," Marie wrote. "Ask her which stones she likes most—sapphires or emeralds?" As a start, she sent Alix an emerald bracelet and a superb jeweled Easter egg.

After ten days of bliss, Nicholas had to say good-by. "What sadness to be obliged to part from her for a long time," he wrote. "How good we were together—a paradise."

IN JUNE, Nicholas went to see Alix in England, and to call on Queen Victoria. They had three days of comparative privacy at Walton-on-Thames in a cottage belonging to Alix's sister. They gathered fruit and flowers from nearby fields, and sat in the garden, Alix embroidering while Nicholas read to her. Years later, both Nicholas and Alix remembered every detail of those three shining days, and the mere mention of the name Walton was enough to bring tears of happiness to Alix's eyes.

They emerged from their private cocoon of happiness to go see "Granny" at Windsor Castle. There Nicholas gave Alix his engagement gifts: a pink pearl ring, a necklace of large pink pearls, and other jewels. Grandest of all was a *sautoir*, or chain with pendant, of pearls, created by Fabergé. Staring at the dazzling display of gems, Queen Victoria shook her head and said, "Now, Alix, do not get too proud."

Nicholas felt that he had to tell Alix about Mathilde. Alix rose to the occasion like a true granddaughter of Victoria. She wrote: "When we are young we cannot always hold our own against temptation, but as long as we repent, God will forgive us. Your confidence in me touched me oh so deeply. May I always show myself worthy of it. God bless you, beloved Nicky."

The six-week visit came to an end. As the Russian ship *Polar Star* slipped past Dover, Nicholas was reading a strangely

347

prophetic line from novelist Marie Corelli: "For the past is past and will never return, the future we know not, and only the present can be called our own."

NICHOLAS found his family in a state of alarm over his father's health. The doctors had recommended the warm climate of the Crimea and Nicholas went with the family to the summer palace at Livadia—where years later, President Franklin D. Roosevelt and his party were housed during the Yalta Conference. At Livadia the Tsar's legs gave way, and he had to take to his bed. Sensing what was coming, Nicholas sent for Alix. She came at once by train and Nicholas brought her to Livadia in an open carriage. They were stopped repeatedly by villagers with welcoming bread and salt and armloads of grapes and flowers.

In his bedroom, seated in an armchair, Alexander III awaited the young couple dressed in full-dress uniform—the only way, he insisted, for the Tsar of Russia to greet a future Russian Empress. Kneeling before the pale, enfeebled giant, Alix received his blessing, and she and Nicholas were formally betrothed.

The life of the household now revolved around the dying Tsar. Alix, feeling an outsider, sat at Nicholas's side while he read the reports submitted by his father's ministers. Doctors and court officials hurried straight from the Tsar's bedside to Empress Marie, scarcely noticing the shy young couple waiting for them. Alix saw that Nicholas, the Heir to the throne, was treated like a nobody. She put her feelings into his diary, in which she now often wrote: "Be firm and make the doctors come to you every day and tell you how they find him so that you are the first to know. Don't let others forget who you are. Forgive me, lovy."

On November 1, 1894, Alexander III died, and the twenty-six-year-old Nicholas inherited his throne. "We embraced and cried together," recalled his cousin and brother-in-law Alexander. "He was Emperor now, and the weight of this terrifying fact crushed him. 'Sandro,' he exclaimed, 'what is going to happen to me, to you, to Alix, to mother, to all of Russia? I never wanted to become Tsar. I know nothing of the business of ruling.' "

While navy guns in Yalta waters thundered a last salute to the dead monarch, an altar was erected on the lawn in front of the palace. Courtiers, officials, servants and family formed a semi-circle and a priest in golden vestments solemnly administered the oath of allegiance to His Imperial Majesty, Tsar Nicholas II. The following day, with the palace draped in black, the Protestant Princess Alix of Hesse became the Russian Orthodox "truly believing Grand Duchess Alexandra Fedorovna" at a special service in the palace chapel and took Holy Communion in her new faith.

As Alexander's funeral train rolled north across the Ukraine, peasants gathered along the track to watch it pass. The train halted in four cities for services. In Moscow, the coffin was carried to the Kremlin, the procession stopping for litanies sung from the steps of ten different churches.

In St. Petersburg, the cortege advanced past silent crowds to the Cathedral of the Fortress of Peter and Paul, where all Romanov Tsars were buried. The new Grand Duchess Alexandra rode alone, thickly veiled, behind the rest of the family. Old women crossed themselves, shaking their heads, and murmured darkly, "She has come to us behind a coffin."

For seventeen days, the body lay in state, while royalty, officials, and thousands of the public paid their respects. The future King George V of England wrote his wife that every day they had another service at the cathedral. "After the service, we went to the coffin and kissed the Holy Picture which he holds in his hand. It gave me a shock when I saw his dear face. He looks beautiful and peaceful, but of course he has changed very much. It is a fortnight today."

Amid the sad faces, the tears, Alexandra suppressed her own small, pathetic happiness. "Our marriage," she wrote, "seemed a mere continuation of the masses for the dead."

The wedding took place one week after the funeral, on Empress Marie's birthday, when protocol permitted a relaxation of mourning. Before a gold mirror used by every grand duchess on her wedding day, the bride was dressed by the ladies of the Imperial family. She wore a heavy, old-fashioned Russian court dress of silver brocade, and a robe and train of cloth-of-gold lined with ermine. From a red velvet cushion, Marie lifted the diamond nuptial crown and put it on Alexandra's head. Together, they walked to the chapel in the Winter Palace where Nicholas waited in the uniform of a Hussar. Each holding the Orthodox lighted candle, Nicholas and Alexandra became man and wife. There was no wedding reception and no honeymoon. The young couple simply returned to Marie's Anitchkov Palace.

The marriage that began that day remained unflawed for the rest of their lives. It was a Victorian marriage, serene and proper, but based on passionate physical love. On her wedding night before going to bed, Alexandra wrote in her husband's diary: "At last united, bound for life, and when this life is ended, we meet again in the other world and remain together for eternity. Yours, yours." The next morning, with fresh, new emotion, she wrote, "Never did I believe there could be such utter happiness in this world, such a feeling of unity between two mortal beings. I love you, those three words have my life in them."

THEY lived that first winter in the Anitchkov Palace, where Marie remained mistress. Although he ruled a continent, the young Tsar conducted official business from a small sitting room while the twenty-two-year-old Empress sat next door in the bedroom working on her Russian.

Nicholas and Alexandra dined with "Mother dear," and Nicholas, trying to comfort the widow, often stayed afterward. At dinner Alexandra was ignored, and Marie treated Nicholas like a schoolboy. She gave advice freely, never suspecting that Alexandra might be resenting her role, since to Marie, Alexandra was still simply an awkward German girl.

As the period of mourning ended, Marie returned to the brilliant lights, the clothes, the jewelry she loved. In Russia, a dowager empress took precedence over an empress. At public ceremonies Marie, blazing with diamonds, walked on the arm of her son while Alexandra followed with one of the grand dukes. The leading role seemed natural to Marie; when she dis-

covered that Alexandra was bitter, she was surprised and hurt.

Alexandra felt and behaved much like any young wife. Shocked by the sudden blow which had struck Marie, her first reaction toward the widow was sympathetic. Before long, however, the strain of living under the same roof and competing for the same man with her mother-in-law began to tell. Despite elaborate politeness between "dear Alix" and "Mother dear," veiled hostility began to appear. Certain crown jewels, for instance, traditionally passed from one empress to the next, and protocol required that Alexandra wear them on formal occasions. But Marie had a passion for jewelry, and when Nicholas asked her to give up the gems, she bristled and refused. Humiliated, Alexandra declared that she no longer cared about them and would not wear them. Before public scandal occurred, Marie submitted.

The domestic tensions eased when Marie left to visit her family in Copenhagen. More important, Alexandra was pregnant. With delight, she and Nicholas began decorating their first real home, in the Alexander Palace at Tsarskoe Selo, fifteen miles south of St. Petersburg. "Sometimes, we simply sit in silence and admire the walls, the fireplaces, the furniture," Nicholas wrote. "Twice we went up to the future nursery. The rooms are remarkably airy, light and cozy." Both Nicholas and Alix marveled at their baby's growth. "It has become very big and kicks about a great deal inside," the Tsar wrote Marie.

As the date approached, Marie returned, bubbling with excitement. "You will let me know as soon as the first symptoms appear?" she wrote to Nicholas. "I shall fly to you, my dear children, and shall not be a nuisance except perhaps by acting as a policeman to keep everybody else away."

Both parents hoped that the new baby would be a son—a Tsarevich. But after a protracted labor, during which Alexandra suffered intensely, a girl was born—the Grand Duchess Olga Nicolaevna. Still, the joy of a baby dispelled the worries about her sex. There was time to have more children. Alexandra nursed and bathed Olga herself, sang her to sleep, and sat by the crib of the "precious little one" knitting jackets, bonnets and socks.

THE NEW TSAR WAS to be crowned in Moscow, after the twelve-month period of mourning. Nothing so meaningful to the nation could be left to the artificial Western-style St. Petersburg. But by tradition, an uncrowned Tsar did not enter Moscow until the day before his coronation. Nicholas and Alexandra went into retreat, outside the city, fasting and praying.

Meanwhile the city inhabitants painted and whitewashed buildings, hung strings of evergreen across doorways and draped the Russian flag from windows. They were buoyant. The coronation meant a three-day holiday, pageantry and feasting, the granting of pardons to prisoners, the lifting of fines and taxes.

The day of Nicholas's entry into Moscow, two ribbons of troops bordered the four-mile line of march, holding back the crowds. Every balcony and window was jammed. Imperial Guard cavalry in golden helmets led the procession. Cossacks came next, wearing long coats of red and purple, curved sabers banging against their soft black boots. Then came the nobility, in gold braid, crimson sashes, jeweled medals. On foot came the court orchestra, the court footmen, and then the court officials.

Nicholas rode alone, on a white horse. He was dressed in an army tunic, and his face was drawn and pale. Behind him rode the grand dukes and foreign and Russian princes. Then came Dowager Empress Marie, and, in a second carriage, Alexandra.

Mathilde was on one of the viewing platforms. "It was agonizing to watch the Tsar pass . . . the Tsar who was still 'Niki' to me, one I adored and who could not, could never, belong to me."

The following day, Nicholas and Alexandra were up at dawn. While Alexandra's hair was being done by her hairdresser, Nicholas sat nearby smoking. She practiced fastening and unfastening the clasps of her heavy coronation robe. Nicholas settled a crown on her head as he would in the cathedral, and the hairdresser used a diamond-studded hairpin to hold it in place. The pin went too far and the Empress cried out with pain, while the embarrassed hairdresser beat a retreat.

Beneath its five golden domes, the Ouspensky Cathedral glowed with light. Walls and ceiling were covered with luminous frescoes; before the altar stood the great iconostasis, a gold and jeweled screen. Light flickered from hundreds of candles. Before the altar stood ranks of metropolitans, archbishops, bishops and abbots, their miters glittering with diamonds, sapphires, rubies and pearls. Nicholas sat on a seventeenth-century throne with 870 diamonds embedded in it; the armrest was set with 85 diamonds, 144 rubies and 129 pearls. Alexandra sat by him on an ivory throne.

The coronation ceremony in which Nicholas swore to rule as Emperor and Autocrat of all the Russias* lasted five hours. (At one point, as Nicholas walked up the altar steps, the heavy chain of the Order of St. Andrew slipped from his shoulders and fell to the floor. Only those standing close noticed, and all were sworn to secrecy, lest it be taken as an unhappy omen.) At last, taking it from the hands of the Metropolitan, Nicholas put on the nine-pound Imperial Crown of Russia, shaped like a bishop's miter, with a cross of diamonds surmounting an enormous uncut ruby. Then Nicholas put it on Alexandra's head for a moment, and replaced it on his own. Alexandra was given a smaller crown. The ceremony ended with the Imperial family approaching to do homage. To Alexandra, the ceremony seemed a mystic marriage between herself and Russia. She now thought of herself not only as Empress, but as *Matushka*, the Mother of the Russian people.

As the monarchs left the church in brocaded mantles embroidered with the double-headed Imperial eagle, a mighty cheer

---

* Nicholas's complete title was: Emperor and Autocrat of all the Russias, Tsar of Moscow, Kiev, Vladimir, Novgorod, Kazan, Astrakhan, of Poland, of Siberia, of Tauric Chersonese, of Georgia, Lord of Pskov, Grand Duke of Smolensk, of Lithuania, Volhynia, Podolia and Finland, Prince of Estonia, Livonia, Courland and Zemgalia, Samogitia, Bialystok, Karelia, Tver, Yougouria, Perm, Viatka, Bulgaria; Lord and Grand Duke of Lower Novgorod, of Chernigov, Ryazan, Polotsk, Postov, Yaroslav, Byelozero, Oudoria, Obdoria, Condia, Vitebsk, Mstislav and all the region of the North, Lord and Sovereign of the countries of Iveria, Cartalinia, Kabardia and the provinces of Armenia, Sovereign of the Circassian Princes and the Mountain Princes, Lord of Turkestan, Heir of Norway, Duke of Schleswig-Holstein, of Storman, of the Ditmarsh, and of the Oldenburg—etc.

came from thousands of throats. Massed cannons thundered and then the thousands of church bells of Moscow clanged. The ringing of the Kremlin bells obliterated all other sound there.

Among the seven thousand noble guests who dined at the banquet afterward, was a room filled with Russians in simple dress: descendants of people who had saved the life of a Russian Tsar. The most honored were the descendants of a servant, Ivan Sousanin, who had refused under torture to tell the Poles where young Michael, first of the Romanov Tsars, was hiding.

For the rest of the day, Nicholas and Alexandra greeted their guests in the great Kremlin halls. The huge coronation crown came down almost over the Tsar's eyes and it gave him a headache. That night there was a ball at which the gowns worn by the Russian ladies were thought by foreigners to be shockingly far off the shoulder. Nicholas's sister Xenia and Alexandra's sister Elizabeth were covered with emeralds. Other women were drowning in sapphires and rubies. Alexandra wore a thick girdle of diamonds around her waist, and Nicholas was draped with an enormous collar made of dozens of clusters of diamonds. Even to those who had seen many kingly fortunes, the jewels which appeared that night brought gasps of awe.

THE NEXT day there was the traditional feast for the people in Khodynka Meadow, a troop training ground crossed with shallow trenches, outside the city. Enameled cups stamped with the Imperial seal were to be given away as souvenirs, and the authorities had ordered hundreds of barrels of free beer.

By dawn, a half million Moscow dwellers waited in the meadow, some already drunk. When wagons loaded with souvenir cups and beer arrived and drew up behind skimpy wooden railings, the crowd moved forward, full of good nature. Suddenly a rumor passed that there would be beer enough only for those who got there first. People began to run. The Cossack guards were brushed aside. Men tripped in the ditches and fell beneath the feet of others. Women and children were knocked down by the crowd and trampled.

By the time police and more Cossacks arrived, the meadow resembled a battlefield. Hundreds were dead and thousands injured. Moscow hospitals were jammed. Nicholas and Alexandra were stunned, and the Tsar's first frantic impulse was to go immediately into retreat in a monastery. He declared he could not possibly go to the ball being given that night by the French Ambassador, but his powerful uncles urged that he not magnify the disaster by failing to appear and thus giving offense to France. Tragically, the young Tsar gave in. It was a painful evening; Alexandra's eyes were red from tears.

Nicholas and she spent the next day going from one hospital to another. Nicholas ordered that the dead be buried in separate coffins at his expense rather than in the common grave customary for mass disasters. The family of every victim received a thousand rubles. But many Russians took the disaster as an unhappy omen, while others thought their attendance at a ball following the tragedy underscored the heartlessness and shallowness of the young Tsar and his "German woman."

Bridge in Paris memorializing
Alexander III

AFTER a coronation, newly crowned monarchs were expected to make state visits and calls on fellow sovereigns. Of all the countries they visited, France gave Nicholas and Alexandra the most emotional and overwhelming ovation. In Paris, Nicholas laid a foundation stone for a bridge, the Pont Alexander III over the Seine. Huge crowds frantically waved and shouted as they went by, even shouting *"Vive le bébé"* and *"Vive la nounou"* when they saw Olga and her nurse. The impression the French left in the mind and heart of the young Tsar would one day serve France well.

Nicholas and Alexandra hated the journey back to Russia across Germany. "At every station in France one heard 'Hurrah' and saw jolly faces, but here everything was dark and boring."

Back at home, Nicholas plunged into "the awful job I have feared all my life." He attacked mountains of papers, wrote comments, signed orders. At first, feeling his way, he relied on Marie for guidance: "The various affairs you left me have all been attended to," he reported faithfully. But he did not always follow his mother's recommendations. When she asked as a favor the loan of one million rubles from the State Bank to a needy princess, Nicholas lectured her sternly on maintaining "the sound condition of our finances."

Far more difficult for Nicholas were his uncles: Vladimir, a gourmet and patron of the arts, and Commander of the Imperial Guard; the charming *bon vivant* Alexis, Grand Admiral of the Russian Navy ("His was a case of fast women and slow ships," people said) and Serge, husband of Alexandra's sister Elizabeth, the reactionary Governor General of Moscow. Only Paul, a mere eight years older than Nicholas, made no trouble for the Tsar.

"Nicholas spent the first ten years of his reign sitting behind a massive desk in the palace and listening to the well-rehearsed bellowing of his towering uncles," wrote the Tsar's cousin Alexander. "He dreaded to be left alone with them. In the presence of witnesses his opinions were accepted as orders, but the instant the door of his study closed on the outsider, down on the table would go with a bang the weighty fist of Uncle Alexis—two hundred and fifty pounds, packed in the resplendent uniform of Grand Admiral of the Fleet. Uncle Serge and Uncle Vladimir had equally efficient methods of intimidation."

Nicholas was now manager of the Imperial estate. His income of twelve million dollars a year came partly from an annual Treasury appropriation and partly from the profits of millions of acres of crown lands—vineyards, farms and cotton plantations—valued in 1914 at some fifty million dollars. Another eighty million dollars was frozen in the form of jewelry bought in three centuries of rule, including the 194.5-carat Orlov diamond set in his scepter, and a superb 40-carat ruby, the Polar Star.

The most admired jewels of all came from the famous court

jeweler, Peter Carl Fabergé, whose creations are now fabulous collectors' items. His workshops in St. Petersburg employed five hundred jewelers, smiths and apprentices. He did an enormous business in silver and gold dinner services, but his lasting fame rests on his jewelry.

It was his genius to subordinate the emphasis on precious stones to the pattern of the work. In their designs, his craftsmen used translucent enamel as the primary material, lining the edges with tiny diamonds. The result was a masterpiece of restraint, elegance and beauty. In Russia, no princely wedding or birthday was complete without a shower of Fabergé jewelry, cigarette cases, writing sets, tiny animals, figures or other miniatures.

The supreme expressions of his art were his fifty-six Imperial

One of Fabergé's masterpieces, this enamel Easter egg was given by Nicholas to Alexandra as an anniversary present. (Panels from it are reproduced, in actual size, throughout this condensation.) Part of the Forbes Magazine Collection of Fabergé, it was shown recently in the Metropolitan Museum's popular exhibition, "In the Presence of Kings."

Easter eggs—shells which opened revealing a "surprise." Inside, there might be a basket of wild flowers made of chalcedony petals and gold leaves. Or the top of the egg might fly open every hour on the hour to elevate a jeweled, enameled cockerel which crowed and flapped its wings.

But the Tsar's private purse was often empty. There were seven palaces to be kept up, fifteen thousand officials and servants to support. There were the Imperial trains and yachts, three theaters in St. Petersburg, two in Moscow, the Imperial Academy of Arts and the Imperial Ballet—all maintained by the Tsar. Every member of the Imperial family received an allowance from him. Each grand duke was given $100,000 a year and each grand duchess received a dowry of $500,000. Hospitals, orphanages, and institutions for the blind depended on Imperial charity. Before the end of the year—sometimes as early as autumn—the Tsar was usually penniless.

In running his family and empire, Nicholas looked to his father and the Russian past, preferring to be Russian down to the smallest details. At his desk, he wore a Russian peasant blouse, baggy breeches and leather boots. Although French was the language of the upper classes, he insisted that his ministers report to him in Russian and was displeased even by the insertion of a foreign phrase. However, he spoke and wrote English to Alexandra, whose Russian was awkward.

In his work habits, Nicholas was solitary. Unlike most chiefs of state—unlike even his own wife—he had no private secretary. On his desk he kept a large calendar of his daily appointments, scrupulously entered in his own hand. When official papers arrived, he opened them, read them, signed them and put them in envelopes himself.

The result of this sense of privacy, plus his hatred of scenes, was that Nicholas never mastered the technique of forceful, efficient management of subordinates. His ministers, in theory, were his servants, and he was free to ignore or to dismiss them without explanation. In practice, they were proud, sensitive heads of large government departments where continuity was an administrative necessity.

Nicholas found it impossible to criticize a man to his face. Even if something was wrong, he preferred to give him a friendly reception and comment gently. Occasionally, after such an interview, a government official would return to his office well pleased with himself, only to receive in the morning mail a letter regretfully asking for his resignation. Not unnaturally, these men complained that they had been deceived.

Because the young Nicholas was influenced at first by his mother, his uncles and his old tutor, who held a high religious office, his enemies declared that he had no will of his own. It would be more accurate to say that he was a man of narrow education, of strong and—unfortunately—unchanging conviction, but of kindly manner and stubborn courage. Even Sergius Witte, the brilliant Minister of Finance, whose abrupt dismissal from office gave him a venomous hatred of Nicholas, nevertheless wrote, "In those days, the young Emperor carried in himself the seeds of the best that the human mind and heart possess."

To the despair of Russian liberals, Nicholas made it bluntly clear that he would abide by his father's autocratic principles in domestic affairs. But Nicholas was anxious for peace and in 1898 he issued a dramatic appeal calling for a conference to study the lamentable effects of the armaments race and to work for "universal peace."

Europe was astonished by this strange proposal from "semi-barbaric" Russia. The Prince of Wales described it as "rubbish," and the Kaiser was frantically hostile. Nevertheless, twenty-six world powers attended the conference at The Hague in 1899. The Russian proposals for freezing armament levels were defeated, but the convention agreed on rules of warfare. This led to the International Court of Justice which still exists.

Building in The Hague where the Peace Conference met.

THE YOUNG Tsar's family grew rapidly. Tatiana was born in June 1898; Marie in May 1899, and Anastasia in June 1901. But along with births, there were illnesses and deaths. Nicholas's brother George died at twenty-seven of tuberculosis, and in the fall of 1900, Nicholas came down with typhoid fever. Alexandra rebelled at the idea of a nurse and nursed him herself.

Scarcely had he recovered when Queen Victoria died. Only the summer before, when the eighty-one-year-old Queen had invited the Empress to England, Alexandra had written to a friend: "How intensely I long to see her dear old face. . . . Never have we been separated so long, four whole years." Alexandra wanted to start immediately for the funeral, but being pregnant with Anastasia, she was persuaded not to go.

The death of her grandmother removed a source of stability and encouragement for Alexandra. Victoria had always worried, for instance, about Alexandra's excessive shyness. This had been a problem ever since Alexandra's first public appearance as Empress, when, standing beside her husband at a ball, her eyes were cold with fright and her tongue stilled by nervousness.

Her receptions for the ladies of St. Petersburg were blighted by the same shyness. As the reception line filed past, the guests confronted a tall figure, standing silent and cold. Her hand hung awkwardly in the air waiting to be kissed. Her tight mouth, her glance down the line to see how many more were coming, plainly indicated that Alexandra's only desire was to get away.

It did not take many balls and receptions before nervousness and uncertainty turned on both sides to active dislike. Alexandra's strict Victorian standards had not prepared her for the gay, loose society of St. Petersburg. Shocked by the all-night parties, the malicious gossip, the flaunted love affairs, she took the palace invitation list and began crossing out prominent names.

Many people in St. Petersburg society quickly dismissed the young Empress as a prude and a bore. They enjoyed the friction between Alexandra and her mother-in-law, Marie, siding openly with Marie and talking longingly of gayer days. There was a story that at one of her first balls, Alexandra had sent a lady-in-waiting to speak to a young woman: "Madame, Her Majesty wishes me to tell you that in Hesse-Darmstadt we don't wear our dresses that way."

"Really?" the young woman replied. "Pray tell Her Majesty that in Russia we *do* wear our dresses this way."

Alexandra's zeal about Orthodoxy embarrassed society. Orthodox from birth, they thought her aggressive collecting of rare icons, her pilgrimages, her talks with abbots and holy hermits were crankish. When she tried to organize a society whose members would knit garments for the poor, most St. Petersburg ladies declared that they had no time for such rubbish.

Everything conspired against young Alexandra. She had lived in Russia barely one month when she came to the throne. She spoke almost no Russian. She made errors in court etiquette and gave offense. Her plans to make friends by giving lunches were interrupted by her difficult pregnancies. After the births, she nursed each child and disliked being far from the nursery.

The Imperial family—closely knit, like most Russian families—resented the way in which the Empress sealed them off from the palace and the Tsar. They were accustomed to frequent visits; but, anxious to be alone with her husband, Alexandra was slow to issue invitations. The family became indignant.

Alexandra's sister, Grand Duchess Elizabeth, who might have acted as a bridge between the throne and society, had moved to Moscow, and between the Empress and the aristocracy it became an unhappy cycle of dislike and rebuff.

But Alexandra told herself that the jaded nobility were not real Russians at all: nor were the striking workers, nor the revolutionary students, nor the difficult ministers. The peasants, the humble people who fell on their knees to pray for the Tsar, were the real heart and soul of Holy Russia. To them, she was certain, she was more than just an Empress; she was truly Matushka, the Mother of the Russian people.

ALEXANDRA's view of life in the Russian provinces, although oversimplified, was generally accurate. The countryside was studded with manor houses of country squires loyal to the Tsar, and with peasant villages which still clung to the traditional patterns of life. At times a current of unrest might run through one of these sleepy provincial towns, but overwhelmingly the prevailing mood was conservative.

Such a town, in the 1880s and 1890s, was Simbirsk, isolated on a hill above the Volga River, among apple and cherry orchards. Yet it was, ironically, the childhood home of two men who would play major roles in the overthrow of Nicholas and Alexandra. One was Alexander Kerensky. The other was Vladimir Ilyich Ulyanov—later called Lenin.

Lenin's father was a successful educator, who, though the son of a freed serf, was given the rank of hereditary nobleman. His mother was a German whose father was a doctor. Lenin was the third of six children. He was a stocky, red-haired boy who would even as a grown man enjoy skating, fishing, hunting, and gymnastics on a pair of crossbars he made himself. He was precise and sarcastic, and an excellent student. When his brothers and sisters brought their marks home, and solemnly reported them to their parents, he simply burst up the stairs, shouting, "Excellent in everything!"

The comfortable Ulyanov household collapsed within a span of sixteen months in 1886–87. Once, replying to a census question about religion, Lenin wrote: "Nonbeliever since the age of 16." This was his age when his father died of a stroke before his eyes. Then, in the spring of 1887, his older brother Alexander was arrested on the charge of trying to assassinate Alexander III with a crude bomb concealed inside a hollowed-out medical dictionary. He was hanged in the spring of Lenin's final year in high school, his mother walking beside him to the gallows, repeating over and over, "Have courage. Have courage."

The effect of his brother's death on Lenin is a subject of dispute, for there is evidence of friction between the two. "Undoubtedly gifted, but we don't get along," Alexander had said of Lenin. He particularly disliked Lenin's arrogance and his mockery of their mother.

Outwardly, at least, unperturbed by the hanging, Lenin graduated at the head of his class. He entered the University of Kazan but was expelled for taking part in a student demonstration. He studied law at home, crammed four years of work into a single year, and passed the law examinations brilliantly. But he failed in his brief attempt at legal practice, and, with his usual intensity, began to study Karl Marx. To his mother's despair, he turned every family meal into a heated discussion of *Das Kapital*. She despaired even more when he announced that since the core of the revolution would be the urban proletariat, he was moving to St. Petersburg.

There he worked in a law office, joined a Marxist study group and, at a traditional Russian Shrove Tuesday supper of blinis, met his future wife, Nadezhda Krupskaya, a round-faced, snub-nosed schoolteacher and also a dedicated Marxist.

In 1895 Lenin visited western Europe and returned to Russia with a false-bottomed trunk stuffed with Marxist literature. He plunged into organizing strikes and printing anti-government leaflets. Arrested that December, he spent a year in jail and then was exiled for three years to Siberia.

If a political exile had money, he could live in Siberia at that time exactly as he always had, and Lenin's three years in a backwater Siberian village were among the happiest of his life. He worked on his first book, and through his enormous mail maintained contact with Marxists in every corner of Russia and Europe. He was delighted to have Krupskaya, now in exile, join him; they were married in Siberia in 1898. Lenin was less happy to welcome his mother-in-law, whom he disliked; but all three of them loved the clear, glowing Siberian air, the peaceful silence of the winter woods.

When his term ended, Lenin, later joined by his wife and mother-in-law, began life in Europe as an influential revolutionary writer and leader. When his followers were victorious at a conference of all revolutionary factions in exile, they took the name of *Bolsheviki*—"Majorityites."

UNLIKE LENIN, Alexander Kerensky, the future Premier of Russia, felt Russia deeply as a child, the traditional Russia with its Tsars and Orthodox Church. He studied at the university in St. Petersburg, and later he wrote, "I doubt whether higher education was so cheap and so accessible anywhere in the world as it was then in Russia. The lecture fees were negligible, laboratory experiments and practical work free." But Kerensky too became caught up in student agitation and strikes. Humanitarian and idealistic, he traveled all over Russia, defending political prisoners.

Before he left St. Petersburg for this work, in 1905, an extraordinary episode occurred. "It was Easter," he wrote later, "and I was returning from the traditional midnight celebration. I cannot attempt to describe the enchanting spell of St. Petersburg in the spring, in the early hours before dawn—particularly along the Neva or the embankments. Suddenly, just opposite the Winter Palace, I stopped involuntarily. On an overhanging corner balcony stood the young Emperor, alone, deep in thought. A keen presentiment struck me: 'We should meet sometime, somehow our paths would cross.' "

LIKE MARIE, the Grand Dukes, and the Tsar's ex-tutor, Kaiser Wilhelm II of Germany tried to take young Nicholas in hand. From the first months of his cousin's reign, Wilhelm peered over his shoulder, flattered him, lectured him and for a time dominated him. Eventually, an older and wiser Nicholas shook off this meddlesome influence, but the harm was done. Urged on by Wilhelm, Russia had suffered a military catastrophe in Asia.

In character, the two cousins were totally unlike. Nicholas was gentle, shy, and painfully aware of his limitations. The Kaiser was a braggart and a bully, restless and vain, and constantly plunging from hysterical excitement to black despair. Nicholas hated the idea of becoming Tsar; Wilhelm all but wrenched the crown from the head of his dying father.

Wilhelm's thin bleak face was partially masked behind his proudest possession, his wide, brushy mustache. This elegant bush helped compensate, in part, for his miniature left arm, caused by an obstetrician's excessive use of forceps. As much as possible, Wilhelm kept the damaged limb out of sight, tucking it into especially designed pockets in his clothes. His good arm became extraordinarily powerful, and his grip was as strong as iron. He increased the sensation by turning the rings on his right hand inward, so that the jewels would bite deep into the flesh of those he greeted.

He scribbled furiously on the margins of official documents: "Lies!" "Rascals!" "False as a Frenchman usually is!" "England's fault, not ours!" and then signed them: "The All Highest." He treated his dignitaries with an odd familiarity, often giving venerable admirals and generals a friendly smack on the backside. "If the Kaiser laughs, which he is sure to do a good many times," wrote one observer, "he will laugh with absolute abandonment, throwing his head back, shaking his whole body, and often stamping with one foot to show his excessive enjoyment of any joke." At a colonial exhibition, he was shown the hut of an African king, with the skulls of the king's enemies impaled on poles. "If only I could see the Reichstag stuck up like that!" blurted the Kaiser, who hated parliaments.

His mother once wrote to *her* mother, Queen Victoria: "You ask how Willy was when he was here. He was as rude, as disagreeable and as impertinent to me as possible."

Nicholas was both repelled and attracted by the Kaiser's flamboyance, and soon the famous "Willy-Nicky" correspondence began. Writing in English and addressing himself to his "Dearest Nicky" and signing himself "Your affectionate Willy," Wilhelm bent himself to undo the anti-German alliance between Russia and France.

"The French Republic has arisen from revolution. Has it not staggered from bloodshed to bloodshed and war to war?" the Kaiser wrote. "Nicky, the curse of God has stricken that people. We Christian kings have one holy duty imposed on us by Heaven: to uphold the principle of the Divine Right of Kings."

Wilhelm sent the Tsar a portrait showing himself in shining armor, a huge crucifix in his raised right hand. At his feet crouched Nicholas clothed in a long Byzantine gown. On the Tsar's face, as he gazed up at the Kaiser, was a look of humble admiration. In the background cruised a fleet of German and Russian battleships. Wilhelm referred to himself as "the Admiral of the Atlantic," and to Nicholas as "the Admiral of the Pacific." He often raved about "the Yellow Peril," and he declared that Russia had a "Holy Mission" in Asia.

Russia's alliance with France withstood Wilhelm's assaults, but on the Pacific the Kaiser was successful. His hatred of Orientals was genuine but there was more to his game than simple prejudice. By turning Russia away from Europe, he left Germany a free hand with France. In addition, wherever Russia moved in Asia, she was certain to get into trouble with Britain or with Japan.

The Kaiser wasn't the only man filling Nicholas's head with expansionist dreams. The temptations were strong for Russia, which had no ice-free Pacific port, to go adventuring in Asia. The decrepit Chinese empire stretched like a rotting carcass along the Pacific, and, to Russia's chagrin, Japan now occupied several Chinese territories Russia coveted, among them the great ice-free harbor of Port Arthur. Russia declared that this constituted a menace to Far Eastern peace, and Japan, unwilling to risk a war at the time, was forced to disgorge the port.

During the Boxer Rebellion in China, Russia "temporarily" occupied Manchuria, and a group of Russian adventurers then resolved to steal Korea. They established the "Yalu Timber Company," and began moving soldiers disguised as workmen into Korea. If they ran into trouble, the Russian government could disown them. If they succeeded, the empire had a new province, and they themselves would have vast economic concessions.

Nicholas still believed in a peaceful settlement with Japan in the Orient—a "flabby" attitude which made the Kaiser bitter— but Japan could not stand by and watch the Russians planting the Tsar's double-headed eagle in every port facing their islands. Soon war became inevitable, but most Russians took it for granted that Russia would easily annihilate the Japanese "monkeys."

On February 8, 1904, without a formal declaration of war, Japanese destroyers suddenly attacked Port Arthur and Japanese infantry stormed its fortified heights. Nicholas's first instinct was to go to the front and place himself at the head of his troops. But his uncles overruled this. "Uncle Alexis thinks my presence with the army is not necessary—still, to stay behind is very upsetting to me." In January 1905, after a long siege, Port Arthur surrendered.

The Russian Far Eastern fleet and the Imperial Japanese Navy were more equal in size; but with the first surprise attack, the Japanese had gained command of the sea. When the remaining Russian fleet appeared in the Strait of Tsushima, between Japan and Korea, Admiral Togo, the Japanese commander, ranged his ships across the head of the Russian columns, and, on May 27, 1905, sent a blizzard of shells into the Russian warships. The ships exploded, capsized or began to drift. Within forty-five minutes the greatest sea battle since Trafalgar was over. All eight Russian battleships were lost, along with seven of their twelve cruisers and six of their nine destroyers.

The Tsar was traveling aboard the Imperial train when the news of the disaster reached him. Recognizing that Russia no longer had a chance of winning the war, he sent for Sergius Witte, a huge, burly man with the ablest administrative brain in Russia, and dispatched him to America to make the best of the peace conference Theodore Roosevelt had offered to mediate. Witte found Americans filled with admiration for the "plucky little Japs," and set out to reverse this image. "I succeeded," he wrote. "I treated every American, of whatever social position, as an equal. This behavior was a heavy strain on me, but it was worth the trouble."

After lunching with President Theodore Roosevelt at Sagamore Hill, Witte described the meal as "almost indigestible. There was no tablecloth and ice water instead of wine." He was struck by Roosevelt's "ignorance of international politics." Nor did Roosevelt care much for Witte. Said the President, "I thought his bragging and bluster not only foolish, but shockingly vulgar when compared with the gentlemanly restraint of the Japanese." But, in fact, Witte had handled the negotiations brilliantly, and the Japanese Komura, who had come as a victor, had to accept a compromise.

The Russian giant staggered back to Europe. The Kaiser was not displeased. The Tsar, with a defeated army, no navy, and an embittered people, was no longer a neighbor to be feared. The Kaiser's influence faded, but Nicholas had lost a war.

VYACHESLAV PLEHVE, Minister of the Interior, had been a professional policeman. He was described by a colleague as "a splendid man for little things, a stupid man for affairs of state." As

Minister, he permitted no political assemblies of any kind. Students were not allowed to walk together in Moscow or St. Petersburg. Any party for more than a few people had to have written permission from the police. He drove many of Russia's five million Jews, a special object of his hatred, into the ranks of revolutionary terrorism.

In July 1904 Plehve was blown to pieces by an assassin's bomb. But his death did not destroy his most inventive project, a workers' movement secretly created and guided by the police. The organization was led by a priest, Father Gapon, whose interest in the people was genuine, and who hoped by his movement to immunize the workers against revolutionary viruses. In his Assembly of Russian Workingmen, grievances were to be channeled away from the government toward the employers. The mass of workers were happy to have any machinery which enabled them to air their grievances.

The humiliating war news had started a wave of protest against mismanagement of the war. In St. Petersburg, a minor strike at a steel works suddenly spread until thousands of workers were out. Swept along by this surge of feeling, Gapon rejected his role as a police agent and rallied the workers with an extravagant theatrical vision of a mass march to the Winter Palace, with a petition to Nicholas. Gapon visualized the Batiushka Tsar, on a balcony above a vast sea of Russian faces, delivering his people from their evil oppressors.

The Gapon petition demanded a parliament, universal suffrage, universal education, separation of church and state, amnesty for political prisoners, an income tax, a minimum wage and an eight-hour day. Gapon informed the government that the march would take place on Sunday, January 22, 1905, and asked that the Tsar receive the petition.

Prince Mirsky, the current Minister of the Interior, became alarmed. He had no intention of having the Tsar there. Nicholas was at his palace at Tsarskoe Selo, and was not even told of the march and the petition until Saturday night. All Mirsky and his colleagues could think of to do was to bring additional troops into the city and hope that matters would not get out of hand.*

Sunday morning, with an icy wind driving flurries of snow, Father Gapon began his march with the workers. Locking arms, they streamed peacefully through the streets in rivers of cheerful, expectant humanity. Some carried crosses, icons and religious banners; others national flags and portraits of the Tsar. They sang hymns and "God Save the Tsar."

They were scheduled to arrive at the Winter Palace at two p.m., but they found their way blocked by lines of infantry, backed by Cossacks and Hussars. Uncertain, but anxious not to be late to see the Tsar, they moved forward. In a moment of horror, some soldiers opened fire. Bullets smacked into the bodies of men, women and children. Crimson blotches stained the snow. The official number of victims was ninety-two dead and several hundred wounded; the actual number was probably several times higher.

Gapon vanished and the other leaders of the march were seized and expelled from the capital. As they circulated through the empire, exaggerating the casualties into thousands, "Bloody Sunday" became a turning point in Russian history. It shattered the ancient belief that Tsar and people were one. As bullets riddled their icons and their portraits of Nicholas, the people shrieked, "The Tsar will not help us!" It would not be long before they added the grim corollary: "And so we have no Tsar." Abroad, the clumsy police action seemed premeditated cruelty.

Father Gapon, from his hiding place, issued a public statement bitterly denouncing "Nicholas Romanov—soul-murderer of the Russian empire." Later, revolutionary leaders, convinced that Father Gapon still had secret ties with the police, sentenced him to death and hung him.

When she heard the news of the massacre, Alexandra wrote, "The Russian people are deeply and truly devoted to their

---

* The era was one of bitter labor strife not only in Russia but in all industrial nations. In the United States, for example, during the Pullman strike, William Howard Taft, the future President, wrote: "It will be necessary for the military to kill some of the mob before the trouble can be stayed." In the end, 30 were killed and 60 wounded.

Sovereign and the revolutionaries use his name for provoking them against landlords, etc.—I don't know how." Nicholas himself was stunned. When Witte suggested that the Tsar disassociate himself by declaring that the troops had fired without orders, Nicholas refused to cast this unfair aspersion upon the army. He decided instead to receive a delegation of hand-picked workers, and lectured them, as father to sons, on the need to reject the wicked advice of treacherous revolutionaries. But when these workers returned to St. Petersburg they were ignored, laughed at or beaten up.

"Bloody Sunday" was the beginning of a year of terror. Three weeks later, Grand Duke Serge was assassinated in Moscow. He had just said good-by to his wife in their Kremlin apartment, and was driving through one of the gates when a bomb exploded on top of him. Hearing the blast, Ella cried, "It's Serge," and rushed to him. What she found was unrecognizable pieces of flesh, bleeding into the snow.

The murder of her husband changed Ella's life. The gay, irrepressible girl who had guided her small, motherless sister Alix, disappeared. Her gentle, saintly qualities came forward. A few years later she built an abbey in Moscow and became the abbess, and wore for the rest of her life a long, hooded habit of pearl-gray wool and a white veil.

Violence now spread to every corner of Russia. In the Black Sea fleet, sailors of the battleship *Potemkin*, angered when they were served some bad meat, threw their officers overboard, raised the red flag and steamed along the Black Sea coast, bombarding towns, until the need for fuel forced them to intern at Constantsa. There was a general strike. "It makes me sick to read the news," said Nicholas. "But the ministers only assemble in council like a lot of frightened hens and cackle about action."

A new workers' organization bloomed. Consisting of elected delegates, one for each thousand workers, it called itself a *soviet*, meaning council. It grew rapidly in numbers and power, and a fiery leader emerged in Leon Trotsky. The revolution was at hand; it needed only a spark.

Nicholas described to his mother what happened next: "The ominous quiet days began. . . . One had the same feeling as before a thunderstorm. There were only two ways open: One was to crush the rebellion, but that would mean rivers of blood and in the end we should be where we started. The other way was to give to the people freedom of speech and press, and to have all laws confirmed by a state Duma—that of course would be a constitution. Witte says it is the only way out, and almost everybody is of the same opinion. Witte drew up an Imperial Manifesto, and after two days of discussion, invoking God's help, I signed it. My consolation is that such is the will of God and this grave decision will lead my dear Russia out of the intolerable chaos she has been in for nearly a year."

SERGIUS WITTE, who gave Russia its first constitution and its first parliament, believed neither in constitutions nor parliaments. "I have a constitution in my head, but as to my heart—" Witte spat on the floor.

But the Imperial Manifesto Witte drafted transformed Russia from an absolute autocracy into a semiconstitutional monarchy. It promised "freedom of conscience, speech, assembly and association." It granted an elected parliament, the Duma. The Tsar, however, retained his prerogative over defense and foreign affairs and the power to appoint and dismiss ministers.

Witte was installed as President of the Council of Ministers, but to his despair, rather than getting better, the situation grew steadily worse. The Right hated him for degrading the autocracy, the Liberals did not trust him, the Left feared that the revolution which it was anticipating would slip from its grasp. Trotsky wrote: "The proletariat rejects the police whip wrapped in the parchment of the constitution."

With the police stripped of many of their powers, violence flared. In the Baltic states, among others, peasants rose against their landlords and proclaimed a rash of little village republics. In the Ukraine and White Russia, bands of Ultra-Rightists began pogroms against the Jews. Soldiers crushed a revolt by the

Moscow Soviet, which proclaimed a new provisional government. Lenin slipped back into Russia to lead the Bolsheviks; the police found his trail and he was forced to flit from place to place. Still, he was gleeful. "Go ahead and shoot," he cried. "Summon Austrian and German regiments against Russian workers. We are for an international revolution."

Nicholas waited impatiently for his experiment in constitutionalism to produce results. As Witte stumbled, the Tsar became bitter. Though Witte tried to recapture his goodwill by cynically chopping away most of the strength from the Manifesto, Nicholas asked for his resignation.

In all these months of war and revolution, Nicholas and Alexandra had had one brief time of unshadowed joy. On August 12, 1904, the Tsar and his wife were finishing their soup at lunch when the Empress was forced to excuse herself and hurry to her room. Less than an hour later, a boy, weighing eight pounds, was born. Nicholas wrote in his diary: "A great, never-to-be-forgotten day. Alix gave birth to a son at one o'clock. The child has been called Alexis."

All across Russia, cannon thundered a salute of three hundred guns. Church bells clanged and flags waved. Alexis was the first male heir born to a reigning Tsar since the seventeenth century. It seemed an omen of hope.

The little Prince, a fat baby with yellow curls and blue eyes, was christened in the presence of most of his large family, including his great-grandfather King Christian IX of Denmark. But six weeks later, Nicholas wrote: "Alix and I have been very much worried. A hemorrhage began this morning without the slightest cause from the navel of our small Alexis. We called the surgeon Fedorov who applied a bandage. The child was quiet and even merry but it is a dreadful thing to have to live through such anxiety."

On the third day, the bleeding finally stopped. But the fear born in Nicholas and Alexandra grew as Alexis began to crawl and to try to walk. When he stumbled and fell, little bumps and bruises on his arms and legs grew to dark blue swellings. Beneath his skin, his blood was failing to clot. The terrifying suspicion of his parents was confirmed.

Alexis had hemophilia.

This grim knowledge, unknown outside the family, would remain in Nicholas's heart for the rest of his life. Those who saw him regularly began to notice his deepening fatalism. Nicholas had always been struck by the fact that he was born on the day in the Russian calendar set aside for Job. "I have a secret conviction," he said once, "that I am destined for a terrible trial." It is one of the ironies of history that the blessed royal birth of an only son should have proved the mortal blow to Imperial Russia.

PART TWO

Family Life

RUSSIAN Tsars and Empresses had created the enchanted village of Tsarskoe Selo near St. Petersburg. It was the supreme symbol of the Russian autocracy, as fantastic as a mechanical toy. Outside its park, bearded Cossacks rode night and day on patrol. Inside, monuments and triumphal arches studded eight hundred acres of velvet green lawn. At one end of a huge artificial lake that could be emptied and filled like a bathtub, stood a pink Turkish bath. Not far off, a red-and-gold Chinese pagoda crowned an artificial hillock. Scattered in clumps throughout the park, lilacs planted by empresses had grown into jungles. When the spring rain fell, the sweet smell of wet lilacs drenched the air. The big Catherine Palace—built by Catherine the Great—was an ornate structure with more than two hundred rooms. In 1812, Alexander I commissioned the smaller Alexander Palace. It was here that Nicholas had brought Alexandra in 1895, the spring after their marriage.

The palace had more than a hundred rooms. In winter, por-

celain stoves warmed them, and the smell of burning wood
mingled with the scent of smoking pots of incense carried by
footmen from room to room. Alexandra filled the palace with
flowers from the gardens and greenhouses. In autumn, blossoms
were brought in by train from the Crimea. Every room had its
swirl of odors: the sweetness of lilies in Chinese vases, the delicate fragrance of violets and lilies of the valley in silver bowls,
the perfume of hyacinths in lacquered pots.

A permanent garrison of five thousand infantrymen guarded
this paradise, and an army of servants and plainclothesmen
moved through it. At every door stood lackeys in pairs in varied
costumes, according to the room to which they were attached.
Protocol was rigid as granite.

Tsarskoe Selo was an elegant provincial town dominated by
the court. A week of excited conversation could follow an Imperial nod, a smile, or a word. There was no greater delight than
to have the telephone ring and hear a palace telephone operator
announce, "You are called from the apartments of Her Imperial
Majesty." Year after year slipped away, wrote Dr. Eugene Botkin,
the court physician, as "the enchanted little fairyland of Tsarskoe
Selo slumbered peacefully on the brink of an abyss."

The minister of the Imperial court, who dispensed favors and
gifts, knew all the secrets of the Imperial family, hushed up the
scandals and paid the debts of the Grand Dukes, was one of the
handsomest, most charming men of his generation, Count
Fredericks. Nicholas and Alexandra were devoted to "the Old
Man." In private, he addressed them as "*mes enfants.*"

But as old age crept over him, Fredericks' energies sagged.
He dozed off in the middle of conferences. He also became forgetful. Once, Prince Bariatinsky arrived to present the Tsar
with the Cross of St. George. On his way from one room to the
other to announce the Prince, Fredericks forgot what he was
supposed to do, and wandered off, leaving the Emperor and the
Prince, bewildered and angry, to wait in separate rooms.

Under the Empress's direction, the family wing of the Alexander Palace had been decorated in cretonnes and chintzes like a

comfortable English country house. But gigantic Negroes, dressed in scarlet trousers, gold-embroidered jackets and white turbans, stood guard outside the Tsar's study and the Empress's boudoir. Although they were referred to at court as Ethiopians, one was an American Negro named Jim Hercules. He took his vacations in America and brought back jars of guava jelly as presents for the children.

In the winter, Nicholas rose at seven, breakfasted with his daughters and disappeared into his study to work. Alexandra spent her mornings in bed or on a chaise longue, reading and writing long, emotional letters to her friends. At her feet lay a Scotch terrier named Eira, who liked to nip at people's heels. Alexandra doted on him and carried him from room to room.

Nicholas and Alexandra's large bedroom opened onto the park. Unlike many a royal couple, they had a double bed. Chairs and couches were covered in flowered tapestry, and there was a thick carpet in mauve—Alexandra's favorite color. A door led to a small chapel used by the Empress for her private prayers; another door led to a dark bathroom where primly Victorian Alexandra insisted that both bath and toilet be kept under cloth covers when not in use.

The most famous room in the palace—for a time the most famous room in Russia—was the Empress's mauve boudoir, her private sitting room. Everything in it was mauve. The furniture, cluttered with books, papers and knickknacks, was painted mauve and white. Masses of white and purple lilacs, vases of roses and orchids, and bowls of violets perfumed the air. The walls were covered with icons. There was a picture of the Virgin Mary and portraits of Queen Victoria and Marie Antoinette.

In this cluttered, cozy room, Alexandra felt secure. Here, in the morning, she talked to her daughters, helping them choose their dresses and plan their schedules. To this room Nicholas hurried to sit with his wife, sip tea, read the papers and discuss their children and their empire. Sometimes through the rooms of the private wing, a clear, musical whistle would sound. This was Nicholas's way of summoning his wife and his children. Early in her marriage, Alexandra, hearing the call, would blush red and drop whatever she was doing to hurry to him. Later, as his children grew up, Nicholas used it to call them.

Next to the mauve boudoir was the Empress's dressing room. Alexandra had six wardrobe maids, but her modesty severely limited their duties. No one ever saw the Empress Alexandra undressed or in her bath. Often it was Grand Duchess Tatiana who combed her mother's hair and piled the long red-gold strands on top of her head. The maids were summoned only to fasten buttons and clasp on jewelry.

For daytime, Alexandra wore loose, flowing clothes trimmed at the throat and waist with lace. She considered the famous hobble skirts of the Edwardian era a nuisance. "Do you really like that skirt?" she asked her friend Lili Dehn, whose husband was an officer on the Imperial yacht.

"Well, Madame, *c'est la mode*," replied the lady.

"It's no use whatever as a skirt," said the Empress. "Lili, run, and let me see how fast you can cover ground in it."

In the evening, Alexandra wore white or cream gowns, embroidered in silver and blue, with diamonds in her hair and pearls at her throat. She disliked filmy lingerie; hers was made of embroidered linen. Her shoes were low-heeled, usually bronze or white suede. Outdoors she carried a parasol to protect her fair complexion, even when wearing a wide-brimmed hat.

For the Imperial children, winter was a time of interminable lessons from tutors. Every morning, before classwork, Dr. Botkin looked at throats and rashes. Later, other doctors cared for the Tsarevich's hemophilia, but Botkin was the children's favorite. A tall, stout man who wore blue suits with a gold watch chain across his stomach, he exuded a strong perfume. The young Grand Duchesses tracked him from room to room by his scent.

At eleven every morning, the Tsar and his children stopped work and went outdoors for an hour of frisking with the Tsar's eleven English collies. In winter, Nicholas joined the children and their tutors in building "ice mountains"—big mounds of snow covered with water which froze and made a handsome run for sleds and small toboggans.

Dinner, the ceremonial meal, was at midday, with the Empress usually absent. The meal began with Father Vassiliev, the confessor to the Imperial family, rising to face an icon and bless the table. Of peasant origin, Vassiliev had never graduated from the Theological Academy, but what he lacked in schooling he made up in fervor. As he shouted his prayers in a cracked voice, Alexandra was convinced that he represented the simple, essential Orthodoxy of the Russian people. And as a confessor, he was comforting. No matter what sin was confessed to him, he smiled beatifically and said, "Don't worry. The Devil neither smokes nor drinks nor engages in revelry, and yet he is The Devil." At the Imperial table, Vassiliev in his long, black robe, with a black beard that reached to his waist, a five-inch silver cross dangling from his neck, gave the impression that a great black raven had settled down at the table of the Tsar.

Cubat, the palace chef, one of the greatest French chefs of his day, labored under a heavy burden, for Nicholas relished the simple food of the Russian peasant—cabbage soup, *borshch, kasha* (buckwheat), boiled fish and fruit—while Alexandra merely pecked at anything set before her. Nevertheless, when an especially elegant dish was being served, Cubat would stand hopefully in the doorway, immaculate in his white chef's apron and hat, waiting to receive the compliments of master and guests.

In the afternoon, when Alexandra often went for a drive in her open carriage with a coachman, two footmen and two grooms, a cumbersome apparatus of police surveillance was alerted. Every tree and bush along her route concealed a crouching policeman. Nicholas preferred to ride out on horseback accompanied by friends. Often he stopped to talk informally to peasants, asking them about village problems and the harvest. Sometimes, knowing that the Tsar rode that way, peasants from other districts waited by the road to hand him petitions or make special requests. In almost every case, Nicholas saw to it that the requests were granted.

At four, the family gathered for tea at small tables set with glasses in silver holders, plates of hot bread and English biscuits. Alexandra complained that "other people had much more interesting teas," but although she was Empress of Russia, she seemed unable to change a single detail of court routine. The same plates of hot bread and butter had been on the same tea tables since the days of Catherine the Great.

"Every day at the same moment," Alexandra's closest friend, Anna Vyrubova, recalled, "the door opened, the Emperor came in, sat down at the tea table, buttered a piece of bread and began to sip his tea. He drank two glasses every day. The children spent most of the hour playing on the floor with toys. As they grew older, needlework and embroidery were substituted. The Empress did not like to see idle hands."

Between five and eight p.m. Nicholas received a stream of callers with, the French Ambassador Maurice Paléologue said, "that gracious and somewhat shy kindness which is all his own." He received most visitors informally, gesturing them into an armchair. He was a careful listener, and, although he often grasped a conclusion before his visitor had reached it, he never interrupted. Precisely at eight, all official interviews ended so that the Tsar could go to supper.

The family suppers were informal, although the Empress invariably appeared in evening gown and jewels. Afterward, she went to the nursery to hear the Tsarevich say his prayers. Then, in the family drawing room, Nicholas read aloud while his wife and daughters sewed or embroidered. These pleasant, monotonous days ended at eleven with the serving of evening tea.

Nicholas wrote in his diary, and soaked himself in the bathtub before retiring. He usually went right to sleep, except when his wife kept him awake, still reading and crunching English biscuits on the other side of the bed.

The Imperial nurseries were directly over Alexandra's mauve boudoir, and were reached by a private elevator and a private stairway. In the morning, she could hear her children's footsteps and the sound of their pianos.

The four Grand Duchesses slept on hard camp beds without pillows and took cold baths. Their nurses were strict, although not without their weaknesses. Marie's English nurse, a Miss Eager, was fascinated by politics and talked incessantly about them. "Once she even forgot that Marie was in her bath and started discussing a political case with a friend," wrote the Tsar's sister, Olga. "Marie, naked and dripping, scrambled out of the bath and started running up and down the palace corridor. Fortunately, I arrived just at that moment, picked her up and carried her back to Miss Eager, who was still talking politics."

OLGA   TATIANA   MARIE   ANASTASIA

Olga, the eldest, was most like her father. She had a good mind, and often borrowed books from her mother's tables before the Empress had read them. "You must wait, Mama, until I find out whether this book is a proper one for you to read," she parried when Alexandra spotted her reading a missing book. She had long chestnut-blond hair and blue eyes set in a wide Russian face. Shy with those she did not know well, she impressed people by her kindness, her innocence and the depth of her feelings.

Tatiana, the tallest and most elegant of the sisters, was closest to Alexandra. She had rich auburn hair and deep gray eyes. She was energetic, assured and purposeful. In public she regularly outshone her older sister. Among the five children she was the one who made the decisions or asked "Papa" to grant a favor. Her younger sisters and brother called her "the Governess."

Marie—"Mashka"—was the prettiest of the girls. She had red cheeks, thick, light brown hair and dark blue eyes so large that they were known in the family as "Marie's saucers." She was merry and flirtatious, and a bit lazy. What Marie liked most was to talk about marriage and children. Had she not been the Tsar's daughter, this warmhearted girl would have made some man an excellent wife.

Anastasia was a short, blue-eyed child renowned in her family chiefly as a tomboy and an impertinent mimic. Witty and vivacious, she also had a streak of stubbornness and mischief in her. She liked to climb trees to dizzying heights, refusing to come down until commanded by her father.

Cloistered at Tsarskoe Selo, without a normal range of friends, the four young Grand Duchesses were closer to each other than most sisters. They chose for themselves a single autograph, OTMA, from the first letter of each name, to use on gifts and to sign letters. Rank meant little to them. They worked alongside their maids in making their beds and straightening their rooms, and when they gave instructions, it was never as a command. They said, "If it isn't too difficult for you . . ."

They took a keen interest in the people of the household. They knew the names of the Cossack guards and the sailors on the Imperial yacht, and, talking to them, learned the names of their wives and children. They listened to their letters from home, looked at photographs and made small gifts. Each had an allowance of only nine dollars a month, so when they gave a present, it meant sacrificing something they wanted for themselves.

Convinced that the girls needed to get away from the palace, Nicholas's young sister, Olga, persuaded Alexandra to let her take them into town. So every Sunday they had a formal luncheon with their grandmother, Marie, at the Anitchkov Palace, and then went on to games and dancing with other young people at Olga's house. Olga wrote, over fifty years later, "I can still hear Anastasia's laughter rippling all over the room." Carefully chaperoned, the girls were also allowed to play tennis, to ride and dance with eligible young officers.

At twenty, Olga, the oldest girl, obtained the use of part of her large fortune. Seeing a child on crutches, she found that the parents were too poor to afford treatment. She began putting aside a monthly allowance to pay the bills.

As they grew up, the sisters made changes in their spare surroundings. The camp beds remained, but icons and pictures went up along the walls. Frilly dressing tables were installed. In their teens, the girls began taking warm perfumed baths. All four girls used Coty perfumes: Olga, *Rose Thé;* Tatiana, *Jasmin de Corse;* Anastasia, *Violette;* and Marie, *Lilas.*

TSAREVICH ALEXIS

"ALEXIS was the center of this united family, the focus of its hopes and affections," wrote Pierre Gilliard, the devoted Swiss tutor who followed the family into exile and degradation. "His sisters worshipped him. He was his parents' pride and joy. When he was well, the palace seemed bathed in sunshine."

The Tsarevich was a high-spirited handsome little boy with dimples, blue eyes, and golden curls which later turned auburn and became straight. But the disease of hemophilia hung over the happy child like a dark cloud. Any bump or bruise rupturing a tiny blood vessel beneath the skin could begin the slow seepage of blood into surrounding muscle and tissue, make a hematoma, or swelling, as big as a grapefruit. Eventually, when the skin was hard and tight, filled with blood like a balloon, pressure slowed the hemorrhage and a clot formed. Then, gradually, a process of reabsorption took place. Minor cuts and scratches were treated by pressure and tight bandaging, but hemorrhages from the inside of the mouth or nose could not be bandaged. Once the Tsarevich almost died from a nosebleed.

The worst pain and the permanent crippling came from bleeding into the joints, where the blood caused pressure on the nerves and nightmarish pain. Alexis would awaken in the morning to call, "Mama, I can't walk today," or "Mama, I can't bend my elbow." At first, as the limb flexed, leaving the largest possible area in the joint for the fluids, the pain was small. Then, as this space filled up, it began to hurt. The Tsarevich was never given the habit-forming morphine. His only release from pain was fainting.

Once inside the joint, the blood destroyed tissue, cartilage and bone, and the limbs locked into a bent position. The therapy for this was exercise and massage—but at the risk of again beginning the hemorrhage. Alexis's treatment also included a grim catalogue of heavy iron orthopedic devices and hot mud baths.*

When he was five, his doctors suggested that Alexis be given male bodyguards to act as nurses. Two sailors from the Imperial Navy, Derevenko and Nagorny, were assigned to protect him. "Derevenko was patient and resourceful, and did wonders in alleviating the pain," wrote Anna Vyrubova. "I can still see the calm-eyed man working for hours to give comfort to the little pain-wracked limbs."

Hemophilia is a fickle disease. For weeks, sometimes months, Alexis seemed well. He was lively and mischievous. As a toddler, he would scoot down the hall and break into his sisters' classroom, only to be carried off, arms waving. At three, he often made the round at the Tsar's table, shaking hands and chattering with each guest. Once he plunged beneath the table, pulled off the slipper of one of the maids-of-honor and inserted an enormous ripe strawberry in its toe. Like any small boy, he filled his pockets with string, nails and pebbles.

"He thoroughly enjoyed life—when it let him—and he was a happy, romping boy," wrote Gilliard. "He was very simple in his tastes and he entertained no false satisfaction because he was the

---

* Today, at the first sign of severe bleeding, hemophiliacs are given transfusions of blood plasma or plasma concentrates. New, non-habit-forming drugs are used to lessen pain. Joints may be protected by intricate plastic and light metal braces. Most of these developments in the treatment are quite recent. Hemophilia today is a severe but more manageable disease, and most hemophiliacs can survive the difficult years of childhood to live relatively normal adult lives. There is a remote prospect that current research into chromosomes will one day help hemophiliacs. If it should become possible to locate, in the chromosomes, the genes responsible—and then to correct or substitute for the faulty gene—hemophilia could be cured.

Heir; there was nothing he thought less about." Still, he understood his own role. Told that a group of officers had arrived to call on him, he interrupted a romp with his sisters. "Now, girls, run away," the six-year-old boy said, "I am busy."

An active child, Alexis was attracted to the very things that involved the greatest danger, though his parents explained to him the need to avoid bumps and blows. "Can't I have a bicycle?" he would beg his mother. "Alexei, you know you can't." "May I please play tennis?" "Dear, you know you mustn't." Then Alexis would cry, "Why can other boys have everything and I nothing?"

There were times when Alexis ignored all restraints and did as he pleased. This risk-taking behavior, common enough among hemophilic boys to be labeled "the daredevil reaction," is compounded of rebellion against over-protection, a subconscious need to prove invulnerability and, most important, the desire to play like a normal child.

Once, at seven, Alexis appeared at a review of the palace guard, riding a secretly borrowed bicycle across the parade ground. The astonished Tsar halted the review and ordered every man to pursue, surround and capture the wobbling vehicle and its delighted novice rider. Again, at a children's party, Alexis led the children on top of the tables and began leaping wildly from table to table. When Derevenko tried to calm him, he shouted gaily, "All grown-ups have to go!" and tried to push him out the door.

Like his father, Alexis was enthralled by military pageantry. As "Hetman of all the Cossacks," he had a Cossack uniform with fur cap, boots and dagger. In the summer, he wore the uniform of a Russian sailor. He wanted to be like one of the ancient Tsars, riding his white horse into battle. But as he began spending more and more time in bed, he realized that he would never be that kind of Tsar.

He kept a number of pets. Once an old Siberian hunter and his wife decided to bring a tame sable to the palace as a present. The couple spent every kopeck they had on the long journey. Later, the old hunter described what happened: "Father Tsar came in. We threw ourselves at his feet. The sable looked as if it understood that it was the Tsar. We went into the children's room. The children began to play with the sable. Then the Tsar asked me questions: What things are like in Siberia, how we go hunting. Father Tsar told me to send the sable to the Hunters' Village at Gatchina. But I said, 'Father Tsar, that won't do. The hunters will want to sell the skin. They will say the animal had an accident.'

"The Tsar said: 'Perhaps you are right. Take it back with you to Siberia. But mind, don't forget to look after the sable; it's my sable now. God be with you!'" They were paid generously and given a watch and a brooch. When they left with the sable, the children were inconsolable; but "Papa had made up his mind."

Pets were only a substitute for what Alexis really wanted: playmates his own age. Carefully selected young military cadets were instructed on the dangers and brought to the palace to play with the Tsarevich. More often, he played with his sisters, or by himself. Once, as he lay on his back staring up at the sky, he said to Olga, "I like to think and wonder. I enjoy the sun and the beauty of summer as long as I can. Who knows whether one of these days I shall not be prevented from doing it?"

Pierre Gilliard's problem as tutor to Alexis was establishing discipline with the quick, sensitive boy. The Empress could not be firm with her son, and Alexis obeyed only the Tsar. His illness interrupted his lessons, sapping his interest. "But," Gilliard wrote, "the more the boy opened his heart to me, the better I realized the treasures of his nature. He was sensitive to suffering in others because he suffered so much himself."

Gilliard worried about Alexis's isolation. "The perpetual presence of the sailors was harmful to the child. It was impossible to guard against everything and the closer the supervision the more humiliating it seemed to the boy." Gilliard told the Tsar and the Tsaritsa that this could turn Alexis into "a characterless individual without backbone. To my astonishment, the parents agreed. They were ready to accept all risks of an experiment on which I did not enter myself without terrible anxiety.

"Then the accident I so much feared happened. The Tsarevich was standing on a chair when he slipped and in falling hit his right knee. The next day he could not walk. The day after, the swelling which formed below the knee rapidly spread down the leg. I was thunderstruck; but the parents did not blame me in the slightest—in fact they tried to keep me from despairing.

"The Tsaritsa was at her son's bedside from the onset of the attack, and the Tsar tried to amuse the boy. But moans and tears began once more. Now and then, one of the Grand Duchesses tiptoed in and kissed her little brother. For a moment, the boy would open his great eyes, and almost immediately, close them again. One morning I found the mother at her son's bedside. He had had a very bad night. His head rested on his mother's arm and his small white face was unrecognizable. At times, groaning, he murmured, 'Mummy.' She kissed him on the hair, forehead, and eyes. Think of the torture of that mother, who knew that she had transmitted the terrible disease, against which science was powerless!"

HEMOPHILIA has come down through the centuries misted in legend and the dark dread of a hereditary curse. In ancient Egypt a woman was forbidden to bear further children if her firstborn son bled to death from a minor wound. The Talmud barred circumcision in a family if two successive male children had suffered fatal hemorrhages.

The condition remains one of the most mysterious and malicious of the genetic, chronic diseases. It is transmitted by women; but while women carry the defective genes, with rare exceptions it strikes only males; though not all the males in a family, for hemophilia is capricious. If the child is a girl, the family cannot know whether she's a carrier until she has children. The secret is locked inside the structure of the chromosomes.

Today in the United States, forty percent of all the 200,000 known cases seem to have no traceable family history of the disease. One explanation for this is that the defective gene can remain hidden for as many as seven or eight generations. A more probable explanation is that the genes spontaneously change or mutate. Some researchers believe this is the result of new environmental factors like modern drugs, or radiation. In any case, hemophilia apparently is increasing.

Queen Victoria was a carrier of hemophilia. The youngest of her sons, Leopold, had hemophilia; he suffered a minor blow and died at thirty-one of a brain hemorrhage. Two of her daughters were carriers, and they and their daughters took the disease into the royal houses of the German states, Russia and Spain.

The British geneticist, J. B. S. Haldane, commented that although the genetic pattern of hemophilia was already known to doctors, this knowledge may never have penetrated the closed circles of royal courts. Nicholas probably knew that Alix had hemophilic brothers, but, because of his narrow education, attached no importance to that fact.

In any case, hemophilia had come to be considered one of the hazards royal parents faced, like diphtheria, scarlet fever and pneumonia. In that era, royal families had many children and, although the death of a child was never a casual experience, they expected to lose one or two in the process of growing up.

In Alexandra's case the mere threat of death to her youngest child involved her totally, and through her, the fate of an ancient dynasty and the history of a great nation. Why was this so?

It is important to understand what the birth of Alexis meant to Alexandra. Her greatest desire had been to give the Imperial family a male heir, for the crown no longer passed down through the female as well as the male line. When Anastasia was born, Nicholas had to walk in the park to overcome his disappointment before facing his wife. The birth of Alexis, then, meant far more than the arrival of just another child. Delirious with joy, Alexandra felt that this beautiful baby was God's blessing on her, on her husband, and on the people of Russia.

Because she had waited so long and prayed so hard for her son, the revelation that Alexis suffered from hemophilia struck Alexandra with savage force. From that moment she lived in the sunless world reserved for the mothers of hemophiliacs. For a woman, there is no more exquisite torture than watching help-lessly as her child suffers extreme pain, crying for her to help him. Almost worse was Alexandra's terrible uncertainty. One minute Alexis could be playing happily. The next, a fall might begin a bleeding episode that would take him to the brink of death. Alexandra's natural reaction was to overprotect her child. (The Spanish royal family put its hemophilic sons in padded suits and padded the trees in the park when they went out to play.) Except when the child was asleep, there could be no relaxation.

The toll on the Empress was like battle fatigue. When this happens to soldiers in war, they are withdrawn from the front to rest. For the mother of a hemophiliac there is no withdrawal. The characteristic reaction when a son is hemophilic is to fight: somehow, somewhere, there must be a specialist who can declare that a cure is just around the corner. The specialists are all consulted. They sadly shake their heads. The mother realizes that she is alone.

The Empress sought answers in the Orthodox Church, which believes in the healing power of prayer. Hour after hour, the Empress prayed, at home, in her private chapel, in crowded churches. When Alexis was well, she cried, "God has heard me." But as hemorrhages followed, she began to dwell on her own guilt. She had transmitted the disease, and God had rejected her prayers; therefore, she must find someone who was closer to God to intercede on her behalf. When Gregory Rasputin, a Siberian peasant who was reported to have miraculous powers of healing, arrived in St. Petersburg, Alexandra believed that God had at last given her an answer.

ONE SUPPORT the mother of a hemophiliac can hope for is understanding friends. But Alexandra had never made friends easily, and now she was on the lofty isolation of the throne. What she longed for was not the stylized attentions and conversations of court ladies, but the simple, profound friendship of the heart which shares the most intimate dreams, hopes and fears.

Outside her own family, the only person Alexandra found to

whom she could open her whole soul was the heavy, round-faced young Anna Vyrubova. Born Anna Taneyev, she was twelve years younger than Alexandra. Her father was Director of the Imperial Chancellery and moved in St. Petersburg society. When, at seventeen, Anna fell ill, Alexandra paid her a routine visit in the hospital, and the romantic girl, overwhelmed by the gesture, conceived a passionate admiration for the twenty-nine-year-old Empress. She was invited to the palace, and began to play and sing duets with Alexandra.

In 1907, Anna was being courted by Lieutenant Boris Vyrubov, a survivor of the Battle of Tsushima. Anna was reluctant to marry him, but Alexandra urged her to go ahead and, with the Tsar, was a witness at the wedding. Within months, the marriage collapsed. Tsushima had shattered Vyrubov's nerves, and the marriage was one in name only.

The Empress blamed herself and devoted much of her time to her lonely young friend. Anna poured her heart out to Alexandra, and Alexandra responded by talking of her own loneliness, her fears for her son. The tie between them grew so strong that they could sit for hours in silence, secure in unexpressed affection. On each side, wounds were healed and faith encouraged.

Anna moved into a small house inside the Imperial park, and often joined in the family's games and reading aloud after dinner. In conversation, she rarely had original opinions, preferring to endorse whatever Nicholas and Alexandra had just said. If husband and wife disagreed, her role was to come down ever so gently on the side of the Empress.

Unlike most royal favorites, she asked nothing for herself except attention and affection. Occasionally, Alexandra made her accept a dress or a few hundred rubles; usually Anna gave the money away. Yet Anna outraged many people at court. Some scorned her naïveté; others felt that an Empress of Russia deserved a more glittering companion than this dumpy, inelegant woman. But for the same reasons that others scorned Anna Vyrubova, the Empress prized her. Where others thought only of themselves, Anna's selflessness was rare and valuable.

Anna had an unqualified devotion to the peasant miracle-worker, Rasputin, who had prophesied the collapse of her marriage. She became convinced that he was divinely blessed. Certain that he could help Alexis, she became his passionate advocate. She telephoned him daily, transmitted his opinions to the Empress and urged them on her.

Later, rumor inflated Anna into a monster of depravity who reigned over sinister orgies at the palace and held major political influence over the Tsar and his wife. But those who dealt with her personally, all described her in the same terms: "a vehicle," "she understood nothing."

As ONE precarious year followed another, emotional stress took a terrible toll on Alexandra's health. As a girl, she had suffered from sciatica; now the battle against her son's hemophilia left her drained. At times of crisis, she spared herself nothing, sitting up day and night beside. Alexis's bed. But once the danger had passed, she collapsed, lying for weeks in bed or on a couch, moving about only in a wheelchair.

When the Tsarevich was four Alexandra developed a whole series of symptoms which she referred to as the result of an over-tired heart. She had shortness of breath, and exertion became an effort. Her sister-in-law Olga wrote, "I often saw her lips turn blue." Dr. Botkin, who listened to her heart twice a day, said years later that the Empress had "inherited a weakness of the blood vessels" which often led to "progressive hysteria." In modern medical terminology, the Empress undoubtedly was suffering from psychosomatic anxiety symptoms brought on by worry over the health of her son.

Alexandra's inability to participate in public life worried her husband. "She does not receive anyone, does not come out to lunches and remains on the balcony day after day," he wrote to Marie. "I am completely run down mentally by worrying over her health." He took her for treatment at the German spa of Nauheim; she came back rested but not cured. For the mother of a hemophiliac, as for the son, no cure has ever been found.

Russians are a compassionate people, warm in their love of children. They did not open their hearts to this anguished mother and her stricken child because they did not know. When Alexis missed a public function, it was announced that he had a cold or a sprained ankle. No one believed these explanations and it was rumored that the boy was mentally retarded, or an epileptic.

A revelation that the Imperial Heir lived under the shadow of death would have put pressures on the autocracy, but the wall of secrecy was worse. Russians viciously misunderstood the power Rasputin held over the Empress, and wrongly ascribed her look of sad remoteness to a haughty distaste for Russia and its people. She had never been understood, and she became steadily less popular. During the war, with national passions aroused, the complaints about her—her German birth, her coldness, her devotion to Rasputin—would blend into a sweeping torrent of hatred.

Beneath a plumed cloth-of-gold canopy, Nicholas and Alexandra follow priests to coronation.

EACH March, the Imperial family left Tsarskoe Selo for the flowering Crimea. In May they moved to their Baltic villa at Peterhof; in June they cruised the Finnish fjords on their yacht; August found them at Spala, Poland, in a hunting lodge; in September they went back to the Crimea; in November, they returned to Tsarskoe Selo.

The Imperial train which bore the Tsar and his family on these trips was a miniature traveling palace—a string of luxurious blue cars with the double eagle emblazoned in gold on their sides. The private car of Nicholas and Alexandra contained a large bedroom, a sitting room and a study. The bathroom boasted a tub designed so ingeniously that water could not slosh out when the train was rounding a curve. The Grand Duchesses and the Tsarevich also had a car; and a paneled lounge car with rugs, charts and sofas served as a gathering place for members of the Imperial suite, each of whom had a private compartment. There was a dining car with a well-equipped kitchen, and an anteroom where *zakuski* (hors d'oeuvres) were served before dinner.

But a trip on the Imperial train was not an unmitigated pleasure. There was always the nagging thought that the train might be blown up by revolutionaries. To make this less likely, two identical trains made every trip, traveling a few miles apart, so potential assassins could not know on which one the Tsar was riding.

The train rattled along at fifteen to twenty miles an hour, so the trip to the Crimea meant two nights and a day of bumping and jostling across the interminable Russian landscape. In summer, the sun turned the salon cars into carpeted ovens, and the train often halted for half an hour to let the passengers get out, stretch their legs and cool themselves. Once, when it was stopped at the top of a high embankment, the children took large silver trays from the pantry and used them to toboggan down the slope.

General Strukov, an aide-de-camp, shouted to them that he would beat them on foot to the bottom. Wearing his formal uniform with his diamond-studded sword of honor in hand, the general threw himself down the bank. He slid for twenty feet, became mired to his knees and gallantly waved as the children glided past, giggling with pleasure, on their silver toboggans.

Nicholas's yacht for cruising along the rocky, pine-forested coast of Finland was a 4500-ton black-hulled beauty named *Standart*. Her gleaming decks were covered with white canvas awnings and lined with wicker tables and chairs. Below were drawing rooms, lounges and dining rooms paneled in mahogany, with crystal chandeliers and velvet curtains. But life aboard the *Standart* was informal. During the day, the girls wandered the decks unescorted, wearing white blouses and polka-dotted skirts. Shipboard flirtations sprang up between young officers and the blossoming Grand Duchesses.

Because of her sciatica, Alexandra rarely left the *Standart*. She spent the days sitting on deck, doing needlework, writing letters, playing Bach, Beethoven and Tchaikovsky at the piano. At first, the girls took turns staying aboard to keep her company: then Anna Vyrubova took over.

At teatime, the Tsar and the children returned with wild flowers, mosses, mushrooms, cups of berries and pieces of quartz. As the last slanting rays touched trees, rocks and water with golden light, Alexandra watched the lowering of the flag and listened to the deep voices of the crew singing the service of Evening Prayer.

The Tsar and the Kaiser saw each other for the last time in June 1912, when the two Imperial yachts *Standart* and *Hohenzollern* anchored in a Baltic port. "William remained three days," Nicholas reported to Marie, "and was very gay and affable."

But, to every other place in Russia, Nicholas and Alexandra preferred the Livadia Palace at Yalta, on a mountainous peninsula washed by the Black Sea. For Alexandra and Alexis, the warm days at Livadia meant recovery from illness and renewal of strength. Here they could live informally. Once, entering a store in Yalta from a rainy street, the Empress lowered her umbrella, which formed a puddle on the floor. The salesman indicated a rack, saying sharply, "Madame, this is for umbrellas." Alexandra meekly obeyed.

When the clothing and equipment of the Russian infantryman was redesigned, Nicholas ordered a kit in his size brought to Livadia. He put it all on and marched alone for nine hours, covering twenty-five miles. Returning at dusk, he pronounced the uniform satisfactory. Later, the commander of the regiment whose uniform he had worn asked Nicholas to fill out a soldier's identity booklet as a memento. Nicholas filled in the form. LAST NAME: *Romanov;* HOME: *Tsarskoe Selo;* SERVICE COMPLETED: *When I am in my grave.*

When possible, the Imperial family spent Easter at Livadia. Easter was the climax of the Orthodox Church year, more holy and joyous than Christmas. On Easter night, huge crowds packed into cathedrals and stood, holding lighted candles, to hear the great choral litany. They waited for the moment, just before midnight, when the priest went in search of the Saviour. Followed by the congregation with a river of candles, he circled the outside of the church, and returning to the door, reenacted the discovery of Christ's tomb when the stone was rolled away. He looked inside the empty church and then turned his face to the crowd. His features lighted with joy, he shouted, *"Kristos Voskres!"* (Christ is risen!) The congregation responded with a mighty shout, *"Voistinu Voskrese!"* (Indeed He is risen!) Everywhere in Russia, this was the moment when peasants and princes alike laughed and wept in unison.

Then they hurried away to the sumptuous feasting which broke the Lenten fast. Any stranger who entered the house was welcome, and the table was set with food night and day. In the Crimea, the Imperial palace became a vast banqueting hall. Nicholas and Alexandra greeted their household with the traditional three kisses of blessing, welcome and joy. Schoolchildren came the following morning to receive Easter cakes from the Empress and her daughters. To members of the court and the Imperial Guard, the sovereigns gave their famous Easter eggs. Some were simply exquisitely painted eggshells from which the yolks had been drawn through tiny pinholes; others were made by the master jeweler, Fabergé.

ALEXIS was so well in 1911 that Alexandra began to hope that her prayers had been answered and he was getting permanently better. He was cheerful and mischievous, and at one social event, Nicholas wrote Marie, drank a glass of champagne unnoticed; "after which he became rather gay and began to entertain the ladies. When we returned to the train, he kept telling us about his conversations at the party and also that he heard his tummy rumbling."

But in the autumn of 1912, when the Imperial family was at Spala, their hunting lodge in Poland, Nicholas and Alexandra were plunged into a crisis that seared them forever. Alexis was convalescing from a fall in a rowboat. Dr. Botkin had found a small swelling just below the groin, and made him stay in bed. A week later, the swelling had dwindled and Botkin believed the incident was closed.

Worried about her son being cooped up in the lodge, Alexandra took him for a drive in the fresh air. The carriage bounced on the sandy roads and Alexis began to complain of pain. Frightened, the Empress ordered the driver to return to the villa. Every time the carriage jolted, Alexis cried out. Alexandra, in terror, urged the driver first to hurry, then to go slowly. Anna Vyrubova remembered the ride as "an experience in horror. The child was almost unconscious with pain."

Botkin found a severe hemorrhage in Alexis's thigh and groin. Specialists arrived from St. Petersburg but none of them could aid the suffering child. Blood flowed steadily from the torn blood vessels inside his leg, forming an enormous hematoma. His leg drew up against his chest to give the blood more room, until there came a point when there was no place else for it to go. Yet still it flowed.

Day and night the boy's screams pierced the walls. Many in the household stuffed their ears with cotton in order to continue their work. For eleven days, Alexandra scarcely left her son's side. His face was bloodless, his body contorted, his eyes rolled back in his head. The Empress never undressed. When she had to sleep, she lay back on a sofa next to his bed. His groans and shrieks dwindled to a constant wail. Through the pain, he called to his mother, "Mama, help me. Won't you help me?" Alexandra sat holding his hand, smoothing his forehead, tears running down her cheeks as she prayed to God to deliver her little boy from torture. During these eleven days, her golden hair became tinged with gray.

Even so, she stood it better than the Tsar. "I was hardly able to stay in the room, but of course had to take turns with Alix, for she was exhausted," he wrote to Marie. "She bore the ordeal better than I did." Once when he came in and saw his son in agony, his courage gave way and he rushed out of the house weeping.

Both parents were certain Alexis was dying. He himself hoped so. "When I am dead, it will not hurt any more, will it, Mama?" he asked. In another moment of relative calm, he said quietly, "When

I am dead, build me a little monument of stones in the woods."

Outside the sickroom, the family played a desperate charade, to conceal from the world the extent of the Tsarevich's illness. Noblemen continued to hunt with the Tsar, and in the evenings, the Empress would briefly leave the bedside and appear, pale but composed, to act as hostess. Despite all precautions, St. Petersburg buzzed with talk, none of it accurate. When the doctor warned Nicholas that the hemorrhage could be fatal at any hour, Count Fredericks received permission to publish medical bulletins. Still, there was no mention of the cause.

Official announcements of the Heir's grave condition plunged Russia into national prayer. Services were held in great cathedrals and in small churches in lonely villages. Before the blessed icon in the Cathedral of Our Lady of Kazan in St. Petersburg, Russians stood and prayed night and day.

Alexis continued to breathe and the agony continued. One night, when his condition was desperate, the Last Sacrament was administered, and the public bulletin sent to St. Petersburg was worded so that the one to follow could announce that His Imperial Highness the Tsarevich was dead.

It was on this night, at the end of hope, that Alexandra asked Anna Vyrubova to telegraph Rasputin in Siberia, begging him to pray for the life of her son. Rasputin wired back: GOD HAS HEARD YOUR PRAYERS. DO NOT GRIEVE. THE LITTLE ONE WILL NOT DIE. DO NOT ALLOW THE DOCTORS TO BOTHER HIM TOO MUCH.

The next morning, Alexandra came down to the drawing room, pale but smiling. "The doctors notice no improvement yet," she said, "but I am not anxious. I received a telegram from Father Gregory and he has reassured me completely." A day later the hemorrhage stopped. It would be a year before he could walk, but the boy was alive.

The part played by Rasputin in Alexis's recovery remains mysterious. None of the doctors present ever discussed it in writing, though one of them, talking to Nicholas's sister Olga later that year, called the recovery inexplicable.

Actually there is a possible medical explanation, for after a prolonged period, hemophilic bleeding may stop of its own accord. Also, Rasputin's advice—"Do not allow the doctors to bother him too much"—was excellent. With four doctors constantly examining him, a clot, still fragile, could easily have been dislodged. When at last the doctors left Alexis alone, the effect could only have been good.

There is another possible factor. That emotion plays a role in bleeding has long been suspected. Until Rasputin's telegram arrived, Alexandra, the only person with whom Alexis had strong emotional communication, was frantic. Alexis must have felt her fear and despair. Her new aura of calm and confidence may have helped his recovery.

Everyone recognized that an eerie coincidence had occurred. But to Alexandra it seemed quite natural: after the doctors had failed and her own prayers had gone unanswered, Rasputin had brought about the intervention of God and a miracle had taken place. From that time, Alexandra was unshakably convinced that her son's life lay in Rasputin's hands.

Procession in honor of Serafim Sarovski, a Russian hermit saint who lived from 1760 to 1833.

WHEN Gregory Rasputin first appeared in 1905 in St. Petersburg's most elegant drawing rooms, he was in his early thirties. Broad-shouldered and muscular, he wore peasant blouses and baggy trousers tucked into heavy boots. His hands were grimy, his beard tangled. His long, greasy hair hung in thin strands to his shoulders. He gave off a powerful, acrid odor. To his devotees, none of this mattered. Women who found him disgusting discovered later that the rough, strong-smelling peasant was an alluring change from pomaded officers and nobles. Others said that his rough appearance was a sign of spirituality; he was a Man of God.

Rasputin's eyes were his most unusual feature. They were pale blue-gray, of exceptional brilliance, at once piercing and caressing, far-off and intent. Friends and enemies alike described their strange power; it was difficult to resist his steady gaze. Prince Felix Yussoupov, who later murdered Rasputin, went to him, coolly announcing that he was sick, in order to learn more about Rasputin's methods of "healing."

"The *starets* (Man of God) made me lie down on the sofa," Yussoupov wrote. "Then, staring intently at me, he gently ran his hand over my chest, neck and head, after which he knelt, laid both hands on my forehead and murmured a prayer. His face was so close to mine that I could see only his eyes. He had tremendous hypnotic power. I felt as if some active energy were pouring heat, like a warm current into my whole being. My body grew numb; I could not speak.

"All I could see was Rasputin's glittering eyes; two phosphorescent beams of light melting into a great luminous ring. I realized that I was gradually falling into the power of this evil man, and I felt stir in me the will to fight his hypnosis; but I could not move until he ordered me to get up, saying, 'Well, that will be enough for the first time.'"

The rise of Gregory Rasputin would have been impossible in any country other than Russia. Throughout Russian history, staretses had walked across the steppes from village to village, living on whatever the peasants might give them. Some preached, others claimed powers of healing. Their poverty, asceticism and self-sacrifice often made them seem holier than the local priests, and all Russians listened to them. Renunciation of the world gave these men freedoms that others lacked. They could rebuke the mighty, sometimes even the Tsars themselves.

Rasputin, however, was a fraudulent starets. He was married and had three children; and his moral behavior was gross. He had only some of the dramatic trappings of holiness: his burning eyes and fluent tongue, a head filled with Scripture, and a deep, powerful voice. He presented himself as a humble penitent, a man who had sinned greatly, been forgiven and commanded to do God's work. It was a touching symbol of his humility, people said, that he kept his youthful nickname "Rasputin," which in Russian means dissolute. His real name was Gregory Efimovich Novykh.

As a young man, Rasputin drank, fought, and made free with the village girls. He became a wagoner, carrying goods and passengers to other villages, an occupation that extended the range of his conquests. His method was direct: he grabbed every girl he met. Naturally, he was frequently kicked and scratched and bitten, but the sheer volume of his efforts brought him notable success.

After he had married, Rasputin turned to farming. One day, while plowing, he saw a vision and declared that he had been directed to make a pilgrimage. He walked two thousand miles to the monastery at Mount Athos in Greece. When he returned at the end of two years, he carried an aura of mystery and holiness. He gave up drinking, curbed his aggressiveness toward women and prayed at length. It began to be said that the profligate was a man close to God. But Rasputin grew bored with village life and again began to wander.

When he appeared in St. Petersburg, a reputation for extraordinary powers had preceded him and he was received by high-ranking churchmen. Rasputin treated all of them with jolly, spontaneous good humor. Put off balance by his simple sincerity, they were also impressed by his gifts as a preacher. He was welcomed as a genuine starets, whom the Church, then trying to strengthen its roots among the peasants, could put to valuable use. Soon Russian society—where mediums and clairvoyants always flourished—also received him with excitement.

Nicholas's cousin-in-law, Grand Duchess Militsa, first brought Rasputin to Tsarskoe Selo in 1905. At first, his reception at the palace caused little comment, since he was introduced from the highest social circles. But no one expected the degree of intimacy with which he came to be accepted. In the hour before dinner when Alexis was playing on the floor in his blue bathrobe, Rasputin usually sat down with the boy and told stories of travels and adventures and old Russian tales. Often the whole family listened. At Alexis's bedtime, Rasputin would pray with him.

Rasputin's manner with Nicholas and Alexandra was respectful but never fawning; he felt free to laugh loudly and to criticize. He larded his language with biblical quotes and Russian proverbs, and referred to the sovereigns not as "Your Imperial Majesty" but as Batiushka and Matushka, as the peasants did. In such ways he deepened the contrast between himself, the Man of God and of the Russian people, and the polished figures of court society whom Alexandra despised.

Nicholas said to one of the officers of his guard, "He is just a good, religious, simple-minded Russian. When in trouble or assailed by doubts, I have a talk with him, and invariably feel at peace afterward."

There was no question that Rasputin more than once brought relief to the Tsarevich. A common belief was that he hypnotized Alexis to make his bleeding stop. No doctor feels that hypnosis alone could stop a severe hemorrhage, but it is possible to produce a contraction of the small arteries by hypnosis. Dr. Oscar Lucas used hypnosis in Philadelphia from 1961 to 1964, extracting teeth from hemophilic patients without a single transfusion, though normally, for hemophiliacs, tooth extraction means a major operation requiring dozens of units of plasma.

Anger or anxiety increases blood flow through the capillaries, and overwrought emotions can adversely affect the strength of the capillary walls. As these break down under stress, the likelihood of abnormal bleeding becomes greater. As a sense of calm returns to a patient, his capillary blood flow declines and the strength of his vascular walls increases.

When Rasputin filled a darkened room with his commanding voice, he cast a spell over a boy overwhelmed by pain. Then, assured in tones which left no room for doubt, Alexis believed that the torment was receding, that soon he would be walking again. The emotional change affected his body; the bleeding slowed, the exhausted child dropped off to sleep and eventually the bleeding stopped. No one else could do it, neither anguished parents nor terrified doctors. Haldane wrote, "Rasputin took the empire by stopping the bleeding of the Tsarevich."

SUCCESS AT TSARSKOE SELO ensured Rasputin's success in society. As his social position improved, his wardrobe became more elegant. He began to wear silk blouses in brilliant colors, some embroidered by the Empress. Black velvet trousers and soft kid boots replaced his peasant breeches. On a chain around his neck he wore a gold cross, a gift from Alexandra. He strode confidently into crowded salons, his rich clothes in striking contrast to his unkempt hair and matted beard. Advancing on acquaintances, he would seize their hands, stare fiercely into their eyes, and begin a familiar banter, studded with impertinent questions. "Do you love your husband?" he asked Nicholas's sister Olga. "Why have you no children?"

In his new finery, Rasputin gloried in remaining the moujik. He used coarse barnyard expressions and enjoyed the gasps they produced. His table manners left people aghast; an aide described his "plunging his dirty hands into his favorite fish soup." But for a jaded, restless society, he was an exotic diversion. Noble ladies, army wives and actresses alike sought the rough caresses of the mysterious and insinuating moujik, and some husbands even considered Rasputin's attention to their wives an honor and a distinction.

Rasputin made it easy for the ladies by preaching his personal doctrine of redemption: salvation is impossible unless one has been redeemed from sin, and true redemption cannot be achieved unless sin has been committed. In himself, Rasputin offered all three: sin, redemption and salvation.

Although the moments were wholly innocent, Rasputin's visits to the palace nurseries touched the Tsar's young daughters with rumors of scandal. On the pretext of saying prayers with the Tsarevich and his sisters, Rasputin sometimes hung about their bedrooms after the girls had changed into their long white nightgowns. The governess was horrified to see a peasant staring at her charges and demanded that he be barred. Alexandra became angry, not at Rasputin, but at the governess who dared to question the saintliness of the "Man of God," but Nicholas instructed Rasputin to avoid his daughters' rooms.

Later, the governess was dismissed and busily spread her story across Moscow. She implored Grand Duchess Elizabeth to speak to her sister. Ella regarded Rasputin as a lascivious impostor, and spoke often to Alexandra, sometimes gently, sometimes bluntly, about the starets. Her efforts had no effect except to open a breach between the two sisters.

By 1911, St. Petersburg was in an uproar over Rasputin. Not all the husbands were complacent, nor did all ladies enjoy his attentions; and doors began to close to him. The Church initiated the first formal investigation of Rasputin's activities and carried the first official complaints to the Tsar. The saintly Bishop Theophan, Alexandra's former confessor, had recommended Rasputin to her. When women began coming to him with their confessions about Rasputin, Theophan advised the Empress that something was fearfully wrong about the "Holy Man." Alexandra sent for Rasputin, who affected surprise, innocence and humility. Soon the aged Theophan was transferred to the Crimea. "I have shut his trap," gloated Rasputin.

Next, the Metropolitan Anthony, head of the Church, called on the Tsar to discuss Rasputin. Nicholas replied that the private affairs of the Imperial family were no concern of the Church. "Sire," the Metropolitan replied, "this is the affair of all Russia." Nicholas nodded. Soon afterward, Anthony fell ill and died.

The most damaging attack on Rasputin came from a flamboyant yet austere young zealot named Iliodor, a fiery church orator. He preached strict adherence to the Orthodox faith and the autocracy of the Tsar, yet he also advocated a vague peasant communism. At first he welcomed the religious fervor manifested by the starets. He invited Rasputin to come with him to his spiritual retreat near Tsaritsyn. There Rasputin as usual boasted of his sexual exploits, and said that the Tsar had knelt before him and told him, "Gregory, you are Christ." He also boasted that he had kissed the Empress.

Rasputin gave Iliodor several letters from Alexandra—or so Iliodor later claimed. Portions of the letters were made public. The most damning was:

My beloved, unforgettable teacher, redeemer and mentor! How tiresome it is without you! I relax only when you, my teacher, are sitting beside me. I kiss your hands and lean my head on your blessed shoulder. Oh how light do I feel then. I only wish to fall asleep forever on your shoulders and in your arms. Where have you gone? Come quickly—I am asking for your holy blessing and I am kissing your blessed hands. I love you forever.

Yours,

M. [Mama].

It is quite possible that the letters were faked; only Iliodor saw them, and his credentials were thoroughly undermined by subsequent events. But, assuming that Alexandra wrote this letter, did it prove that she and Rasputin were lovers? No serious historian has accepted that charge. Alexandra wrote to all of her intimates in this florid, emotional style. Such sentences could have been addressed, for instance, to Anna Vyrubova.

Despite Iliodor's disgust, he and Rasputin remained friendly until 1911, when Rasputin attempted to seduce and finally to rape a nun. Iliodor and Bishop Hermogen, of Saratov, confronted him with the story and he mumbled, "It's true, it's true, it's all true." Hermogen beat Rasputin with a heavy, wooden cross and dragged him into a little chapel, where he and Iliodor made him swear on an icon that he would leave women alone and stay away from the Imperial family. Rasputin swore.

Within a few days Rasputin was back at the palace, giving his version of the episode. By Imperial order, Hermogen was sent to seclusion in a monastery. Iliodor was ordered into seclusion also, but he refused to submit. Instead, he wandered from place to place, hysterically denouncing Rasputin. It was while he was in this mood that Alexandra's alleged letters appeared. Growing even more wildly erratic, Iliodor was excommunicated and fled into exile.

In spite of his great influence, Rasputin was no longer a frequent visitor. When he came to Tsarskoe Selo, it was usually to the little house of Anna Vyrubova. This was because it was impossible even to creep up a back staircase in the palace without the news going all over St. Petersburg. In later years, so rarely did Rasputin come that Gilliard never met him there. Nevertheless, despite the fact that Alexandra saw Rasputin infrequently, and then under circumstances ideal for him, she refused to consider that there might be another side to her Man of God. "Saints are always calumniated," she told Dr. Botkin.

Alexandra wrote the Tsar, "They accuse Rasputin of kissing women, etc. Read the apostles; they kissed everybody as a form of greeting." A monarchist member of the Duma wrote later: "Rasputin was a Janus. To the Imperial family he turned his face as a humble starets; to the country, he turned the drunken, unclean face of a satyr."

The Holy Coronation of Nicholas and Alexandra in the great golden Ouspensky Cathedral.

IN 1906, THE Prime Minister was an elderly bureaucratic relic named Ivan Goremykin, who believed that ministers were mere servants of the Tsar, appointed to execute, not initiate, policy. He soon foundered, and he recommended to the Tsar that the Minister of the Interior, a bearded, burly country squire named Peter Arkadyevich Stolypin, be appointed in his place.

If any man could have saved Imperial Russia, it was the eloquent, courageous, sincere Stolypin, who served from 1906 to 1911. No Russian statesman of the day was more admired. A passionate monarchist, he was also a realist and sensed that the monarchy would survive only if the government could adapt to the times. He set about transforming an absolute autocracy into a government more responsive to the popular will.

But before he could attack the root problem of the peasants' thirst for land, the terrorist revolutionaries had to be suppressed.

Stolypin established field courts-martial. Before the end of the summer, six hundred men had been strung up and Russians had named the hangman's noose "Stolypin's necktie"—but the terrorists had previously murdered no less than sixteen hundred officials, officers and policemen.

Now Stolypin could attack the land problem. Most Russian peasants lived in village communes. It was a ridiculously inefficient system, since a single peasant might farm as many as fifty small scattered strips, each containing a few thin rows of corn or wheat. Stolypin decreed that any peasant could withdraw from the commune, claim a plot of ground for himself, and expect to hand it along to his sons.

Nicholas strongly approved Stolypin's program and—over some family opposition—sold four million acres of crown lands to the government to sell to the peasants on easy terms. He waited hopefully for the nobility to follow his example. None did so, but by 1914, nine million peasant families owned their farms—a new class of small landowners. The most vociferous troublemakers were often the first to claim land, and thus became supporters of law and order. There was a new atmosphere of stability.

For five fruitful years, nature smiled on Stolypin. The crops were the best in Russia's history. Government tax revenues rose, roads expanded rapidly. American firms like International Harvester and Singer Sewing Machine established offices in Russia. The Duma established free primary-school education, censorship of the press was lifted, and the government became more liberal in the sphere of religious tolerance.

For Lenin and his dwindling band of exiles, the Stolypin era was a time of fading hope. Gloomily, wandering from library to library through Europe, Lenin watched the success of Stolypin's land reforms. To other Marxists, too, it seemed that the dream of a Russian revolution was dead.

WHEN the Russian parliament, the Imperial Duma, first met in 1906, it was alien to everything that had gone before in Russia. A constitution, parliament and political parties had to be constructed overnight, and it was not surprising that neither the Tsar nor the members of the fledgling representative body knew quite how to behave.

Scarcely had the First Duma members taken their seats in a hall of the Tauride Palace than they formulated an aggressive "Address to the Throne." To Nicholas's horror, it demanded universal suffrage, radical land reform, the release of all political prisoners, and the appointment of ministers acceptable to the Duma. Disgusted, Nicholas rejected everything and dissolved the Duma. He would have been happy to end the whole experiment, but Stolypin insisted that the Tsar had made a solemn promise to the nation in his Manifesto creating the Duma. Grudgingly, Nicholas gave permission for new elections.

As the Second Duma met for the first time, the ceiling of the hall caved in over their heads. It was an appropriate beginning. The leftist parties formed more than a third of the membership. They turned the Duma into a madhouse of shouts, insults and brawls. When there was an appeal to the army to join the people in overthrowing the government, Nicholas had had enough. The Duma was again dissolved, and a new electoral law abandoned all pretense of universal suffrage, concentrating power largely in the hands of the country gentry. As a result, the Third Duma, elected in 1907, was a thoroughly conservative body.

However, the Duma, while more cautious, remained independent. The members showed a growing courage and initiative and achieved a mutual understanding with the autocracy. There was surprise at the simplicity with which differences that had seemed formidable could be removed when people worked together for the good of Russia.

But influences were at work to poison the relationship between the Tsar and Stolypin. Reactionaries kept telling the Tsar that the Duma was a blot on the autocracy and that Stolypin was a secret revolutionary. Unfortunately, Stolypin had also angered the Empress. Alarmed at Rasputin's influence, he had ordered an investigation into his life and presented a report to the Tsar. Nicholas read it but did nothing. Stolypin commanded Rasputin to leave

St. Petersburg anyway. Alexandra protested, but Nicholas refused to overrule his Prime Minister. Rasputin departed on a pilgrimage to Jerusalem, during which he scrawled lengthy flowery and mystical letters to the Empress. To Alexandra, it seemed that Stolypin had deliberately severed the bond on which her son depended for life.

Stolypin found it frustrating to work with a Tsar who was a fatalist and mystic. Nicholas, for instance, returned a document to Stolypin with the note: "Despite most convincing arguments an inner voice insists that I do not accept responsibility for this matter. 'A Tsar's heart is in God's hands.' Let it be so."

Stolypin, weary, his health waning, began to complain that he was being ignored or slighted at court. When he and Vladimir Kokovtsov, Minister of Finance, accompanied Nicholas to Kiev to unveil a statue, the Tsar was surrounded by guards and police, but the carriage in which the two ministers were riding was completely unprotected. "You see, we are superfluous," Stolypin said.

By a coincidence, Rasputin, back from Jerusalem, was in Kiev that day, observing the procession. As Stolypin's carriage clattered past, Rasputin called out in a dramatic voice, "Death is after him! Death is driving behind him!"

The following night, Peter Stolypin joined the Imperial party at the Kiev Opera House. Nicholas was sitting with Olga and Tatiana in a box; Stolypin and other officials were in the first row of the orchestra. During the second intermission a young man in evening clothes walked down the aisle from the rear of the house, drew a revolver and fired two mortal shots in Stolypin's chest. The assassin was hanged as a revolutionary, but the suspicion always remained that Stolypin's murder was the work of powerful reactionaries. Kokovtsov was named his successor.

WHEN Stolypin had investigated Rasputin's activities, the outcry against the starets was still a matter for private conversation. But by 1912, with Kokovtsov in Stolypin's office, the scandal had burst into the open. Soon the "Rasputin question" dominated the political scene. Newspapers openly printed accusations from his victims and cries from their anguished mothers. Unprintable stories about the Empress and Rasputin passed from mouth to mouth. "Grishka" (the diminutive of Gregory) appeared in obscene drawings chalked on walls. He was the subject of a hundred smutty rhymes. "My poor daughter-in-law does not perceive that she is ruining both the dynasty and herself," Marie said to Kokovtsov, weeping.

Inevitably the demand rose for an open debate in the Duma on Rasputin. The Duma President, Michael Rodzianko, a massive figure weighing 280 pounds, was a former cavalry officer of aristocratic family. To him, the idea of such a debate seemed highly offensive. Before having an audience with the Tsar about it, he prayed in the cathedral before the icon of Our Lady of Kazan. At the palace, he bravely told the Tsar that he had to speak to the Tsar about the starets. Nicholas looked away and murmured, "Speak." Afterward, moved by Rodzianko's honest fervor, he authorized a new investigation of Rasputin's character and activities. Rodzianko eventually wrote a report, but when he asked for another audience to present it, the request was denied.

Actually, when he first came to St. Petersburg, Rasputin had no plan for making himself the power behind the Russian throne. He was an opportunist, living from day to day, and he was indifferent to politics until his own behavior became a political issue. Then he sought political influence in self-defense. With ministers of state, Duma, Church and press all attacking him, he counterattacked in the only way open to him—by going to the Empress—and Alexandra faithfully tried to dismiss all his enemies.

Two years after his appointment, Kokovtsov was toppled from power, his political career poisoned by Rasputin. His successor was the aged Goremykin. "I am like an old fur coat," Goremykin said. "I had been packed away in camphor. Now I am being taken out merely for the occasion."

IN 1913, the aristocracy of Europe still moved through a world of spas, yachts, top hats, tailcoats, long skirts and parasols, but the old monarchs who had given character to this world were vanishing. Austrian Emperor Franz Joseph was eighty-seven; Queen Victoria and Edward VII were in their graves. The Kaiser was now the dominant monarch in Europe, reveling in his preeminence and scorning the pair of gentle cousins who occupied the thrones of England and Russia.

The nations ruled by these kings had grown into industrial behemoths. New machines had given the rulers vastly greater power to make war—and war, as Lenin remarked, would be splendid for the hoped-for revolution. Even without war, the stresses produced by industrialization promised storms.

Yet the great tercentenary celebration of the Romanov dynasty, in 1913, astonishingly confirmed Alexandra's belief in the bond between the Tsar and his people. Huge crowds flooded city boulevards to cheer Imperial processions, and in the villages, moujiks flocked to catch a glimpse of the Tsar. In some towns Grand Duchess Olga saw workmen fall down to kiss the Tsar's shadow as he passed. Alexandra decided Nicholas's ministers were cowards to frighten him with threats of revolution. "We need merely to show ourselves to the people," she said, "and their hearts are ours."

But the celebrations had been in the nature of a family party, with controversial issues forgotten for the moment. The Duma still felt that the Tsar must realize that conditions had changed. The future Premier, Kerensky, now a member of the Fourth Duma, wrote: The whole of Russia was now covered with a network of labor and liberal organizations." In July 1914, one and a half million Russian workers were on strike. In St. Petersburg, mobs of strikers smashed windows and put up barricades in the streets. The German Ambassador assured the Kaiser that in these chaotic circumstances Russia could not possibly fight.

By the spring of 1914, the nine-year-old Tsarevich had made a good recovery from the desperate attack at Spala, eighteen months before. His leg had straightened and, to his parents' delight, he walked with only a trace of a limp.

Despite her shyness and the close family circle that surrounded her, there was now talk of a possible marriage between eighteen-year-old Olga and Crown Prince Carol of Rumania, since this match would give Russia a chance of detaching Rumania from her alliance with Germany and Austria-Hungary. On June 13, the Imperial family paid a brief, formal visit on the *Standart* to the Rumanian port of Constantsa. There were ceremonies all day, and the Rumanians stared at Olga, aware that they might be observing their future queen.

But in that sense, the visit was a waste of time. Even before the *Standart* arrived in Constantsa, Olga spoke to Gilliard. "Do you know why we are going to Rumania?" she said. Tactfully, the tutor replied that he understood it was a matter of diplomacy. Tossing her head, Olga declared that Gilliard obviously knew the real reason. "I don't want it to happen," she said fiercely. "I don't want to leave Russia. I am a Russian and I mean to remain a Russian."

In the end, Olga's parents respected her feelings. Alexandra explained their viewpoint to the Foreign Minister: "You know how difficult marriages are in reigning families. I was once threatened with the danger of marrying without love or even affection, and I shall never forget what I suffered when I met the man for the first time. My grandmother, Queen Victoria, took pity on me, and I was left in peace. I feel it my duty to leave my daughters free to marry according to their inclination, if the Emperor considers the marriage suitable."

Rebuffed by Olga, Carol later suggested to Nicholas that he marry Marie, then sixteen. Nicholas laughingly declared that Marie was only a schoolgirl. In the end, Carol married three times—his last bride being his longtime mistress, Magda Lupescu.

THE SUMMER of 1914 was marked by glorious weather. Millions went off on holidays, forgetting their fears of war in the warmth of the sun. Kings and emperors continued to visit each other, dine at state dinners, and bounce each other's children on their knees. Beneath the surface, however, differences were detectable. In their entourages, the chiefs of state brought generals and diplomats who sat down quietly with their opposite numbers to compare plans and confirm understandings.

Then, on June 28, Serbian nationalists in Sarajevo assassinated Archduke Ferdinand, the heir to their overlord, Emperor Franz Joseph of Austria. The government of the Austro-Hungarian empire reacted violently to crush "the Serbian viper." Franz Joseph wrote the Kaiser: "Serbia must be eliminated as a political factor in the Balkans."

THREE days before the events at Sarajevo, Alexis, jumping for a ladder on the *Standart,* caught his foot on a rung and twisted his ankle. Toward evening, he began to feel serious pain and by the following morning the joint was swollen and rigid. Alexis was weeping, and every few minutes he screamed. Alexandra's face was white. Despite the illness, the cruise continued, and it was aboard the yacht that Nicholas and Alexandra learned what had happened at Sarajevo. But revolution, conspiracy and assassinations were the normal ingredients of Balkan politics. Like most Europeans, neither the Tsar nor his ministers expected the assassination to lead to a world war.

On July 19, the *Standart* returned its passengers to shore, Alexis still with a swollen ankle. The French President Raymond Poincaré was arriving for a state visit. Before he came, the Tsar told the new French Ambassador, Maurice Paléologue, that he didn't believe the Kaiser wanted war. "If you knew him as I do!" the Tsar said. "If you knew how much theatricality there is in his posing!" Later President Poincaré agreed with Nicholas that "notwithstanding appearances, the Emperor Wilhelm is too cautious to launch his country on some wild adventure and the Emperor Franz Joseph's only wish is to die in peace."

But at seven a.m. on July 25, Paléologue was informed that Austria had presented Serbia with an ultimatum—one purposely so outrageous that Serbia would be forced to reject it. The Austro-Hungarian empire had decided to make war.

Serbia had appealed to Russia, for Nicholas had personally guaranteed Serbian independence, and besides, Russia traditionally protected Slavic states. But with Russia's unpreparedness in mind, the Tsar instructed Foreign Minister Sazonov to play for time. Sazonov attempted to persuade Germany to mediate the Balkan quarrel. Germany refused. He then proposed a conference in London, but again Germany refused. Finally Sazonov advised the Serbian Premier to accept all the Austrian demands which did not actually compromise Serbian independence.

The Serbs, also anxious to avoid a military showdown, then sent such a humble reply to the ultimatum that it took the Austrian Chancellor Count Berchtold by surprise and he hid the document for two days. On July 28 Austria reached a decision. Rejecting the Serb reply, it declared war.

In St. Petersburg, Nicholas ordered all Russian military districts along the Austrian frontier mobilized. But the long frontier with Germany, running through Poland and East Prussia, still slumbered in peace. The Tsar was sure that the Kaiser did not want war; and actually, Wilhelm still expected to bluff his way. He saw the abject Serb reply to Austria's ultimatum on July 28, and he exulted, "Now all grounds for war have disappeared." But that same night Austria declared war on Serbia. The Kaiser was astonished and frustrated. Nevertheless, the war was still only an affair in the Balkans, and unless Russia moved, Germany need not become involved.

The Tsar's telegram announcing that Russia had mobilized against Austria therefore put the Kaiser into a rage. To Nicholas's plea, "We need your strong pressure on Austria," he scribbled, "No, there is no thought of anything of that sort!!!"

Sazonov sadly told his sovereign that a general war was unavoidable. Germany and Austria were determined to increase their power by enslaving Russia's Balkan allies and making Russia dependent on the will of the Central Powers. "I don't think," he ended, "Your Majesty can postpone the order for general mobilization." Nicholas's face showed a terrible inner struggle. At last, in a choked voice, he said, "You are right." When Russia did not reply to a German ultimatum to halt mobilization, the Kaiser declared war.

PART THREE

War Comes to Russia

ON AUGUST 2, 1914, the Tsar issued a formal proclamation of hostilities at the Winter Palace. The great palace square was packed with excited people carrying banners, flags and icons. Crowds swarmed along the bridges and quays, singing and cheering; the Neva teemed with yachts, steamers, sailboats and rowboats, all carrying flags and crowded with spectators.

When Nicholas and Alexandra arrived by yacht from Peterhof, waves of cheers rose: "Batiushka, Batiushka, lead us to victory!" Nicholas wore the plain uniform of an infantry regiment. Alexandra, in a white dress, had turned up the brim of her picture hat so that the crowds could see her face. The four girls walked behind. The Tsarevich, still unable to walk, remained at Peterhof, weeping in disappointment.

Inside the palace, a crush of people lined the grand staircases and wide corridors. As Nicholas passed, men and women dropped to their knees and frantically tried to kiss the Tsar's hand. A service was held in a great salon jammed with five thousand people, before an altar holding the miraculous icon of the Vladimir Mother of God, said to have turned back the Mongol conqueror, Tamerlane, in the fourteenth century. Nicholas invoked its blessing.

Afterward, raising his right hand, he pronounced in a low voice the oath taken by Alexander I against Napoleon: "I solemnly swear that I will never make peace so long as a single enemy remains on Russian soil."

Then Nicholas and Alexandra went out to the balcony and, far below them, the great crowd knelt and began to sing the Imperial anthem whose chords make up the final crescendo of Tchaikovsky's "1812 Overture": "God save the Tsar, Mighty and powerful, . . ."

Hand in hand, the man in the khaki uniform and the woman

in the white dress stood on the balcony and wept with the crowd.

So war was declared, and "all at once, not a trace was left of the revolutionary movement," Kerensky wrote later. Workmen exchanged their red flags for icons and portraits of the Tsar. Peasants said, "If we don't destroy the Germans, they'll harness us to their plows." A million wildly enthusiastic people lined the streets in Moscow when Nicholas went to ask God's blessing in the Kremlin.

The same heady emotions surged through Paris, London and Berlin. But when war began its stern testing of the nations, Britain, France and Germany could call up deep reserves of national strength. In Russia, behind the massive facade, the social structure was too primitive to withstand the terrible strain of war.

Two shrewd Russians sensed the danger. Rasputin guessed what the war would cost in peasant blood. He telegraphed from Siberia: LET PAPA NOT PLAN WAR, FOR WITH THE WAR WILL COME THE END OF RUSSIA AND YOURSELVES AND YOU WILL LOSE TO THE LAST MAN. The Tsar angrily tore the message to pieces; but again Rasputin sent an ominous prophecy, scrawled in almost illegible letters: "A menacing cloud is over Russia. . . . Thou art the Tsar Father of the People don't allow the madmen to triumph and destroy themselves and the People. . . . Terrible is the destruction and without end the grief."

And former Prime Minister Witte said bluntly: "This war is madness. . . . Even a victory means the proclamation of republics throughout central Europe—the end of Tsarism. I remain silent as to what we may expect in defeat. . . ."

But Nicholas's own optimism was keenly shared by Russian army officers. Many were frantic lest it all be over before they got to see action. Guards officers leaving for the front asked whether they should pack their dress uniforms for the victory parade in Berlin. They were advised to let them follow by courier.

Day after day the capital trembled to the cadence of marching men. Outside the city, columns of troops, baggage carts, ammunition wagons, ambulances and field kitchens moved out across the dry, summer fields in a jumbled confusion of dust, shouts, horses' hoofs and rumbling wheels.

It was the men rather than the officers who often sensed what was coming. Many a Russian soldier marched to war suffused with a melancholy knowledge that he would never see his family or his village again.

Sometimes women with children followed for the first few miles. "One . . . was very young," Paléologue reported. "She was pressing a baby to her breast, striding out as well as she could to keep pace with a fine, muscular fellow at the rear of the file. They did not exchange a word, but gazed fixedly at each other with loving, haggard eyes. Three times I saw the young mother offer the baby to the soldier for a kiss."

DURING three years of war, 15,500,000 men marched away to fight for the Tsar and Holy Russia. Newspapers called them "the Russian steamroller"; but in every respect except numbers, Russia was unprepared. There were limited reserves of weapons and ammunition; at one point, Russian artillerymen were threatened with court-martial if they fired more than three rounds per day. The railroads were hopelessly inadequate, and Russia's industry was small and primitive.

The Russian army was commanded by two men who hated each other: Vladimir Sukhomlinov, the Minister of War, and Grand Duke Nicholas Nicolaievich, commander in chief in the field.

General Sukhomlinov's reputation was a mournful joke. He was a small chubby man, scented and pomaded. Although almost seventy, he retained a strong taste for expensive pleasures, including a voluptuous wife thirty-two years his junior. "He enjoyed life and disliked work," a colleague wrote.

Sukhomlinov believed the cavalry should charge with sabers, the infantry with bayonets—machine guns and modern artillery he thought unworthy of brave men. As a result, the Russian army entered the war with a fraction of the heavy artillery of the Germans. But Sukhomlinov was enormously charming and reassuring to the Tsar. His reports were full of assurances that army morale and equipment were in splendid condition, and Nicholas, watching the superb regiments of the Imperial Guard march

417

past on parade, could not believe that the Russian army was unready for war.

Grand Duke Nicholas, although born to great wealth and position, had devoted his life to the army. Six feet six inches, thin, fiercely energetic, with blazing blue eyes and a steel-trap mouth, a dagger or sword hanging from his belt, he seemed an ancient warrior chieftain. He was the most admired man in the army. Sukhomlinov, who had hoped to be commander in chief, did what he could to undercut the Grand Duke.

German strategy was to destroy France before the clumsy Russian colossus could move. "Lunch in Paris, dinner in St. Petersburg," the Kaiser said. Through the hot weeks of August, the cream of the German army, one million men in gray uniforms, moved across Belgium and France. In less than a month, the advance guard stood thirty miles north of Paris.

The French began to urge the Russians to attack at once: to wait would mean disaster for France. Because of the need for haste, the Russian offensive was assembled piecemeal. Russian cavalry with lances and sabers, and Russian infantry with bayonets willingly charged heavily armed positions—and were scythed down like rows of wheat. After five months of war, one million Russians had been killed, wounded or taken prisoner.

The Russians began the war as a gentlemanly undertaking. Captured enemy officers were not questioned; it was considered improper to ask a brother officer to inform on his compatriots. Russian officers considered it cowardly to take cover. Attacking in the face of murderous enemy fire, the officers made their men crawl forward on the ground while they themselves stood erect and walked into enemy bullets. The flower of Russia's aristocratic youth was killed. One division soon lost ninety percent of its original officers.

Much of the power and resilience of the Russian army lay in a simple, unquestioning religious faith which permeated all ranks. "With prayer—" a Russian general said to his officers while discussing tactics "—with prayer you can do anything." One German attack near the Baltic began on Easter. Artillery pounded the

Russian trenches and gas was released into them. The Russians lacked both gas masks and steel helmets, and after five hours, battalions of 500 men were reduced to 90 or 100. Yet the German infantry advance was met by a bayonet charge. That night the Germans heard the Russians singing the Easter hymn, *"Christ is risen from the dead, conquering death by death."*

The Russians managed to penetrate Prussia and attack Austria before their famous defeat at the Battle of Tannenberg. There they lost 110,000 men, including 90,000 prisoners—but they had diverted German forces from the Western front, distracted the Germans from their overwhelming lunge at Paris.

GRAND DUKE NICHOLAS established permanent field headquarters in a forest of birch and pine near a railway junction midway between the German and Austrian fronts. The camp—*Stavka*—was set up on a branch line. From his private railway car spread with bearskins and Oriental rugs, with more than two hundred icons on the walls, the Grand Duke dominated the life of the camp.

The Tsar came often to Stavka. When his train glided slowly onto a siding alongside the Grand Duke's, Nicholas stepped happily into the routine of army life. He loved the professional talk at the officers' mess, the rough, hardy, outdoor life. He took long walks or rowed on the Dnieper. Occasionally he challenged other officers to a race. Nicholas liked to win, but he would row only against men who had a chance of beating him.

In the autumn of 1915, the Tsar brought the Tsarevich with his tutor to live with him at Army Headquarters. His reasons were both sentimental and shrewd. The Russian army, battered from the terrible losses in East Prussia, needed a lift in morale. His presence with them, symbolizing Holy Russia, raised tremendous enthusiasm among all who saw him, and he hoped the appearance of his Heir, symbol of the future, would further bolster their drooping spirits. Alexis's presence did cause great excitement, and the point that made the greatest impression was that the child wore the uniform of an army private.

But the Tsar was also thinking of his son. Alexis lived in a world of adoring women. He had not been out of his mother's sight for more than a few hours in his entire lifetime. By bringing Alexis into the bracing air of beards, leather and uniforms at Stavka, Nicholas hoped to broaden the education of a future Tsar.

The Tsarevich now bounced in automobiles over dirt roads, walked long distances and stood for hours as thousands of men marched by. No doctor would have permitted this activity for any other hemophiliac, and Alexandra's letters to the Tsar were filled with concern: "See that Tiny doesn't tire himself.... Tiny loves digging and working and he is so strong and forgets that he must be careful...."

A series of German victories in the summer of 1915 forced the headquarters to relocate in the house of a provincial governor on a hill overlooking the Dnieper River. As the building was crowded, Nicholas reserved only one bedroom and an office for himself. A cot was placed for Alexis in the bedroom.

"It is very cosy sleeping side by side," Nicholas wrote to Alexandra. "I say prayers with him every night.... He says his prayers too fast and it is difficult to stop him.... I read all your letters aloud to him. He listens lying in bed and kisses your signature. Thank God he looks so well and has become sunburnt. He wakes up early in the morning and begins to talk quietly to me. I answer drowsily, he settles down and lies quietly until I am called." For father and son, the room became a haven of peace and affection. "His company gives light and life to all of us," Nicholas wrote.

Every morning the Tsarevich did lessons with Gilliard. Afterward, he played in the garden. "He carries his little gun with him and marches backwards and forwards on the path, singing loudly," wrote Nicholas. "At the table, he sits on my left hand and behaves well but sometimes becomes inordinately gay and noisy."

On hot days they swam in the Dnieper: "We found a lovely place with soft sand where Baby ran about shouting. Dr. Fedorov allowed him to go barefoot. Naturally, he was delighted. Did he describe to you how the peasant boys played all sorts of games with him?"

S. Pasquilini

The Allied military attachés adopted the high-spirited boy as their mascot. "I had expected to find a very delicate and not very lively boy," wrote General Sir John Hanbury-Williams of Britain. "But in periods of good health, he had all the spirits and the mischief of any ordinary boy. . . . As time went on and his first shyness wore off, he had always some bit of fun with us. With me it was to make sure that each button on my coat was properly fastened, a habit which naturally made me take great care to have one or two unbuttoned, in which case he used at once to stop and tell me I was 'untidy again,' and carefully button me all up again. . . . At the table, his bread pellet attacks risked the Imperial china. If, however, he had a stranger sitting next to him he had all the courtesy and charm of his father, talking freely and asking sensible questions."

In October 1915, to show his son that war was not all games, the Tsar took Alexis on a month-long trip the length of the battlefront. They made a visit to a frontline dressing station lit only by torches. Moving from one bandaged body to the next, Nicholas spoke to the men, many of whom could scarcely believe that the Tsar was walking among them. Later, standing before a field of men on parade, Nicholas asked those who had served since the beginning of the war to raise their hands. "Very few hands were lifted above those thousands of heads," wrote Gilliard. "There were whole companies in which not a man moved. This made a very great impression on Alexis."

The Empress made occasional visits to headquarters with her daughters, living aboard the royal train. Hanbury-Williams found Alexandra much easier to get on with than he had expected. She was shy at first, but the moment one began to laugh over things, she brightened up and talk became easy and unaffected: "It seems extraordinary how little it takes to cheer her up."

The Tsar carried the day-to-day burden of caring for his son's health. In July 1916 he wrote that Alexis's elbow would not bend. "This morning he took his temperature and calmly announced that he had better stay in bed all day." And in November: "The Little

One is suffering from a strained vein in his right leg. During the night, he kept waking and groaned in his sleep." The situation was unprecedented—the commander in chief of the world's largest army spending his time caring for a suffering child.

But for the most part all went well, and Nicholas enjoyed the deceptive sense of calm which often comes to the parents of hemophiliacs. The capricious disease awaits precisely such moments to strike.

It was when Nicholas and Alexis were on the train heading for an inspection that the boy, who had a cold, had a heavy nose-bleed. Dr. Fedorov could not stop the bleeding and by the next morning Alexis's state was so alarming that it was decided to take him to Tsarskoe Selo. His temperature went up, and "when he swooned I thought the end had come," Gilliard recalled.

Anna Vyrubova described the return of the Emperor and the boy to Tsarskoe Selo: "I can never forget the waxen, grave-like pallor of the little pointed face as the boy was borne into the palace and laid on his little white bed. Above the blood-soaked bandages his large blue eyes gazed at us with unspeakable pathos, and it seemed to all around the bed that the last hour of the un-happy child was at hand. In despair, the Empress sent for Rasputin. He came into the room, made the sign of the cross over the bed and, looking intently at the almost moribund child, said to the kneeling parents: 'Don't be alarmed. Nothing will happen.' Then he walked out of the room and out of the palace. The child fell asleep, and the next day he was so well the Emperor left for Stavka. The doctors told me afterward that they did not attempt to explain the cure."

Although Gilliard gave more credit to the doctors for succeed-ing in cauterizing the scar at the spot where a little blood vessel had burst, the Empress again was convinced that her son had been saved by Rasputin.

The Emperor missed his "Little One" terribly, and in May 1916 Alexandra reluctantly allowed him to return to headquarters. He was promoted from private to corporal. "He is more mischievous than ever," reported Hanbury-Williams. "At lunch he pushed all the bread, toast, etc., he could get hold of across to me and then called to his father to count all the pieces I had."

On December 20, 1916, the Tsarevich paid his last visit to Army Headquarters. A few days later, he was to leave for the winter for Tsarskoe Selo. On that night, General Hanbury-Williams received word from England that his eldest son, a British officer, had been killed in France. As the general sat alone with his grief in his room, the door quietly opened. It was Alexis, saying, "Papa told me to come to sit with you as he thought you might feel lonely tonight."

Nicholas unveils a monument to Peter the Great in the Latvian city of Riga.

VICTORY on the Marne and disaster at Tannenberg had dimmed the result of a third great battle in the early stages of the war. The main Austro-Hungarian army, one million strong, had launched itself north to try to amputate Poland from Russia. Within less than three weeks, the Russians had smashed this invasion, and Russian cavalry was riding onto the great Danube plain toward Budapest and Vienna. In terror, the Austrian government appealed to Berlin for help, hinting it might be forced to a separate peace.

Four army corps were sent south from Prussia, under Hindenburg, but even this help might not have been enough if the Russian offensive had not suddenly halted. France wished Russia to press a direct offensive against Germany, so Nicholas commanded the triumphant Russians to begin receding from the Austrian front, and to begin a fruitless attack on German Silesia. It was another gallant, expensive gesture toward hard-pressed France, and Russia's great chance to crush Austria-Hungary was lost.

Having failed to destroy France in 1914, the Germans selected 1915 as the year to drive Russia out of the war. While the Russians again attacked the Austrians, with brilliant success, the German generals calmly and efficiently massed men and artillery in southern Poland and opened fire. Within four hours, 700,000 shells fell into the Russian trenches, and the Russian division stationed there was reduced from 16,000 to 500. Reserves brought in were also almost wiped out, and in the maelstrom, the Russian line disintegrated. In the retreat, men lost their rifles; the shortage quickly became desperate. A general reported that a third of his men had to wait until their comrades fell before they could find weapons. A private said, "This is not war. This is slaughter."

Now nothing could stem the German columns advancing through the deep summer dust of Poland, with tragic columns of refugees fleeing ahead. In that spring and summer of 1915 half the Russian army was destroyed.

There were few great balls that winter in the gray cities of Russia. Instead, there were silent groups standing in the cold reading the casualty lists posted in shopwindows. The thrilling sense of national unity evaporated. In its place surged all the old suspicions. Worst was the hatred of everything German. In St. Petersburg—now renamed Petrograd by the Tsar—the works of Bach, Brahms and Beethoven were banned. The Holy Synod banned Christmas trees as a German custom. In Red Square, a mob shouted insults at the Imperial family, demanding that the Empress be shut up in a convent, the Tsar deposed, Rasputin hanged and Grand Duke Nicholas crowned as Nicholas III.

To those who knew her, there never was any question of Alexandra's Russian patriotism. "It is the country of my husband and my son," she explained to a lady-in-waiting. "All my heart is bound to this country." But bitter stories were told about the German-born Empress. One had a general come upon the Tsarevich, in the Winter Palace, weeping. Patting the boy on the head, the general asked, "What is wrong, my little man?" The Tsarevich replied, "When the Russians are beaten, Papa cries. When the Germans are beaten, Mama cries. When am I to cry?"

There were political repercussions to military defeat. General Sukhomlinov was swept away. Even the faithful Grand Duke Nicholas was under attack, for Alexandra had never liked the fiery, impetuous soldier who towered over her less colorful husband. He was the strong man of the Imperial family; worse, he hated Rasputin. Once, Rasputin, hoping to gain favor with him, telegraphed the Grand Duke offering to come to headquarters to bless an icon. "Yes, do come," replied Grand Duke Nicholas. "I'll hang you."

Against this powerful enemy Rasputin fought back skillfully through Alexandra. The Grand Duke, he said, is deliberately overshadowing Nicholas so one day he can claim the throne. The Grand Duke cannot succeed on the battlefield because God will not bless a man who has turned his back on me, the Man of God. If the Grand Duke keeps his power, he will kill me—and then what will happen to the Tsarevich, and Russia?

All summer, Alexandra's letters to the Tsar maintained a steady drumfire of criticism of the Grand Duke: "Having gone against a Man of God, his work can't be blessed or his advice good. . . . Nobody knows who is the Emperor now; N. settles all. . . ."

Nicholas did not share his wife's views. He respected the Grand Duke and had full—and thoroughly justified—confidence in his loyalty. Nevertheless, as the retreat continued, the Tsar decided to take personal command of the army: it was his duty, he felt, to unify civil and military authority and take on his own person the full weight of responsibility for Russia's destiny. The ministers were aghast at this proposal. What would happen to governmental machinery if the head of state spent all his time more than five hundred miles away? Moreover, he should not take command at a moment when the army was being defeated. Nicholas, his brow covered with perspiration, thanked them. Then he announced quietly, "Gentlemen, in two days I leave for Stavka."

He wrote a public letter to the Grand Duke, explaining his decision. Eloquent and felicitous, it managed to spare the Grand Duke's pride while gracefully easing him out of his post and making him commander in chief in the Caucasus. "God be praised," said the Grand Duke when he read it. "The Emperor releases me from a task which was wearing me out." He greeted the Tsar when he came to Stavka with a smile.

The fall of the great soldier and strategist was a source of grim satisfaction to the Germans. It was hailed by Alexandra as a supreme personal triumph. When Nicholas left for Stavka, he carried with him a letter of ecstasy from Alexandra. "Forgive me, my Angel," she wrote, "for having left you no peace on this but I too well know your marvelously gentle character. . . . A sovereign needs to show his will more often. This is the beginning of the great glory of your reign, our Friend says so . . . Sleep well, my Sunshine. Remember last night how tenderly we clung together. I shall yearn for your caresses. . . . Your very own wife, Sunny."

By going to the army, the Tsar had given up all but a vague, supervisory control over civilian affairs. In an autocracy this was impossible; a substitute had to be found. Uncertainly at first, then with growing confidence, this role was filled by Alexandra. At her shoulder, his "prayers arising day and night," stood her Friend, Rasputin. Together they would finally bring down the Russian empire.

In the Russian army, it was understood that the Tsar would be a figurehead. His choice for chief of staff, the man who would make the actual decisions, was reassuring. General Michael Vasilevich Alexeiev was a soldier of humble beginnings. Short, with a simple, wide Russian face, he had risen to the top by sheer ability and hard work.

Soon after the change of command, the German offensive began to lose impetus. Russian troops, fighting now on the soil of Mother Russia herself, gave ground slowly, contesting every river, hill and marsh. When winter closed down most of the front, Alexeiev had managed to stabilize a line which became almost precisely the western frontier of Soviet Russia until the Second World War.

Assuming that their losses had broken the Russian army, the Germans transferred their main effort to France. In February 1916 they hurled the great mass of German artillery and a million infantrymen at the French fortress Verdun. To the dismay of the Kaiser's generals, no sooner were they committed in the west than the Russians attacked again in the east. By July, eighteen German divisions had to be transferred back to the east and Verdun was saved. But the cost to the Russian army of the 1916 campaign was a terrible one: 1,200,000 men.

After the war, Hindenburg paid tribute to the bravery and sacrifices of his Russian enemies. "Sometimes," he said, "we had to remove mounds of enemy corpses from before our trenches in order to get a clear field of fire against fresh assaulting waves." Later, a careful analysis of Russian casualties showed 7,900,000 men killed, wounded or taken prisoner.

THE HUGE Catherine Palace at Tsarskoe Selo was converted into a military hospital; eighty-five hospitals operated under Alexandra's patronage in the Petrograd area alone. Many Russian ladies became hospital patrons, but only a few followed the Empress's example by enrolling in nursing courses and coming daily in person to tend the wounded.

The Empress, who used to stay in bed nursing her own ills until noon, now was up for Mass at seven. At nine, dressed in the gray uniform of a nursing sister, she arrived at the hospital, with Olga, Tatiana, and Anna Vyrubova, for her nursing course. Every day, Red Cross trains brought long lines of wounded men back from the front. They were patient men, gentle, grateful as children. "*Nichevo*—it is nothing, little sister," they responded to sympathy. Only rarely did the nurses hear a low-voiced "I suffer, little sister."

"I saw the Empress of Russia in the operating room," wrote Anna Vyrubova, "holding ether cones, taking from the hands of busy surgeons amputated legs and arms, removing bloody, vermin-ridden field dressings, enduring all the sights and smells and agonies of a military hospital in the midst of war. Nevertheless I never saw her happier than on the day, at the end of her two months' training, when she marched at the head of the procession of nurses to receive the Red Cross diploma of a certified war nurse."

After a morning in the operating room, Alexandra spent the

afternoon visiting other hospitals. The wounded men reached out bandaged hands to touch her; they wept as she kneeled beside their beds to pray. Men facing amputations cried from their beds, "Tsaritsa, hold my hand, that I may have courage." To Alexandra, this was Russia itself, bleeding and dying, and she was the Matushka of all the brave men and boys.

She wrote to Nicholas, "I had a wretched fellow with awful wounds—scarcely a man anymore, so shot to pieces. I washed and cleaned and painted with iodine and bandaged all up. I did three such—one's heart bleeds for them—it's so sad, being a wife and mother I feel for them quite particularly—a young nurse I sent out of the room."

Six hundred and thirty of the Empress's letters to the Tsar were found in a black leather suitcase in Ekaterinburg after her death. They were written with no inkling that anyone else would ever read them. Today, they offer a window into a soul; a portrait of a woman none of her contemporaries in Russia could possibly have seen. She wrote in English, voluminously, in a bold, rounded hand, breathlessly, the punctuation largely dots and dashes. The intense fervor of some passages is strong evidence of her passions, but not—as some have charged—proof that the Empress was mad. Phrases plucked from a mass of verbiage can make a loquacious woman seem hysterical.

A remarkable feature of the letters was the freshness of Alexandra's love. After two decades of marriage, she still wrote like a young girl. Shy, even icy, in public, she released all her romantic passion for Nicholas in her letters: "My sweetest treasure . . . I yearn for your kisses, for your arms and shy Childy [Nicholas] gives them me only in the dark and wify lives by them." She was in anguish whenever he left for the front.

The letters usually reached Nicholas with flower petals pressed between their pages. "We have lived through so much together in these years. . . . In thoughts I gently kiss your sweet face all over. For an old married woman it may seem ridiculous, but I cannot help it. With the years, love increases. . . ."

Nicholas's replies, if more restrained, were no less tender. "My beloved Sunny, I don't know how I could have endured it all if God had not decreed to give you to me as a wife and friend. It is difficult to speak of such things and it is easier for me to put it down on paper, owing to my stupid shyness. . . . Ever your old hubby, Nicky."

Knowing how much he missed his children, Alexandra wrote of them. "Baby improves on the balalaika. . . . The girls are sprawling on the floor with the sun shining full upon them to get brown. From whom have they got that craze?" But then: "Baby woke up from pain in his left arm and from 2 on scarcely got a moment's sleep. . . ."

FOR A WHILE, Rasputin's influence had dwindled because of his opposition to the war. But in the winter of 1915, Anna Vyrubova was left in critical condition following a train wreck. Her legs had been crushed and her skull and spine badly injured. At the hospital a surgeon said she was dying. Nicholas and Alexandra came to her bedside and waited for the end.

When Rasputin heard about the accident, he drove to the hospital, and entered Anna's room. She was in a delirium, murmuring, "Father Gregory, pray for me." He took her hand and called, "Annushka! Annushka! Annushka!"

The third time he called, Anna slowly opened her eyes. Rasputin ordered, "Now wake up and rise." She made an effort to get up. "Speak to me." She spoke in a feeble voice.

"She will recover, but she will remain a cripple," said Rasputin. Then he staggered from the room and collapsed in a wave of dizziness and perspiration.

Anna recovered, but thereafter used crutches or a wheelchair. The episode overwhelmingly revived Alexandra's conviction that Rasputin was a saint, capable of accomplishing miracles.

During 1914–1916, Rasputin lived in a working-class apartment house in Petrograd. His apartment was small and simply furnished. The narrow bed had a red fox fur bedspread, and there were lamps burning before an icon. Portraits of the Tsar and Tsaritsa hung on the walls, along with crude engravings of biblical scenes.

When he had not been drinking late, Rasputin rose early and went to Mass. By the time he returned for a breakfast of bread and tea, the first of his petitioners were climbing the stairs: bankers, bishops, officers, society women, actresses, speculators, peasants, old women who had traveled miles to get his blessing. Many waited in line on the staircase. If Rasputin decided to help a visitor, he scrawled a few lines: "My dear and valued friend. Do this for me. Gregory." These scraps of paper were all that was needed to win a promotion or a contract. Some of them went straight to Alexandra who forwarded them to the Tsar.

Because he wrote poorly and slowly, Rasputin did not name the service to be performed, leaving this to the petitioner. Eventually, to save time, he made up a supply of these notes in advance and simply handed them out.

In return for his services, the wealthy put bundles of money on the table and Rasputin stuffed them into a drawer, to accumulate a dowry for his daughter, Maria, who lived in a room in his apartment. But if his next petitioner was in need, he might pull out the bundle and give it away. He had little need of money.

For pretty women, there were other methods of payment. Many an attractive visitor rushed out of his apartment, weeping or trembling with rage, and went to the police to complain that Rasputin had attacked her. But he was never punished.

Whatever else he might be doing, Rasputin took care to preserve the image of piety he had created at Tsarskoe Selo. Sometimes a call from the palace would upset his evening plans; even when thoroughly drunk, he managed to sober himself and rush off to consult with "Mama" on matters of state.

Rasputin was one of the most enigmatic men on earth, an overwhelming personality, and a superbly convincing actor. He caroused at a pace that would kill a normal man, and whenever he felt himself threatened by the many scandalous stories about him, he played on Alexandra's fears and her religious nature. "Neither the Emperor nor you can do without me," he said. "If I am not here to protect you, you will lose your son and your crown within six months." Alexandra would not take the risk.

Rasputin's political advice was usually confined to endorsing policies which the Empress already believed in, rephrasing the idea in his own language so it would seem freshly inspired. Where his ideas were original, they represented peasant Russia. He often warned of the shortage of food, a shortage which was mainly a problem of distribution. At one point, he urged Alexandra to have all passenger trains cancelled for three days so that food and fuel might flow into the cities.

The area in which Rasputin exercised his most destructive influence was in the choice of ministers. He simply nominated men for the highest government positions because they liked him, or at least did not oppose him. In time, every appointment in the highest echelons passed through his hands.

Nicholas greets members of the first Russian parliament—the Duma—at the Winter Palace.

ALEXANDRA scarcely knew her husband's ministers during her first twenty-one years as Empress. She had shown little interest in politics unless Rasputin was threatened. When she filled the administrative gap Nicholas left behind, it was not a formal regency, but a division of family duties wholly within Russian tradition. This was the way Nicholas regarded her role. He wrote, "My wify, will you not come to the assistance of your hubby now that he is absent? What a pity that you have not been fulfilling this duty long ago. . . . I am so happy to think that you have found at last a worthy occupation. Now I shall not worry over internal affairs."

Inexperienced, narrow and stubborn, Alexandra made numerous, outsized mistakes, but as she went along, her self-confidence improved and she delightedly wrote to the Tsar, "I am no longer the slightest bit shy or afraid of ministers and speak like a waterfall in Russian." Rasputin was still her yardstick for measuring men. "Good" men esteemed his advice. "Bad" men hated him. "Good" men would be blessed, and should be appointed to high office. "Bad" men were sure to fail, and those already in office should be driven out.

Any sign that a minister disagreed with the Tsar also made her suspicious; the thought that the ministers and the Duma might be working together drove her frantic, since she considered the very existence of the Duma a stain on the Emperor's autocracy.

During the next sixteen months there was a sad parade of dismissals, reshuffles and intrigues. In that time, Russia had four prime ministers, five ministers of the interior, four ministers of agriculture and three ministers of war, and the government almost ceased to function.

When an obscure, reactionary bureaucrat, Boris Stürmer, was suddenly named Prime Minister, Paléologue thought him simply a tool for Rasputin. He wrote: "Third-rate intellect, mean spirit, low character, doubtful honesty, no experience . . . but a rather pretty talent for cunning and flattery."

Stürmer supplied Rasputin with four high-powered War Office cars, too fast to be followed by the police. Alexei Polivanov, the Minister of War, Russia's ablest military organizer, sternly objected to this, and soon Alexandra was writing to Nicholas, "Get rid of Polivanov. Any honest man better than him. Lovy, don't dawdle, make up your mind." So Polivanov fell. For Russia, it was a disaster. "Oh, the relief! Now I shall sleep well," the Empress said when she heard the news.

The next to go was Foreign Minister Sergei Sazonov, a cultivated, liberal man, trusted by the Allied governments. Alexandra suspected, rightly, that he wanted a less autocratic government in Russia. She kept up a barrage against "long-nosed Sazonov" and his downfall came in 1916, because he backed autonomy for Poland. At the start of the war, Russia had promised the Poles a virtually independent Polish kingdom, linked to Russia only by the Tsar. But now Alexandra, spurred by Rasputin, argued that "Baby's future rights" were being challenged, and Sazonov was abruptly dismissed, Stürmer taking on his office in addition to the Premiership.

But the key ministry in troubled times was the Ministry of the Interior, which was responsible for the police, informers and counterespionage. The Tsar, urged by Alexandra and Rasputin, appointed Alexander Protopopov to this critical post. He was a small, sleek man with white hair, bright black eyes, and an ingratiating air which had charmed the Tsar. In office, he became wholly eccentric. Beside his desk he kept an icon which he addressed as a person. "He helps me do everything; everything I do is by His advice," Protopopov once explained to Kerensky, indicating the icon. Even more astonishing was the sudden transformation of a liberal into an arch-reactionary. He was determined to become the savior of Tsarism, and he hoped to provoke a revolution in order to crush the revolutionaries.

Alexandra—without consulting Nicholas first—gave the ineffectual Protopopov responsibility for Russian food supplies in the critical winter of 1916–1917. "Our Friend said it was absolutely necessary," she wrote the Tsar. "Gregory says Protopopov will have all in his hands and by that will save Russia. . . . Stürmer and Protopopov both completely believe in our Friend's wonderful, God-sent wisdom," she added happily.

Alexandra also began to trespass into the area of military operations. "Sweet Angel," she wrote, "long to ask you heaps about your plans concerning Rumania. Our Friend is so anxious to know." General Alexeiev was less than charmed to hear of Rasputin's interest in the army, and the Tsar begged Alexandra not to pass on to Rasputin the military details he told her. Alexandra assured him that Rasputin wouldn't mention them "to a soul." With supreme self-confidence, Rasputin passed from asking questions about the army to transmitting instructions as to the timing and location of Russian attacks, using inspirations that came to him in dreams. His intervention appeared most conspicuously during the great Russian offensive of 1916 against the Austrians, an attack that inflicted a million casualties, and prevented the Austrians from exploiting their great victory over the Italians at Caporetto. The cost to Russia of the attack was heavy, and it seemed to the Empress and to Rasputin that Russia was choking in her own blood. Repeatedly she attacked "this useless slaughter," and after long hesitation, Nicholas finally gave in and the great Russian offensive ground to a halt.

By October 1916, Russia was beginning to disintegrate. There were mutinies in the army, and a growing economic breakdown. Nicholas, more perceptive than the Empress, had seen this coming for months. "Stürmer cannot make up his mind to do what is necessary for munitions and railways," Nicholas wrote. "Prices are soaring and the people are beginning to starve." Under the pressure of his dual role as Tsar and commander in chief, Nicholas's health and morale were beginning to suffer. He grew pale and thin under his unbearable load.

In November he went to Kiev to inspect hospitals. His sister, Grand Duchess Olga, worked in the ward of one of the hospitals he visited. "We had a young, wounded deserter, condemned to death," she wrote. "Two soldiers were guarding him. All of us felt troubled about him—he looked such a decent boy. . . . Nicky put his hand on the boy's shoulder and asked why he had deserted. The young man stammered that, having run out of ammunition, he had got frightened and ran. We all waited, our breath held, and Nicky told him that he was free. The lad scrambled out of bed, fell on the floor, his arms around Nicky's knees, and sobbed like a child.

"I never saw Nicky again."

While the Tsar was in Kiev, the Duma met and the storm began to break. From extreme right to revolutionary left, every party opposed the government. A right-wing liberal quoted the Russian author Alexander Pushkin: "Woe to that country where only the slave and the liar are close to the throne." The outrage in the Duma could not be ignored, and, giving Alexandra a pain-

435

ful shock, the Tsar finally dismissed Stürmer and appointed Alexander Trepov, a conservative monarchist but a stern enemy of Rasputin. Trepov won the Tsar's promise that Protopopov would be dismissed, but Alexandra entreated Nicholas desperately, and, after a painful scene between them, Protopopov was allowed to remain.

Alexandra, sending her husband back to the front, felt pleased with this triumph. During the following days, a torrent of exhortation poured from her pen. "Be firm. . . . Russia loves to feel the whip—it's their nature—tender love and then the iron hand to punish and guide. . . . Be Peter the Great, Ivan the Terrible, crush them all under you."

Rather acidly, Nicholas replied: "Tender thanks for the severe scolding. I read it with a smile, because you speak to me as though I was a child. Your 'poor little weak-willed' hubby, Nicky."

PETROGRAD society began to show a deep loathing of Rasputin and a growing indifference to the war. The crowds drinking champagne at the hotels included many officers who should have been at the front, for now there was no disgrace in shirking.

Society gathered at the Maryinsky Theatre to watch the ballet, with Kschessinska, the Tsar's early love, as prima ballerina. A twelve-year-old ballet student, George Balanchine, was taken to the Imperial box to be presented to the Tsar and the Empress. Fifty years later, Balanchine, now director of the New York City Ballet Company, struggled to convey his impression of the Empress. He said, "Beautiful, beautiful—like Grace Kelly."

To most of Russia, however, Alexandra was an object of contempt and hatred. They believed a secret pro-German cabal was betraying them from the top. The Tsar was not suspected, but she was. She was openly described as Rasputin's mistress, and Rasputin, everyone assumed, was a spy. This seems unlikely; but he was probably drained of information by others who were German agents. He was loud and boastful, and it was not difficult to infiltrate his circle.

General Alexeiev warned the Tsar that censorship of soldiers' letters revealed that they were writing continuously of his wife and Rasputin. She was referred to everywhere as *Nemka* (the German woman), just as Marie Antoinette had been known as *L'Autrichienne* (the Austrian woman).

The growing peril to the monarchy was obvious to the rest of the Imperial family and they tried in vain to get Nicholas to broaden the government's support in the Duma, remove Rasputin's influence and give Russia a constitutional monarchy. Nicholas refused, saying that he had sworn at his coronation to deliver his autocratic power intact to his son.

The most poignant of all the warning visits was that of Grand Duchess Elizabeth. Dressed in the robes of her religious order, she came from Moscow to speak to her sister about Rasputin. At the mention of his name, the Empress's face grew cold. She was sorry, she said, to find her sister accepting the "lies" told about Father Gregory; if that was all she had to discuss, her visit might as well end. Desperate, the Grand Duchess persisted, whereupon the Empress rose and ordered a carriage to take her to the station. It was their last meeting.

THE GRAND DUKES, the generals and the Duma all agreed that Rasputin had to be removed. There was a standing ovation when Vladimir Purishkevich, an ardent monarchist, roared in the Duma, "Revolution threatens—and an obscure moujik shall govern Russia no longer!" But amid the storm of cheers a slender young man in the visitors' box remained silent. Another visitor noticed that Prince Felix Yussoupov was pale and trembling.

At twenty-nine, Yussoupov was heir to the largest fortune in Russia. Dinner parties at the Moika Palace brought two thousand guests to sit before golden plates and be served by Arab and Tartar footmen. There were three other Yussoupov palaces in Petrograd, three in Moscow and thirty-seven Yussoupov estates scattered across Russia. The family's mines, oil fields and factories churned out wealth which exceeded that of the Tsars. "One of our estates," wrote Yussoupov, "stretched for one hundred and twenty-five miles along the Caspian Sea." Once, on a whim, Prince

Yussoupov's father had given his mother the highest mountain in the Crimea as a birthday present.

For centuries, the Yussoupovs had been standing at the elbows of Russia's Tsars. A Yussoupov mansion in Moscow had been a hunting lodge for Ivan the Terrible; it was connected by tunnel with the Kremlin several miles away, and there were sealed underground chambers which, when opened in Felix's boyhood, revealed rows of skeletons hanging in chains. Felix's ancestor Prince Nicholas Yussoupov had been an adviser to three Tsars. His estate near Moscow was a city in itself, with a zoo, glass and porcelain factories, and a private theater where Nicholas could, with a wave of his cane, produce an extraordinary effect: his company of dancers would suddenly appear on stage, stark naked. A gallery on the estate contained portraits of the Prince's three hundred mistresses.

Felix was a spindly, lonely child. Princess Zenaide, one of the most famous beauties of her day, had borne three previous sons, of whom only one survived, and had prayed that her next child would be a girl. She kept Felix in long hair and dresses until he was five. In adolescence he was described as "the most beautiful young man in Europe." He tried opium, and a liaison with a charming young girl in Paris; then he became the family heir when his older brother was killed in a duel, and returned to Russia to marry Princess Irina, the niece of the Tsar.

Yussoupov had achieved a reputation as a bohemian. Whenever friends visited, he played the guitar and sang gypsy songs, and he and Rasputin caroused together at dubious night spots. According to Yussoupov, Rasputin often spoke of his Imperial patrons, and had suggested that Nicholas should abdicate in favor of Alexis, with the Empress installed as regent. For a year before he acted, Yussoupov had felt that Rasputin was destroying the monarchy and had to be killed.

The morning after Purishkevich spoke in the Duma, Yussoupov called on the orator in a fever of excitement. When he said that he planned to kill Rasputin, Purishkevich enthusiastically agreed to help. Others were brought into the plot, including a doctor named Lazovert, and the charming, elegant young Grand Duke Dmitry, Nicholas's cousin.

The date they chose was determined by Grand Duke Dmitry's heavy social calendar; December 15 (Old Style) was the first evening he had free. To cancel one of his previous engagements, the conspirators decided, might arouse suspicion. The place selected for the murder was the cellar of the Moika Palace. Yussoupov was to bring Rasputin there in a car driven by Dr. Lazovert disguised as a chauffeur. In the cellar, Yussoupov would feed Rasputin poison; then the others, waiting upstairs in his parents' apartment, would take charge of removing the body.

THE EBULLIENT Purishkevich bubbled with hints to Duma members that something was about to happen to Rasputin. Catching rumors of this, Rasputin became moody and cautious. Once after a walk along the Neva he declared that he had seen the river filled with the blood of grand dukes. In his last meeting with the Tsar, he refused to give Nicholas his blessing, saying, "This time it is for you to bless me, not I you."

Then Rasputin wrote a prophetic letter, its warnings directed at Nicholas: "I feel that I shall leave life before January 1. I wish to make known that if I am killed by common assassins . . . you, Tsar of Russia, have nothing to fear. But if it was your relations who have wrought my death then no one of your family will remain alive for more than two years. They will be killed by the Russian people. Pray, pray, be strong, think of your blessed family."

When Yussoupov invited Rasputin for the evening of the fifteenth, he readily accepted. Yussoupov had encouraged his belief that Princess Irina, widely known for her beauty, would be present. Actually she was in the Crimea for her health, but, as Yussoupov wrote, "I thought Rasputin would be more likely to accept my invitation if he thought he had a chance of meeting her."

By evening the cellar was prepared. It had an open fire, a low vaulted ceiling, gray stone walls and floor, carved oak chairs, and a cabinet of inlaid ebony with a crucifix on it. There was a Persian carpet and, in front of the cabinet, a white bearskin rug. On the table at which Rasputin was to drink his last cup of tea a samovar smoked, surrounded by plates of Rasputin's favorite cakes and dainties. Bottles and glasses sat on a sideboard.

Yussoupov wrote later, "I took from the ebony cabinet a box containing the poison and laid it on the table. Doctor Lazovert put on rubber gloves and ground cyanide of potassium crystals to powder. Then, lifting the top of each cake, he sprinkled the inside with a dose of poison which, according to him, was sufficient to kill several men instantly."

When Yussoupov went alone at midnight to get Rasputin, he found the starets dressed in his best embroidered silk blouse, black velvet trousers and shiny new boots. As he took his victim to the palace and down into the cellar, Yussoupov said that Princess Irina was upstairs at a party but would be down shortly. From overhead came the sounds of "Yankee Doodle" played on a phonograph by the "party."

Yussoupov nervously offered his victim the poisoned cakes. Rasputin gobbled two. Yussoupov expected to see him crumple in agony, but Rasputin merely asked for the Madeira, which had also been poisoned. He swallowed two glasses, with no effect. He took some tea to clear his head, and, while sipping it, asked Yussoupov to sing and play his guitar. The terrified murderer sang gypsy songs while Rasputin sat nodding and grinning with pleasure. Huddled at the top of the stairs, the conspirators could hear the quavering sound of Yussoupov's singing and the murmur of the two voices.

After two and a half hours, Yussoupov rushed upstairs in desperation to ask what he should do. Lazovert had no answer: his nerves had failed and he had already fainted once. Grand Duke Dmitry suggested giving up and going home. Purishkevich, the steadiest of the group, declared that Rasputin could not be allowed to leave half dead. Steeling himself, Yussoupov volunteered to complete the murder.

Holding Dmitry's revolver behind his back, he went back down the stairs and found Rasputin calling for more wine. Yussoupov led Rasputin to the mirrored cabinet, and showed him the crucifix. "Gregory Efimovich," he said, "you'd better say a prayer." Rasputin glared at the prince, then turned to look again at the cross. As he did so, Yussoupov fired into the broad back. With a scream, Rasputin fell onto the white bearskin rug.

Yussoupov's friends rushed into the cellar, and Dr. Lazovert, clutching Rasputin's pulse, pronounced him dead. The diagnosis was premature. When Yussoupov was temporarily alone with the "corpse," Rasputin's eyes fluttered open. "I then saw the green eyes of a viper staring at me with an expression of diabolical hatred," Yussoupov wrote. Foaming at the mouth, Rasputin suddenly leaped to his feet, grabbed his murderer by the throat and tore an epaulet off his shoulder. In terror, Yussoupov broke away and fled up the stairs. Behind him, clambering on all fours, roaring with fury, came Rasputin.

Purishkevich heard a savage, inhuman cry. It was Yussoupov: "Purishkevich, fire, fire! He's getting away!" Purishkevich ran to the stairs and almost collided with the frantic Prince, who hurled himself into his parents' apartment. Purishkevich dashed outside. Rasputin was running across the snow-covered courtyard, crying, "I will tell everything to the Empress!" Purishkevich fired twice, missing. He bit his left hand to force himself to concentrate, and a third bullet stopped Rasputin. A fourth shot probably hit him in the head. "He fell into the snow, tried to rise, but could only grind his teeth," Purishkevich wrote. Yussoupov reappeared and struck hysterically at the bleeding man with a club.

At last the body lay still in the crimson snow. It was rolled up in a blue curtain, bound with a rope and taken to the Neva, where Purishkevich and Lazovert pushed it through a hole in the ice. Three days later, when the body was found, the lungs were filled with water. Gregory Rasputin, his bloodstream filled with poison, his body punctured by bullets, had died by drowning; and before he died, he had struggled with sufficient strength to free one of his hands from the rope around him. The freed arm was raised above the shoulder; the effect was a sign of benediction.

In his excitement, Purishkevich had again forgotten the need

for secrecy. After his four pistol shots had brought a policeman to the palace, he had thrown his arms around the man and shouted, "I have killed Rasputin, the enemy of Russia and the Tsar!"

Detectives, entering the Moika Palace later, found the trail of blood, which Yussoupov now explained as the result of a wild party at which one of his guests had shot a dog; the body of a dog was lying in the court. Protopopov advised Alexandra that Rasputin had probably been murdered and she ordered Dmitry and Felix confined to their houses. She wrote to her husband, "I cannot believe that He has been killed. God have mercy. Come quickly. . . ."

In Petrograd, confirmation that the Beast was slain set off an orgy of rejoicing. In the provinces, however, where the peasants knew only that a man like themselves had become powerful at the court of the Tsar, Rasputin became a martyr. They said, "He defended the people against the court folk, so they killed him."

Nicholas was horrified that "the hands of my kinsmen are stained with the blood of a peasant." And almost fifty years later, Grand Duchess Olga said: "There was nothing heroic about Rasputin's murder, it was premeditated most vilely. . . . It proved how low we had fallen."

Grand Duke Dmitry was ordered to leave for duty with the troops in Persia; the sentence saved his life by putting him out of reach of the Revolution. Yussoupov was banished to one of his distant estates. Later, he left his homeland with Princess Irina, taking with him a million dollars in jewels. Purishkevich was allowed to go free. To strike down a member of the Duma who had also become a hero was no longer possible for the Tsar.

Rasputin was buried in a corner of the Imperial park. The Imperial family were there, dressed in mourning. The Empress, pale and in tears, had two objects placed on Rasputin's breast. One was an icon, signed by herself, her husband, her son and her daughters. The other was a letter: "My dear martyr, give me thy blessing that it may follow me always on the sad and dreary path I have yet to follow here below. And remember us from on high in your holy prayers. Alexandra."

FOLLOWING RASPUTIN'S MURDER, the Tsar suffered something close to nervous collapse. He remained secluded, speaking vaguely and avoiding decisions. Paléologue wrote, "Nicholas II has abdicated inwardly and is resigned to disaster."

Alexandra told a friend, "I think my heart is broken." But the face she showed was calm and resolute. While life remained, she would persevere in her faith, her devotion to her family and her resolve to maintain the autocracy. Steeled for the shocks to come, she continued to dominate political affairs. The main telephone in the palace was not on the Tsar's desk but in her boudoir.

Felix Yussoupov's father-in-law, cousin and brother-in-law of the Tsar—the "Sandro" of Nicholas's gay youth—went to Tsarskoe Selo to plead that the Empress withdraw from politics. He found her lying in bed in a white negligee. The Tsar sat quietly smoking on the other side of their large double bed. Grand Duke Alexander spoke plainly, telling the Empress that she was harming Nicholas—that all classes were opposed to her. "Please, Alix," he ended, "leave the cares of state to your husband." But the interview ended badly, with Alexander shouting in a rage: "I realize that you and your husband are willing to perish, but you have no right to drag your relatives with you."

Then Rodzianko, President of the Duma, went to the Tsar, warning him of grave upheavals. "Sire," he said, "there is not an honest man left in your entourage. Hatred of the Empress is growing. To save your family, Your Majesty must find some way of preventing the Empress from exercising any influence on politics. Do not compel the people to choose between you and the good of the country."

Nicholas pressed his head between his hands. "Is it possible," he asked, "that for twenty-two years I tried to act for the best and that for twenty-two years it was all a mistake?"

Rodzianko summoned his courage and said, "Yes, Your Majesty, for twenty-two years you followed a wrong course."

A month later, on February 23, 1917, Rodzianko saw Nicholas again, for the last time. The Tsar's attitude had grown harsh and Rodzianko, in turn, was blunt. Announcing that revolution was imminent, he declared, "I consider it my duty, Sire, to express to you my profound conviction that this will be my last report to you." Rodzianko was curtly excused.

Rodzianko's was the last of the great warnings to the Tsar. In Nicholas's mind, the many people who had come to him did not represent the peasant masses, the real Russia. Most of all, he felt that to give way during the war would be taken as a sign of weakness which would only accelerate revolution. Perhaps, when the war was ended, he would modify the autocracy. "But I cannot act now," he said. "I cannot do more than one thing at a time."

On March 8 Nicholas returned to Stavka to plan the spring offensive. Four days later, the Imperial government collapsed.

PART FOUR

Revolution

THE UNDERLYING problem in Russia was still the shortage of food and fuel. The war had taken fifteen million men off the farms, and the railroads, barely adequate in peacetime, were collapsing. The cities suffered more than the countryside, and Petrograd, farthest from food- and coal-producing regions, suffered most. Ironically, no organization had made any serious revolutionary plans. Lenin, living in exile in Switzerland, declared gloomily that while "popular risings must flare up in Europe within a few years . . . we older men may not live to see the decisive battles of the approaching revolution."

But no plan for a revolution was needed in the growing hunger and bitterness of the people. In the grip of thirty-five-degree-below-zero cold, long lines of women waited outside the Petrograd bakeries for their daily bread ration. Workers whose factories had closed for lack of coal milled in the streets. In the barracks, soldiers gathered around stoves and listened to agitators.

445

On March 8, as Nicholas's train was carrying him back to head-quarters, the long-suffering breadlines suddenly erupted. People broke into the bakeries and helped themselves. A procession chanting, "Give us bread," marched across the Neva bridges, and filled the Nevsky Prospect. Next morning, more bakeries were sacked and Cossack patrols appeared, but without their whips, the traditional instrument of mob control in Russia. They assured the crowd, "Don't worry. We won't shoot."

On March 10, huge crowds surged through the streets, carrying red banners and shouting, "Down with the German woman! Down with the war!" The Cabinet begged Nicholas to return from the front and appoint a ministry acceptable to the Duma. Misinformed by Protopopov as to the seriousness of the situation, Nicholas only telegraphed brusquely: I ORDER THAT DISORDERS IN THE CAPITAL, IN-TOLERABLE DURING THESE DIFFICULT TIMES, BE ENDED TOMORROW.

The Tsar's order meant that troops were to be used to clear the streets. But the quality of the troops at that time could not have been worse. The pre-war army had long since perished, and the Petrograd garrison consisted of raw recruits and young country boys, all in training. Despite this, the military governor, General S. S. Khabalov, prepared to obey the Tsar's command. Early risers, venturing into the streets on Sunday morning, found huge posters bearing his order: All assemblies and public meetings were forbidden and would be dispersed by force.

Ignoring the posters, huge crowds swarmed into the heart of the city, and lines of soldiers began issuing from their barracks. There was shooting on the Nevsky Prospect that day and two hundred people died. Many of the soldiers obeyed orders reluctantly. One company refused to fire into a crowd, and emptied its rifles into the air; another shot its officer.

That night, Rodzianko sent an anguished telegram to the Tsar: THERE IS ANARCHY IN THE CAPITAL. THE GOVERNMENT IS PARA-LYZED. A PERSON TRUSTED BY THE COUNTRY MUST BE CHARGED IM-MEDIATELY TO FORM A MINISTRY. Nicholas said scornfully to General Alexeiev, "That fat Rodzianko has sent me some nonsense which I shall not even bother to answer."

446

On March 12 the final crisis came with the massive defection of 66,000 Petrograd soldiers. With red flags fastened to many bayonets, they joined the disorderly mobs. The gates of the Arsenal burst open with a crash. The Military Government Building and a score of police stations were set on fire; the prisons were opened and all the prisoners liberated. By nightfall the Fortress of Peter and Paul had fallen. The Cabinet adjourned itself—forever as it turned out—and most ministers went to the Tauride Palace to place themselves under the protection of the Duma.

Events now moved with breathtaking speed. Crowds of workers and soldiers, carrying red banners and singing the "Marseillaise," swarmed into the Tauride Palace and engulfed the Duma. "Can I say that the Imperial Duma is with them?" the moderate revolutionary, Alexander Kerensky, cried to Rodzianko. "That it takes the responsibility—that it stands at the head of the government?" Rodzianko had little choice but to agree; and so power passed from the Tsar to the Duma, with Kerensky emerging as its leader.

But on the same day there arose a rival assembly, the Soviet of Workers' and Soldiers' Deputies. Kerensky felt that the Duma needed representatives from the more violent rebels to be able to reestablish order. By nightfall the Soviet sat under the same roof as the Duma. Kerensky wrote, "Two different Russias settled side by side: the Russia of the ruling classes who had lost (though they did not realize it yet) and the Russia of Labor, marching towards power, without suspecting it."

During the first days of the Revolution, Kerensky averted a massacre. "The Duma was full of the most hated officials of the monarchy," he wrote. "If I had washed my hands of it, Russia might have been drenched in torrents of blood as it was under Lenin in October." When a stream of prisoners were arrested, Kerensky said, "The Imperial Duma does not shed blood."

Petrograd had fallen. But Russia was immense and Petrograd only a tiny corner of the Tsar's empire; and even in that city the revolutionaries were less than a quarter of the population. Nicholas had lost his capital, but still he kept his throne.

BUT AT HEADQUARTERS, NICHOLAS was simply writing to Alexandra about the Tsarevich. "Here in the house it so still," he wrote. "No noise, no excited shouts. I imagine him sleeping—all his little things, photographs and knickknacks, in exemplary order in his bedroom."

Nicholas's last letters as Tsar, written from the brink of the abyss, have been cited as evidence of incorrigible stupidity. But the Tsar had far less information than aristocrats who continued blithely to attend parties in Petrograd. He had been told only that the capital was afflicted with "street disorders." Nicholas had faced "street disorders" innumerable times in his reign. They were a matter for the city police.

Then, on the 12th, a jolting telegram arrived from Alexandra: CONCESSIONS INEVITABLE. MANY UNITS GONE OVER TO THE ENEMY. ALIX. At midnight Nicholas ordered his train and at five a.m. he was under way for Tsarskoe Selo. The news continued to grow worse, and finally the Tsar sent Rodzianko the offer he had so long refused: a ministry acceptable to the Duma. It was too late. The Duma and the Soviet had already agreed that Nicholas must abdicate in favor of his son, with the Tsar's brother Michael as regent. When the telegrams announcing that army leaders concurred were brought to the Imperial train and laid before the Tsar, his face became white. He turned away and walked to the window. The car was absolutely still.

It was the advice of his army comrades, that abdication would be an act of patriotism, that swung his decision. He cared far more about winning the war than he did for his crown. A civil war, with the hated Germans looking on, would be a negation of all that he deeply believed. He spun around from the window and announced in a clear, firm voice, "I shall give up the throne in favor of my son, Alexis." He made the sign of the cross and the others in the car crossed themselves.

At this point, Nicholas assumed that he would be allowed to retire with his family to his palace at Livadia, in the Caucasus, and that Alexis would remain with them until he had finished his education. But now Dr. Fedorov said that the Tsar and the

Empress would almost certainly be exiled, and that the government would never allow its new sovereign to be educated abroad.

Fedorov's words confronted Nicholas with a heartbreaking dilemma: He could not abandon Alexis to strangers ignorant of all the ramifications of his disease. For the second time that day Nicholas made a dramatic decision: He abdicated in favor of his brother Michael. He signed a document splendidly illuminated by his patriotism: "For the sake of Russia, and to keep the armies in the field, I decided to take this step."

In England and France, where Nicholas was seen as a tyrant wielding the knout, liberals were exuberant at the news; and Woodrow Wilson spoke glowingly of the "majesty and might" that the Russian people had added to the forces fighting "for freedom in the world." But this optimism was not shared by one brilliant Englishman. A decade later Winston Churchill wrote: "It is the shallow fashion of these times to dismiss the Tsarist regime as a corrupt, incompetent tyranny. . . . Nicholas II was neither a great captain nor a great prince. He was a true, simple man of average ability, of merciful disposition, upheld in all his daily life by his faith in God. But in spite of errors vast and terrible, the regime over which he presided had won the war for Russia. . . . Belittle his efforts, asperse his conduct, insult his memory; but pause then to tell us who else was found capable. Who or what could guide the Russian state?"

The reign of the thirty-nine-year-old Michael was ludicrously brief. The Soviet had already decided that replacing one Romanov with another was not enough. Michael consulted Kerensky and Rodzianko, who said they could not vouch for his life if he accepted the crown. Michael abdicated and the Romanov dynasty was swept away.

Haggard and hollow-eyed, Nicholas said good-by to his officers and wrote a farewell to the troops, urging them to support the Provisional Government. To assure their own safety, the Provisional Government in Petrograd had resolved to "deprive the deposed emperor and his consort of their liberty."

Nicholas's mother had arrived for a visit and the Tsar, comforting her, had a last luncheon with her alone. Then, at three p.m., the express from Petrograd arrived bearing the government envoys who would take the Tsar to Tsarskoe Selo. Nicholas tenderly kissed his mother good-by as she cried unrestrainedly. Both hoped that they would soon be reunited either in the Crimea or in England. They were never to meet again.

A famous St. Petersburg palace made by Alexander III into a museum which still exists.

ALEXANDRA, already at Tsarskoe Selo, had paid less attention than usual to events in Petrograd. Protopopov had assured her that matters were under control, and besides, Alexis, Anna Vyrubova and two of the girls had bad cases of the measles. The Empress nursed the invalids herself. When Rodzianko warned her that she and her children were in danger and should leave as soon as possible, Alexandra refused to go because of the children's health. Hours later, the railway lines around Tsarskoe Selo were in the hands of the revolutionaries.

Even before that day, March 13, was over, it seemed that Alexandra's decision to stay would lead to calamity. From Petrograd, a crowd of mutinous soldiers set off by truck for Tsarskoe Selo to seize "the German woman" and her son and bring them back to the capital. But arriving in the village of Tsarskoe Selo, they became distracted and began looting and drinking.

Count Alexander Benckendorff, the senior court official present, ordered a battalion of the *Garde Equipage* and two battalions of the Imperial Guard, about 1500 men, to take up defensive positions around the palace. The Empress was reassured, and her daughters, seeing the familiar faces of the marines, declared happily, "It's just like being on the yacht again."

At nine p.m. a telephone call advised that the rebels were on their way. The sound of firing grew steadily closer. The Empress went out to speak to the guards. Walking from man to man, a black fur cloak over her white nurse's uniform, she told them that she trusted them completely, and that the life of the Heir was in their hands. She looked radiant, Count Benckendorff said. "They are all our friends," she kept repeating.

The mutinous soldiers, hearing rumors that the palace was defended by immense forces and many machine guns, lost their nerve and withdrew; but the loyalty of the troops guarding the palace was deteriorating, and on March 15 they deserted. Alexandra said brokenly, "My sailors—my own sailors—I can't believe it."

Next day, leaflets announcing the Tsar's abdication and the establishment of a Provisional Government reached the palace. The Tsar's uncle, Paul, arrived and went straight to the Empress. Alexandra's friend, Lili Dehn, waiting in the next room, heard agitated voices. "Then the door opened and the Empress appeared," wrote Lili. "Her face was distorted with agony. . . . Leaning heavily against a table and taking my hands in hers, she said brokenly: '*Abdiqué!* . . . What he has gone through! . . . And I was not there to console him.'"

On the morning of March 21, General L. G. Kornilov came to the palace to place Alexandra Fedorovna under arrest, to safeguard her and her children from the excesses of the Soviet. Her husband, he said, would be returning to Tsarskoe Selo the following day. As soon as the children's health permitted, the Provisional Government intended to send the family to Murmansk, where a British cruiser would be waiting to take them to England.

Kornilov told the palace suite that those who wished to leave were free to go; those who stayed would be placed under house arrest with Her Majesty. A majority rose and left the hall. Kornilov, disgusted, muttered under his breath: "Lackeys!"

"The soldiers of the new guard were horrible," said Benckendorff. "Untidy, noisy, quarrelsome. The officers were afraid of them." That night, from the park, came the sounds of rifle shots; it was the soldiers of the new guard killing the tame deer. There were songs and drunken shouts. Lili Dehn offered to sleep outside the Empress's door. "I went to the mauve boudoir," she wrote. "As the Empress watched me trying to arrange my bed on the couch, she came forward, smiling. 'Oh Lili, you Russian ladies don't know how to be useful. My grandmother, Queen Victoria, showed me how to make a bed. I'll teach you.'"

When Nicholas's train finally pulled into the private siding at Tsarskoe Selo station on March 22, the representatives of the Duma turned him over to the new palace commander. As the Tsar was taken away, the members of his suite scuttled away from the train in all directions. Only Prince Vassily Dolgoruky, Benckendorff's son-in-law, chose to accompany his former sovereign to whatever awaited him at the Alexander Palace.

The palace gates were locked. The sentry called an officer, who came out and shouted, "Who is there?" The sentry bawled back, "Nicholas Romanov." "Let him pass," cried the officer.

Nicholas entered an antechamber filled with soldiers. Some were smoking, others did not remove their caps. By habit, as he walked through the crowd, Nicholas touched the brim of his cap, returning salutes which had never been given.

Upstairs, the Empress's door flew open and a servant, in a tone which ignored the events of recent days, boomed out: "His Majesty the Emperor!"

With a cry, Alexandra sprang to her feet and ran to meet her husband. Alone, in the children's room, they fell into each other's arms. With tears in her eyes, Alexandra assured him that the husband and father was infinitely more precious to her than the Tsar. Nicholas finally broke. Laying his head on his wife's breast, the ex-Emperor sobbed like a child.

COUNT BENCKENDORFF, knowing the Tsar's need for outdoor exercise, had arranged for a section of the park to be used for this, but each excursion had to be arranged in advance so sentries could be posted. The Empress, watching from an upstairs window, saw Nicholas marching briskly across the park and a soldier stepping up and blocking his path. Surprised, the Tsar made a nervous gesture with his hand and started in a different direction. Another sentinel appeared and ordered him back. A moment later, Nicholas was surrounded by six armed soldiers, pushing him this way and that. "You can't go there, *Gospodin Polkovnik* (Mr. Colonel). Stand back when you are commanded, *Gospodin Polkovnik*." The Emperor looked from one to another and then with dignity turned and walked back to the palace.

That night, a band of soldiers broke into Rasputin's tomb. They took the coffin to a clearing, pried off the lid and drenched the remains with gasoline and set them on a pine-log fire. For more than six hours, the body burned while an icy wind howled and clouds of pungent smoke rose from the pyre. Earlier, Rasputin had predicted that he would be killed and his body burned, his ashes scattered to the winds.

THE SMALL GROUP which remained with the family included, among others, Anna Vyrubova, Lili Dehn, the Benckendorffs, Prince Dolgoruky, Baroness Buxhoeveden, Pierre Gilliard and Dr. Botkin. They were entirely isolated. Letters passing in and out were read by the commander of the guard. All telephone lines were cut except one connected to the guardroom. It could be used by the captives only if both an officer and a private soldier were present and the conversation was in Russian. Every parcel entering the palace was examined; jars of yogurt were stirred by dirty fingers and pieces of chocolate bitten apart.

The guards were shaggy, unshaven. Their blouses were unbuttoned and their boots filthy. Off duty, they wandered freely through the palace. Baroness Buxhoeveden awoke one night to find a soldier in her bedroom, pocketing gold and silver trinkets from her table. Groups of soldiers kept tramping into the nursery saying, "We want to see the Heir."

Alexis had been abruptly and cruelly deserted by Derevenko, the sailor who devotedly, it seemed, had lived for ten years at the boy's side. He did not leave without an act of heartless vengeance. "I passed the open door of Alexis's room," Anna Vyrubova wrote, "and saw sprawled in a chair the sailor Derevenko. He bawled at the boy insolently to bring him this or that, to perform any menial service. Dazed, the child moved about trying to obey." Nagorny, the other sailor-attendant, was outraged by the betrayal and remained after Derevenko left the palace.

The tranquillity of Nicholas's behavior during his imprisonment has since attracted both glowing praise and contemptuous scorn. But those who were close to Nicholas and saw him as a man regarded his calm as evidence of courage and nobility of spirit. Everyone knew that Nicholas had wept and then, for a moment, they felt an anchor was gone. But he recovered and his bearing became once again the anchor which held everyone else. "No word of reproach ever passed his lips," said Gilliard. "His whole being was dominated by one passion—his love of country. . . . He was ready to forgive anything to those who were inflicting humiliation upon him so long as they were capable of saving Russia."

Nicholas helped tutor his children, played with them, shoveled snow, read the Bible. At night, he read aloud to Alexandra and his daughters from the Russian classics. After the midnight service on Easter Eve, Nicholas asked the officers of the guard to join his family for the traditional Easter meal. There, he embraced them as Russian and Russian, Christian and Christian.

But Alexandra faced the captivity with bitterness. Thin, proud and silent, she remained most of the day on a sofa in the girls' room. In the evening, she traveled by wheelchair to visit Anna, with Nicholas usually pushing the chair. Everything spoke to her of her humiliation. Used to filling her rooms with flowers, she was now forbidden "luxuries unnecessary for prisoners." When a maid brought her a branch of lilac, she wept in gratitude.

For weeks, Alexandra remained convinced that the Russian peasants and the army remained faithful to the Tsar. Then gradually, with a kind of bitter humor, she let Nicholas show her reality. "He would laugh at the idea of being what he called 'an Ex,'" said Lili Dehn. Alexandra picked up the expression. "Don't call me an Empress—I'm only an Ex," she would say. One day at lunch when an especially unpalatable ham appeared on the table, Nicholas made everyone laugh by saying, "Well, this may have once been a ham, but now it's nothing but an ex-ham."

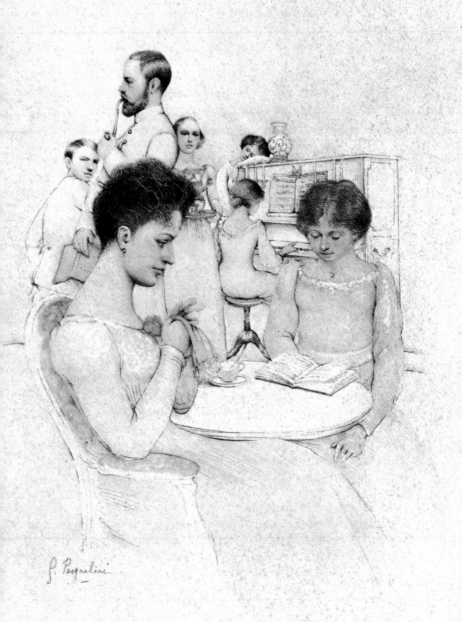

G. Pasqualini

With Nicholas and Alexandra now the focus of popular hatred, the Provisional Government placed the responsibility for their safety on Kerensky. He decided to take a look at them, and drove out in one of the Tsar's own automobiles from the Imperial garage. Alighting at the kitchen door, he assembled the soldiers and the palace servants and delivered an impassioned speech, asking them to report everything suspicious that happened in the palace. His manner abrupt and nervous, he had the Emperor's rooms searched, then the rooms of the ladies-in-waiting. Eventually, he came to the door of Anna Vyrubova.

She had been having lunch with Lili Dehn when the confusion in the palace signaled Kerensky's arrival. In terror, she grabbed a pile of her private papers and threw them into her fire, then jumped into bed and pulled the covers up to her head. A moment later, Kerensky, entering, noticed the fireplace filled with the glowing ash of burning paper and had her arrested. Lili Dehn was also arrested, but was released next day. Anna spent five chilling months in the Fortress of Peter and Paul.

Kerensky, extremely nervous about meeting Nicholas, was conducted to the Imperial family, who were in the schoolroom. He wrote that when he saw them, his feelings underwent "a lightning change." They were standing around a small table, in a "huddled, perplexed little group." The Emperor walked forward to meet him, then stopped in confusion. He didn't know how to act.

"With a smile, I shook hands with the Emperor and he led me to his family. His daughters and the Heir Apparent were obviously burning with curiosity; their eyes were glued to me. But Alexandra Fedorovna stood tense and erect—proud, domineering, irreconcilable. She held out her hand to me unwillingly. I inquired after their health and told them to have complete confidence in the Provisional Government. The Emperor wished us success in our difficult new task."

Kerensky began an investigation of the Empress's "treasonable, pro-German" activities, and found her innocent. He said later that during the weeks of interrogation he was affected by Nicholas's unassuming manner and courtesy, and his "wonderful eyes, deep and sorrowful." Alexandra began to share the Emperor's confidence in Kerensky. Nicholas said, "He is a man who loves Russia; I wish I could have known him earlier because he could have been useful to me."

SPRING melted the snow, and the family began to go out together into the park. They filed out, under guard, the Empress in her wheelchair, through a gauntlet of soldiers, many of whom snickered as they passed. Crowds lined the iron fence to jeer at the Imperial family. Once, when Nicholas pedaled his bicycle along a path, a soldier thrust his bayonet between the spokes. The Tsar fell and the soldiers guffawed.

Yet Nicholas was friendly even to those who insulted him. He always said "Good morning" and held out his hand. "Not for anything in the world," declared one soldier turning his back. "But, my dear fellow, what have you got against me?" asked Nicholas, genuinely astonished. The humiliation of his father was hard for Alexis, who blushed with shame whenever an incident occurred.

Alexandra, too, flushed deeply when her husband was insulted, but she learned to be silent. When the weather was fine she sat on a rug, surrounded by a ring of curious soldiers. Once one of the men dropped with a belligerent grunt onto the rug beside Alexandra. He accused her of "despising" the people, of not traveling about, showing that she did not want to know Russia. Alexandra explained she had had five children and nursed them all herself; she had not had time to go about the country. After more conversation, the soldier got up and took the Empress's hand, saying, "Alexandra Fedorovna, I was mistaken about you."

In May, Colonel Eugene Kobylinsky of the Petrograd Life Guards assumed command of the palace. He did much to buffer the family from shocks. Once when Alexis was playing outside with his toy rifle, soldiers began to shout, "They are armed!" and walked off with the gun, leaving Alexis in tears. Kobylinsky was furious. Carefully, he took the gun apart and, carrying it under his coat, returned it piece by piece to the Tsarevich. Nicholas wrote to his mother that Kobylinsky was "my last friend."

The family began digging up part of the lawn to plant a vegetable garden. Together, they turned the soil, planted the seeds and brought water in tubs from the kitchen. The servants helped; so did some of the soldiers who discovered more pleasure in working beside the Tsar than in mocking him. Later, Nicholas turned to sawing up the dead trees in the park for firewood.

But there was tension at Tsarskoe Selo. The sentries believed a rescue attempt might be made at any moment, and the prisoners lived from day to day, wondering whether the following morning would find them flung into a Soviet dungeon.

They still hoped to be sent abroad. This was what the Provisional Government had promised, hoping to send them to England. The British Ambassador, Sir George Buchanan, had wired London asking for asylum for them. But the fiery Welsh Prime Minister, Lloyd George, was exuberant over the fall of the autocracy. Finally, asylum was grudgingly offered, but the news was received coldly by the Labour Party and many liberals, and the British government began backing away.

George V had wanted to help his relatives, but he was concerned about the widespread indignation in England against the Tsar. He suggested to Lloyd George that he inform the Russian government that Britain was obliged to withdraw its offer.

When the murder of the Imperial family outraged the King, memories tended to blur. The Duke of Windsor recalled, "There was a very real bond between my father and his first cousin Nicky. It hurt my father that Britain had not raised a hand to save his cousin. 'Those politicians,' he used to say."

IN SWITZERLAND, Lenin's reaction to the revolution in Russia was skepticism. In his view, the replacement of an autocracy by a bourgeois republic was not a genuine proletarian revolution. The fact that they intended to continue the war confirmed in his mind that they were no more than tools of Britain and France. He telegraphed instructions to the Bolsheviks in Petrograd: OUR TACTICS: ABSOLUTE DISTRUST. NO SUPPORT OF THE NEW GOVERNMENT. KERENSKY ESPECIALLY SUSPECT.

Lenin became desperate to reach Russia. Through the German minister in Berne, he arranged to travel through Germany to get to Sweden, Finland and Russia. Germany needed a regime which would make peace, and this Lenin promised to do. On April 9, Lenin and eighteen other Bolshevik exiles left Zurich to cross Germany in a sealed train. "The German leaders," said Churchill, "turned upon Russia the most grisly of all weapons. They transported Lenin in a sealed truck like a plague bacillus from Switzerland into Russia."

After ten years away from Russia, Lenin arrived in Petrograd at the Finland Station. He stepped from his train into a vast crowd and a sea of red banners. In an armored car, he drove to Kschessinska's mansion, now a Bolshevik headquarters. From the dancer's balcony, he addressed a cheering crowd, shouting that the war was "shameful imperialist slaughter."

Although Lenin had been welcomed like a returning prophet, other revolutionaries believed that some degree of cooperation should be shown the Provisional Government. But Lenin gained ascendancy over his colleagues by sheer force of intellect and physical stamina. He demanded an end to the war. "Peace, Land, All Power to the Soviet," was his slogan.

Terrified of Russia's withdrawal from the war, the Allies exerted heavy pressure on the Provisional Government. The U.S. government extended loans of $325 million; but the terms were: "No war, no loan." The Provisional Government, with Kerensky now Prime Minister, prepared another offensive, but German reserves checked their rapid advance. And while Soldiers' Committees debated the wisdom of further attacks, whole divisions refused to move. When the enemy counterattacked, there was no resistance. The new Russian retreat became a rout.

In Petrograd, on July 16, half a million people marched through the streets carrying huge scarlet banners proclaiming DOWN WITH THE WAR! and DOWN WITH THE PROVISIONAL GOVERNMENT! But the Provisional Government crushed the uprising, mainly by circulating a document purporting to prove that Lenin was a German agent. The Bolshevik strongholds were stormed and occupied, and Lenin escaped over the border into Finland disguised as a fireman on a locomotive.

"The July Uprising" was over, but it made plain to Kerensky the danger of delay in moving the Imperial family away from Petrograd. Nicholas had asked if they might go to Livadia, but Kerensky settled on Tobolsk, an old-fashioned town in western Siberia where they would be relatively safe.

Without telling Nicholas where he was being taken, Kerensky warned that they would leave within a few days and should take warm clothes. Nicholas replied quickly, "We trust you." He instructed Benckendorff to see that the vegetables they had raised at Tsarskoe Selo and the piles of sawed wood were fairly distributed among the servants.

August 12 was Alexis's thirteenth birthday. At the Empress's request, an icon was brought from the Church of Our Lady of Znamenie, with a procession of clergy to ask prayers for the safe journey of the Imperial family. "All were in tears," wrote Benckendorff. "The soldiers themselves seemed touched and approached the holy icon to kiss it."

On the night before the departure, Kerensky came to supervise the final arrangements. He addressed the restless, uncertain guards: "Remember: no hitting a man when he is down. Behave like gentlemen." Grand Duke Michael arrived to say good-by to his older brother. They were deeply moved, but they plunged into that irrelevant small-talk which is so characteristic of short meetings. "How is Alix?" "How is Mother?" They stood opposite each other, shuffling their feet in embarrassment, sometimes getting hold of one another's arm or coat button. Ten minutes later, Michael walked out of the room in tears, and stopped to kiss Alexis good-by.

The night was confused and sleepless. By six a.m., the train was ready and the baggage loaded. The train bore Japanese flags, and placards proclaiming: JAPANESE RED CROSS MISSION. The family walked to the first car where, for lack of steps, the men lifted Alexandra and the other women in. The train began moving toward Siberia.

PART FIVE

Imprisonment

IF THE TRAIN was not of Imperial quality, it was nevertheless a luxurious vehicle, with sleeping cars, a restaurant car stocked with wines, baggage compartments filled with rugs, pictures and knickknacks. The Imperial family and suite were accompanied by two valets, six chambermaids, ten footmen, three cooks, four assistant cooks, a butler, a wine steward, a nurse, a clerk, a barber, and two pet spaniels. Colonel Kobylinsky rode aboard the Tsar's train. Most of his 330 soldiers followed on a second train.

Deferring to the habits of the Imperial family, every day the train was stopped in open country so that Nicholas and the children could walk the dogs. Alexandra sat fanning herself by an open window and was delighted one afternoon when a soldier reached up and handed her a cornflower.

For four days, the train rolled eastward through heat and dust. East of the low, forested hills of the Urals the Empress and her children saw for the first time the Siberian steppe meadowlands stretching to the horizon. In late afternoon, the immense dome of sky overhead turned bright crimson and gold as the last rays of sunset glowed on the white trunks of the birches and the green marsh grass.

On August 17, the train puffed into Tyumen, on the Tura River, two hundred miles southwest of Tobolsk. The family boarded the river steamer *Rus* for the two-day journey. At Pokrovskoe, Rasputin's home, they gathered on deck to see the prosperous village. Rasputin's house, two stories tall, loomed above the simple peasant huts. Long before, he had predicted to the Empress that one day she would visit his village.

Late the next day, the steamer docked at Tobolsk, a town of twenty thousand people, with an old fortress, onion-bulb-domed churches, log houses and wooden sidewalks. The governor's house, where the royal family would live, was a big, white, two-story structure fringed with second-floor balconies. Most of the entourage lived in a house across the street.

The soldiers objected to any freedom at all for the prisoners, so Kobylinsky reluctantly built a high wooden fence around the house, enclosing a section of a small street. In this muddy, tree-less compound, the family took its exercise. The suite was per-mitted to come and go freely, and Sidney Gibbs, the Tsarevich's English tutor, arrived from Petrograd.

Evening prayers were held in a corner of the drawing room which was decorated with icons. A local priest came in to con-duct services, but because there was no consecrated altar he was unable to offer Mass. Kobylinsky arranged for the family to attend a private early Mass at a church. They walked there be-tween two lines of soldiers. People standing behind the soldiers crossed themselves and some dropped to their knees. The people of Tobolsk were still strongly attached to the Tsar. Merchants openly sent gifts of food, nuns brought sugar and cakes, and peasants arrived regularly with butter and eggs.

In September, two commissars, Vasily Pankratov and Alex-ander Nikolsky, arrived to take charge of the captives, although Kobylinsky kept his command of the military guard. Pankratov, a small, earnest man, pitied the Tsar and was genuinely fond of the children. But the rough, embittered Nikolsky blamed the Tsar for his own earlier imprisonment in Siberia as a revolutionary. He burst into rooms without knocking, and bellowed at the Tsare-vich, who had seldom been yelled at.

In October, the long Siberian winter descended upon Tobolsk. As the days grew shorter Nicholas morosely followed the local newspaper stories of the rapid crumbling of Kerensky's Provisional Government. The Bolsheviks had now gained control of the Petro-grad Soviet. From Finland, Lenin urged another lunge for su-preme power, and on October 23, he slipped into Petrograd in disguise, to attend a meeting of the Bolshevik Central Commit-tee. The Committee voted 10 to 2 for insurrection.

On November 6, the Bolsheviks struck. The cruiser *Aurora*,

flying the red flag, anchored in the Neva opposite the Winter Palace. Without bloodshed, armed Bolshevik squads occupied the railway stations and other public buildings. Kerensky left the Winter Palace in an open car to try to raise help from the army. The remaining ministers stayed in the Winter Palace, protected by a women's battalion and a troop of cadets. The *Aurora* fired a single blank shell, and the women's battalion surrendered. Two more shells whistled into the palace, slightly damaging the plaster. Next day the ministers gave up.

This skirmish was the Bolshevik Revolution, magnified in Communist mythology into an epic of struggle and heroism. A flick of Lenin's finger had finished Kerensky. After months in hiding, he left via Murmansk to begin his long exile.

Nicholas, at first, could not believe that Lenin and Trotsky were formidable. To him, they were simply German agents sent to try to overthrow the Russian government. When they became the rulers of Russia, he was gravely shocked, and for the first time felt that his abdication had done his country an ill turn. This idea was to haunt him more and more.

At first, the Revolution had little effect on the lives in far-off Tobolsk. The Imperial family had settled into a routine which was almost cozy. "Lessons for the children begin at nine," the Empress wrote Anna. "I sew, embroider, paint, read good books and the Bible. The others are all brave and uncomplaining, though Alexei's socks are in holes, Father's trousers torn and darned, and the girls' underlinen in rags. I make everything now. . . . But God is in all, and nature never changes. I see all around me churches, and hills; the lovely world. I feel old, oh, so old, but I am still the mother of this country, and I love it in spite of all its sins and horrors. God have mercy and save Russia."

In December, the full force of the Siberian winter hit Tobolsk. The thermometer dropped to 68 degrees below zero Fahrenheit. A fire burned all day in the drawing-room grate but the temperature inside the house remained 44 degrees. In spite of this, Alexis was lively and in excellent health all winter. He went out every morning and wandered through the sheds attached to the house, collecting old nails and pieces of string. "You never know when they might be useful," he said.

For the four young Grand Duchesses—Olga was twenty-two, Tatiana twenty, Marie eighteen and Anastasia sixteen—life was acutely boring. Gilliard and Gibbs began directing them in scenes from plays. Soon, everybody participated. After dinner, the little group huddled near the fire, trying to keep warm. Nicholas read aloud while the others played quiet games and the Grand Duchesses did needlework. "In this atmosphere of family peace," said Gilliard, "we passed the long winter evenings, lost in the immensity of Siberia."

At Christmas, the Empress and her daughters presented to the suite and servants the gifts on which they had been working for weeks—knitted waistcoats and painted ribbon bookmarks. On Christmas morning, at early Mass, the priest offered the prayer for the Imperial family which had been dropped from the service after the abdication. The soldiers became angry at this and thereafter refused the family permission to go to Mass. This was a great hardship, especially for Alexandra.

As the meaning of the Revolution penetrated to Tobolsk, many of the guards became hostile, and surveillance grew stricter. Then the Bolshevik government issued an order demobilizing all older soldiers of the Imperial Army, so the ones most friendly to the Tsar had to leave. The new young guards were excited revolutionaries. Many enjoyed offering little insults to the captives. They carved obscene words into the wooden seats of swings used by the Grand Duchesses. Nicholas removed the seats and thereafter the soldiers drew lewd pictures and inscriptions on the fence.

On March 1, a telegram announced that the Imperial family must be put on ordinary soldiers' rations. Each member of the family would receive only 600 rubles a month from their personal estate. So Nicholas faced the novel task of drawing up a family budget. Ten servants were dismissed. Butter and coffee were excluded as luxuries. The townspeople began to send more eggs and delicacies, which the Empress called "gifts from Heaven."

At times it seemed to the exiles that they were living on a separate planet; forgotten, beyond all help. Yet they still cherished a hope that loyal friends would attempt their release. And never would the situation be more favorable for escape than now, for there was no central government representative at Tobolsk, and it would be easy to trick the insolent but careless guards.

Actually, monarchist organizations both in Moscow and in Petrograd were secretly planning a rescue. But as the idea of escape grew, Nicholas raised a serious obstacle by insisting that the family not be separated. An escape involving a number of women and a handicapped boy would require horses, food, soldiery, possibly a train.

The monarchist organizations began sending agents to Siberia. Former officers under assumed names, mysterious bearded visitors with Petrograd accents, mingled with the shopkeepers of Tobolsk, bringing money, sending messages into the governor's house, making vague promises and then disappearing, accomplishing nothing. For there were too many groups, each jealous of the others—among them Dowager Empress Marie's and Anna Vyrubova's. Acting independently, they dissipated their energy milling about and arguing about who was to have the honor of rescuing the Imperial family.

Eventually, a leader seemed to appear in the person of Boris Soloviev. Alexandra trusted him implicitly, for he was Rasputin's son-in-law. He established contact with the Empress through one of her maids, raising her hopes by promising that "Gregory's family and his friends are active." When he insisted that all agents and funds be channeled through him, this was done.

But there were four suspicious officers who did not trust Soloviev. Why, they asked, was he passing his messages through a parlormaid, when the devoted Dr. Botkin was available? Why did he assure Petrograd and Moscow that no more men were needed, since he had "converted" eight regiments—but that still, they should advance more money? The officers put these questions to Soloviev. By that time Bolshevik officials had control of the area. Immediately, three officers were shot; the fourth escaped. Kerensky later wrote that Soloviev was a traitor working for the Bolsheviks. In the end, when the moment came for a well-planned and coordinated escape organization to swing into action, it did not do so—because it did not exist.

And now an enemy older than the Bolsheviks rose up. Alexis had a bad fall and began to bleed into the groin. The hemorrhage was the worst since Spala five and a half years before, and the pain became excruciating. Alexis gasped between his screams, "Mama, I would like to die. I am not afraid of death, but I am so afraid of what they will do to us here!"

Without Rasputin, Alexandra could do nothing. She wrote to Anna Vyrubova: "I sit all day beside him holding his aching legs. . . ." And in her last letter to Anna, a few days later, the Empress wrote: "Yesterday for the first time, Alexei smiled and talked with us, and slept two hours during the day. A great number of new troops have come. They hint to us that we shall have to travel either very far away or to the center of Siberia. But our souls are at peace. Whatever happens will be through God's will."

LENIN's control over Russia was still precarious. To consolidate his grip, he had to have peace at any price. The price set by the Germans was a terrible one: loss of most of the territory won by Russia since the days of Peter the Great, including Poland, Finland, the Baltic States, the Ukraine, the Crimea, and most of the Caucasus—more than one third of the population of Russia. But Russian soldiers were deserting by the millions, and a German arm, was so close to Petrograd that the capital was moved to Moscow. To save the revolution, Lenin had to agree to the humiliating treaty of Brest-Litovsk. When Nicholas heard the news, he was overwhelmed with grief and shame. It was, as Lenin was well aware, a total rejection of Russian patriotism.

Nicholas was still a pawn with potential value. To the Kaiser, ashamed of dealing with the Bolsheviks, a pliable Nicholas willing to endorse the Treaty of Brest-Litovsk would have had great value; while the Bolsheviks wanted to keep the Tsar beyond the Kaiser's reach in any bargaining that still lay ahead.

On April 22 Moscow sent Commissar Vasily Yakovlev to Tobolsk. A tall, muscular man, with jet-black hair, he arrived at the head of 150 horsemen. Though he seemed cultured and addressed Nicholas as "Your Majesty," the prisoners felt his arrival was an evil portent. At Yakovlev's request, Kobylinsky took him to see Alexis. The Tsarevich was lying in bed, his leg badly flexed from the recent hemorrhage. The commissar seemed disturbed by this. He summoned an army doctor, who assured him that the boy was seriously ill.

On April 25, Yakovlev finally revealed his mission to Kobylinsky. He had been assigned to take the whole Imperial family from Tobolsk to Moscow. After discovering how ill Alexis was, he had been communicating with Moscow by telegram. Now he had received an order to take only the Emperor.

When he told the Emperor this, Nicholas refused to go. But Yakovlev said that force would then have to be used. "Be calm," he added, "I am responsible with my life for your safety. You can take with you any people you wish. We start at four a.m."

When Yakovlev left, Nicholas said bitterly to Alexandra, "They want to force me to sign the Treaty of Brest-Litovsk. I would rather cut off my right hand."

The Empress was in a painful dilemma. She couldn't let the Tsar face the Bolsheviks alone; but suppose some complication set in with her son? Gilliard assured her that if she went with the Tsar, he and the others would take good care of Alexis, who was over the worst of the crisis. Later, he wrote, "Tortured by indecision, she paced up and down. At last she agreed." The girls themselves decided that Marie would go with her parents. Olga was not well enough, and Anastasia was too young to be helpful. Tatiana would be needed to supervise the household.

Meanwhile, Alexis was lying upstairs awaiting the visit his mother had promised after lunch. Frightened when she did not appear, he began to call, "Mama, Mama!" his shouts ringing through the house. She came into his bedroom at last, her eyes reddened, and explained that she and his father were leaving.

The family spent the rest of the afternoon and evening with

Alexis. Alexandra, her hope for earthly rescue fading, prayed for help from heaven. The suite joined them for evening tea. The girls' faces were swollen from crying, but Nicholas and Alexandra were calm. "This wonderful faith proved infectious," said Gilliard. At 11:30 they came downstairs to say good-by to the servants. Nicholas embraced every man, Alexandra every woman.

Lights blazed throughout the night. Near dawn, the clatter of horses and the creak of wheels signaled Yakovlev's arrival. The vehicles, which were to carry the Tsar and the Empress across two hundred miles to the railroad at Tyumen, were crude, peasant carts. The servants swept up straw from the pigsty and spread it in the carts as cushioning. Yakovlev himself was infinitely courteous, repeatedly touching the brim of his hat in salute to the Tsar and Empress. Nicholas started to climb into the same cart with his wife, but Yakovlev insisted that the Tsar ride with him in an open cart. Marie rode with her mother.

The drivers flicked their whips and the carts lurched forward with their cavalry escort. Gilliard heard Olga, Tatiana and Anastasia climb slowly back up the stairs and pass, sobbing, to their room. He found Alexis, his face to the wall, weeping uncontrollably. There was no rescue, no "friends of Rasputin." Only a boy and his sisters, frightened and alone.

The journey was exhausting. The cavalcade crossed the river Irtysh on melting ice, with wheels sloshing axle-deep in water. At another river, where the ice was beginning to crack, the entire party dismounted and crossed on foot. They changed horses frequently. The last remount station was Pokrovskoe, where the change was carried out beneath the windows of Rasputin's house, with the family of the man who had done so much to destroy the Tsar looking down, waving handkerchiefs. Rasputin's widow looked directly at Alexandra and made the sign of the cross.

In Tyumen a special train was waiting. Yakovlev was afraid that if he took the direct route to Moscow, his train would be stopped in Ekaterinburg, where the Ural Soviet, fiercely militant Bolsheviks, were anxious to lay hands on the Tsar. The Bolsheviks had no proper administrative machinery as yet, and had to let such regional Soviets have their way. Yakovlev decided to go east to Omsk and then double back on another line to Moscow.

But as soon as the train left Tyumen, the Ekaterinburg Soviet were somehow informed that the "traitor" Yakovlev was traveling in the wrong direction. Desperate telegrams from the Ural Soviet addressed: TO ALL, TO ALL, TO ALL, were sent all over the region, and the West Siberian Soviet in Omsk was specifically asked to block Yakovlev. It agreed to do so. When Yakovlev's train was sixty miles from Omsk, it was surrounded by troops, and he was told to go to Ekaterinburg. Unhitching the engine and one coach, Yakovlev went to Omsk to call Moscow. He was told that under the circumstances he had to give in. Sadly, he rejoined the stranded train and told Nicholas and Alexandra the news. "I would have gone anywhere but to the Urals," said Nicholas. "People here are bitterly hostile to me." Yakovlev himself defected later and became a White Russian army officer, fighting the Bolsheviks. He was later accused of being a secret Royalist who had tried to take the Tsar all the way east to safety at the Pacific.

Monument at Poltava, Ukraine, memorialized 1709 defeat of Swedish invasion by Peter the Great.

THE CITY of Ekaterinburg lies on a cluster of low hills. Atop the highest, a merchant named Ipatiev had built a handsome, two-story house. Even as the Tsar left Tobolsk, Ipatiev was suddenly given twenty-four hours to vacate his home. A high wooden fence was erected, shutting off the house and garden from the street, and the upper floor was sealed as a prison, with the windowpanes painted white so that those inside could not see out. The lower floor was converted into guard rooms and offices. The house was given the ominous designation "The House of Special Purpose."

When Yakovlev's train arrived in Ekaterinburg, officials of the Ural Soviet took charge, and after some threats, Yakovlev was allowed to go back to Moscow. At the door of the Ipatiev house was an official of the Ural Soviet. He said ironically, "Citizen Romanov, you may enter."

In Tobolsk, the children waited anxiously to hear what had happened. A letter from the Empress said that all were well and advised the girls to "dispose of the medicines as agreed." "Medicines" meant jewels: Alexandra, having been roughly searched, was advising them to sew their jewels into cloth buttons, bodices and corsets.

A bullying young commissar named Rodionov was sent to Tobolsk to bring the remainder of the family to Ekaterinburg as soon as Alexis could travel. As soon as Rodionov arrived, he went to see the boy. Finding Alexis in bed, he stepped out of the room, waited a minute and then reentered, thinking he might be using his malady as a pretext for not moving.

By May 19, Alexis could travel. The following day, Nagorny carried him aboard the steamer *Rus*, which had brought them to Tobolsk the previous summer. On the voyage to Tyumen, Rodionov padlocked Alexis and Nagorny into their room.

Gilliard had a last glimpse of the children when their train from Tyumen reached Ekaterinburg. "Nagorny the sailor passed my window carrying the sick boy; behind him came the Grand Duchesses, loaded with valises. I tried to get out but was roughly pushed back by the sentry." Tatiana came last, carrying Anastasia's pet spaniel, Jimmy, and struggling to drag a heavy valise. "I saw her feet sink into the mud at every step. A few minutes later carriages drove off with the children." Gilliard, with Baroness Buxhoeveden and Sidney Gibbs, was ordered to leave Ekaterinburg. Later, in Tyumen, they were rescued by the advancing White army.

At the Ipatiev house, the children's arrival brought a burst of happiness, though twelve people would be crowded into five rooms. Marie slept on the floor that first night so Alexis could have her bed.

Outside the house fence, the guards were ordinary Red soldiers. Inside, they were hard-core Bolshevik shock troops. Night and

day, three of them, armed with revolvers, kept watch outside the family's rooms. The leader of the inner guard, Alexander Avadeyev, was a thin-faced ex-commissar who habitually referred to the Tsar as "Nicholas the Blood-Drinker." With his men, he drank heavily and pilfered the family's baggage. There was no privacy, the guards entering the rooms whenever they liked, telling dirty jokes or singing lewd ditties. When the girls went to the lavatory, the soldiers followed with loud guffaws to "guard" them. Inside the lavatory, they scrawled obscene pictures of Alexandra and Rasputin.

The family rose at eight for morning prayers. Breakfast was black bread and tea. The main meal, soup and cutlets, arrived at two p.m. from the Soviet soup kitchen. While the family ate, Avadeyev and his men came often to watch. Sometimes, Avadeyev would brush past Nicholas's face to fetch himself a piece of meat from the pot. "You've had enough, idle rich," he said.

One of the guards noticed, hanging from Alexis's bed, a thin gold chain on which the boy had strung his collection of Holy Images. The man began to take the chain, but the sailor, Nagorny, outraged, stopped him. It was his last service to Alexis. He was sent to prison. Four days later, he was shot.

Now it became Nicholas's task to carry Alexis into the garden each afternoon. There, the Tsar placed his son in a chair and the others walked back and forth under the eyes of the guards. In time, Nicholas began to change the impressions of these seasoned revolutionaries. One, later captured by the White army, said that the guards found Alexandra haughty, but Nicholas kind and simple. "I began to pity them. I kept saying to myself, *Let them escape. . . .*"

And there were still people anxious to rescue the family. Two letters are quoted by General M. K. Dieterichs of the White army, who assisted with an inquiry into the Tsar's murder. One is from a White officer to the Tsar, suggesting a plan, and the other is the Tsar's answer, giving information about the house and the guards.

On June 27, Nicholas wrote in his diary: "We spent an anxious night, fully dressed, because a few days ago we received two letters in which we were told to get ready to be rescued by some devoted people. But nothing happened and the waiting and the uncertainty were very painful."

ON JULY 4, uncertainty turned to fear. Avadeyev and his guards were replaced by a squad of ten of the Bolshevik Cheka, or Secret Police. Five of them were prisoners of war, hired for jobs at which Russians might balk; but their leader, the chillingly cold Jacob Yurovsky, was Russian. The fate of the Imperial family was sealed. These men were executioners.

The Ural Soviet had long since decided unanimously that Nicholas should be executed, but, unwilling to take the full responsibility, they sent to Moscow to learn the attitude of the central government. Moscow was toying with the idea of holding a public trial. Before this could be arranged, however, civil war and foreign intervention began to challenge the Bolsheviks' feeble grip on Russia.

To prevent stores of supplies in Russia from falling into German hands, a small Allied force landed in the north. After Russia made peace, this force was enlarged and began to support counterrevolutionaries. The White volunteer army, with the fiercely independent Don Cossacks, had been organized in the Ukraine. In Siberia, a Czech Legion had taken Omsk and was rapidly advancing westward toward Ekaterinburg.

The Ekaterinburg Soviet asked their local military commander how long the city could hold out against the Czechs. He reported that it might fall within three days. The Soviet decided to shoot the entire Imperial family as soon as possible, and to destroy all evidence.

Yurovsky and another official spent three days in the outlying woods, looking for a suitable place to hide the remains. They discovered an abandoned mine shaft with water in it, close to four pine trees known as the "Four Brothers." Peter Voikov, another member of the Ural Soviet, began buying quantities of gasoline and sulfuric acid.

Yurovsky appeared to have no strong feelings about his cap-

473

tives. They were simply his next assignment. Two women who came to scrub the floors saw Yurovsky sitting with the Tsarevich and asking about his health. Yet that same day, Yurovsky had been at the "Four Brothers" supervising preparations.

On July 16, Yurovsky ordered the kitchen boy sent away from the house. He summoned the Cheka men into his room and told them, "Tonight, we will shoot the whole family. Notify the guards not to be alarmed if they hear shots."

The family went innocently to bed at ten thirty. At midnight, Yurovsky awakened them, telling them to dress and come downstairs. He said the Czechs and the White army were approaching Ekaterinburg and they must be moved. Still unsuspecting, the family dressed and Nicholas and Alexis put on their military caps. Nicholas came down the stairs first, carrying Alexis. The sleepy boy had his arms tightly around his father's neck. The others followed, with Anastasia clutching her dog, Jimmy. Yurovsky led them to a small basement room, with a heavy iron grill over the window, and produced three chairs. He asked them to wait until the automobiles arrived.

Alexandra sat in one chair. Nicholas took another, his arm and shoulder supporting Alexis, who lay back across a third chair. Behind Alexandra stood the four girls, Dr. Botkin, the valet, the family cook, and Demidova, the Empress's maid, clutching a pillow. In the feathers inside, was a box of jewels.

Yurovsky reentered the room, followed by his Cheka squad carrying revolvers. He stepped forward and declared quickly, "Your relations have tried to save you. They have failed and we must now shoot you."

Nicholas, his arm still around Alexis, begin to rise from his chair to protect his wife and son. Yurovsky fired at the Tsar's head and Nicholas died instantly. Then the entire squad began to shoot. Alexandra had time to make the sign of the cross before she too was killed by a single bullet. Olga, Tatiana and Marie died quickly, with Dr. Botkin, the cook and the valet. Demidova, the maid, survived the first volley, and the executioners, rather than reload, pursued her with bayonets. Screaming, running back and forth like a trapped animal, she tried to fend them off with the cushion. At last she fell, pierced more than thirty times. Jimmy, the spaniel, was killed with a rifle butt.

The room became suddenly quiet. Blood was running in streams from the bodies on the floor. Then there was a movement and a low groan. Alexis, lying on the floor, still in the arms of the Tsar, tried to clutch his father's coat. Savagely, one of the executioners kicked him in the head. Yurovsky fired two shots into the boy's ear.

At that moment, Anastasia, who had fainted, regained consciousness and screamed. The entire band turned on her with bayonets and rifle butts. In a moment, she lay still.

The bodies were wrapped in sheets and placed in a truck. At the "Four Brothers," each body was cut into pieces with axes and saws, then placed in a gasoline-fed bonfire. The process was neither easy nor quick; many of the larger bones had to be dissolved with the sulfuric acid. For three days, Yurovsky's ghouls labored at their work. Finally, the residue was thrown into the water at the bottom of the mine shaft. Voikov, who later became Soviet Ambassador to Poland, proudly declared: "The world will never know what we did with them."

EPILOGUE

EKATERINBURG fell to the advancing White army, and a group of officers rushed to the Ipatiev house. It was empty and sinister. The basement room had been scrubbed but the walls and floors bore the scars of bullets and bayonets. It was obvious that a massacre had taken place, but impossible to tell how many victims there had been.

A search for the family led nowhere. Not until January 1919 did a thorough investigation begin. Then Admiral Kolchak, head of the White government in Siberia, selected Nicholas Sokolov, a legal investigator, to undertake the task. Sokolov, assisted by the Tsarevich's tutors, Gilliard and Gibbs, located the mine and uncovered a wealth of tragic evidence. For Gilliard the work was excruciating. "But the children—the children?" he cried when Sokolov told him of the preliminary findings. "The children have suffered the same fate as their parents," replied Sokolov sadly.

Hundreds of objects and fragments were identified and catalogued. Among them were the Tsar's and Alexis's belt buckles, an emerald cross of the Empress's, fragments of a sapphire ring which had become so tight on Nicholas's finger that he could not take it off, small icons worn by the Grand Duchesses (on each icon, the face of the saint had been destroyed by heavy blows), and Dr. Botkin's eyeglasses.

The investigators also collected an assortment of nails and tinfoil, which puzzled them. Gilliard identified them as part of the pocketful of odds and ends collected by Alexis from the sheds at Tobolsk. Finally, mangled, but not burned, the little corpse of the spaniel Jimmy was found at the bottom of the pit. To confirm this evidence, the Whites added the depositions of captured members of the guard at the House of Special Purpose. Sokolov's findings were also confirmed later by the Chairman of the Ekaterinburg Soviet.

After the massacre, a telegram to Moscow reported only that Nicholas would be shot and the family "transferred to a place of greater safety." But Lenin and Jacob Sverdlov, the head of the Soviet cabinet, already knew that the entire family was dead, for in their haste to evacuate Ekaterinburg, the Bolsheviks left behind copies of several telegrams exchanged with the Kremlin after the murders. Said one: OFFICIALLY, THE FAMILY WILL PERISH DURING THE EVACUATION.

A YEAR later, the Bolsheviks admitted that the entire Imperial family was dead. Hypocritically—as one of them later admitted—they brought to trial twenty-eight members of another party, the Social Revolutionaries, charging them with murdering the Tsar to discredit the Bolsheviks. Five of them were executed. The link between the Moscow leaders who authorized the murders and the Ural Soviet, which determined the time and method, was later described by Trotsky, who said that Lenin felt he shouldn't leave the Whites a live banner to rally around.

The same ruthless logic dictated the murder of every member of the Romanov family on whom the Bolsheviks could lay their hands. Nicholas's brother Michael was shot six days before the Tsar. Alexandra's sister, the nun Elizabeth, Nicholas's uncle Serge and four sons of other Grand Dukes were thrown, still living, down an abandoned mine shaft, with heavy timbers and hand grenades thrown after them. A peasant who crept to the mine after the murderers had left heard hymns being sung at the bottom of the shaft. When the bodies were removed by the White army, the injured head of one of the boys was found to have been carefully bound with Elizabeth's handkerchief.

In January 1919, Paul, the Tsar's uncle, and Grand Duke Nicholas, the liberal historian, were executed in the Fortress of Peter and Paul. The writer Maxim Gorky pleaded that Nicholas's life be spared. Lenin refused, declaring, "The Revolution does not need historians."

Within a very few years, the Revolution did not need Lenin or Trotsky. Lenin died in 1924, after a series of strokes; Trotsky, exiled, wrote that Lenin had been poisoned by Stalin, an accusation about which Lenin's biographers still argue. Trotsky's assassination—by an ice pick—was ordered by Stalin. So it was Stalin who inherited the Revolution and for thirty years ruled Russia more cruelly than any Tsar since Ivan the Terrible.

Sverdlov, who had arranged the murders, died within six months of them. The town of Ekaterinburg was renamed Sverdlovsk. For years, the House of Special Purpose was kept as a Bolshevik museum. In 1959, a group of American correspondents accompanying Vice President Nixon on a tour of Russia found that Sverdlovsk was now a huge, grimy coal and steel metropolis. The museum had been closed. It was over Sverdlovsk, in May 1960, that the U-2 piloted by Francis Gary Powers was shot down.

As the Red Army approached the Crimea, in 1919, Nicholas's

mother, Marie, left on board a British battleship and returned to her native Denmark, to live in the royal palace of her nephew King Christian X. The two disliked each other and argued over money. Marie had brought many of her jewels from Russia, and the King suggested that she sell them to pay her expenses. The Empress adamantly refused and kept the jewels in a box under her bed. She died at eighty-one, never accepting the "rumors" that Nicholas and his family were dead.

Nicholas's sisters, Xenia and Olga, also left Russia on British warships. Xenia came to London, where her servants, upon first seeing King George V, fell on their knees, believing him to be the Tsar miraculously resurrected. She lived in a mansion provided by the Royal Family, and she died at eighty-five. Olga eventually went to live with a Russian couple in an apartment over a barbershop in Toronto. She died there at seventy-eight.

Nicholas's first cousin Cyril had been the first Romanov to fly the Red flag over his palace. But in 1924 he proclaimed himself "Tsar of all the Russias" and established his "court" in a village in Brittany. Today, his son Vladimir, who lives in Madrid, is head of the House of Romanov. The former Russian commander in chief, Grand Duke Nicholas, left Russia with Marie and died at Antibes in 1929. Dmitry, whose life was saved by his banishment to Persia after Rasputin's murder, married an American heiress, and became a champagne salesman in Palm Beach. He died of tuberculosis in Switzerland.

Prince Dolgoruky disappeared, but a body answering his description was found. Baroness Buxhoeveden and Sidney Gibbs crossed Siberia and reached safety in England.

Of the Tsarist ministers, the aged Goremykin was caught by a Petrograd mob in 1918 and strangled on the spot. Protopopov was shot. Rodzianko, the Duma President, got away and died in Belgrade, harassed to the end by Russian monarchists who blamed him for the overthrow of the autocracy. Rasputin's assassin Purishkevich fought with the White army in southern Russia and died there of typhus.

Only when he felt sure the Imperial family were dead, did

Count Benckendorff attempt to leave Russia. He died in a border town hospital. Count Fredericks was allowed to return to his native Finland, where he died in 1922 at the age of eighty-four.

Anna Vyrubova, after being imprisoned several times, escaped to Finland and died there at the age of eighty. Pierre Gilliard returned to Switzerland and became a noted professor at the University of Lausanne. As for Rasputin's daughter, Maria, she left Russia with her husband, Boris Soloviev, and became a lion-tamer, billed as "the daughter of the famous mad monk." She now lives in obscurity in Paris.

Only a handful of major characters in this historical drama remain alive. Mathilde Kschessinska, who married Grand Duke Andrei at Cannes in 1921, for thirty years conducted a ballet studio in Paris, instructing, among others, Margot Fonteyn. Today, the young ballerina who rode through the snowy nights in a troika beside Nicholas II lives in Paris. She is ninety-four.

Prince Felix Yussoupov and his wife, Princess Irina, have lived mostly in Paris, where Yussoupov's generosity to other Russian émigrés has become legend. Alexander Kerensky, still vigorous at eighty-five, lives in New York City.

Rumors persist that some members of the Imperial family are alive, and dozens of claimants have stepped forward. The pathetic story of Anna Anderson's lifelong attempt to prove herself to be Anastasia is famous. Olga, who had been closer to her niece than any other Romanov survivor, interviewed Mrs. Anderson, and after four days sadly pronounced her false.

KERENSKY once said, "If there had been no Rasputin, there would have been no Lenin." And if there had been no hemophilia, there would have been no Rasputin. This is not to overlook the backwardness and restlessness of Russian society, the clamor for reform, the battering of a world war, the gentle, retiring nature of the last Tsar. Even before the birth of the Tsarevich, autocracy was in retreat.

But had it not been for Alexis's hemophilia, had it not been for the desperation which made his mother turn to Rasputin, first to save her son, then to save the autocracy, might not Nicholas II have continued moving into the role of constitutional monarch so happily filled by his cousin King George V? This was the direction in which Russian history was headed. Absolute power was struck from the hands of the Tsar with the creation of the Duma. In the era of Stolypin and the Third Duma, cooperation between the throne and parliament held high promise for the future. But Alexandra, goaded by Rasputin, objected to any sharing of the Imperial power. By giving way to his wife, by denying every plea for responsible government, Nicholas made revolution inevitable.

Why Alexandra placed the fate of her son, her husband and his empire in the hands of a wandering holy man, why Alexis suffered from hemophilia—these are the riddles of this historical tale. All of them have answers except, perhaps, the last.

"It really began eleven years ago . . ."

by Suzanne Massie

My husband, Robert Massie, *Nicholas and Alexandra* eleven we both learned that our little son, old, had hemophilia. We had only vague and false notions about the condition, such as: "If he cuts his finger he will bleed to death." When we began to cope with the difficult and frightening ramifications of Bobby's illness, one thing that helped was learning all we could about the disease and about others whom it had touched. Both my husband and I are journalists — Bob has been at *Newsweek* and *The Saturday Evening Post* and I at Time Inc—so we interviewed doctors and research scientists and wrote several magazine articles about hemophilia.

In time, my husband became more and more interested in the most famous hemophiliac of all — Alexis Romanov. The more Bob read, the more he was struck by the fact that although all historians thought Alexis's disease important, no one had really explained its effect on his parents, and through them, on Russia. Nicholas and Alexandra's preoccupation and withdrawal is a common reaction among parents of hemophiliacs. It was to lead to enormous consequences for the world.

This book also combines other experiences and interests of ours. Bob was trained as a historian. A Kentuckian, he studied history at Yale and later at Oxford, as a Rhodes Scholar. I am Swiss by birth, and my mother had lived in Russia from 1913 to 1918. I had studied the language, and we have always had many Russian friends.

Once we began, the research took five years. Bob read, absorbed and considered more than two hundred books. Together we ran down leads, combed newspaper files, and even made an extensive trip to Russia, trying to visit all the scenes and fit together all the pieces of the drama.

Bob has no filing cabinets. As the piles of notes and papers grew they began to fill many grocery store cartons in our house in Westchester County, outside New York City. Along a window seat and on the floor, piles of papers were arranged in neat stacks. For a while, it was a marital crisis to make room when I wanted to have guests to dinner. All of this material was distilled and redistilled; sometimes a chapter was rewritten six times, until we both felt it was right.

During these years, Bob became so absorbed that he spent whole days shut up in the library, playing Russian music constantly as he wrote. One day, the younger of our little girls looked at the closed door from behind which she heard the familiar Russian music and uttered her first word. "Daddy," she said knowingly and toddled away.

The

Gabriel Hounds

Danger and romance waited inside

the forbidden gate of Dar Ibrahim

A condensation of the book by
Mary Stewart

illustrated by Joe De Mers

In a North of England legend, the
"Gabriel Hounds" run in a pack which
hunts through the sky with Death. . . .
In this tale of suspense, however,
the hounds are hunting the Lebanon—
a land of sharp contrasts and, in
this case, violence.

Here, to a mysterious valley, come
two young and headstrong
relatives in search of their
eccentric aunt, a recluse who lives in
a crumbling Arabian Nights palace.
What starts out as a lark on their part,
soon becomes a very dangerous
matter indeed—and one which changes
the lives of spirited young Christabel
and her cousin Charles.

A story written with all the
atmosphere and excitement that make
each new novel by Mary Stewart
an international event.

I

I MET him in the street called Straight.

I had come out of the dark shop doorway into the dazzle of the Damascus sun, my arms full of silks. I didn't see anything at first, because the sun was right in my eyes and he was in shadow, just where Straight Street becomes a dim tunnel under its high corrugated iron roof.

The souk was crowded. A group of youths went by, eyeing me and calling comments in Arabic, punctuated by "Miss," " 'Allo" and "Good-by." A donkey pattered past under a load of vegetables three times its own width. A taxi swerved, horn blaring, past the donkey, and aimed without slackening speed at the bottleneck where the street narrowed sharply between jutting stalls.

A man had been standing at a jeweler's stall, but at the blast of the taxi's horn he glanced up and stepped quickly out of the way, full into the sun's glare. With a queer jerk of the heart, I saw who it was. I had known he was in this part of the world, but I stood there gazing blankly at the profile, four years strange to me, yet so immediately familiar.

485

The taxi vanished with another yell of its horn. Between us the dirty, hot street was empty. I saw his eyes widen; then, ignoring the stream of bad English which the jeweler was shouting after him, he came to me. He said, with the intonation with which he had, as a small boy, daily greeted his even smaller worshiper, "Oh, hullo! It's you!"

I wasn't a small girl anymore. I was twenty-two, and this was only my cousin Charles, whom of course I didn't worship anymore. For some reason it seemed important to make this clear. I tried to echo his tone. "How nice to see you. How you've grown!"

"I shave nearly every week now." He grinned. "Christy love, thank goodness I've found you! My mother said your package tour was coming here, but no one seemed clear when. I phoned the hotel where you told your mother you'd be and they said your group had gone to Jerusalem; and *there* they referred me back to Damascus. You cover your tracks well, young Christy."

"I'm sorry," I said. "Our itinerary was changed and we're doing the tour back to front. So they had to change hotels here. Oh, blast—we leave for Beirut tomorrow. Have you been here long?"

"Only since yesterday. The man I have to see in Damascus isn't coming home till Saturday, but I thought you might be here so I came straight up. Why don't you cut loose from your group? We'll do Damascus together and then go on to Beirut. What on earth are you doing in a package tour, anyway, Christy?"

"Oh, I wanted to see this part of the world, and I didn't know a thing about it, and they plan everything, and there's a courier who speaks Arabic. And I couldn't very well come on my own."

"Don't look at me with those great big helpless eyes. If any female was ever capable of looking after herself, it's you."

I regarded him with pleasure. "Oh, Charles, it'd have been lovely to have some time here with you, but I'd better stay with the group. We're adding Baalbek on the way, and besides, there's all that silly business with visas here. Mine's dated tomorrow, and it's a group passport, too. Still, I could stay on in Beirut after the group goes home on Saturday."

"I'll see you in Beirut, then. Look, what are we standing here for? Any minute we'll be mown down by a donkey. Come and have tea in my little pad." He grinned. "Which is the nearest thing to a palace you ever saw. I'm staying with a man I knew at Oxford, Ben Sifara. Ben's father is a V.I.P. in Damascus—his brother-in-law is Minister of the Interior. The family's what they call a 'good family' here, which in Syria just means stinking rich."

"At that rate you and I would be well up in the studbook."

"Well, aren't we?" my cousin said crisply.

Our family of merchant bankers has been stinking rich for three generations, and it is surprising how many people are willing to overlook the very mixed blood that pumps through the Mansel veins.

"What are you looking for here?" I asked. "A ring for Emily?"

"A jewel for my love, certainly. A blue bead for my car. Blue beads ward off the Evil Eye. If camels and donkeys wear them, why not the car?" He laughed. "Never mind, I can get one anytime. Let's go where we can talk. Where is your party?"

"I don't know. We were trailing through the souks and I stopped to look at a stall, and then they'd sort of gone. I doubt if they'll miss me before dinner. They're used to my wandering off."

"Still the same spoiled little madam I love?"

"I just don't like crowds. Anyway, look who's talking! My parents always said you were spoiled rotten." (They also said, I could have added, that he had considerable intelligence when he chose to use it—which was, they insisted, about once a month, and then entirely in his own interests.)

"Dear Uncle Chris," said my cousin placidly, taking my arm.

Charles's car was at the end of the street, instantly recognizable by the six-deep crowd of small boys who stood round it. It proved to be a white Porsche, and because I loved my cousin, I promptly gave him his cue. "What a beauty! How do you like her?"

He told me. He opened the hood and showed me. He almost stripped her down to demonstrate to me. The small boys crowded in, openmouthed. I watched Charles's face and remembered all the other times I had watched it—with the electric-train set, the first wristwatch, the bicycle . . . He straightened up, hauled a

487

couple of boys out of the engine, shut the hood, and paid off the biggest, who had presumably been on guard for him, speaking to them in Arabic. We drove off.

"What was that boy saying?"

"Just 'thank you.' In other words, 'The blessing of Allah be upon you, your children, and your children's children.' " We turned down a narrow, rutted street. "That means you, more or less. I hope we're still engaged?"

"I seem to remember that you broke it off yourself, and in writing, when you met that blond model—what was her name?"

"Samantha? But that was four years ago."

"No one else in my way? What about Emily? I'm sure Mummy said Emily—or was it Myrtle? The *names* you pick."

"I can't see that any of them are worse than Christabel."

I laughed. "You have a point there."

"As far as I'm concerned," said my cousin, "we're still pledged as from the cradle. We'll keep that lovely money in the family, and our mutual Great-Grandfather Rosenbaum, on whom be peace, can stop whirling in his whited sepulcher."

"You take a lot for granted. Just because I stayed faithful all my teens, even when you had spots."

"A lot of chance you had to be anything else. You were as fat as a seal puppy. I must say you've improved." He gave me a sideways, brotherly look, with less sexual appraisement than a dog-show judge. "In fact, you're rather gorgeous, love. Well, blight my hopes if you must."

The Porsche turned into a small courtyard, where the sun struck blindly down into the dust. He parked the car in a wedge of indigo shade. "Front entrance, Damascus style."

At one side of the stifling courtyard a big archway was forbiddingly blocked by a timber door with massive wrought handle and hinges. Charles opened the door on a black passageway, which gave at the other end on an arch of light. We went through, into a second courtyard about the size of a tennis court, with Moorish arches on three sides holding a shady cloister, and on the fourth, a raised dais behind a triple arch. At the back and sides of this dais were rug-covered couches and low tables—the "divan" where men of the East meet and talk. Low tables stood in front of the couches. The tiled floor was blue and white, and the colonnade glittered with mosaics in blue and green and gilt. There were orange trees and a fountain. A turtledove crooned somewhere. The court was cool, and smelled of orange blossom.

"Come into the divan," said Charles. "It's rather lovely, isn't it? Arab building is all poetry and passion and romance, but elegant. Like their literature. What would you like? Tea?"

"I'd rather have coffee. Do you clap your hands for slaves?"

"More or less." He rang a brass bell on an inlaid table, and when a young Arab in white appeared, ordered coffee. Then he prowled restlessly—he had always been restless—while I sat down and watched him.

He hadn't changed. As children we were always supposed to be very much alike, Charles and I. This had always infuriated Charles, who in those days had been aggressively masculine, but to me, worshiping my clever cousin as only a small girl can, it had been a delight. As we grew up the resemblance had faded, but there were still similarities: dark hair, high cheekbones, slightly aquiline nose, gray eyes and spare build. Charles's eyes were beautiful, dark gray and thickly fringed; his eyelashes were (in Nature's unfair way) longer and thicker than mine. He had now reacted from the aggressive masculinity of adolescence into a casual elegance which oddly enough was no less male. And what we still certainly had in common was the "spoiled" quality we were so quick to recognize in one another; flippancy and an arrogance that did not spring from pride of achievement but was, I am afraid, the result of having too much too young; a fierce rejection of personal ties, which we called independence, but which was really a fear of possessiveness; and something we called sensitivity, which probably only meant that our skins were too thin for comfort.

I should explain that our relationship was at once close and distant. We were second cousins, with nothing nearer than a great-grandfather in common; but we had been brought up together almost from birth. Charles's father, Henry Mansel, had been the senior member of the family, the other male members being his twin cousins, Charles and Christopher. Christopher was my father. Charles—"Chas"—had no children; so when Henry and his wife met with a fatal accident only a few months after Charles's birth, Uncle Chas brought the baby up as his own. When Henry Mansel's death left vacant the family house in Kent, Chas took it over, and my father built one for himself nearby.

So Charles and I had been brought up together until four years ago, when my father had exported Mummy and myself to Los Angeles. We occasionally came back to stay at Charles's home, ours being rented, but Charles had spent his vacations from Oxford abroad, indulging a flair for languages which he intended to turn to account when he went into one of the family's banks on the Continent. I had not flown so high. I brought nothing home from Los Angeles except three years' experience as producer's assistant in a small company which called itself Sunshine Television Incorporated, in blissful ignorance of the fact that it was normally referred to by its initials, *S. T. Inc.*

Now here we were, back without effort on the same terms. What held us so easily together was, paradoxically, that each recognized and respected in the other a refusal to be claimed. This had made tolerable—even funny—the thin-worn family joke about our marriage, which would keep the family money in hand. We never knew whether the idea was anything more than a joke. I had heard my father insisting that the family characteristics were bad enough singly, and squared would be lethal; whereupon Uncle Charles would retort that since my mother was partly Irish, and Charles's had been part Austrian, part Russian, part French, the stock would be strong enough to stand a match a good deal closer than ours.

Charles and I had watched with amusement and derision each other's brief romantic adventures. Sooner or later a girl would start assuming a claim on Charles, and be dropped without trace. Or my own pinup would simply lose his gloss. Our parents bore with us lovingly and took off the strings, possibly because they wanted freedom from us as urgently as we thought we wanted freedom from them. The result was that we went back to them at intervals like homing bees, and we were happy. Perhaps they saw the basic security in our lives which made our restlessness nothing more than the taking of soundings outside the family harbor.

The young Arab brought in a tray with an urn and two small cups which he set in front of me. When he went out, my cousin came quickly up the steps and sat down beside me. "Smoke?"

"Not now, thanks. Heavens, what *are* those? Hashish?"

"Harmless Egyptian. They do look awful, don't they? Now, tell me all that you've been doing." He accepted coffee from me and curled back on the rug-covered seat.

We had never been letter writers and I suppose more than an hour had gone by before Charles stubbed out another Egyptian cigarette and said, "Where are you staying in Beirut?"

"At the Phoenicia, once I'm on my own."

"I'll join you there. Book in for me, will you? What do you plan to do, apart from going up to Dar Ibrahim?"

"Dar Ibrahim?" I repeated blankly.

"Great-Aunt Harriet's place. Surely you knew? It's on the Nahr Ibrahim, the Adonis River, where it meets the El Sal'q about thirty miles away from Beirut, towards the Adonis Source. I haven't been there, but I'm planning to go."

"Well, I'd certainly intended to see the Adonis Valley and the place where Venus and Adonis met—but I'd forgotten all about Aunt H's place. I hardly remember her. We were in Los Angeles when she was home last, and before that it was—heavens, all of fifteen years! And Mummy never said a thing—she probably didn't realize Beirut was so near." I put down my cup. "Well, I might go with you and put flowers on the old dear's grave."

"She'd kick you in the teeth if you tried," said Charles.

I stared. "She's alive? But she died just after New Year's."

He laughed. "If you're thinking about that will the family received, she's sent them round every few months lately. She finally cut everyone off with sixpence—except me, that is." He grinned.

"I'm to have the Gabriel Hounds and her copy of the Koran because I 'show signs of interest in the real civilizations of the world.' That's because I know some Arabic."

"You're kidding."

"Indeed I'm not. She's renounced her nationality and us. She told us she is now Muslim, and has built a private cemetery where she can rest forever in the peace of Allah among her beloved dogs. And would we please inform the London *Times* that the paper of the overseas edition is too thin to allow her to do the crossword puzzle properly."

"You can't be serious."

"As an owl," said my cousin.

"But what are Gabriel Hounds? I seem to remember a story—"

"A legend in that book we had, *North-Country Tales*. The Gabriel Hounds are supposed to be a pack of hounds that run with Death. When someone's going to die, you hear them howling over the house. I think the idea must have come from wild geese. In full cry overhead they sound like hounds, and the old name for them was 'gabble ratchet.' Perhaps 'Gabriel' came from 'gabble'; after all, Gabriel wasn't the angel of death. . . . You shivered."

"One of them gabbling over my grave, I expect."

"Well, Great-Aunt Harriet had a pair of Ming china dogs that I christened the Gabriel Hounds, because they were like the illustrations in that book. They're museum pieces, and I had the good taste to fall flat in love with them at the age of six. Great-Aunt Harriet with even better taste fell flat in love with me at the same time, so she promised them to me. And mad though she may be, she seems to have remembered." He made a restless movement. "Oh, it doesn't really matter; they make a good excuse for going to see her, that's all." He gave me an odd slanting look from under the long lashes. "It sounds like an intriguing setup."

"Well, I'll go with you, out of sheer roaring curiosity. Let's hope she remembers you. She must be a hundred."

"Not a day over eighty. She's a local legend, goes galloping about the countryside on horseback; has Tibetan Terriers and Salukis—Persian greyhounds, the dogs Arab princes used for hunting. And she's turned Arab all right, male at that; dresses like an emir, never sees anybody except at night, and lives in this dirty great palace—"

"Who does she think she is? Lady Hester Stanhope?"

"Exactly. But how did you know about Lady Hester?"

"When we spent last Christmas at your house, I read everything you had about her, and nice snappy reading it was, compared with some of your tomes."

He grinned, undeceived. "Don't work so hard at not being clever. I'm not one of your muscle-bound blond beaus."

"No, you aren't," I said. Our eyes met. There was a tiny silence, in which the fountain sounded oddly loud. Then my cousin got up and reached a hand. "Come and see the water lilies now the sun's gone. They shut while you watch."

I followed him into the coolly shadowed court. The lilies were pale blue, and their glossy leaves overlapped the still surface like tiles of jade. A powder-blue petal shut, and another, till one by one the lilies were turbaned up, stiff and quiet for the night. A late bee, almost caught by a folding flower, wrestled his way angrily out of the petals, and shot off like a bullet.

I watched absently. The picture Charles had given me of Aunt Harriet blended with my vivid mental pictures of Lady Hester Stanhope. She had gone to the Middle East in the early eighteen hundreds, an earl's daughter, and a masculine, peremptory woman. After traveling round with a large retinue, she had purchased a mountaintop fortress near Djoun, in Syria. There she dressed as an emir, and ruled her entourage of servants, guards, companions, slaves, grooms and personal doctor with a rod of iron and at times, literally, a whip. Fearless, arrogant, she defied the local emirs and placed herself—with some success— above the law. In the end she died alone, old and destitute, her fortress rotting, her servants robbing and neglecting her. But she left a legend that persists to this day.

It was intriguing to think that it might persist in my own Great-Aunt Harriet. She would fit the role quite well. She had wealth and personality, and had traveled widely. She had married an archaeologist, Ernest Boyd, and superintended his "digs." After his death she returned to England, but continued to finance archaeological expeditions in the Middle East. Two years of English weather had been enough. She had gone off to the Lebanon, where she had bought her hilltop refuge. I thought she had died. I regarded my cousin doubtfully. "You think she'll see you?"

"Oh, she'll see me. My mother was always sarcastic about Great-Aunt Harriet's penchant for young men; and if I tell her I've come to demand my Gabriel Hounds, it'll appeal to her. She always liked people who stuck out for their dues. Let's make a date of it for Monday."

"It all sounds intriguing—if I can believe a word of it."

"Sober truth. This is a country where *anything* can happen."

I glanced at my watch. "Heavens, it's dinnertime and I've things to do." I stooped for my handbag.

"I'll drive you back," said my cousin.

We crossed the court. The far murmur of city traffic, no louder than the humming in a shell, made a background to this still quiet, where the only sound was the trickle of the fountain. A bird crooned itself to sleep above the arcade in a rustle of leaves.

"A turtledove, do you hear it?" Charles said quietly. "The poets say she calls all the time for her lover—'*Yusuf, Yusuf,*' till her voice breaks in a sob. . . . I'll ring you Saturday, at the Phoenicia, to tell you when I'm coming."

"I hope we get our Arabian Nights' entertainment at Dar Ibrahim. Is there the faintest reason why she should want to see *me?*"

"She'll be delighted to see you," said my cousin generously. "I was even quite pleased to see you myself."

II

CHARLES WAS right about the Dar Ibrahim "legend." Saturday, the day I moved to the Phoenicia Hotel to plan my brief independence and wait for Charles, I wanted to do some shopping. On Sunday I planned to hire a car and driver to take me exploring up into the Lebanon range to the source of the Adonis River.

494

When I approached the desk clerk to arrange the trip, he entered into my plans with enthusiasm, assessing my clothes, room number and probable bill. There were temples to see at the Adonis Source. "And," he added, "if you make a slight detour on your way back you'll be able to see Dar Ibrahim."

He misunderstood the surprise on my face, and explained quickly, "Dar Ibrahim's a palace where an English lady lives. In the old days it was possible to visit some parts of the place. But now, alas, she is very old, and they say a little—" he touched his forehead. "It is a long time since anyone has seen her."

"But she's still there?"

"Certainly. I have heard talk of a companion, and there are still servants. Once a month supplies are sent up to Sal'q—that is the nearest village—and taken across the stream by mule." He smiled. "I am only recommending the view. It is very fine."

I said, "I know some relatives of the old lady's in England. Perhaps I might write her a note and ask if I could visit her." Something—I'm not quite sure what—forbade me to explain my relationship to the clerk.

He shook his head doubtfully. "They say the porter at the gate lets no one through at all. For a long time she has received no one except the doctor."

"The doctor? Is she ill?"

"About six months ago the doctor went up each day. But she recovered."

She had been well enough, I reflected, to draft another snappy will at Christmas. "Do you know the doctor's name?" I asked. "I might get news of her from him."

It was a Dr. Henry Grafton, he said, who lived near Martyrs' Square. Back in my room, I got the number. A man's voice answered in Arabic, then French, and finally English. Dr. Grafton had left Beirut for good, some time back. A silence. Could he help me . . . ?

"I was just making inquiries about a relation of mine," I said. "A Mrs. Boyd. She lives at a place called Dar Ibrahim."

The voice quickened. "Lady Harriet? As far as I know she's

fine, but she's not my patient. Normally, I would have attended her after Grafton left, but she wrote me she had made other arrangements." Another silence. "May I know who is calling?"

"Her great-niece, Christabel Mansel. Is Dr. Grafton still in the Lebanon?"

"I'm afraid not. He went back to London."

"I see. Well, I might try to look her up myself."

There was a slight pause. Then the voice said, carefully expressionless, "One gathers she lives very much retired."

"So I understand. Thank you for your help. Good-by."

"Good-by," said the voice. I grinned as I put the receiver down. What was implicit in the pleasant voice was, unmistakably, "and the best of luck."

Charles telephoned that evening to say that Ben's father had been delayed, so he couldn't get up before Sunday evening at the earliest. "But in the name of all the gods at once," he finished impressively, "I'll be with you Monday or perish in the attempt."

"Don't say that until you've bought your blue bead. You told me this was a country where anything could happen."

I didn't mention my own inquiries, or that I was developing a lively curiosity about Great-Aunt Harriet.

THE DESK CLERK had done his best to get me a nice, expensive trip. The car was a vast American affair with air conditioning—and blue beads. The driver, a lively young man called Hamid, told me we would go from sea level to about eight thousand feet in one fell swoop, since the Adonis Source was up in the High Lebanon. I settled down beside him and watched his altimeter with fascination as the road turned away from the coast at Byblos.

Hamid had underestimated the number of fell swoops required. At first the road bored its way reasonably up through terraced fields, where apple trees stood knee-deep in growing crops, and dark-eyed children played among the hens in the dust. Then it climbed more steeply through a last belt of cultivation, with neat terraced walls and fruit trees in meager bloom. On the more exposed terraces, thin blades of grain were almost smothered by sheets of spring flowers. Hamid stopped the car and let me explore them with rapture: orchids, cyclamens, flax-blue geraniums, tulips, and the red anemone that flowers for Adonis himself.

Presently we were running, in crystal-clear air, along switchback ridges where gray shrubs clung to the rock and the only flower was the yellow broom. We saw sheep grazing with glossy black goats, each flock bunched round its shepherd, a solitary figure, arms crossed over his stick, watching as we went by.

Still the road climbed. The car swerved terrifyingly round bends, rocks threatening to scrape the inside fenders and, on the other side, a sheer abyss where crows and ravens tilted and croaked below us. Then suddenly we were running along the hogsback of a dizzyingly exposed ridge with, to the left, white rock and blue distance and crest on crest of wooded mountain to the sea; and deep down on our right, ice-green, flashing and hiding and flashing again, as it rushed down its great forested gorge, the Nahr Ibrahim, the Adonis River.

And presently, dipping down through rocky gorges deep in red anemones, we came to the Adonis Source itself. It has been magic, time out of mind. To the people of a thirsty land, the sight of that white torrent bursting straight out of a roaring black cave half up a massive cliff, suggested gods and demons and power and terror—and fertility. Where the water bursts from the rock, all is suddenly green with trees and flowering bushes; and the red anemone grows along the torrent side. So here came Venus—Aphrodite—to fall in love with the shepherd Adonis. And here a wild boar killed him, and where his blood splashed, anemones grew; and to this day, every spring, the waters of the Adonis run red right down to the sea.

We left the scene of white water and blazing rock, the massive ruins of Aphrodite's temple and the bright flowers blowing in the wind, and turned homeward by a different track, to meet a final touch of Eastern fantasy. A little way below the Adonis Source, up a path which was a white scratch on the rock, went a bright chestnut Arab horse, the white burnous of its rider filled out like a sail, the scarlet and silver of the bridle winking in the sun. At the horse's heels cantered two beautiful fawn-colored dogs with long silky hair—Salukis. Then a curve of the road hid them.

We saw the rider again, on our way down the other side of the valley after lunch. He must have used some shortcut. As we picked our way between potholes into a tiny village, I saw him below, walking his horse through a field of sunflowers. Then the squat, peeling houses of the village hid him from view.

WE STOPPED in the village to buy oranges. They would, Hamid said, be straight from the tree, warm with the sun, and divinely ripe. "I shall buy them for you as a present," he said, drawing the car to a halt in the shade of a mulberry tree.

The village was just a handful of mud-brick houses, but some of Aphrodite's fertility had spilled over into the place. It was full of fruit blossom; not only of enchanting glossy trees of oranges and lemons, but the snow of pears and the sharp pink of almond, and everywhere the blush pink of apple.

A crowd of very small and rather engaging children gathered round the car. Otherwise the place seemed dead with the afternoon deadness. No one was in the fields. Apart from the children and some skinny hens, the only creature moving was an old man smoking a pipe. His eyes turned up slowly, half blind, to Hamid, as my guide asked him a question in Arabic, presumably who would sell us the fruit on the lovely trees. Then the old man mumbled something, and Hamid grinned at me. He said, "I won't be a moment," and vanished into a dark doorway.

I wandered up the street. Below a six-foot retaining wall were the terraced fields where I had seen the rider. The sunflowers were tall and thickly planted, and there were wild irises and a blue lily at the foot of the wall. I climbed down and the children followed and helped me hunt for flowers. There was a great deal of conversation, Arabic and English and Stone Age grunts, and we all understood one another. The clearest thing was that I was expected to hand over something substantial in return for the flowers.

"A shilling," said Hamid from the road above me, amused.

It seemed very little, but he was right. The children grabbed the coins, and melted away.

"I'll walk down now and meet you on the road as you drive down. Did you get the oranges?"

"Yes." Then, "Don't hurry; I'll wait for you below."

The path where I had seen the rider was a narrow chasm between the head-high sunflowers. Between them some other plant with glaucous green leaves and plumes of brownish flowers fought its way up towards the light. I made my way down to the last terrace where sunflowers gave way to the more familiar corn. Standing sentinel where the crops divided was a silver-boughed fig tree, its buds just bursting into young green. Against the stem some wild vine clung, with flowers as red as the anemones. I stopped to pick one. A hank of the vine pulled away from the trunk, uncovering something. On the exposed fig stem, scrawled in red, was a crude but lively sketch of a running dog—unmistakably a Saluki.

It is a common experience that once something has been brought to your attention it crops up again and again, often with an alarming coincidence, or fate. Once Charles had mentioned them, were Salukis going to haunt me through the Lebanon? I went on down to the road. Hamid was sitting on a low wall, smoking. He got up quickly. "Would you like an orange?"

"I'd love one. Oh, aren't they gorgeous! . . . Hamid, why do they grow sunflowers here?"

"For cooking oil. Also, the government uses them to make margarine. It's part of a campaign to stop the growing of hemp."

"Hemp? That's hashish, isn't it?"

"Oh, yes. There has always been a lot grown in these hills. A certain amount is grown legally, with a license for medical use. But it's always been easy for the peasants in these wild parts to grow more than they declare, or to harvest the crops before the government inspectors come." He lifted his shoulders. "It pays, and there are always men who will take big risks for big money." He dropped his cigarette and trod the butt into the dust. "The old man I spoke to, he was smoking it, and there was some growing beside his house, among the potatoes."

"What's it look like?" I asked.

"A grayish plant, with a brownish spike of flowers."

I sat bolt upright. "There was some growing under the sun-flowers!"

"It will be gone before the inspectors get here," he said in-differently. "Shall we go?"

It had been a strange and heady day, and it seemed inevitable that as I got into the car I should say, "You know, I'd like to see Dar Ibrahim on the way home."

And I told him why I was interested.

ABOUT FOUR o'clock we slid into the village of Sal'q. Hamid stopped the car where the land dropped away to give another of those staggering views of the Adonis Valley. "There," he said.

I looked where he pointed. The valley was wide, the swift river cutting down between banks of trees. From somewhere to our left, the El Sal'q river fell to meet the Adonis. Between the two streams, a high, dry, wedge-shaped tongue of land thrust out, and on its tip sprawled the palace, a vast collection of almost windowless buildings.

"You have to cross the El Sal'q ford at the bottom," Hamid said. "If you wish to go up to the palace, I will come with you. I be-lieve that the porter there speaks nothing but Arabic."

"I'd be terribly grateful," I said. He locked the car, and pock-eted the key.

The path to the ford led round the wall of the village mosque, past a little Moslem graveyard with its slender stone pillars. Stone turbans indicated the graves of men, lotus carvings the women. Past the graveyard, the track turned downhill in steep zigzags. The whole barren width of the valley seemed to be filled with hot, dry silence.

Round a steep turn in the path we disturbed a herd of sleepy goats, grazing on heaven knows what on that barren slope. Their narrow, wicked, clever faces gave the impression that we were walking through a colony of creatures who lived here by right. When one of them strolled into the middle of the path, I got off and walked round it. It didn't even turn its head.

The swiftly running Nahr el Sal'q was about twenty feet wide here. Though shallow in places, in others it was tumbling with foam, and dark green in breast-deep pools. The foundations of an old bridge could be seen deep in the clear water. There was little left above but some large square stones, which had been re-arranged to make stepping-stones about a yard apart. Hamid took my hand to help me across, then led the way up a wide path through tangles of wild fig and yellow broom. There was no sound except the water running below us, the scrape of our steps, and our breathing.

We came to the great bronze entrance gates set under a wind-fretted arch. The high, blind, palace walls showed here and there the remains of colored decorations, ghostly patterns and mosaics, and broken marble plastered over and painted a pale ocher color which had baked white with the strong sunlight.

Hamid said cheerfully, "If the porter isn't asleep, I might get him to take a message. I will say, 'My name is Hamid Khalil, from Beirut, and I have driven this young lady up to see your mistress. She is no ordinary visitor, but the daughter of the Lady's brother's son, whom you cannot turn from the door. You must tell the Lady that Miss Christy Mansel has come to see her.' "

He tugged a bellpull. In the silence, we could hear a hollow clang just inside the gate. A hound barked somewhere, and we heard the whispering shuffle of slippers, then the sound of bolts being dragged back. The gate creaked cautiously open a crack on a dark passage and a thin bent figure robed in white. For one mad moment, I thought the man had no face; then I saw that he was dark, almost black, and against the blackness of the passage only his white robes showed. He peered out into the light, an oldish man, his skin wrinkled like a prune under the folds of the kaffiyeh, the Arab headdress. He mouthed something at Hamid, and started to shut the gate again.

"Wait." With one stride Hamid had a tough shoulder against

the gate. His quick-fire Arabic sounded urgent, but from the porter's lips came, in answer, only strangled sounds—the struggles of someone with a severe speech impediment. Hamid raised his voice and spoke again, sharply. Curiosity showed now in the old man's face as he turned to stare at me. Then he shook his head violently, mouthing at Hamid and flapping his hands at us like someone driving hens.

"As far as I can make out," said Hamid, "he's saying, 'The doctor says no one is to go in.' "

"The *doctor*? Then I must see the doctor—or anyone else who can talk. Tell him I insist."

After more wrangling, the porter, palms thrown up to disclaim responsibility, let us through at last. Behind us the gate creaked shut, and there were the sounds of bolts being replaced.

We were in a dim, barrel-roofed tunnel, with doors opening off it, and ending in another heavy door. The old man took us through and into a big arched courtyard—the *midan*, or outer court, where once people gathered with gifts or petitions for their ruler, the emir. Under some of the archways were stables and perhaps quarters for soldiers. In its heyday, the midan would have been an impressive place. Now it was quiet and empty, but the scuffed dust showed recent hoofmarks of horses.

The porter led us across the midan, through another door and another darkened passage. Corridors went off to left and right; in one, a skylight shed a glimmer on sacks and boxes and a stack of broken chairs. The passage took three right-angled turns in this labyrinth into a small courtyard, where a rat streaked by. A heavy, dusty silence slept over everything; and as we followed the shuffling guide along yet another dim, filthy corridor, I began to wish fervently that I had not come. The thought of coming face-to-face with the combination of helplessness, senility, and perhaps sickness which must live at the center of all this decay filled me with nothing but dismay.

Suddenly we were in a marble-floored courtyard about fifty feet square, with blue-tiled arcades, pretty pillars and a pool. Thistles grew in gaps in the floor, and the pool was empty. Grass and some tightly clenched, grayish buds grew in the troughs meant for flowers. To one side was the usual dais, with unpadded marble seats, and here the porter indicated that we should sit. Then, with more grotesque yammering, he turned and went.

"Smoke?" asked Hamid, producing cigarettes. He lit mine and squatted down with his back against a pillar. After a time he said, "If she does not receive you, what will you do?"

"Go away, once I've seen the doctor. I haven't seen her for fifteen years, and she may not even remember my name."

"Here is the porter," said Hamid, rising. "And praise be to Allah, he has brought someone with him."

The "someone" was a young European, perhaps twenty-four years old; tall, thin, and carelessly dressed, with light sun-bleached hair. He had the confused air of someone startled from sleep, and I remembered Great-Aunt Harriet's alleged nocturnal habits. Perhaps the staff slept by day. The man dismissed the porter with a gesture, and approached us with apparent reluctance. However, his voice was friendly enough. "Good afternoon. I gather from Jassim that you have an urgent message for Lady Harriet?"

I stood up. "It's not exactly a message. My name's Christy Mansel, and Lady Harriet is my great-aunt. I'm visiting in Beirut and so I came to see her. If she'd spare me a few minutes, I'd be very pleased."

He looked surprised and, I thought, guarded. "Christy, did you say? She's never mentioned anyone of that name."

My voice was tart. "Should she have, Mr.—er . . . ?"

"My name's John Lethman. I—I look after your great-aunt."

"You mean you're the doctor?" He looked taken aback, so I went on, "The porter said the doctor wouldn't allow anyone to see my great-aunt. Did he mean you?"

"I suppose he did. . . ." He shook his head sharply as if to wake himself, and gave me an embarrassed smile. His eyes appeared unfocused, with wide, myopic-looking pupils. "I'm sorry, I'm still a bit stupid. I was asleep."

"I *do* apologize; I forgot the siesta habit. I hope my great-aunt isn't ill, Dr. Lethman. I mean—if you have to live here?"

504

"Look," he said, "I'm not a doctor really, unless you count psychological medicine—" A quick look. "And I'm not here in *that* capacity either! Your great-aunt's pretty fit, and all I do is see to things generally, and provide her with a bit of company. What happened was that I came to the Lebanon to do research for a paper, and was marooned up here one day last July, nearly a year ago, by a flash storm. Your great-aunt took me in. Then somehow one thing led to another, and I stayed." His smile was oddly disarming. He added, "Can you think of a better place to write?"

I could think of a million better places but I said only, "I see. Well, I'm glad she's all right. So I can see her?"

He gave that odd little shake of the head again, and ran his hand over his brow, as if smoothing away a headache. "Let's sit down, shall we?" he said. We sat down in the shade of the Divan, and he went on, "How long since you have seen or heard from your great-aunt?"

"The last time I saw her I was only seven, but my family hears from her now and again."

He was frowning down at his hands. "I only asked because . . ." A pause, then he looked up suddenly. "Miss Mansel, how much do you know about the way she lives here?"

"Very little, except that she's perhaps getting more eccentric as she gets older. All this Lady Hester Stanhope imitation—"

He looked immensely relieved. "I wondered if you knew about that. When your aunt first settled here she did keep a bit of state and the locals started calling her Lady Harriet. She was amused at first, I gather, and then she discovered it suited her to be a 'character.' Gradually it grew beyond the point where she could treat it as a joke, even to herself. She let Dar Ibrahim be used as a halt for caravans on their way from High Lebanon to the sea and received 'distinguished travelers'—mostly archaeologists. When I turned up out of the blue, with part of a medical degree, she was delighted—I would be the 'resident physician' who plays such a large part in the Lady Hester Stanhope story. Of course, if she *did* need medical attention, I'd get it from Beirut."

"Who does she have now that Dr. Grafton's gone?"

"Dr. Grafton?" He sounded quite blank, and I looked at him in surprise.

"Don't you know him?"

"Oh, yes; I was only wondering how you knew the name."

"Someone at the hotel said my aunt had been ill, so I got Dr. Grafton's name and called him. But he'd left Beirut."

"She hasn't needed anyone lately, I'm glad to say." He smiled again. "Don't worry; I look after her quite well, and run the place for her—as far as one can with five courtyards, three Turkish baths, a mosque, stabling for fifty horses and twelve camels, several miles of corridors and more rooms than I've managed to count. I use radar to get from the Prince's Court to the Seraglio."

I laughed. "Don't you have slaves to go with the decor?"

"Only myself and three others—Jassim, the porter; a girl called Halide, and Halide's brother, Nasirulla, who lives in the village and comes over for the day. But Halide looks after your aunt pretty well. You don't need to worry about her."

"I'm not worried. I just want to see her for five minutes so I can tell my family all about it."

He shifted on the hard seat. "Yes. Well, the point is, we've standing orders to stall everybody off. And what she says about her family doesn't lead me to think she'd make an exception."

"Can't we let her decide for herself? I take it she doesn't know I'm here yet? Or did Jassim get that across to her?"

"He came straight to me; but he gets more across than you'd think, and he's pretty useful as a staller-off. Anyway, we can't get anyone much to stay here nowadays. There isn't much money, you know."

There was something odd about the way he said this, but he seemed relaxed enough now. His clothes were inexpensive, but he wore a really magnificent gold watch. I found myself remembering Aunt Harriet's penchant for young men, and some corner of my mind came up with the phrase "undue influence." Was there really very little money left? Perhaps Lethman looked on my arrival as a threat to his own position. . . . In that case Charles might be even less welcome. I decided not to mention him yet.

"Jassim wouldn't have been able to see your aunt yet, in any case," Lethman was saying. "She sleeps during the day, like Lady Hester." He cleared his throat. "I suppose I ought to warn you that she's—well—difficult. And some days are worse than others. Halide wakes her at six, but she's at her best between ten and midnight, and after that she's often up all night. If she receives anyone at all, that's when she sees them."

"You mean that if I'm to see her, I must stay here all night?"

"Until pretty late, at all events. Could you?"

"I could, but I can hardly keep Hamid. Can you put me up?"

There was a pause. Then Lethman said, agreeably enough, "We can find you a room."

I looked at Hamid. "Do you mind? You could tell the Phoenicia I must stay here tonight. Are you free tomorrow?"

"For you, yes," Hamid said. "But I don't like going away and leaving you. Surely, if she wakes at six—"

Beside me, Lethman straightened suddenly. His voice held genuine exasperation. "Look, I'm not making this difficult just for fun. When I was taken to your aunt at midnight the first time I wondered what sort of loony bin I'd landed in. She keeps her bedroom—the Prince's Divan—pitch-dark most of the time, just as Lady Hester did *her* room, out of vanity. And lately she's taken to—" He stopped, and seemed to be examining the tip of one shoe with great attention. "How well do you remember her?"

"Only that she was tall and dark and had piercing black eyes. She had a black shawl, and she wore a diamond pin. I remember Mummy saying that her diamonds were filthy."

"Any diamonds, I'm afraid, have gone long since." He sounded regretful. "Actually she's not so very tall, though I suppose she'd seem so to a child. And as for her clothes . . ."

"Oh, I know, she dresses in Arab men's clothes. Well, why not?" I held out a trousered leg. "I dress like a European man."

"I wasn't fooled," said Mr. Lethman, with the first really human glimmer he had shown. He stood up. "Well, it's after six; I'll try to persuade her to see you straightaway. If she won't, we'll arrange for you to spend the night." He smiled perfunctorily and left us.

I sat down beside Hamid. "Funny setup," he said. "Did you know he'd been smoking hashish when we came? He was finding it hard to think. I smoke it myself sometimes; everybody does in the Lebanon."

"*Do* you?"

He smiled. "Don't worry; not when I'm driving. And not much; it's dangerous. Did you hear him say he was writing a paper? If he smokes hashish, he will think for years that he will start it tomorrow; but he never will. He will end up like Jassim, coughing in the sun and dreaming dreams. . . . What will you do if the old lady won't see you at all?"

"I don't quite know."

"I'll tell you what I would do. Say you wish to hear this from the old lady herself. If he will not allow this, then tell him that you wish a doctor from Beirut to see her straightaway. Tomorrow."

I stared at him. "What are you suggesting?"

"I do not suggest anything, me," said Hamid dryly. "But I have a very unpleasant nature. And she *was* very rich."

"And if he is smoking hashish—" I took a breath. "You're right, I must insist on seeing her."

"There's no need."

I jumped. Lethman had come back with Jassim. He looked wide-awake now, even brisk. "She'll see you, but I'm afraid it'll have to be later tonight—it's not a good day for her. She's had a touch of bronchial asthma lately, but she won't let me call the doctor, and since we still have a prescription from last autumn I haven't overruled her. Anyway, the idea of a visit from you cheered her up a good deal, though to tell you the truth, she doesn't remember much about you. Now, if you'll come with me, Jassim will show your driver the way to the gate."

As I said good-by to Hamid, I thought I saw Jassim looking at me as if he would have liked to throw me out, too. But he shuffled off into the shadows with Hamid, and Lethman led me off the other way, towards the rear of the buildings.

"I'm putting you in the old harem—the Seraglio. It's the best end of the palace." He smiled down at me, suddenly charming.

"Actually, I'm delighted you're staying. It would be nice if she took a sudden shine to you and pressed you to stay on. Then *you* could read the Koran to her at three in the morning, and give *me* a night off. Shall I suggest it to her?"

"I'll let you know in the morning."

He laughed, pushed open a gate under a weed-grown arch and ushered me into a courtyard. "Do you like the Seraglio Garden?"

"*Like* it!" I drew a breath and stood still.

The garden was a riot of green and flowers around the shimmer of cool water. The courtyard itself was huge. Apparently, with the Seraglio rooms, it filled the whole width of the palace on the flat plateau. On three sides ran arched colonnades, throwing their pattern of sun and shadow over the harem doorways. To the north a row of closely latticed windows looked out across the Nahr el Sal'q towards the village. The garden pond was almost a lake, with a small island at its center crowned with a grove of trees. In the grove, I saw the gilded tile roof of an exotic summer-house: a Persian-style kiosk with an onion dome.

There had once been a bridge to the island but now, halfway over, a gap yawned. Around the brink of the lake went a wide paved walk where ferns and briers thrust up the cracked marble slabs. From the roofs of the arcades hung festoons of jasmine, bougainvillea and roses, and on every cornice doves called, "*Yusuf, Yusuf.*"

"It's gorgeous!" I said. "And to think I was always sorry for those poor harem women. Well, that settles it, Mr. Lethman; I'll move in tomorrow for a long, long stay."

"Wait till you've seen your rooms before you commit yourself!"

He led the way. The rooms were on the south side of the garden. The first one had a high ceiling, a checkered marble floor, and mosaic walls. Unlike the other rooms I had seen, it was light and clean, with bookcases and a triple window. The window was barred, but not heavily, for obvious reasons: the south wall apparently rose straight from the edge of the rock above the Adonis.

"The bedroom's next door," said Mr. Lethman, "and then the baths—the *hammam:* steam rooms, cold rooms, massage rooms, the lot." He grinned. "Guess what—no steam! But there *is* running water, straight off the snow. I'll send Halide along to bring you some towels." He glanced at his watch. "Explore where you like, except for the Prince's rooms, of course. I'll send some wine to you straightaway, and join you for supper in about half an hour."

When he had gone I sat down on the Divan cushions, looking out over the gorge where the last of the light tipped the trees with gold. Shortly, a stocky young Arab in white robes, presumably Halide's brother, Nasirulla, came with a tray which held a lighted lamp, two glasses, and a bottle of the light, dry wine of the Bk'aa, about the best that Lebanon produces. I began to think kindly of John Lethman. Nasirulla set the lamp in a niche, sketched a salaam and went out.

I sat curled on the window seat, sipping the golden wine. Soon, the sky was like black velvet spangled with stars. In the garden the doves had fallen silent in the still air. But I could smell jasmine and roses.

Lethman came back, and with him Nasirulla with the supper tray. There was scalding-hot soup, and grilled mutton flavored with vinegar, lemon, onion and cardamom seeds. With this came a salad, unleavened bread, butter, goat cheese and apples.

When Nasirulla left, I asked, "Where do you usually eat?"

"Here, quite often. You'll probably find out, so I may as well tell you: these are my rooms. But I was going to sleep on the Prince's side tonight anyway."

"Mr. Lethman, I don't know what to say! Turning you out of—"

He cut me short by serving the soup, and refilled my wineglass. Then, almost as if he were making amends for his earlier reluctance to let me in, he became a lively host, chatting entertainingly about Dar Ibrahim. He said very little about Aunt Harriet, but I thought I could sense respect and liking for her. He was certainly interested in everything I could tell him about the family. I still did not mention Charles and his planned visit. I intended to tell Aunt Harriet myself and so bypass the difficulties of persuasion at second hand.

Halide brought coffee at nine, with the information that

Nasirulla had gone back to the village and that my bedroom was ready. She was dark-skinned, with huge eyes outlined with black, a slim neck and delicate hands. Her dress was of bronze-green silk, and like many Arab women, she wore her bank account on her wrists, which jingled with thin gold bracelets. As she told Lethman, in softly accented English, about the room, she looked me over and the message passed, clear from female to female in any language: "Not that he'd look at you, but keep off—or I'll make you sorry."

Then, eyes modestly lowered, she said to Lethman, "When you have finished, the Lady would like to see you again."

She went out, leaving the door open. I watched her vanish into the shadows of the arcade, but then I saw a movement reflected in the waters of the lake. She was waiting among the bushes. Lethman got to his feet. "I'll come back to take you across."

He turned his head sharply as a bell pealed violently deep in the buildings. From somewhere nearer, startled by the bell, came a furious baying of dogs. Big dogs, by the sound of them.

"What on earth's happened?" I demanded, startled.

"The bell means your great-aunt is getting impatient."

"Those dogs sound dangerous."

"They're our watchdogs. Don't worry, they're only turned loose at night, and they can't get into the Seraglio if you keep the main door shut. You'll be quite safe." He flashed me a smile and went. I heard the wooden gate shut behind him, and a moment later his voice calling to the dogs. The baying stopped.

Halide appeared, glimmering in her green silk. She began to stack the dishes on the tray, watching me with wary hostility. Irritated, I concentrated on John Lethman's books. They were not light reading: volumes on Lady Hester, on Lebanon, on mind-changing drugs. . . . No medical textbooks—presumably too bulky to carry out here.

I turned. Halide was carrying the tray to the door. "I'll shut it for you," I said, moving to do so, but she paused in the doorway.

"You really travel alone?"

"Why not?"

She ignored this. "You—you stay here long?"

Curiosity made me less than truthful. "As long as she'll let me," I said, watching her.

She said quickly, "She is not well. You must go tomorrow."

I raised my brows. "Mr. Lethman asked me to stay."

The black eyes flared. "But that is not possible! He—"

Imperative, sounding very bad-tempered, Great-Aunt Harriet's bell jangled once more, and, still obviously at large, the watchdogs bayed. The girl started violently. "I must go!" Then, almost fiercely, as I made a move to follow and open the gate for her: "Stay here! I can manage, I can manage!"

I stared thoughtfully after her. Whether or not John Lethman had a stake in Great-Aunt Harriet, Halide had a stake in John Lethman. And I wasn't sure how that added up for Aunt Harriet.

When Lethman came for me, he was armed with an enormous, very powerful electric torch. "Ready?" he asked.

He led me back to the courtyard where Hamid and I had waited. From there we seemed to walk forever, up corridors, up and down steps, and across more courts. In the last, I heard, from behind a closed door, a scratching sound followed by a deep whining yelp that made me jump. "It's all right, I shut them up." He shone the torch momentarily towards the door, and in the gap at its foot I saw the gleam of a dog's damp nose snuffling at the air. "Sofi! Star! Quiet! Watch your step, Miss Mansel; the threshold's broken here. Here is the Prince's Divan."

Dim orange light shone from a doorway between two tubbed trees. He stood aside for me. His voice sounded different—wary and deferential: "I've brought Miss Mansel, Lady Harriet."

I went past him into the room.

III

THE PRINCE'S DIVAN was enormous. It had a sort of luxurious squalor. The marble floor was strewn with dirty Persian rugs; the walls were of intricate mosaics with recesses which must have held statues or lamps but were now empty except for rubbish—

cartons, papers, medicine bottles, candle stubs. A boarded-over fountain did duty as a table. It held the remains of a recent meal. On the floor was an empty bowl labeled Dog. A mahogany chest of drawers, covered with more bottles and pillboxes, stood against the wall. There were one or two kitchen chairs and a big throne-like affair in red Chinese lacquer.

Up three steps, on the dais, was a huge bed, with a high carved headboard. Velvet curtains sagged in heavy loops. A figure reclined on the bed in a welter of rugs and blankets.

I had not expected anything quite so grotesque as this. John Lethman had warned me that Aunt Harriet would have shrunk, and this was so; though I might have recognized the jutting nose and black eyes which peered at me from the shadows, nothing had prepared me for her sheer outlandishness.

She was wearing a silk bedgown, a loose velvet coat and an enormous cashmere shawl. Her skin was sallow and her lips sunken, but the lively black eyes showed none of the signs of old age. She was lavishly powdered, and a towering white turban, occasionally slipping a little to one side, exposed a shaved head—somehow the final touch of grotesqueness.

I did remember the ring on her left hand. It was a Burma ruby, the size of a thumbnail and immensely valuable. She wore it always. It flashed in the lamplight as, wheezing a little, she beckoned me with a large, pale hand to a stool near the bed.

"Well, Christy?" The voice, little more than a whisper, had an asthmatic breathiness, but the black eyes were live and curious. "Sit down and let me look at you. Hm. Yes. You always were a pretty little thing. Why aren't you married?"

"Have a heart, I'm only twenty-two!"

"Is that all? One forgets. John tells me I forget things all the time. He's always trying to make out that I'm getting senile." She darted a look at Lethman, who was watching her, I thought, uneasily. The sharp gaze came back to me. "You've a look of your father. How is he?"

"Fine, thank you. If he knew I was here, I'm sure he'd send his regards."

"Hm. An attentive family, the Mansels, wouldn't you say? Well?" And again, when I didn't speak, "Well, girl?"

I sat up straighter on my stool. "Aunt Harriet, you know quite well my people write to you *just* as often as you write to them— even if it's only to thank you for the latest edition of your will!"

The eyes glittered. "My will? Ha! Come to collect, have you?"

"Well, I'd have a job, since you're still alive, wouldn't I?" I grinned at her. "Anyway, it's a long way to come for sixpence."

I caught a glance from John Lethman, half amused, half apprehensive, as she stirred suddenly, plucking at her coverings. "I could have died out here for all they'd have cared. Any of them."

I said quickly, "Aunt Harriet, if you wanted or needed us, you had only to let us know: it's only six hours from London to Beirut. We've just let you live the way you want to—and you seem to be making a pretty good job of it, if you ask me!"

She laughed openly then, the cocoon of coverings heaving to her wheezing breaths. The big hand went up, and the ruby flashed. "All right, child; I was teasing you! I always did like a fighter. But if you're so full of this 'live and let live,' why were you so insistent about getting in to see me?"

I grinned. "Call it curiosity. You're a celebrity. Everybody talks about you, and Dar Ibrahim is one of the sights of the Lebanon. When I realized I had an excuse to bulldoze my way in here, nothing short of boiling oil could have stopped me."

"Make a note of that, John; boiling oil is what we need. A Mansel to your claw tips, aren't you? So everybody talks about me, do they? Who's everybody?"

So I told her about the desk clerk and my phoning Dr. Grafton to try to get news of her health.

"A lot of use that would have been," she said. "The man was a fool. A very good thing he's gone back to London. Much better now, much better." The shawl had slipped; she pulled at it irritably, muttering, "Calling up about me," and "Chattering about me in hotels," in a whisper which all at once seemed vague and blurred. I longed to escape, but I would not leave until I had spoken of Charles. I wondered she hadn't spoken of him herself.

"Christy . . ." she was saying. "Stupid name for a girl. What's it short for?"

"Christabel. The nearest they could get to Christopher."

"Oh." I got the sharp impression that the eyes in the shadows were by no means forgetful; that this was a game she played. The impression wasn't pleasant. "What were we talking about?"

John Lethman leaned forward quickly. "Don't you think you should have a rest, Lady Harriet? And it's time for your tablets. I'll see Miss Mansel back."

"No," said Great-Aunt Harriet uncompromisingly. "I won't take the tablets yet; they make me sleepy. Stay where you are, child, and entertain me. How long have you been in Beirut?"

I was telling her amusing stories about the group tour when she suddenly reached out and yanked at a bellpull. The building echoed the familiar clanging peal, and then the noise of the baying hounds. I stopped talking, but she said almost snappishly, "Go on. What's happened to your party?"

"They went back to London on Saturday morning."

"So you're on your own now? Where's that stupid girl? Ah, there you are! Where the devil were you?" Halide came quickly across the room. She looked scared.

"I want my pipe," said Great-Aunt Harriet irritably.

Halide scurried to the dressing chest. I looked after her with surprise. It wasn't easy to see how anyone could frighten Halide, short of the whip-and-club methods used by Lady Hester Stanhope. But then two sets of pegs on the wall above the bed caught my eye. On them lay a stick and a rifle. I blinked at them in disbelief. Even here, surely, in the mid-twentieth century . . .

The girl pulled open a drawer, took out a wooden box and a mouthpiece, and fitted the mouthpiece into a nargileh, a kind of hubble-bubble pipe, by the bed. I saw her throw a quick glance at Lethman, and receive an irritable nod. So this was the cause of her nervousness; she was in the awkward position of the servant who is bidden by one master to do what the other disapproved.

Lethman said in my ear, "I can't offer you a cigarette; she only approves of herbal tobacco. I'm afraid it smells vile."

Aunt Harriet sucked at the pipe. "Did you like Damascus?"

"So-so. But something nice happened; I ran into Charles."

"Charles?" Her voice was sharp, and Halide and Lethman looked at one another quickly. "What the devil's my nephew Charles doing here?"

"Oh, not Uncle Chas," I said quickly. "Charles, my cousin. He'll be in Lebanon tomorrow, and he's terribly keen to see you."

The pipe bubbled and she blinked at me through the smoke. The air was stuffy and acrid; I really must get out of here soon.

"You *do* remember Charles?" I said. "He was your favorite."

"Of course. I always liked handsome boys. Yes, yes." She smoked in silence, nodding as if to herself, then relinquished the mouthpiece of the pipe to Halide. The black eyes were fixed on me now. "You're like him. *Very* like him." She was still nodding to herself, her hands unsteady with her shawl.

"Lady Harriet," said Lethman, abruptly, "I must insist you take your tablets now, and rest for a little. Miss Mansel—"

"Of course," I said, getting to my feet. I felt waves of heat coursing over my skin. "Now what shall I say to Charles?"

"You may give him my regards." The whisper was harsh.

"But—" I regarded her blankly. "May he come up tomorrow evening and wait till you're ready to receive him? Or Monday?"

"No. I won't receive him. I have received you, and it's been a pleasure, but this is enough." She added, more kindly, "I'm an old woman and I can be arbitrary. I have chosen my way of life."

"But Charles will be terribly disappointed. You are his favorite relative."

"I have spoken." The ruby flashed.

I gave up. "I'll tell him. He'll be glad you're so well."

"Child, you may go now; I'm tired. When I'm dead John will let you know. You're a pretty girl and I've enjoyed your visit."

"I've enjoyed it, too. Thank you for letting me come."

"Good night. . . . Halide! You're taking all night with my pills!"

Lethman already had shown me to the doorway. I glanced back. Halide was shaking something from a small bottle into her hand. Beyond her the bed was a towering obscurity. Then some-

517

thing moved towards the bed, small and gray and quick. For one flesh-creeping moment I thought there were rats even in the bed-room; but then a half-grown cat leaped on the bed. The large pale hand came forward and stroked it.

A cat! No wonder I felt hot and shaky. I have a true cat phobia. I love their looks but I cannot be in the same room with them, and on the rare occasions when I have tried to touch a cat, it has almost made me ill. Cats are my nightmare.

I hurried out in the wake of John Lethman's torch. I imagined myself telling the family: "She's ill, she's old; and this recluse thing—" None of the phrases fitted the odd tone of the interview. And for her to refuse to see Charles . . .

John Lethman's torch flicked upwards for a moment to light my face. "What is it? Are you cold?"

"Oh, no. But that tobacco—"

"Was that all it was? The interview didn't upset you?"

"In a way, I was upset," I admitted. "And I was a bit tactless. Did I upset *her?*"

"Oh, it takes more than that. She enjoyed the conversation. But I wish you'd told me earlier about this cousin Charles. I might have managed to persuade her."

"Yes, it was silly of me," I said ruefully. "I had some idea of finding out first how the land lay. Charles will be furious with me. She's talked of him, surely?"

"Oh, yes. Well, tell him to leave it for a few days. I'll do what I can, and get in touch with you."

"Thank you," I said. "I'll tell him. When she's had time to think it over, I'm sure she'll change her mind."

"Stranger things have happened," said John Lethman.

IV

A FLASH OF lightning and a crack of thunder woke me that night. I sat up. There was no wind, only the thunder and the vivid white rents in the black sky which made the window arches flicker dramatically. Then rain began to splash on the floor in great hammering drops. I hurried across the chilly floor and slammed the casement shut.

I heard the sudden howl of a big dog. It is one of the weirdest of all sounds, bringing with it race memories of wolves and countless legends of death and grief. The voice was rising in a throbbing wail; it was joined by the long tremolo of another. The watchdogs, of course, upset by the storm. But I thought of the legend Charles had reminded me of, the Gabriel Hounds, Death's pack hunting through the sky. . . .

Then, as suddenly as if a tap had been turned off, the rain stopped. A bird sang in the garden, full and loud and echoing from the water and the enclosing walls. Another joined it, and then a third; waterfalls of song rinsing the clear air. I padded out. The nightingales' song filled the garden, welling out of the tangle of soaked and glittering creepers.

A pair of white pigeons rocketed from their roost and vanished with a clap of wings over my head. Someone was walking softly along in the darkness under the western arcade. It must be John Lethman come to see how I'd made out in the storm. I waited for him, but he didn't come over. The garden, but for the nightingales, was quiet and still.

I shivered suddenly. I went into my room, shut my door against the nightingales, and rolled back onto the bed.

I WOKE to cheerful sunlight and a tapping on the door. It was Halide, with a plate of unleavened bread, cream cheese, apricot jam and coffee. She looked tired, and when I thanked her, she only nodded sullenly and went out.

I carried the tray out into the blazing sunshine by the lake. A peacock, his tail spread, studied his reflection there, and a small golden bird flirted over a rose laurel. The little kiosk on the island, freshly washed, showed its gilded dome and a glimpse of bright blue tiling.

I wondered how John Lethman had got in and out last night, and why. He came a half hour later. He looked alert and greeted me almost gaily. "Good morning!"

"Oh, hullo." I picked up my handbag. "I had just decided to look for you—hoping the dogs were shut up!"

"Always, by day. Did they wake you last night? It was a bit rough, I'm afraid. Did you sleep through it?"

"In the end," I replied.

"Your aunt was very set up by your visit. She kept me talking quite a time. No change about your cousin Charles, I'm afraid, but give her time."

We moved towards the front gate. "Did she keep you very late?" I asked.

"Not very, no. I'd gone to bed before the storm broke. It never even woke me."

"I enjoyed its aftermath. The garden looked wonderful."

A quick sideways glance. "You went out?"

"Only for a moment, to listen to the nightingales."

We were crossing the courtyard where Hamid and I had waited. In the marble flower troughs, where the gray buds had been, was a blaze of red anemones, shiny as fresh blood. "Oh, look at the anemones," I cried. "Is that because of the rain?"

"My Adonis Gardens," said Mr. Lethman. "You know, Adonis was a fertility god. The Adonis Gardens here, which spring up and die in a few days, are symbols of death and resurrection. They are supposed to help the harvests in a magical way."

"Why did *you* plant an Adonis garden? It's the kind of romantic notion that appeals to *me*, but what has Adonis to do with psychological medicine?"

"Oh, I'm writing a paper on the ecstatic religions of the Near East. Whenever I'm let off the chain, I ride out into the hill villages. I've found some quite interesting stuff here."

We were in the midan now. He nodded across it. "There's still a horse here. Hullo! The stable door's still shut. Nasirulla's late. I'll open it and give Kasha some air." He pulled open the upper half-door. In the dim interior a chestnut Arab horse stood dozing.

"Do you wear Arab dress when you ride?" I asked.

He looked surprised. "Usually. It's cooler. Why? Wait a minute—did you see me up at the Adonis Source yesterday?"

"Yes. I recognize the horse." I smiled. "You looked terribly romantic with the Salukis. I may tell you, you made my day."

"And now I've spoiled the picture? Not an Arab emir; just a drifter who's found a lazy billet in the sun."

I didn't answer. John Lethman must know that his job would expire with Great-Aunt Harriet. Or was he playing for Dar Ibrahim itself, and a dilettante life on his own?

There was no sign of Jassim at the gate. Lethman pulled back the bolts and opened the bronze door. The sun blazed white on the empty plateau. "Your driver isn't here yet," Lethman said. "If you'd rather come back in and wait—" The light eyes met mine and slid away.

"I think I'll just walk down to meet Hamid," I said. "Good-by, and thank you for all you've done."

"Good-by."

The big door shut and the palace had sealed itself off once more behind me.

When I got down to the Nahr el Sal'q, there was no sign of Hamid—and I saw why. The river was in spate. Where yesterday the stones from the old bridge had stood a foot clear of water, there was nothing but angry, broken water streaked with red mud.

I stared about helplessly. This was why Nasirulla hadn't turned up for work. And unless I could make my way up the valley between the roaring Nahr el Sal'q and the bigger Adonis and cross where the stream was narrower, I was marooned. Meanwhile I could only wait for Hamid to appear.

It was then that I saw the boy across the stream—a sturdy, ragged boy with a shock of wild dark hair. He was standing beside a bush, leaning on a stick, with goats moving slowly around him, and he seemed to be staring straight at me. I picked my way to the river's edge. "Hullo there!" My voice whirled away in the roar of the water. I tried again. "Do you speak English?"

He nodded, a curiously dignified nod. Then, with a small boy's movement, he thrust down his stick and pole-vaulted down to the far side of the stream. I tried again. "Where can I cross?"

He shook his head. "Tomorrow." He waved the stick upstream

towards the towering cliffs at the head of the valley, then down to where the two rivers rushed together in a wrangle of white foam stained with red. "All bad!" he shouted. "You stay there with the Lady. Your father's father's sister?"

Through Nasirulla, of course, everyone in the village would know all about me by now. "Yes," I said. "You live in the village?"

A gesture at the barren landscape. "I live here."

"Can you get me a mule? A donkey?" I shouted.

That shake of the head again. "No mule. Donkey too small." Then he pointed towards the village. I saw Hamid, a slim figure in dark blue, detach himself from the dense shadow under the village wall and start down the path.

I turned back to the boy. The goats were still there, the river roared, the distant village wavered in the heat; but on the bank there was only a shaggy black goat, staring at me with those cold yellow eyes. . . .

A country where anything can happen.

I said aloud, "I could do with your being here, cousin dear."

And a second later I realized that the figure coming down the slope was not Hamid but Charles himself.

I stood still, watching him, as he raised a hand to greet me. Then he turned. A patch of shade resolved into a black goat and, squatting cross-legged beside it, the herdboy. Charles had a short conversation with him, then the two of them came down together to the riverbank. We surveyed one another across the turbid water. "Hi!" said Charles.

"Hi!" I shouted. Then, not very brilliantly, "We're stuck."

"Serves you right. Stealing a march on me with Aunt H."

"But Charles, what are we going to do?"

"I'll come over." He started to undo his shirt buttons.

I yelled in alarm, "Charles, you can't! Besides, she says she won't see you!"

"She actually told you that?" I nodded, and Charles spoke to the boy. Then he turned back to me and raised his voice again. "Ahmad says a man can cross further up. Can you make it upstream on your side?"

"I'll try," I shouted.

I turned and began to make my way up the Nahr el Sal'q through a thick growth of trees. I caught only glimpses of Charles and Ahmad before they vanished, apparently following some goat track up into the thickets. The stream entered a narrow gorge with a series of rapids and Charles and the boy reappeared, but the water was so loud that we could not hear each other. The boy kept pointing upstream in an Excelsior kind of way, and Charles jerked an encouraging thumb. We toiled on, separated by the loud white rush of water, until the stream seemed to run right up against a cliff.

In fact, the spring which fed the Nahr el Sal'q roared *out* of the cliff and tore down among the white boulders of the gully. A few hanging bushes, soaked with spray, waved in the breeze of the fall. The sun lit the cascade above us into glittering brilliance, but where we stood the place was in shadow and chilly.

I stared about in dismay. Communication was impossible here, and to cross the torrent would have been suicide; while above the cascade towered a craggy, sunlit cliff as high as a cathedral. Ahmad pointed at this, and to my alarm, I saw Charles approaching it. My wild gesture reached him, for he stopped and nodded his head at me, with a thumb-up gesture. Then I remembered that climbing had been another of the games with which (said my father) my cousin had wasted his time all over Europe. I hoped he had, as he usually did (said my mother), wasted his time to good effect.

It seemed he had. He went carefully, because in places the rock was wet or loose, but it was not long before he had gained my side of the river. He came down in a scramble to land safely beside me. "Hullo, Aphrodite," he said.

"Adonis, I presume?"

"Sweet coz, I've got to talk to you. Let's get up into the sun. I'll tell the boy—why, where is he? Did you see him go?"

"That's not a boy, that's a faun. Invisible at will."

"Very likely," agreed Charles calmly. "Well, he'll turn up when he wants his tip."

I followed him up the side of the gully. We emerged on a stony plateau where hot sun struck the tumbled ruins of some forgotten temple: a portico, a stretch of broken floor, and two honey-colored pillars. We sat in the shade of one of the pillars. "Oh, Charles, I'm awfully glad you came!" I said. "The faun told me the water won't go down till tomorrow."

"So I gather. He tells me there's some kind of track on this side, going up into the High Lebanon, but it's very far, and if I took the car up the road on the other side, you'd never find me."

"Nothing," I said, "will get me to clamber up into the High Lebanon. It's probably full of wild boars."

My cousin leaned back lazily against the pillar. "So there's only one thing to do—go back to the palace. Ben's father telephoned me again last night to say he had to go on to Aleppo and possibly Homs, and so I told Ben I'd go back to Damascus later. I came up to Beirut at the speed of sound, and found your driver was in the hotel lobby when I checked in. He told me about you, so I said I'd come and fetch you. Now, what the devil do you mean by stealing a march on me, young Christy?"

I sat up. "Oh, Charles—when we got to El Sal'q, the palace looked so near to me, and so weird and romantic! Look, you can see why from here." We were looking down on the back of the palace. "See the green courtyard and the lake?" I said. "That's the Seraglio where I slept." In that brilliant air even the branches of the feathery trees were clearly visible. It was not more than three-quarters of a mile distant from us.

I told Charles my story then, omitting nothing. When I ended, he regarded me frowningly. "Well, we expected a queer situation. But it's queerer even than you think."

"Meaning?"

He asked flatly, "Did she strike you as sane?"

I have often read about moments of "revelation"—and in a minor, very personal way, I had a revelation now. There was the boy I had known ever since I could remember. I had seen him smacked. I had jeered at him when he fell off the orchard wall and cried. Later, I had regarded him with a tolerant, familiar indifference. Now, suddenly, I saw, as if I had never seen them before, the gray long-lashed eyes, the slightly arrogant and wholly exciting cut of nostril and upper lip, the vivid intelligence and humor and force of the man's face.

"What's the matter?" he asked, irritably. "I asked you if Aunt H struck you as sane."

"Oh." I pulled myself together. "Yes, of course she's sane. She's odd and forgets things, but . . ." I hesitated. "However peculiar she is, Charles, her *eyes* are sane."

He nodded. "That's what I mean. I called the family up Friday evening. I told them that you and I were coming up to see Great-Aunt H. Well, my mother said they'd had a letter from her, dated two months ago. Mother told me she'd forwarded it to me in care of Cook's, in Beirut." His hand went to his inside pocket. "I picked it up this morning. Tell me if it makes sense to you."

He handed me the letter. It seemed to be written on wrapping paper. The handwriting was spidery but perfectly legible:

My dear Nephew:

My dear Husband's colleague, Humphrey Ford, tells me that Henry's boy Charles is at present studying the languages of the East. Humphrey also informed me that young Charles will be traveling this yr in Syria. If he wishes to call on me, I shld make a point of receiving him. Charles is a clever boy, and there is much to interest him here in the study of Eastern Life and Manners.

I do well enough here with my small but attentive Staff and a man from the village who looks after the dogs. Samson cannot abide my Dr. Young Chas will remember Samson.

Regards to yr Wife also to my other Nephew and Wife—the little girl must be well grown by now. A strange little thing.

Yr affec Aunt,
Harriet Boyd

Post Scriptum—*The Times* continues flimsy so that I cannot believe Yr. Representations were sufficiently decided.

Post Post Scriptum. I have purchased an excellent Tombstone locally.

I gaped up at my cousin. "From the postmark," he said, "it looks as if she didn't mail the letter straight off; but it was certainly written after that last will. Wouldn't you say that was an open invitation to me?"

"I certainly would. Something's happened to change her mind."

"John Lethman? Would you say he was honest?"

"I don't think you need worry about him. He may be feathering his nest, but I swear he couldn't stop her from doing anything she'd set her heart on. Charles, it's perfectly possible she really *has* forgotten you."

He stirred. "Oh, I don't care, as long as things are going the way she wants them, but I'd like to have seen for myself. She gave no reason for her embargo on me?"

"None whatever. I got the impression that, having seen me, she'd satisfied her curiosity, and wanted to get back to her own life. I quite like John Lethman, and Aunt H did seem perfectly happy and not ill, apart from being absentminded and wheezing a bit. I wasn't feeling too good myself in that stuffy room. Oh, Charles, I forgot—there was a cat in the room. When I felt queer I thought it was Aunt Harriet's tobacco and the room, but that must have been what it was."

"*Cat?*" His turn to stare. "Good Lord, was there?"

So Charles hadn't forgotten the grotesque horror I have of cats. He doesn't share my phobia, but he understands.

"It jumped up on the bed beside her just as I was leaving," I said, "and she started stroking it. It can't have been there all the time, or I'd have felt rotten earlier. There must be another door into the room." Charles said nothing and I went back to the letter. "Who's Humphrey Ford? And Samson?"

"Ford is Professor Emeritus, Oriental Studies. Oxford. A nice old chap. And Samson is a Tibetan Terrier. She got him last time she was home, as a mate for Delilah."

I handed the letter back. "I never saw the dogs. They were shut up except at night. Lethman said they were dangerous."

He put the letter back in his pocket. I got the impression that he was talking slightly at random. "Samson was a savage little brute, except with the family. You'd have been all right: don't they say there's some sort of family smell that they recognize?"

"Do they?" I leaned back with my face lifted to the sun. "Charles, why don't you come back with me here and now? We can show Lethman the letter and he can hardly stop you. . . . Charles, are you *listening?*"

He was looking away from me, down the bright distance of the valley towards the palace. "Look over there."

At first I could see nothing except the crumbling ruin sleeping in the heat. Then among the rocks and tangled bushes at the lip of the Adonis Gorge I saw a man in Arab dress making his way on foot towards the palace. He disappeared from time to time in the thick overgrowth, but presently emerged on the open plateau behind the palace. He seemed to have a bag over his shoulder.

"The faun is right," I said. "There's a path on this side."

"You never wondered how Lethman got back to the palace before you did yesterday?"

"I never thought of it. I remember now, there was something about the palace being on an old camel route from the High Lebanon to the sea."

The man had reached the back wall of the palace. He made for the corner where the walls grew out of the cliffs of the Adonis Gorge, and vanished into a clump of trees.

"He can't get round that way!" I exclaimed. "It's a sheer drop to the river."

"He's got a rendezvous," said Charles.

I narrowed my eyes against the brightness. Then I saw the Arab among the trees with another man, this one in European dress. "John Lethman?" asked Charles.

"Must be. Look, there's someone else, in white, moving among those trees. That must be the doorman, Jassim. I don't understand. Have they been waiting out there for the visitor? If they'd come round from the front gate, we'd have seen them. A path skirts the north palace wall below the Seraglio arcade."

"There must be a postern door at the back of the palace."

"Tradesman's entrance?" I said. "I suppose you're right. Look, he's handed over his pack, whatever it is. He's going now. Will they see us if they look this way?"

"Not a hope. We're in the shadow of this pillar, and what's more, the sun will be in their eyes. Yes, he's going."

The Arab had turned and was making his slow way back among the rocks, and the other two had vanished. There must indeed be another way into the palace. I said suddenly, "Quite honestly, I don't want to go back there. Couldn't you somehow convoy me across the cliff?"

"I wouldn't, even if I could. Too risky. It's obviously the will of Allah that you should go back to Dar Ibrahim. I'll go there tonight and *you* are going to let me in the postern. Was the ford where we met this morning out of sight of the palace?"

"Yes. But Charles—"

"And when you first saw me, you thought I was your driver?"

"Yes, but Charles—"

"If they were looking out this morning, all they would see was your driver, walking down from the village."

"Yes, but Charles, you can't—"

"Now be quiet and listen. You go back to the palace and tell Lethman what's more or less the truth. Say you couldn't cross the stream, but you and your driver went up the Nahr el Sal'q to see if there was a way across. But there wasn't any place to cross, even with the driver's help." He grinned. "True so far. So you told your driver to call for you tomorrow when the stream had gone down. You told him to tell your cousin that you would stay here tonight and join him tomorrow at the Phoenicia."

"But Charles—"

"Lethman can hardly refuse to take you in. So you get back into the palace. He said you could explore anywhere you liked except the Prince's rooms. Well, you'll have hours of daylight this time. See if you can find this back door. It must come from your end of the palace, because whoever was in the gardens last night didn't go out past your room to the main door. If you find the door, see that it's unlocked after dark tonight. If you can't find it— you said there's a path on the north side?"

"There is, but the windows are all barred. Don't forget it was a harem."

"Aren't any of the grilles broken? Or could they be broken?"

"Yes, I think so. But they're up high in the wall, and—"

"I've always wanted to climb into a harem," said Charles. "If the wall's in bad repair there'll be footholds."

"But why not try the main gate first with me?"

"Because I'd sooner bypass Lethman." I started to ask why, saw my cousin's face, and decided to save time and energy. I asked instead, "Well, once you're in, what if you're caught?"

"All that'll happen is a bit of a row and I'll risk that." He got decisively to his feet. "If they're interested, they'll see me going back towards the village. Now, you said you'd finished supper by about ten, and Aunt H didn't send for you until about twelve. Just in case she decides to receive you again, we'd better say that I'll be at the back of the palace from ten thirty on. If the postern isn't unlocked, I'll give a couple of barks like a hill fox. If it's all clear for me to climb up, hang out a towel or some other light-colored cloth I can see. Now let's get back, shall we?"

"What about the faun?"

"I daresay I can buy his silence. And no one in the village is going to be able to cross the Nahr el Sal'q to report that a white Porsche has been standing in the village street all day."

"Charles, I don't want to spend another night without even a nightie."

"I'll bring you a toothbrush tonight, but I'm darned if I'll climb back across the rocks carrying a nightie. You can borrow a djellaba from Great-Aunt Harriet."

And on this unfeeling note he led the way back into the gully.

V

IT WAS almost too easy. Jassim let me in with only a bit of sulky muttering, and in a moment I was telling John Lethman about trying to find a way across the Nahr el Sal'q.

"How stupid of me not to have expected this," he said, "when

Nasirulla couldn't get here. Of course you must stay. So your driver's gone back to Beirut until tomorrow?"

I nodded. "I sent a message for my cousin not to come up here, because Aunt Harriet wasn't well enough to see him. I'll explain better when I see him. Are you going to tell her I've come back?"

He hesitated, then turned up a hand, smiling. "I'm not sure. Let's defer the decision until she wakes up, shall we?"

We went back to the rooms in the Seraglio Court, and Halide soon arrived with a tray set for two. She thumped it down on the table and stood smoldering at me and directing a stream of Arabic at Lethman which sounded like the spitting of an angry cat. He took it calmly and finally, with a glance at his watch, made some statement that sent her flouncing away. Lethman was looking embarrassed. "I'm sorry about that."

I helped myself from a dish of *kefta*, savory meat balls on a mound of rice, and luncheon passed easily and impersonally, much to my relief: I didn't want to strain my talent for deception too far. As soon as lunch was over Lethman got to his feet. He had things he must see to. . . . If I would excuse him now . . . ? I reassured him, almost too eagerly. I would sit in the garden, I told him, and doze over a book. And if I might do a bit of exploring later on? A chance I might never have again . . . and of course I wouldn't dream of disturbing Aunt Harriet. . . .

We parted on a note of mutual relief, Lethman taking the tray with him. I collected some cushions and took them into the quiet garden. I settled myself at the edge of the pool under a tamarisk tree and slept.

About an hour later I woke. Sleepy heat seemed to have overtaken the whole place: there was no sound at all. I got up from my cushions and set out to explore.

The postern was apparently hidden in the trees at the southeastern corner. When I looked out of my bedroom window, I could see the treetops level with the sill. The Seraglio was a story and a half above the plateau, so the postern must open on some corridor below the palace, or at the foot of a flight of steps.

A hunt along the eastern arcade and into the recesses of the hammam on the corner convinced me that there was no staircase there, nor a door that could lead to one, so I abandoned the Seraglio, and set out to investigate the twisting stairs and narrow dark corridors of the palace building.

I very soon lost all sense of direction. Every time I came to a window I looked through it to get my bearings, but many of the rooms were lit only by skylights, or by narrow windows giving on corridors; and after wandering for nearly two hours, careful to preserve the air of an innocent and random explorer, I was no nearer finding any door or staircase to the postern. I came across several locked doors and stairways in plenty that led crazily from one level to another, but I found nothing that could be called a lower story—or a postern.

Quarter to five. I sat down wearily on a deep windowsill. It simply hadn't come off: Charles would have to climb in after all. At least I had met no one all afternoon, and in the heat the hounds, doubtless, slept too.

I heard the sound of a door opening on the far side of the corridor. The siesta was over; the place was waking up. I started back to my room.

Light steps on stone, and the gleam of scarlet silk. Halide paused in a doorway, languidly adjusting the gilded belt at her waist. This time her dress was scarlet over pale green, and her gilt sandals had high heels and curved Persian toes. The bird had on new plumage.

Mating plumage, at that. I heard Lethman's voice in the room, and a moment later he came to the door. He was wearing a long Arab robe of white silk, open to the waist. The girl said something, and laughed, and he pulled her to him and made some reply against her hair.

I edged away from the window, hoping they were too absorbed to look up. But almost immediately I froze at the sound of the bell from the Prince's Divan, and after it, inevitably, the clamor of the hounds.

Halide and Lethman raised their heads, but stayed where they

531

were. Halide let forth a stream of Arabic, punctuated by laughter. Now Lethman was laughing too, and the hounds fell quiet. Then he pushed the girl away from him with a gesture which obviously meant "You'd better go." Still laughing, she put a hand up to push the tumbled hair back from his brow, kissed him, and went, not hurrying.

I stared after her, wholeheartedly glad for the first time about Charles's fantastic proposal for tonight's break-in. I could hardly wait to tell him what I had seen.

For as Halide had lifted her hand to John Lethman's hair I had seen Great-Aunt Harriet's ruby ring. I had a sudden picture of the lamplit room last night: the old woman huddled on her bed; Halide with that wary look; and behind me John Lethman. . . .

He went back into the room and shut the door. I gave it three minutes, then made my way back to the Seraglio Court.

AT FIRST I thought that Charles's alternative plan—using a window—was also doomed. In the brief time left before darkness I explored the north arcade carefully. Looking as if I was interested only in the view, I wandered from window to window examining the heavy six-inch squares of the metal grilles. Here and there, it is true, a bar was broken or the grille had rusted; but there was no gap that would let in anything larger than a cat.

I reached the end window. This one wasn't barred, but it was boarded up with heavy shutters and, across them, a heavy plank held with four nails as big as rivets. I peered at the window anxiously and fingered the nails. To my joy they were not nails but big-headed screws. I might manage them. Surely there was something here that would do the job?

I remembered a nearby room like an abandoned junk shop, its dusty floor covered with a clutter of useless-looking objects. I picked my way into it over a camel saddle and an old sewing machine. On a chest of drawers was a dagger with an inlaid handle and a steel blade. I ran back with it to the window.

The lower screw I tackled first was rusty and had bitten deeply into the wood. I abandoned it and attacked the other. This came out eventually. I had to stand on tiptoe to deal with the other two screws, but I got one out and the other loosened. I didn't bother with the rusted screw; I could use it as a hinge. There was no point in opening the shutters yet, before John Lethman had been and gone.

I went back to my room and hid the dagger under the cushions of the window seat. Then Jassim arrived, carrying a lighted lamp, a tray, and a note from John Lethman to say that he had to dine with Aunt Harriet, but would come along at ten to make sure I had everything I wanted for the night. The note concluded: *I didn't tell her you'd come back. It didn't seem quite the time. I'm sure you'll understand.* I put the note in my handbag. I understood very well.

He came as he had promised, chatted for half an hour, and left shortly after ten thirty, taking my supper tray with him. Just after eleven I heard again the furious peal of Aunt Harriet's bell, and somewhere in the palace the sound of a slammed door. Thereafter, silence. I turned out my lamp, and, carrying a towel to use as a signal, went out into the garden.

The night was warm and scented, and there was a crescent moon. A couple of nightingales sang in a wild, angelic counterpoint. I nearly fell over a sleeping peahen, which went blundering off, disturbing a covey of rock partridges which exploded in their turn through the bushes. Frogs dived in the lake with a noise like the popping of champagne corks.

By the time I reached the shuttered window I was waiting, with every nerve jumping, for the hounds to add their warning to the rest. But they made no sign.

I tackled the window. The screw I had loosened answered easily to the dagger. I lowered the bar and pulled the shutters open.

Except for a few inches of iron, the grille on the window had gone completely. I hung over the sill and strained my eyes to see. The window was about thirty feet above the path, but here and there ferns and plants had thrust the mortar from between the stones of the walls, and the rock below, though sheer, looked rough enough to provide holds for a clever climber.

I hung the white towel over the windowsill and turned to hurry back along the arcade.

Something moved in the bushes near the end of the broken bridge. I stood still, my heart thumping. It forged through the crackling thicket, out onto the flags, and stood staring at me. One of the hounds. Almost immediately I heard a splashing sound, followed by the swift scrabble of paws on stone, and the other hound came racing round the edge of the lake and stopped beside him.

I stayed where I was, frozen. It didn't occur to me to be afraid of the big, alert dogs themselves; I assumed John Lethman to be behind them, and what frightened me was the thought of the window behind me, with the All Clear towel hanging in it for Charles.

But nothing moved; they must be patrolling on their own. Lethman must have left the main door open when he went, and like a fool I hadn't checked. Of course, if they did give tongue, Charles would hear them and be warned. Or if they attacked me, and I screamed for John Lethman . . .

The only thing to do was to stand perfectly still and stare back at them. Moonlight reflected brilliantly from their eyes. "Good dogs," I said falsely, putting out a reluctant hand.

There was a horrible pause. Then the bigger one gave a sudden little whine, and in dazed relief I realized that his plumed tail was stirring. The smaller hound seemed to take a cue from this. Her head went down and she crept towards me, wagging her tail.

Weak at the knees, I sat down on the edge of a stone flower tub and said breathlessly, "Oh, *good* dog!" What were their names? Softy? Sofi, that was it, and Star. "Star!" I said. "Sofi! Come here . . . That's right . . . Keep quiet, you idiots—you dangerous brutes. Oh, you horrible dog, you're wet. . . ."

We fussed damply over each other. Then I got to my feet and took their collars to put them out. "Come along now. Back on the job! We've got a burglar coming any minute now and I want you brutes out of here."

At that moment, below the north wall, I heard the sharp double bark of a hill fox. The Salukis' heads went up, and the bigger one stiffened. But Charles must have sounded to them a fairly unconvincing fox, for when I murmured soothingly, they allowed me to pull them towards the gate. I tried to hurry, but they hung heavily against their collars, making little whining noises. At length I got them to the gate—to find it firmly shut. The hounds must have found their way in through some hole in the walls.

Eventually I managed to get the gate undone and with a final pat pushed both hounds outside and dropped the latch into place. For a moment all was stillness, though I thought I saw movement in the far shadows. A moment later I heard Charles's soft footsteps. I had started to meet him when to my horror I heard the dogs begin to bark just outside the gate, the eager scrabbling of their paws on the wood as loud as a charge of galloping horses. They still sounded absurdly friendly—too friendly. Even the burglar from outside rated a noisy welcome. I could see him fairly clearly now, coming rapidly along the eastern arcade. I ran to meet him. "I'm sorry, the dogs got in somehow and now they're making a ghastly noise, and I don't know what to do with them!"

I stopped abruptly. The shadowy figure had come up to me.

"I'm fearfully sorry," he said. "Did they frighten you? That idiot Jassim left a door open and they got through."

The newcomer was John Lethman.

It was a good thing that the dark hid my expression. There was a long, ghastly pause, while I did a desperate mental recap of the way I had greeted him, and decided it hadn't given much away. Thanking Allah I hadn't called him Charles, I settled on attack as the best form of defense. "How in the world did you get in?"

He hesitated a moment. "There's a door in the far corner. Hadn't you found it in your wanderings?"

"No. Was it open?"

"Afraid so. It's not a door we use; it gives on a warren of empty rooms between here and the Prince's Court. Nothing there but rats. That's probably why the dogs went ramping through."

He was speaking softly, as I suppose one does instinctively on a quiet night. I wondered if the sounds I had heard before had in fact been Charles, or only John Lethman. If the latter, had Charles heard him too, and waited at the foot of the wall; or was he likely to erupt at any minute from the window? I raised my own voice to normal pitch. "Why in the world did you tell me the dogs were savage? They're actually terribly friendly."

He laughed, a bit too easily. "They can be sometimes. Your Aunt Harriet used to have a terrier, but he died just last month. You mightn't have got away with it if he'd been around." Again the abrupt laugh. "I really am terribly sorry about this. You weren't in bed, I take it?"

"No. I'd just put the lamp out, and I came out to look at the garden. Can you smell the jasmine? And don't the roses ever go to sleep?" I moved determinedly towards the gate as I spoke, and he came with me. "If it comes to that, don't you? Were you coming to see me, or trying to find the dogs?"

"Both. I was wondering whether you were counting on seeing your great-aunt again."

"No. I wasn't staying up for that, honestly; I quite understand about it. Good night, Mr. Lethman."

"Good night. And don't worry that you'll be disturbed again. I've locked the other door."

"I'll lock this one myself," I promised.

The gate closed behind him and strangled yelps of welcome from the dogs receded into the palace. At least I had an excuse for locking the Seraglio gate on the inside. The key turned with a satisfying *clunk*, and I fled back towards the open window.

It was my night for shocks. I'd got two-thirds of the way there when a soft "Christy" brought me up short, and my cousin's shadow detached itself from a dark doorway. I turned on him furiously, and quite unjustly. "You nit! You scared me silly! I thought—when did you get *in*?"

"Just before he did. That was Lethman?"

"Yes. He came from Aunt Harriet's rooms, through a door in the far corner."

"He did not. He came from the island," Charles said curtly. "I saw him. I heard some noises, so I took a quiet look over the sill before I climbed in. I saw you and the dogs making off down the path. I couldn't hang on much longer, so I heaved myself in through the window. Next thing, I saw him coming across the bridge from the island. I jackknifed down by a prickly pear, and after he'd gone by me I went into one of the rooms and hid."

"But if he was on the island all the time, he must have seen me open the window—and guessed why. Charles, I don't like it! *Why didn't he wait for you?* What has he gone to do?"

"Dear girl, don't get so steamed up. If he had seen you at the window he'd obviously have asked what you thought you were doing, and stopped you. So obviously he didn't."

"I suppose so. . . ." I added quickly, "Come to think about it, the dogs could have been on the island: Sofi was wet. Perhaps Lethman went across to get them . . . ? No, then he'd have seen me. But if he'd come by a door in the far corner, he'd have seen me, too. Oh, I give up. Charles, why should he lie?"

"I don't know. Is there really a door in the corner?"

"I didn't see one, but it's overgrown, and I didn't really search because it wasn't the right place for the postern."

"Supposing we look, then? But we'll do without my torch as long as we can. Can you see in the dark, love?"

"Just about, by this time. And incidentally, so can Lethman. You'd think he'd use a torch in this boneyard of a place."

We walked on. "Watch it," said my cousin, "there's a prickly pear on your near bumper." He dropped a casual arm round my shoulders to steer me. "And there's that door, I think." He turned on his torch. "Under that luxuriant herb, whatever it is."

"Jasmine, you ignorant peasant. But there certainly is a door."

There was; but neither dog nor man had been through it for a very long time. The hinges looked like spindles of wool, so thickly were they cocooned with cobwebs.

"And a web across it, too," said Charles. "This door hasn't been opened since the last time the old emir tottered along to the harem in 1875. So he didn't come *this* way, our John Lethman."

I said blankly, "But there *can't* be a way in from the island!"

"We can but look," said Charles reasonably. "Hullo!" The beam of the torch speared down at the foot of the wall to light a small slab set into the masonry, with a name deeply tooled: JAZID. The torchlight skidded along a couple of feet. Another stone: OMAR. Then ERNIE . . .

"A graveyard, no less," said Charles. "I remember Ernie. He was one of her King Charles spaniels." He was thinking hard, but not about what he was saying. The torchlight moved on. "Ah, here she is. DELILAH. Alas, poor Delilah. That's the lot."

"They can't have got round to Samson yet. John Lethman says he died last month. . . . What are you looking for?"

The torchlight drifted along a tangle of creepers and the ghostly pale faces of flowers. "Nothing," said Charles. He snapped the light out, and swung back an armful of stems to let me back through. "Curse these roses; my trousers must look like a yak's pelt by now. I suppose that's a nightingale singing its ducky little heart out up there?"

"What does it take to make you romantic?"

"I'll tell you someday. Can you manage this?" "This" was the bridge to the island. The broken gap wasn't as wide as I had thought; perhaps three feet. Charles jumped it first and caught me as I jumped after him. Soon, with a hand in his, I was on the rocky shore.

The island was very small: an artistically placed tumble of rocks, bushes and shrubs long gone wild, but designed to lead the eye up to a grove of shade trees which overhung the circular pavilion. Wide shallow steps led up from the shore, and creepers hung across an arched doorway. My cousin let go my hand, pulled some of the tangle aside, flashed his torch on and led the way in.

The interior was empty except for a small basin in the floor where there must once have been a fountain, and filthy, cushionless couches. The wall opposite the doorway was painted in the Persian style, with flowering trees, seated figures clad in blue and green robes, and a hunting leopard leaping after a gazelle.

The scene was in three panels; at one edge of the center panel, all down the side of a tree trunk, a dark line showed.

"Here we go," said Charles, approaching it.

"You mean it's a door?"

He made no reply. He played the light slowly over the picture, his hand patting the surface. Then he gave a grunt of satisfaction. From the middle of a painted orange tree, leaves seemed to detach themselves in his hand: the ringbolt of a door. He turned it and pulled. The panel opened on quiet, accustomed hinges, showing a gap of blackness behind.

My heart beat fast. "Where can it possibly go?"

He jerked a thumb downwards and I whispered, "An underground passage?"

"What else? These old palaces had as many secret exits as they had wormholes. Besides—this is the harem. The emir would have a private stairway. So this must be how Lethman got in—and the dogs. The door probably pushes open easily from the tunnel, but I don't trust it, and I don't want to be locked down there forever. I'll find something to wedge it open with." He picked up a stone.

"We're not going down?" I asked in alarm.

"Why not? There's a flight of steps here, in good repair; even reasonably clean." He took my hand and I stepped carefully over the sill after him.

The steps spiraled steeply down round a richly carved central column. On the curved outer wall there were more paintings. I could see a pale flower-dotted ground where a racing camel carried a mustachioed warrior waving a saber, and a lady unconcernedly playing a zither. A handrail was riveted to the wall by elaborate lizards or small dragons.

It was certainly a royal staircase, the Prince's own.

"Wait—" I hung back against Charles's hand. "Don't you realize—if this is the way from the Prince's rooms, that means Aunt Harriet's, and she'll be wide-awake, probably with Lethman reading aloud to her."

He stopped. "You've got a point. But this must go somewhere else as well. The dogs came this way, and I doubt if they're allowed to roam the old lady's bedroom at night. This might be a way to the postern."

"Of course! But if we met someone . . ."

"You're right," said Charles, "we'd better leave it for a bit." He followed me back up into the pavilion, shut the painted door and switched off the torch. "What time does she settle down?"

"I've no idea. But Lethman'll be around for a bit yet. Are you going to try and see her when he's gone?"

"Not tonight. It'd be enough to frighten an elderly person into fits. But on the basis of what's happened, I'm not clearing out without a good look round."

We were at the bridge. No shadow moved. He started softly across, and I followed. "I'm interested in the part of the palace they didn't let you loose in," Charles whispered. He jumped the gap and I followed, slipped on landing, and was caught and held. I hadn't realized how strong he was. We climbed down off the bridge and pushed our way through the rustling bushes.

He said, "Just in case we don't find the postern down there— I think I saw a rope in that room full of junk along here. It would make life easier on the downward trail."

We turned towards the room and Charles slanted a look at me. "Why didn't you go to the island before? It's dead romantic."

"I meant to, but when I saw the gap in the bridge . . ." I paused. "You mean that's what John Lethman counted on? And even if I had jumped over, I'd never have realized the painted wall was a doorway. But if it was so important that I shouldn't find the staircase, why put me in this court at all?"

"Because the Seraglio was designed as a sort of five-star jail. There are probably a million ways in and out of every other corner of the palace, so he had to put you in here and spin you the story about the savage dogs to keep you in. What's more," he added, not sounding worried about it all, "we'll almost certainly find there's another door at the foot of the spiral stairway, and it'll equally certainly be locked now."

I glanced at him. "And if it is?"

"Well . . ." said my cousin, and left it at that.

I asked sharply, "You mean you could pick the lock?"

"That's the first note of honest admiration I've heard from you since the time I blew the apple-loft door open. Why, lock picking is a required study at Mansels' bank."

"Naturally. But—" I paused. "Then you think there really *is* something wrong going on. . . ."

As I followed him along the arcade, I told him quickly about seeing Halide and Lethman and the ruby ring. He listened attentively but made no comment. As we reached the junk-room door, he said only, "Stay out here, love, and keep your ears open while I go in and look for a rope." And he vanished.

I looked after him thoughtfully. I knew every tone of Charles's voice. There was something he knew, or thought, that he didn't propose to share with me.

"Found it," he said, from inside the room. He emerged, wiping dirt off his hands. "And now a wash, and a wait. We'll give it an hour. I must get out of here by first light. . . . It's even possible the river may have gone down by then, and I can cut straight across it before anyone sees me."

"Where's your car this time?"

"Pretty well out of sight in a small quarry near the village. I'll tell Hamid to come up for you at half past nine tomorrow, and I'll wait for you in Beirut. Now show me your bathroom, Christy mine, and we'll listen to the nightingales while I get my picklocks sorted out."

VI

THE THIN MOON had drifted higher when we made our way back to the pavilion. Charles wedged the painted door open with the stone. Our torchlight speared ahead as we started down. The paintings slid past; domes and minarets, gazelles, Arabian stallions, fruit trees, singing birds . . . and at the bottom a door.

Shut, of course. But when Charles pulled cautiously, it opened with the same well-oiled silence as the one above. It had been secured by a padlock, but on one side the hasp had been pulled

543

away from the crumbling jamb, probably by the dogs earlier tonight, for splinters and sawdust showed on the floor. "Good for the Gabriel Hounds," I breathed.

Charles smiled, and beckoned. I soft-shoed after him into the darkness of a great arched passage at the end of a sort of underground T junction. Our door closed one end of the cross shaft of the T. A few yards from us on the left, an open archway led off into a black passageway down which came a draft of air. Straight ahead, and also closing the top bar of the T, was a bronze door in a carved archway. To either side of it were ornate iron brackets which must once have held torches, and beneath these we saw recesses in the wall, man-high, like sentry boxes.

"Must be the Prince's Door," I whispered. "See if it's locked."

But he shook his head and sent the light towards the passageway on the left. "Line of retreat first. This way to the postern, what do you bet?"

The tunnel was long and curved, with rough stone walls and, at intervals, rusty iron brackets for lights. The floor was worn, filthy, and treacherous with holes. The passage bent to the left, turned uphill, and met another passage at right angles. We paused here. Our passage was the main stem of another T junction. Charles put the torch out, and we stood for a moment listening. The air was fresher here, and it was an easy guess that this corridor was open to the upper air. From somewhere to the right I heard, faintly, the whine of the hounds.

Charles flashed the light that way momentarily, to show wide and very shallow steps mounting presumably to ground level. "That probably goes up to the midan gate, which means, unless I'm wrong—" He turned the beam to the left; it focused on a scattered trail of droppings, horse or mule. "I'm not wrong," said my cousin. "This way. You see? A ramp up from the plateau—a secret emergency door—and then the long passage leading under the Seraglio and up to the midan." A few minutes later we were at the postern gate. It was a heavy affair, locked and barred, but the key was in the lock. Charles opened it and we looked out through the grove of trees at the edge of the Adonis Gorge. A steep ramp, just wide enough for a laden beast, led down through the grove, and a buttress hid the ramp from the plateau.

"Well, this'll save me a climb." Charles closed the gate. "We'll leave it unlocked." He glanced at his watch. "After two. They can't stay up all night, surely?"

"If anyone's still awake, it'll be Aunt Harriet."

"Yes," said my cousin. "Well . . ." He was looking at the ground, fiddling with the flashlight. As it came on again, I caught a bleak expression. He glanced up suddenly. "Shall we go back to the Prince's Door?"

"That'll be locked, too, I expect."

"Possibly, though I doubt if they'd have the place sealed up internally, so to speak. Christy—if you'd rather go back to the Seraglio and leave this to me—"

"No. I'm not afraid of Lethman, even if you are."

He started to say something, apparently thought better of it, and grinned. We went on.

The Prince's Door wasn't locked. It opened silently, and beyond it was another long, vaulted corridor, pitch-black and very still. Charles hesitated a moment, then went forward. On either side, at intervals, were doorways, most of them gaps of darkness. Charles shone the light into the first of these, which seemed to contain nothing but large earthenware jars.

"Nothing there but the Forty Thieves," he commented. "And here's Aladdin's cave. Half a minute, let's look." The torchlight probed past dreary clutter to a pile of less dusty books on a rickety chest of drawers. Charles turned the thickest volume spine upwards. "I thought so. *Chambers's Dictionary*." He picked up a smaller book with tooled leather covers. He handled this gently, and when he blew the dust off I caught the gleam of gilding.

"What is it?"

"It's a Koran. Take a look."

The paper was expensive, and the beautiful Arabic script was enhanced by the ornate designs which headed the suras, or chapters. It was certainly not a book anyone would throw into a dusty room to be forgotten. Charles laid it down without comment, and the light strayed further over the debris. It halted suddenly at a battered violin and a tangle of leather bridles. Behind these I saw two half-hidden objects. China dogs.

I stared at them. "Charles! Not your Gabriel Hounds?"

"Indeed and indeed." He knelt down in the dust. "Hold the torch." He took one of the ornaments gently in his hands, and began to wipe the dust away with his handkerchief. "Well, who'd have thought it?" he said.

The creature was a dog or lion, about six inches high, in glowing yellow porcelain. It sat back on its haunches with one paw down and the other poised delicately on a fretted ball. The head was turned over one shoulder, ears back, wide mouth grinning. It had a kind of playful ferocity. Its mate on the floor had a plume-tailed pup under her paw instead of a ball.

"These are known as dogs of Fu, or Buddhist lions," Charles said. "Nobody seems sure exactly what kind of creatures they were, but Fu was the Buddha himself, and these are the only creatures in the Buddhist mythology that are allowed to kill, and then only in the Lord Buddha's defense. They're officially the guardians of his temple." He turned the glowing creature over in his hands. The wrinkled pansy face grinned over the pretty ball.

"But why have they been shoved out here? I'd have thought—"

"Yes," said Charles. He set the dog down on the floor, straightened up abruptly, took the torch out of my hand and led the way quickly back into the dark corridor. Ahead of us, the torch picked out another arched doorway. But this arch was blocked with a brand-new oak door, solid as a ship, and locked with a brass padlock. Treasure chambers? I wondered.

The light paused, then moved along the wall. Stacked there were a dozen or so cans, with bold black lettering on them: FINEST COOKING OIL. *Ideal for Frying, Mayonnaise, Salads.* And below this, a red design of a running dog. I said, "Charles, I've seen that running-dog design before."

"Where?"

I looked at him in surprise. He sounded sharply interested. I said, "Sunday afternoon, up at the village Hamid took me to. A sunflower field had a sign on a tree, a red dog that I thought looked like a Saluki." We stooped closer. Under the dog I could see: HUNTING DOG BRAND. BEST QUALITY. BEWARE IMMITATIONS.

"Sal'q," said my cousin. "The word Saluki is the Arabic *salūqīy* or *slughi*. It means 'hound.' I imagine Nahr el Sal'q is a corruption meaning 'Hound River.' Local produce, in other words."

I straightened up. "Sunflower oil, I suppose, and what I saw was a field marker for peasants who can't read. Heavens, this must be about ten years' supply! What on earth *do* they use it all for?"

He lifted one of the cans and put it down again. "Empty," he said shortly, and turned away. "Let's get on with it, and we'd better stop talking."

We rounded a curve in the corridor, going warily, and saw a wide stairway leading up to a landing. A door was standing open there, with a heavy curtain hanging across it, and at one edge a line of light. We stopped, listening. Even our breathing sounded loud to me. Then, shielding the torch with his fingers so that only a crack of light showed to dance like a glowworm, Charles mounted the stairs and inched his way to the curtain. He paused, with me at his elbow. The torch was out now, the only light the streak at the curtain's edge.

I could smell the curiously pungent scent of Great-Aunt Harriet's tobacco, so this must be the Prince's Divan. Charles drew the edge of the curtain back a couple of inches. He laid an eye to the crack, and I stooped to look.

This was the curtain at the back of Aunt Harriet's bed. The room was exactly as last night: the red lacquer chair, the unwashed dishes on the table, the dish on the floor with Dog, now half full with milk for the cat, and on the bed . . .

For one breathless moment I thought Aunt Harriet was within a yard of us, sitting where she had sat last night. Then I saw the room was empty. The dark bed held only a welter of blankets, her velvet coat and her fleecy shawl.

A moment later it hit me again, the cold wave of sickness as the cat lifted its head and eyed us from the tumbled bed. Charles saw it at the same moment. As I backed sharply away he let the curtain fall and his arms went round me. "It's not coming here. You're all right, love; relax."

I was shivering, and the arms tightened. The top of my head came just up to his cheekbone. "Give it a minute," he whispered, "then we'll go." He held me till the shivering quieted. It was very dark and still. I knew from the sound of his breathing that he had turned his head, and was watching and listening. I felt him draw a breath to speak. Then abruptly his cheek came down against my hair. "Christy—"

"Yes?"

A tiny pause. The breath went out like a light sigh, stirring my hair. "Nothing. All right now?" I nodded. "Come along then. We'll go back.

"I'm so sorry, Charles."

"So you should be." His whisper mocked me gently. "Brace up, love. Charles'll fight the nasty cat for you."

The terror receded. I laughed. "I'm fine now, thank you."

"Then back to your harem, girl."

THE AIR on the island was wonderfully fresh and sweet. We crossed the bridge to the gap, and I jumped it after him. He didn't let me go straightaway. "Christy . . ." He spoke softly, quickly. "I've been making a few guesses and I *know* there is one thing very wrong here. I'm not going to tell you about it yet—for the simple reason that you've got to stay in this place until morning. Now, listen, Christy—you've got to meet John Lethman tomorrow and be civil and normal to him."

"Civil and normal? Then there *is* something wrong involving him and the less I know the better? Is he Aunt Harriet's lover or something?"

"Heavens," said Charles, "if that were all . . ."

"Come on, you've got to tell me!" But, of course, he wouldn't. He let me go and prepared to jump back across the gap.

I said, "Why don't you just shin down from the window with the rope?"

"It's easier this way. Close the shutters, but don't put the bar

548

back yet, just in case. I'll see you at the hotel in the morning." He seemed to hesitate. "You're not scared, are you?"

"Scared? Why on earth should I be scared?"

"Well, as long as you're not," said Charles, and left me.

VII

I WENT to bed and was out like a light for the five hours or so until my breakfast came. It was a glorious morning, but I woke to a faint shadow of apprehension coloring the day ahead. The sun-lit Seraglio Court, the whole palace locked in its hot valley, afflicted me with a sort of claustrophobia, and I swallowed my coffee quickly, eager to get back to the color and bustle of Beirut. And to Charles.

It was barely half past eight, but Nasirulla had already appeared with my breakfast, so the river must be passable this morning. I decided to go down immediately and meet Hamid in the village. I let myself out of the Seraglio. Nasirulla must have told John Lethman I was leaving early, for he came to meet me in the second courtyard, where the anemones of the Adonis Gardens had already withered and died. I thought he looked the worse for wear this morning, and wondered if the same could be said of me.

"You're up early," he said. "Did you sleep all right after the alarms and excursions?"

"After the—? Oh, the dogs. Yes, thanks. It's just another romantic episode to think about later."

"It may have been a mistake to shut them up last night."

I didn't want to ask, but it was certainly the natural question. "Why?"

"We found the back gate open. Anyone could have got in."

"The back gate?"

"There's a gate opening out on the plateau at the back. What with that, and letting the hounds into the Seraglio, Jassim seems to have had himself a ball yesterday."

I said, as casually as I could, "You found signs of a break-in?"

"Oh, no. But universal trust isn't a habit of mine, particularly in this country. What time is your driver coming?"

"Nine," I said, lying, "but I think I'll start over and meet him in the village. You've been good to put up with me for so long."

"It's been a pleasure." He didn't even try to sound, today, as if he meant it. He seemed harassed and edgy. "I'll see you out," he said, and hurried me on with quick, nervous strides, a hand going to his face in that gesture I had noticed the first day, as if the skin was tender.

"Did Aunt Harriet say anything more about my cousin?"

"Not a word." Short, sharp, and to the point. He walked out of the main gate with me and right to the edge of the plateau, and stood there to watch me start down the path. When I reached the ford I looked back, and saw him still there, watching as if to make sure I really went.

The stepping-stones were clear now, but the high water still ran blood red for the dead Adonis. As I gained the far side of the stream I saw Hamid—this time unmistakably Hamid—coming down the path towards me. We met in the shade of a fig tree where three goats were sleeping in a dusty heap. I asked him if he had seen Charles or the white Porsche that morning.

He smiled. "He is very like you, that one. No, I saw nothing on the road this morning except a black car with an Arab driver, and a Land Rover with three Maronite fathers. You mean your cousin has also been for the night at the palace?"

I nodded. "This means he probably got away before he was seen. Hamid, don't tell anyone about this, promise." And I gave him the main facts about Charles's break-in. "We explored a bit," I ended, "and then he let himself out by the postern. I hope he got his car away before anyone saw it."

"I don't think you need worry. I know the quarry he mentioned and I'd have noticed if the car was there when I went by."

We had been climbing as we talked. Now I saw what I had been looking for: a patch of shadow under a tree where goats stood or lay, chewing and eyeing us with supercilious boredom. Among them the faun, grinning, squatted cross-legged in the dust and chewed a leaf with the same kind of disenchanted thoroughness as the goats. "There you are!" I said.

"I am always here," he said simply.

Hamid regarded the boy doubtfully. "If he saw your cousin, the whole village will know where he spent the night."

"I don't think so. In any case, if Nasirulla had known, you can bet Mr. Lethman would have had something to say this morning." I called out, "Ahmad, did you see the Englishman leave Dar Ibrahim this morning?"

"Yes. Just after daylight."

"He must have stayed on for a bit, then. I wonder why. He went up to the village?"

"Yes. He came from the gate at the back of the palace and got in the car which was in the quarry."

There was no curiosity in his voice, but he was watching me intently.

"Did he speak to you?" I said, relieved.

"No. I was over there." A jerk of the head seemed to indicate some inaccessible rocks a quarter of a mile away.

I regarded him thoughtfully. "And no one else saw him?"

"No one, only me." A brief flash of the white teeth, clenched on the green leaf. "And I have forgotten."

I fished some notes out of my bag and laid them on the rock beside me. "Thank you very much. May Allah be with you."

Before I had got more than two steps away there was a flash of brown limbs and the notes had disappeared into the dirty kaftan. Dignity, it seemed, took second place to common sense. "The goats would eat them," Ahmad explained. Then, in a rush of Arabic which Hamid laughingly translated for me as we moved on: "And the blessing of Allah be upon you and your children and your children's children and your children's children's children and . . ."

IT WAS heaven to be back in my modern, characterless, comfortable room at the Phoenicia, to throw off my horrible clothes and climb into a bath. I broiled myself happily before dressing carefully in the coolest frock I had, then rang for coffee. When the boy brought it, he also delivered a letter from Charles. It was ordinary, unexciting—and infuriating.

Dear Coz,

I'm fearfully sorry about this. Was nearly caught just after I left you. Aunt H, a weirdie now, as you say, but active enough, came down the underground corridor with Halide just as I was letting myself out. I was tempted to pop out and have a word, but it might have scared the daylights out of them, so I stayed where I was till they went in the Prince's Door, then let myself out. Picked up the car and got down here without seeing a soul. Rang Aleppo to see if I could catch Ben's father. Was told he'd left for Homs and is due home today.

Something I heard Aunt Harriet say to Halide explained quite a bit to me. But there's still a problem, and the only person I can take it to usefully is Ben's father. He'll be leaving home again almost straightaway, so I've gone down to Damascus to catch him. I'll be back as soon as I can; tomorrow or Thursday morning. Wait for me till then, and don't, *please* don't, do *anything* else except extend your hotel booking. When I get back, I think I'll get to see Aunt H after all.

Love and one kiss,

C.

I read the letter twice, and decided that Charles was lucky he was halfway to Damascus. I reached for the phone. I was, of course, completely independent, and didn't need help or advice, and I didn't even particularly like Aunt Harriet. . . . But it would be nice to tell Daddy all about it. I put a call through to Christopher Mansel at Mansels of London.

Daddy's advice, when I read him the letter, was short and to the point. "Wait for Charles."

"But Daddy—he might have waited for me! It's so exactly like him to play it the selfish way."

"Certainly," said my father. "But if he was anxious to catch Ben's father he couldn't afford to wait for you, could he? I'd leave matters to Charles. He knows what he's about, and he's certainly clear on one point."

"Meaning?"

"Meaning don't do anything fatheaded just because Charles has annoyed you," said my parent frankly. "And don't dream of going up to the palace again without him."

"Daddy, I can look after myself *perfectly* well."

"Then try not to be more of an idiot than Nature made you," said my father crisply. "Now go and enjoy yourself, my child, and wait for your cousin. He's got a lot of sense."

"You always said he was spoiled rotten and lived for nothing but pleasure."

"If that doesn't show sense I don't know what does."

"And don't I?"

"Lord, no, you take after your mother," said my father.

"Well, thank goodness for that," I said acidly. He laughed and rang off, leaving me, for some absurd reason, relieved and immensely cheered.

I was annoyed that I had been left alone to see Beirut, but there was nothing else to do with the afternoon, so, after lunch, I went out. I soon found that the Beirut souks are dirty and crowded and about as dramatic as Woolworth's. The Souk of the Goldsmiths was best, and I almost decided to start a bank account like Halide's—so lovely and so cheap were the thin gold bracelets tinkling and glittering in their hundreds along rods that spanned the windows. But I resisted them, and emerged with nothing to show for the afternoon but a gold-mounted turquoise bead, bought as a charm for Charles's Porsche before I remembered that I was furious with him and the sooner the Evil Eye got him the better. . . .

Perhaps he had phoned? I taxied back to the hotel. The first person I saw there was Hamid, leaning gracefully against the counter talking to the desk clerk. Hamid smiled at me and said something to the clerk. Before I had crossed to the desk the clerk had checked my pigeonhole and was shaking his head. My face must have given me away, for Hamid asked quickly, "Were you expecting a message?"

"From my cousin. He's coming back to Beirut Wednesday or Thursday, but meantime he's had to go to Damascus and I thought he might have phoned."

"Miss Mansel," the clerk interrupted, "there was a call from Damascus about an hour ago. I understood it was for *Mr.* Mansel, but it might have been *Miss* Mansel. They didn't leave a number, but if they call again, I'll have you paged. I'll tell the switchboard right away." He picked up the phone and began to talk into it in Arabic. He turned back to me. "Here is some luck. The call just came again. It *is* for Mr. Mansel, but the caller will speak to you. You may take the call in the booth over there."

The booth was an open stall. Just beside it, two women were discussing the ruins of Byblos, another group of Americans was talking about Lebanese food, and in the booth next to mine a sad-faced Arab was apparently failing, in sullen Arabic, to get the connection he wanted. I put a hand over my free ear.

It was Ben, and in the general hubbub it was some time before we could sort ourselves out. "Charles? Here? Not yet."

"He hasn't telephoned? He wanted to talk to your father about something fairly urgent."

"That's what I was calling *him* about. My father's due home tomorrow from Homs. I promised I'd let Charles know."

I said, puzzled, "But Charles seemed to think your father was due home today. I'm sorry to bother you, but could you ask him to call when he does arrive?"

"Look, I've been longing to meet you. Why don't you come down and join Charles here? It would be lovely to have you. I'll show you Damascus, and if Charles doesn't turn up, so much the better."

"It sounds very tempting." I hesitated. "You know, I think I'd like to, very much."

"That's settled then! I'll see you tomorrow." And he gave me his address and spelled the name SIFARA, and I read it all back. "Come anytime," he ended.

The line went dead, and the Arab in the next booth, clinging to his receiver, regarded me with sour envy as I emerged from my booth.

Hamid was still at the desk. I said, "Could you take me to Damascus tomorrow, please, at ten a.m.? I'm going to see friends of my cousin's named Sifara; here's the address. I won't come back the same day, but I'll pay you for the return trip."

"Don't trouble; I'll arrange in Damascus to bring back a one-way fare to Beirut. But if the cousin rings?"

"Let him ring," I said. "We still go to Damascus."

But there was no call from Charles that night.

VIII

AND NO call in the morning.

At ten the big car slid to the door and I slipped into the seat beside Hamid. He gave me a cheerful greeting and swung the car through the narrow streets and onto the long curve of the Route de Damas—the Damascus Road, which climbs through the summer gardens of the rich to the foothills of the Lebanon. Then the road divides, north for Baalbek, and southeast for the pass by Mount Hermon where the frontier lies.

I had crossed this frontier before, on the way to Beirut, so I was prepared for the four tedious halts and the frenzy of sus-picion that the frontiers of the Arab countries demand. We were fourth in line at the Lebanese side, but two hundred yards away, across no-man's-land, I could see quite a queue of northbound vehicles, including a bus, waiting in the hot dust in Syria.

Hamid took the car's papers and my passport, and vanished into the concrete hutments of the frontier post. Time crawled and it was hot in the car. I got out and sat on a boulder above the road. The hotel had provided a picnic, and I sat munching a sandwich till I met the eyes of a thin dog, eyeing me wistfully from the road. I held out the remains of the sandwich. He looked at it with his soul in his eyes, but stayed out of stick distance. I started to throw it down to him, but at the movement of my hand he flinched violently away. I went down to the road, and placed it carefully in the dust, then retreated to the car. The dog inched forward and took the food. The faintest movement of his tail thanked me, and I suspected it was the first time he had wagged it for years. I put another sandwich in the dust and he snatched it, more confidently this time. Then he turned and fled as Hamid approached the car, shaking his head.

"They say we cannot pass. You have no entry visa for the Lebanon; in fact, no exit from Syria. You're not officially in this country at all, so he can't give you an exit. You came through here with a group, and they do not always stamp the individual passports. You did not ask them for a stamp, no?"

"I never thought of it. But my name is on the list."

The bus arrived from the other side, churning up dust. I went on angrily, "The smaller the country the more silly fuss it makes today. . . . I'm sorry, Hamid, I didn't mean to be rude. It's just so *infuriating*. I'm sorry."

"You're welcome," said Hamid, meaning it generously. He looked troubled. "But the cousin will come back tomorrow, no?"

"I wasn't even thinking about the cousin," I snapped.

But I was, of course, and Hamid had known it before I did. He said gently, "I know these frontiers are annoying to foreigners, but we have big problems here; among other things, drug smuggling."

"I'd forgotten that this road is called 'the hashish run.' "

"I'm afraid it isn't only hashish. Opium is still grown in Turkey and Iran and smuggled through to the sea. The controls are getting tighter now, so things are a little fierce at the frontiers. Recently, two English tourists were arrested. They're still in prison in Beirut. In Turkey and Egypt, the penalty for smuggling drugs is death."

"But you said nobody thought it very wrong to smoke hashish."

"This is not a moral problem to the governments but an economic one," said Hamid. "The addict is pretty useless as a worker, you know." He smiled. "So you see why things are difficult—and for the customs men, too. Do you see the bus?"

It was immobilized at the Lebanese barrier. The passengers were standing about with the air of people prepared to wait all day, and one could see why, for on top of the bus were what looked like the household goods of every person on board: bundles of clothing, filthy bags once labeled AIR FRANCE or B.O.A.C., and a wicker cage full of unhappy-looking hens.

"They have to search all that," explained Hamid, "because there are hundreds of ways in which the hashish can be disguised. Last week, a cobbler was stopped with a large suitcase full of leather soles. They were made of hashish, powdered and then stamped into this shape. Sometimes the drug looks like gum, or jam, or sheep droppings."

"Well," I said, "anyone caught carrying a suitcase full of sheep droppings through a frontier ought to be locked up anyway."

"That is very true," said Hamid gravely. "And now, if you like, we can try to explain about the list on the group passport."

We went into the hut. It was small, stiflingly hot, and full of stout, olive-colored men all talking at once. The head official nodded understandingly; he even commiserated with me; but no entry stamp: a rule was a rule. We gave up at last, fought our way back out of the shed, and walked over to the car. I wondered crossly what to do. I should go back, of course; this was disappointing, even infuriating, but it really didn't matter.

But by the pricking of my thumbs, it did.

I met Hamid's eye. I said abruptly, "I know I'll see him tomorrow, but I want to see him today, *now*. Don't ask me why; I can't tell you in any way that makes sense, but . . ."

He said quickly, "You think he is in trouble?"

"Oh, no. How could he be? I told you I can't explain. And Hamid—I've just thought—what's going to happen when I leave here for London? Shouldn't I get a visa at once anyway?"

"I think you're right. I'll ask the official here what you should do. Who knows, you might even be able to come back and get through to Damascus by nightfall."

I smiled. "Thanks a million, Hamid. You're very good!"

"For a smile like that," said Hamid, "I would be very bad. The cousin is lucky." He disappeared into the building, where I could see a shoving, vociferous crowd round the counter.

Hamid might be some time, so I climbed the bank again above the road, going higher this time but still keeping the car in sight. Sparse grass moved in the breeze here, with gray whorls of thistles, drifts of some small white flower, blazing golden broom, and everywhere, thrusting up boldly, the simple familiar hollyhock, crowding wild among the Lebanese rocks.

From this height I could see farther beyond the Syrian frontier; and as I looked, I suddenly stiffened and stared at a point where a dusty track met the main road. Just off the road, by a bridge, was a small thicket of trees, and under those trees was a parked car. A familiar car. Charles's Porsche. The screen of leaves prevented me from seeing if he was in the car, but I was almost sure I caught a glimpse of movement.

I made a hasty way down to the road, arriving with a thump in the dust just as Hamid came back. He started without preliminary. "Must go to the Chef de Sûreté, on the Rue Badaro in Beirut, so— Is something the matter?"

Exitement had made me breathless.

"I've just seen my cousin's car, from up above there! It's parked about a quarter of a mile past the Syrian frontier, in some trees by a humpbacked bridge. It's a white Porsche, and they can't be common. Do you suppose Ben's told him I'm coming, and he came to wait for me?"

"Perhaps."

"Or maybe when he found out that Mr. Sifara was in Homs, he went up there instead of to Damascus. If he called the hotel this morning and heard I had gone, he might have decided to drive down this way, save time by getting himself through the border, and then settle down to wait for us. But I can't get through to tell him our problems!"

"No," said Hamid, "but I can." He smiled reassuringly. "You wouldn't mind being left here?"

"Of course not—and I'd be terribly grateful. Hurry, in case he goes! I'll take the rest of my lunch up the hill and wait."

"And your handbag—and the jacket in case you need it—" He was already fishing for them in the car. "If there is a crowd at the frontier, it may be a long wait." He got into the car, started the engine and was off. I panted back to my perch above the road. The Porsche was still there.

I peered down at the Lebanese barrier immediately below me. It was already lifting, no doubt to Hamid's bribe, and the big car sailed, windows flashing, through the stretch of no-man's-land. It checked at the Syrian barrier, and I saw Hamid hurry to the buildings to show his papers.

I looked the other way just in time to see the Porsche break out of the trees in a swirl of dust and shoot off down the road towards Damascus.

I felt as if I had been dropped, dazed, into the dust of its wake. I pulled myself together, and looked to see how far Hamid had got. His car was already through the barriers and gathering speed down the road. He hadn't missed the Porsche by more than a few minutes. I saw the dust mushroom up as he braked, got out and looked in the trees where Charles's car had been. He turned, hand to eyes, to stare down the valley, then whipped back into the car, slammed the door and was out of sight down the twisting road.

It was a safe guess that he had glimpsed the Porsche on the road ahead. And it was anybody's guess how long it would take for him to catch it.

I sat down and finished as much lunch as I wanted. Before I started on a peach, I glanced at my watch. Half past one, and the road still empty either of Hamid or the returning Charles.

At two o'clock it was still empty. At half past two I got to my feet and began to pick up my things. Either Hamid was still determinedly pursuing the Porsche, or there had been some sort of mishap. And if I waited much longer, there would be no possibility of getting to Beirut in time to visit the Sûreté office.

I walked downhill to the road. The thin dog was lying in the shadow of a parked car. He watched me with recognition, but without hope. I dropped the last of the sandwiches for him as I passed. He snatched it and bolted out of the way. Passengers from the bus were still standing about in the heat, apathetically, as customs men examined their household goods.

I went into the frontier post, to be met by an unwelcoming stare from behind the counter. It took a few minutes to find someone in the crowd with sufficient English to pass on what I wanted to ask, but I managed.

"What time does this bus get to Baalbek?" I asked.

"Half past three."

I thought for a moment. Baalbek was well off the direct road, but there would be a good chance of getting a car there, and then the shorter mountain route would get me to Beirut before the Sûreté closed. "Where do I find a taxi in Baalbek?"

"At the temples, or in the main street. Or ask at the Adonis Hotel, where the bus stops."

I remembered the Adonis. The group had gone there for lunch, and the manager, I remembered, spoke reasonably good English.

I said, "If anyone asks about me, tell them I'm going to the Sûreté office in Beirut, and then back to my hotel." I said a thank you all round, and went out.

The bus's engine was roaring, and black smoke poured from the exhaust as I got in. Seconds later, with a shaking roar and a smell of soot, we headed for Baalbek.

It was a horrible journey, but it ended perforce where the bus finished its run, in a dirty hot street within shouting distance of the ruined temples and just in front of the Adonis Hotel. I got out, shaking the creases from my skirt with a strong feeling that I was dislodging fleas in clouds. The bus went off to turn and the other passengers dispersed. The street was empty except for a sleek black limousine parked at the curb, and just beyond it, incongruously, a white camel with a ragged Arab holding the headrope.

The Arab bore down on me now to offer me a ride on his camel for the paltry sum of five English pounds. I beat him off, parried a second offer, to pose for a snapshot for only ten shillings, and ran up the steps into the hotel.

I found the manager drinking beer with a companion under the pines in the little restaurant garden. He was a small, round-faced Arab with a thin line of mustache. His companion looked English. The manager rose and came hurrying to meet me. "Mademoiselle— You are back again? But I thought your party had left the Lebanon?"

"You recognize me?" I exclaimed. "What a memory!"

"How could I forget you, mademoiselle?" A bow, a gallant look. Then he added, frankly, "I have only been here since the beginning of this season. So far, I remember all my guests. Please—will you join us?"

"No, thank you very much. I came for help, monsieur."

"Anything. Of course."

He obviously meant it. But to my dismay, as soon as I explained my difficulty and mentioned a taxi, he made a grimace of doubt.

"I will do all I can, naturally; but at this time of day most of the cars are already hired. It is possible there is one at the temples. I could send someone to—"

"Forgive me." The other man set down his glass and rose. "I couldn't help overhearing. I am going to Beirut, and would be delighted to offer you a lift."

"Why, thank you—" I was slightly taken aback, but the manager intervened quickly, sounding relieved and pleased.

"Of course; an excellent idea! May I introduce Mr. Lovell, Mademoiselle—? I'm afraid I don't know your name."

"Mansel. How do you do, Mr. Lovell."

"How do you do." Mr. Lovell's voice was English and cultured. He was a man of middle height, somewhere in his forties, with a face made Arab-olive by the sun, and dark hair receding from a high forehead. He was well dressed and wore heavy-rimmed dark glasses. Something about him was faintly familiar, and I thought I must have met him somewhere.

Even as the thought crossed my mind he said, smiling, "As a matter of fact we've met before, though without an introduction. It was in Damascus, last week, in the Great Mosque. You were

561

with a group, weren't you? I'd been talking to your guide while you ladies were admiring the carpets, and then he had to intervene in some minor international incident, and we exchanged a word or two while it was going on. You wouldn't remember, why should you? But tell me—did the stout lady allow herself to be parted from her shoes as the custom requires?"

I laughed. "Oh, *that* 'international incident!' Yes, and even admitted she wouldn't have wanted that crowd walking on *her* carpets in outdoor shoes. You know, I had a feeling I'd met you. Are you really going to Beirut?"

"I was just leaving for an engagement there." He indicated the limousine parked below the garden wall. An impassive Arab was now at the wheel.

"I'd love to come with you," I said.

The manager came with us to the car, the driver whipped round to open the rear door, and Mr. Lovell handed me in and settled beside me. We said good-by to the manager, and the car moved off.

We threaded the narrow streets quickly, then gathered speed along the road to Beirut. In a few minutes a great sweep of hill and valley stretched brilliant in the afternoon sun.

"Where are you going in Beirut?" Mr. Lovell asked.

"To the Sûreté in the Rue Badaro. I don't know where it is, but perhaps you do?"

"Of course. It's practically on the way. I'll drop you."

"Thank you very much," I said. I explained briefly about my visa, and cast a worried glance at my watch. "Have you any idea what the hours are?"

He didn't answer, but glanced at his own wrist, then leaned forward and said something in Arabic to the driver. The car surged forward smoothly at an increased pace. Mr. Lovell smiled at me. "You should be all right. In any case, I might be able to help you."

"You mean you know someone there?"

"You might say so. I doubt if there will be any difficulty, but if you like, I'll come in with you and see you through it."

"Oh—would you really? It's terribly good of you!" I found myself stammering in a sort of confusion of relief.

"Think nothing of it," he said calmly. "A cigarette?"

"Thank you. Oh, are they Turkish?"

"No, latakia—it's the best Syrian tobacco. Try it."

I took one, and he lit it for me, then lit one for himself, and leaned back beside me. His lighter, cigarette case and cuff links were of heavy gold. A man of substance, and certainly of self-assurance. Someone of importance? He had that air. I stopped worrying about the visa.

We sat for a while smoking in silence, while the big car took the High Lebanon pass in its stride and began to nose downhill towards Beirut. I was content to sit back and stop thinking. This was a gap in time before the next effort, and the next effort would be eased for me by the pleasant and competent Mr. Lovell.

It was only then, as I found my tension melting, that I realized how senselessly keyed up I had been over Charles—over things which could have been no more than my own imagination. As the car sailed on, and the sun beat warm through the window, and the breeze feathered the smoke from my cigarette away in veils of blue nylon, I was content to lift a lazy hand to wave it away from my eyes. I felt tranquil, without thought.

My companion, seemingly as relaxed as I, was gazing out of his side of the car where the land rose through terraced fields of gold and green and dark-gold to more stony heights, and gray seams of snow. The poplars along the road's edge winked past like telegraph posts, bare and lacy against the far snow and the hot blue sky.

"How romantic!" Mr. Lovell whipped off his dark glasses, and shaded his eyes to stare down the mountainside.

"What is it?" I asked.

"Something straight from 'The Arabian Nights.' Rather a pretty sight. An Arab on a bright chestnut horse with a pair of Salukis. Beautiful things."

It must be pure coincidence, of course. We must be miles on the wrong side of Beirut, with Dar Ibrahim a long way away.

"Where?" I leaned across him to see down the hill. He sat back, indicating a point below us and some way off. "I can't see anything," I said.

"There—just going into the trees."

I strained to see and as I leaned close across him his left arm came quietly round me and held me fast.

For a moment I thought he was supporting me against the swing of the car on a bend. But, as I tried to pull away, the arm held me like iron against him.

"If you keep still you won't be hurt." The voice, whispering now, was recognizable and the eyes, uncovered, stared into mine. The long nose, the olive face that would look pale in lamplight . . .

But if it was mad to suppose John Lethman was riding out here, forty miles from Dar Ibrahim, it was still madder to suppose that my Great-Aunt Harriet, disguised as a man, was holding me with this ferocious strength with one hand, while the other came up holding something that gleamed. . . .

I screamed, but the Arab driver drove smoothly on without even turning his head. "What are you doing? Who are you?" I gasped.

I twisted in his grip, fought as hard as I could, as the car rocked, swinging wide on the next bend. But the dizzy swoop of the car, the flicking shadows as the poplars whipped by, the unheeding silence of the driver, all combined in some curious but merciful way to insulate me from the nightmare of what could not—could not possibly—be happening.

He was grinning. From a few inches away, his teeth looked like something in a horror film. Great-Aunt Harriet's dark eyes blinked and glittered as he fought to hold me.

"Who are you?"

It was a last gasp on the edge of hysteria, and I saw him recognize the fact. His voice was smooth. "I told you we'd met before, but we weren't introduced properly. Henry Lovell Grafton, if you want it in full. . . . Mean anything to you? Yes, I thought it might. Now hold still, or I'll hurt you."

His right hand flashed down at my bare arm. Something pricked, was withdrawn. He dropped the hypodermic into his pocket, still holding me tightly. "Pentothal," he said. "You have ten seconds, Miss Mansel."

I was to find that Dr. Henry Grafton had a habit of overestimating. It took about seven seconds to put me under.

IX

WHEN I WOKE, I opened blurred eyes on a dark wall where shadows moved like rags in a draft. A warm, heavy, airless quiet conveyed to me the sense of being shut in. A small moth, fluttering, pattered into my semiconscious mind. It worried me. I must move and let the poor creature out, and let in the air.

But not yet. My body felt heavy, my head was aching, and I was cold. I was lying on blankets, so I scruffled a couple of them over myself, and turned on my face, cold hands against throbbing forehead. I felt that a dark and terrifying idea loomed and gibbered just out of reach; but I checked my groping mind and shut my eyes. . . .

My second return to consciousness was final, sharp, and altogether frightening. I was suddenly wide-awake, and now knew I was back at Dar Ibrahim. The smell told me first—dead air, dust, lamp oil, and the indefinable sharp smell of Great-Aunt Harriet's tobacco. I looked around. I was in a windowless room lit only by a faint light from a small barred opening above a massive door. I must be in one of the locked storerooms under the Seraglio lake, in the underground passage where Charles and I had gone exploring.

That was the gibbering thought I had been refusing to face. The Prince's Divan. Aunt Harriet. Henry Grafton . . .

I could think of only one reason for Henry Grafton's grotesque masquerade, for the abandonment of the Chinese dogs and the beloved books, for the glimpse I had had of the ruby ring on Halide's hand. My skin crawled cold.

Aunt Harriet was dead—and for some reason the death had to

be concealed. And Charles, who had apparently suspected the truth—Charles was miles away. Even if Hamid caught up with him, it would be some time before they would find my trail. No one would miss me at the Phoenicia; and Ben had said, "Come when you can. . . ." Christy Mansel, sunk without trace, like Aunt Harriet and the little dog, Samson.

I slapped my drugged nerves down hard, sat up and looked about me. A low, cobwebbed ceiling, a stretch of stone wall where harnesses hung from rusty hooks; stacked shapes of crates, boxes, cans . . . The tiny, flickering, mothlike sound I had heard came again from outside: the fluttering of a wick in an oil lamp.

I had been right about where I was. I held myself still, listening. I was stiff and sore. The headache was gone, but it was followed by an awareness, worse and more painful—a feeling of nerve-end vulnerability, like a snail that has been torn from its shell and wants nothing better than to creep back inside. . . .

The silence was suffocating, complete. You would think I had been buried alive.

The cliché struck home like a poisoned dart. With it came a vision of the tons of rock and earth and water above me. The weight must be terrific. If there was the slightest movement of the earth above me . . . Then with cold prickling over my skin, I heard it through the silence, the tick of settling earth.

I was on my feet, rigid and sweating, before I became aware that the ticking was merely my watch. I stretched up on tiptoe near the door, holding my wrist high towards the light from the ventilator. The little watch face was like a friend. It brought sanity—and the knowledge that it was just short of six o'clock. It had been four in the afternoon when I had accepted the lift from Henry Grafton, so I had been unconscious for more than twelve hours. . . .

A sound came now: a key in the lock. By the time the door opened I was sitting on the bed, trying to conceal, with straight back and poker face, that I didn't trust my legs to let me stand My lips were dry and my heart thumping.

It was John Lethman, carrying a lamp, and behind him Halide

as ever with a tray. He put the lamp up in a wall niche, and the girl came past him to set the tray down on a packing case. Her big kohl-rimmed eyes slid sideways to look at me, and I saw pleasure there. I ignored her, and said abruptly to Lethman, "Great-Aunt Harriet was murdered, wasn't she?"

I saw the silk of Halide's dress shimmer as she started, and Lethman turned quickly to look down at me. His back was to the lamp, and I couldn't see him clearly, but his voice was edged with nerves. "She died of natural causes," he said stiffly. "Dr. Grafton was her doctor. He'll explain."

"You're so right he will," I said.

He had been moving towards the door, but my tone brought him round again to face me, with a startled reappraisement. The light was on him now and I saw alarm on his face. He opened his mouth to say something, then shut it again. There was pouched flesh under the eyes, and lines I had not noticed before. And what had certainly not been there before was the swollen bruise at the corner of his mouth and a nasty-looking weal from cheek-bone to ear.

Halide said venomously, "Don't let her talk to you like that. You are the master here."

I laughed. "If so, who's been knocking you about? You think I'm the one who's in trouble? Well, you'll learn. And I assure you it'll pay you to listen to me and get me out of here. At once."

He drew a sharp breath. "You'll stay here. Dr. Grafton will see you later."

"He'll see me now. *After* I've washed. And what's more, I'd like my handbag back."

"It's there, by the bed. Now stop being stupid. There's some food. If you behave yourself you'll come to no harm."

"I don't want food!" I said angrily. "I want to wash up!"

He started out, Halide sliding past him with a final gleam at me that made me want to slap her face.

I stood up and said sharply, "Don't be a clot, Mr. Lethman. I want the lavatory. The w.c. Do I have to spell it out?"

I saw with pleasure that he looked disconcerted. "Well, come along then, but don't try anything. It won't do you any good."

"... Because the dogs would tear me limb from limb?" I laughed with a derision that got him right between the eyes, and sent my own morale rocketing. I went out with him, my exit somewhat spoiled by the fact that I stumbled over a broken flagstone, for my head swam dizzily with the aftermath of the drug. We went up the stairs to Aunt Harriet's room, and as we reached the heavy curtain and he drew it aside, I gave an exclamation of surprise. It was not morning, as I had expected, but golden afternoon: six o'clock of a blazing day. The pentothal must have laid me out for barely two hours.

Lethman stepped carefully through onto the dais, and handed me after him. "I'm surprised it's daylight still," I said. "Tell me, Mr. Lethman, did you carry me over from the village in broad daylight?"

"The car didn't touch Sal'q at all. There's a negotiable track down this side of the valley from the High Lebanon. You only had to be brought a couple of kilometers from the car."

"Down the path behind the palace? I suppose that's why I'm as stiff as a board. What did you bring me on, a mule?"

Absurd though it may seem, I was angrier at that moment than I had yet been. There was humiliation in the knowledge that these men had manhandled my unconscious body. So far, the thought made me want to run away and hide; but perhaps later on the anger would help.

He said only, "The hammam's next door, off the Prince's Garden."

I escaped into its alabaster and stained-glass labyrinth like a rabbit scuttling down a safe burrow. Within, the murmur of water trickling through shallow channels and dripping into marble basins echoed like the sea in the corridors of a cave. I threaded my way to the center of the cool maze. Here water splashed into a blackened shell that had once been silver, and a stone faun leaned out with a cup of wafer-thin alabaster. I took it from him, filled it, and drank. Then I took off everything but pants and bra and washed deliciously in the cool water, drying myself on my slip. I shook my dress out and put it on, did my face and hair, and put my shoes on again. I took another drink of water, rinsed the cup for the faun, and went out to meet John Lethman.

He was sitting on the edge of the dry fountain in the Prince's Garden. He got quickly to his feet and started to speak but I cut in abruptly, "You needn't think you're going to get me back into that foul little room. If Dr. Grafton wants to see me, he can see me here. And you can have that girl bring coffee." I marched into the Divan. I sat down in the red lacquer chair, while Lethman, giving me a look of acute dislike, pulled the bell.

The familiar peal ricocheted through the stillness with, inevitably, the clamor from the hounds. Somehow, the noise was comforting; Aunt H's dogs, who had known my voice and step, and who (the thought lit my mind like a sudden flare) perhaps disliked "the Doctor" as much as Samson had—and so were kept shut away except to keep nosy Christy Mansel within bounds—might actually be on my side.

Before the echoes of the bell had died, the heavy curtains at the head of the bed were pulled violently back and Henry Grafton came in like a genie erupting from Aladdin's lamp. He said furiously, "What the devil's happened to that girl?" Then he stopped short, like someone running into a wire. He gave me a long look I by no means liked. "What's she doing here?"

"She asked for the bathroom," John Lethman said.

"Oh." He seemed as disconcerted as Lethman had been.

"You rang?" said Halide, at the garden door. At least I suppose that's what she was saying in Arabic. She was wearing Aunt Harriet's ring.

I answered in English. "Yes, we rang. You may bring some coffee for me."

She spat something at me and whirled furiously on Grafton. "Why do you let her sit there like that and give orders? Are *you* afraid of her too?"

"Shut up," I said wearily. "Stop yelling and get my coffee. And heat it before you bring it."

The look she gave me this time was pure boiling oil and I was

569

glad to have deserved it. She swung back to Grafton, simmering like a kettle, but he cut her short. "Do as you're told. John, can't you clout some sense into her? It won't be long now." He added something in Arabic to Halide, more conciliatory in tone, and after a while she went, scowling.

Lethman gave a sigh, half relief, half exasperation. "She'll come to heel when the time comes." He dabbed at his face, winced, and dabbed again. "Shall I take the girl back?"

"No. I'll talk to her here. Afterwards—" He finished the sentence in Arabic. Lethman's reply was wordless and quite horrible. He merely drew the edge of his hand across his throat. Henry Grafton laughed. "If you can," he said in English.

Lethman went out. I wanted to keep what miserable initiative I could, so I spoke immediately. My voice came out harsh with nerves, and surprisingly formidable. "Well, Dr. Grafton, you've got a bit of explaining to do."

My rudeness didn't even ruffle him. He eyed me with an appraising, almost clinical look, and his manner was pleasant as he brought a chair over, and sat opposite me.

"Cigarette? It'll help compose your nerves."

"Who said they needed composing?"

"Oh, come, Miss Mansel!"

"All right. My hand's shaking. Does that please you?"

"Not at all." He lit my cigarette. "You're a fighter and I admire that. I don't mean you any harm. I had to get you back here and talk to you."

"Oh, come off it, Dr. Grafton! You could have talked to me in the car." I drew on my cigarette and felt my nerves beginning to relax. "Now let's have it. What happened to Aunt Harriet?"

He looked at me, frankly apologetic. "Miss Mansel, you've every ground for suspicion and anger, but only on your *own* account. As far as your aunt is concerned, there's nothing to worry you. She died quite peacefully a fortnight ago. I was with her all the time, and so was John."

"What did she die of? Heart? Her asthma? Plain neglect?"

He answered with the same pleasant appearance of frankness.

"The asthma was a fiction, Miss Mansel—a story that allowed me to speak to you in a whisper. And the picture I had to give you of a forgetful, very strange old lady was far from the truth. Your aunt was fully in possession of her faculties right up to the time of her death."

"What was it, then?"

"Primarily her heart. She had a very slight coronary last autumn, and another in late February. Then she had had gastric attacks lately; and she had a bad one three weeks ago. Her heart simply wouldn't take it. She was, after all, over eighty."

I stared at him, drawing on my cigarette. "You went to pretty fair lengths to conceal her death. Why?"

He turned up a hand. "I don't blame you if you don't believe it, but far from wanting your aunt out of the way, I did a lot to keep her alive. I liked her; and besides, her death was damned inconvenient and could have cost me a fortune." He tapped ash on the floor. "Hence the masquerade. It didn't suit me to have lawyers or family invading the place, so we've allowed people to think she's still alive."

"And then I turned up at the wrong moment. But the wrong moment for *what*, Dr. Grafton? You'd better start from the beginning."

He leaned back in the chair. "Very well. I was your aunt's doctor for about six years, coming up once a fortnight, sometimes oftener. She was very fit and active, but something of a hypochondriac; and besides, she was, in spite of her fanatical independence, a bit lonely. I may say I enjoyed my visits. She could be very entertaining. I finally moved in here last fall."

"And John Lethman? He told me how he got taken on here, but I don't believe it."

"Ah, yes. One of the few times John has managed a bit of lightning thinking. He knows about as much as you do about psychological medicine; he's an archaeologist. He was working on the Adonis cult, and that's what suggested the 'ecstatic religions' nonsense he gave you. Apart from that, he told you the truth about being caught by a storm and coming to Dar Ibrahim. Your aunt took a fancy to him, and asked him to stay on; and somehow he started looking after the place for her. I must say, it made my job a lot easier." There was the ghost of a smile I didn't quite like. "A nice boy."

"So *you* were the 'resident physician' in her acting out of the Lady Hester story—John Lethman certainly made a quick recovery on that one! I *was* puzzled, because the dogs like Lethman, and she wrote us that her dog couldn't abide the doctor."

"Oh, that was the wretched little brute that I—that died. . . . Yes, indeed, I was the 'resident physician.' On occasions, your aunt's impersonation of Lady Hester got a little trying."

I glanced above the bed to the stick and the rifle. "Is it too much to hope that like Lady Hester she really used them on Halide?"

He laughed. "You mustn't be too hard on Halide. She's working very hard for what she wants."

"John Lethman? Or Dar Ibrahim?" I leaned forward to stub out my cigarette on a saucer. "You know, I do believe you meant my aunt no harm. For one thing, you don't seem to have censored her letters, since you obviously never saw the one inviting Charles to visit her." I half expected him to ask what I was talking about, but he simply watched me steadily. "And I'm inclined to pass John Lethman," I said. "But are you sure Halide didn't want my aunt out of the way?"

"No, no, that's nonsense," he said. "Halide looked after her devotedly. The late-night sessions were a fact and the girl was sometimes run off her feet. To suggest that Halide . . ."

He broke off as Halide came in. She set the coffee down on the table, then, without looking at either of us, went straight out of the room. I drank a cup, and felt better.

"What's more," said Henry Grafton, "John and Halide, as partners in my—my business—had reason to wish Lady Harriet alive."

"Meaning," I said, "that they're in a racket with you?"

"You could put it like that."

"Did my great-aunt leave a will?" I asked bluntly.

He grinned. "She made them every week. Apart from cross-word puzzles, it was her favorite amusement. She used to hide them in odd corners. You're welcome to look."

I said, in surprise, "You'll let me look around?"

"Naturally. All this may belong to you or your cousin now."

"Or to John Lethman?"

He shot me a look. "As you say. She was very fond of him. But there's little left of value. You may care to unearth one or two personal souvenirs from the general chaos."   .

"Such as the ring that Halide's wearing?"

He looked surprised. "The garnet? It was certainly your aunt's favorite, but I understood she herself gave it to Halide. Well, Halide probably wouldn't mind . . ."

"It has sentimental value, and I'm pretty sure that the family would fight to get it back."

"Then you must certainly have it. I'll speak to Halide."

I felt suddenly very tired, as if the conversation were slipping away from me. "Will you show me where my aunt is?" I said.

He got to his feet. "Of course. She's in the Prince's Garden, as she wished to be." He led the way into the court. Over the outer wall fell a tangle of white jasmine, and beside it a blinding curtain of yellow roses. In their shade was a flat white stone, with the turban of the Moslem dead. I stared at the slender column with its man's turban. Somehow of all that I had seen this was the most alien. I thought of the lichened stones in the old churchyard at home. . . . *I have purchased an excellent Tombstone locally.* . . .

"At least she's near her friends," I said. "I saw the dogs' graves in the Seraglio Garden." I turned away, still feeling tired. The strain of the day was weighing on me.

"Come in out of the sun." His dark eyes were peering at me. They looked very intent. Somewhere, behind those oil-black eyes, was something not as calm, as pleasant as Dr. Henry Grafton would like me to believe. "Come along now," he said.

The room seemed comparatively cool after the garden. I sat down in the lacquer chair and leaned back. Dr. Grafton poured water into a glass.

"Drink this. Are you all right? Here, have another cigarette. It'll help you."

I took it automatically, and he lit it for me. Somehow, the doctor-patient gesture had put him back, subtly, on top. I made an effort, through the invading fatigue, to resume the attack.

"Dr. Grafton, for the time being I'll accept that my aunt's death was a natural one. Now, why did you conceal it?"

He regarded his clasped hands for a minute. Then he looked up. "When you rang up my house, did they tell you anything about me?"

"No, but from their silences, I gather you're in trouble."

"True. A little matter of selling medical supplies illegally. You can get away with murder here more easily."

"You wouldn't just have been deported to England?"

"As it happens, I'm a Turkish national. I had to get out of the Lebanon—and fast. But I had assets in the country, and I wouldn't leave without realizing them. I'd been afraid this might happen one day, so I'd been using Dar Ibrahim as my—my storeroom—for some time, and over the past few months I had also managed to—" a flick of the brown eyelids "—engage John's interest.

"My getaway from Beirut was easy. I was driven to the airport and checked in. Someone else took over my ticket and boarded the flight. Then John drove me up here by the back road. I'd spun your aunt a story about procuring drugs without charge for my poorer patients. Like Lady Hester, she had the highest disregard for the laws of this country, so she took me in and kept it secret. As for Halide, she had her eye on John as a one-way ticket out of Sal'q, and her brother was employed by me already. Jassim's silence one hardly has to buy. So I was sitting pretty, due to check out at the end of the summer. . . ."

I leaned forward to flick ash into the saucer. It missed, and went onto the dusty table.

He went on: "Then came your great-aunt's death. For you to think I'd killed her! I spent nine hours solid at her bedside, fighting for her life. . . . Well, she died—and her death could have thrown me to the lions. So we decided to try to keep it secret—

just for the couple of weeks needed to cut our losses and complete the current operation. But then—*you* came."

The sun's last light sloped in a bright shaft across my feet. I watched it idly. Dr. Grafton seemed oddly remote.

"You're a persistent young woman. John and I were afraid you would whistle up lawyers and heaven knows what else, so we thought we hadn't much to lose by trying the masquerade. And it worked."

I nodded, remembering the hoarse whisper disguising the man's voice; the sunken mouth, from which presumably he had removed some false teeth; the alert black eyes. Halide's and Lethman's nervousness had not been for the reasons I imagined. "So at supper John Lethman was finding out all he could about the family, to fill you in. You knew I hadn't seen Aunt H since I was a child, but Charles had seen her recently, so naturally 'she' couldn't receive him. Oh, clever, Dr. Grafton." I blew a long cloud of smoke. "Lethman tried to hurry me out, but you wouldn't let him; you were enjoying yourself too much making a fool of me."

He was grinning. Grotesquely, it was Aunt Harriet's face. I said, "All right, you fooled me. So why drag me back like this?"

"Because we hadn't fooled your cousin. Don't give me that great big innocent look. He was here Monday night. Yes, my dear, that stare's a bit more genuine."

"How do you know?"

"He told me all about it."

I stared. The room seemed to be swirling round me.

"He was to have left by the back gate that night, wasn't he? Well, he didn't. John and I came across him in the passageway below here, trying to force one of the padlocked doors. . . . So he's been safely locked away in the palace prison cell ever since."

"Charles *here*? He can't be!" I felt as if I were groping through smoke. I put a hand to my forehead. "He left a letter for me in Beirut. He went to see Ben's father. . . . And we saw him. . . ."

"He wrote that letter only to ensure that you kept away from Dar Ibrahim and didn't start hunting for him when he failed to turn up at the Phoenicia. . . ."

575

The conversation no longer seemed to have much to do with me. As I stared at him, I saw the yellowish grin widen. He was talking again, fragments of information drifting like torn paper to lie in a crazy pattern: John Lethman—no doubt the "Englishman" seen in the distance by the faun—had driven Charles's Porsche down to Beirut in the early morning, hidden it, then been driven back by Yusuf, who later got the letter delivered to the hotel, and went himself to ride herd on me. . . .

"But you, my dear, didn't stay out of the line of fire. You even telephoned England. And after Yusuf heard your conversation with Damascus, we decided to remove you."

"Yusuf. The Arab in the red tarboosh. In the next booth?"

"Certainly. We didn't want any eyes turning to Dar Ibrahim, so we decided to let you disappear. So Yusuf got the Porsche out and drove it through the frontier to wait. Bait, of course."

"If he's harmed *Hamid*—!"

"Not if Hamid is sensible." Grafton laughed. "Your being stopped at the frontier worked out like a dream. I was there, so I sent my driver through to tell Yusuf to get rid of the Porsche. But as luck would have it you'd seen it and told your driver to go after it. My car came back, but since neither Hamid nor the Porsche did, I gather Yusuf must have made him listen to reason." A grunt of amused satisfaction. "Then you told everyone within hearing that you were going to the Adonis Hotel to get a car for Beirut, so I simply drove there first and waited for you. The manager may be new, but I made sure that by the time you turned up, he was sure he'd known me all his life. I hope you appreciated the touch about the Great Mosque? You told 'Aunt Harriet' about it."

"Oh, you're clever!" I said. "Have you hurt Charles?"

"There was a bit of a rough-up last night."

"No wonder John looks the worse for wear! Good old Charles! And oh, poor Auntie Harriet! Did he hurt *you* much?"

His smile vanished and a vein in his temple began to beat. "He didn't touch me. I had a gun. John Lethman isn't much use because he drugs."

"Drugs?" My brain simply wasn't working. Grafton was gigantic, standing over me. His voice was vicious. "Yes, *drugs*, you silly spoiled little brat. I said 'medical supplies,' didn't I? There's a fortune in hemp lying in the cellars, waiting for collection tonight; and another fortune in the fields above Laklouk. If your aunt hadn't died, and I'd been able to hang on till harvest—" He drew in his breath. "And not only hemp. Opium, morphine, heroin. . . . I've a pipeline across Syria, to Turkey and Iran. With a bit of time and privacy for processing . . ."

My cigarette stub fell through my fingers to the floor. It seemed to fall in slow motion, and I sat there, looking down at my hand, which seemed not attached to my body at all.

" . . . and that privacy is just what we had, till you came. We've been working like slaves putting the stuff through the lab downstairs. And the caravan comes through tonight. . . ." I heard him laugh again. "Feeling a bit far away, are you? That was a reefer—hashish—you had in the car; and you've just smoked two more, my pretty. Now you're going back to your room to sleep them off . . . till tonight's over."

I ought to care. Fragments of pictures were there in smoky darkness: John Lethman's defeated young face; the patch of hemp; the label of the racing dog; the crates in the cellar. . . . But I was safe; beautiful and powerful as an angel, floating on the ceiling, while down there below a vaguely smiling girl sat slackly in a red lacquer chair. . . . Poor silly brat; she was in danger, and she didn't even look afraid.

Not even when Lethman came in and asked, "Is she out?"

"Well taken care of. And the man?"

"Blocked. Cell blue with smoke and he's out cold."

Grafton laughed. "Safe till it's over. And you, young John, you've just had your fix, by the look of you. Well, that's the last hard stuff you'll get till that cargo's safely through Beirut. D'you hear me? Right. Now, take her back."

The girl moved her head dreamily and smiled at the younger man. "I must say," said John Lethman, "I like her better this way. What a family! She reminds me of the old lady on her bad days."

He leaned over the lacquer chair. At his touch, I came down from where I had been floating. I said with dignity, "Can manage qui' well, thank you."

He said with impatience, "Of course you can't." He yanked me out of the chair and heaved me over his shoulder, and I laughed like an idiot upside down all the way back to my dungeon. . . .

X

MY WATCH said almost eleven. The hours had passed like smoke from those cigarettes. Now I felt firmly enough based—too firmly. I sat on my prison bed, holding my head, with a crashing hangover.

They had left me a lamp this time. In the swimming light, I could see that the room was even bigger than I had thought, and literally stacked with boxes, cartons and tins. The device of the running dog stood out clear and damning, with its misspelled warning stenciled below: BEST QUALITY. BEWARE IMMITATIONS.

So John Lethman's role in the business was pathetically clear: he was a victim. He was hooked on the hard drugs that would ensure his dependence—his willingness to watch the crops in the hills, and deal with growers like the man Charles and I had seen approach the palace.

And I was afraid that there were going to be more victims. People have been murdered for a lot less. Whether Grafton yet realized it, he would have to kill Charles and me to keep this fortune and save his own skin.

The door swung open. Halide was standing there with a tray in her hands. "Here is your food," she said. "And do not think you can get away. The back gate is locked this time, and the key out of it, and the men are in the Lady's room."

"If you knew how funny that sounds in English!" I said. I watched her as she set the tray down on a box.

"Halide," I said, "did John warn you what the penalties are for running drugs?"

She smiled. "Everybody knows this, but everybody does it in

the Lebanon. For many years, my brother used to bring the
hashish down from the hills. Only brave men like him are the carriers to the sea."

She spoke as if they were Robin Hoods. To the peasant,
hashish brought pleasure and money. If the government was unreasonable, why, then the government must be fooled—just as we,
in more sophisticated societies, assume that tax and speed laws
are made to be broken.

"You need not be so afraid," Halide added now, contemptuously. "They do not mean to kill you."

"I'm not afraid." I met her look as steadily as I could. "But you
had better be, Halide. Where can you go with John Lethman?
Not into Syria—they'd catch you in no time. Not into Turkey or
Egypt—there's a death penalty there for running drugs. Don't
think John can take you to England, either; you'd soon be picked
up there. Any minute now the Beirut police will start looking for
us, and the trail leads first to Dar Ibrahim."

"But it is nearly midnight, Wednesday," she said. "The caravan
is already on its way. The palace will be empty by daylight!"

"I suppose it will," I said. I pressed a hand to my forehead as if
that would clear my thoughts. "Listen, Halide. My family is
wealthy. I can offer the help which you and John are badly going
to need."

"You!" she blazed. "You are only a stupid woman, too stupid
even to get a man!" And she spat at me.

That was all it needed. My head cleared miraculously, and I
laughed. "As a matter of fact I *have* got a man. He's the grandson
of your Lady's eldest brother, and probably the legal owner of
this palace and its contents. So for a start you can hand over my
great-aunt's ring."

It was obvious that Grafton had already spoken to her. Her face
darkened and then she drew the ring off. "Take it. It is nothing.
Take it!"

She threw it at me with the gesture of an empress—and it
landed slap in the bowl of soup.

"Well," I said cheerfully, "that should sterilize it." I fished it out, dunked it in the glass of water, and dried it on the napkin. Then I noticed the silence and looked up.

Halide spoke urgently and I knew, with surprise, that something had put her out. "Let me bring you more soup. Please allow me— Any minute you will be taken out of here and put with the man, so you must eat while you can." There was an abject quality in her eagerness that spoke suddenly of generations of slavery and the whip.

"But I don't want the soup, thank you. Bread and cheese will do very well." I noticed with self-contempt that when she was insolent I was angry; as soon as she crept into her place, I could afford civility.

"I will take it back, then, just in case—" She reached for it, and, inches apart, our eyes met. I shot out a hand and took hold of her wrist. Her tiny intake of breath told me that—incredibly— I was right.

"What's in it?" I demanded.

"Nothing! Chicken and herbs. Let me go!"

"And a drop or two of poison to top it up?"

"Poison? Where would I find poison?"

"What's this about poison?" Grafton said from the doorway.

She swung round to face him, hands out as if to ward him off.

I said, "Just a guess on my part—but perhaps you would like to analyze that soup in your lab?"

Grafton looked at Halide, his black eyes bright and deadly. Her hands clutched the silk of her robe together at her throat as if for warmth. She said, "There is nothing in the soup—only chicken and herbs. . . ."

"Then," said Grafton, "you wouldn't object to drinking it yourself?" He whipped the bowl from the tray, advanced on the girl and held it up to her mouth.

She backed away from him until she was against a stack of crates, staring at Grafton like a mesmerized rabbit.

Suddenly she gave in. "All right. I *did* put something in it, but it is only a purge, to give her pains. Why should she have the ring, when she is rich already? I put the oil in the soup only to make her suffer a little ... just a little ..." Her voice faltered. Then she finished in a rush: "I would drink it myself, but tonight you will need me to help you. We will give the soup to a dog, or to Jassim, so that you will see ..."

Grafton spoke evenly. "Where did you get the oil?"

"I forget. From her room, perhaps ... All those bottles ..."

"There were no purges, nothing harmful in Lady Harriet's room. I saw to that. Come on, what was in it?"

"It was nothing—a black bottle, in John's room. He will tell you it was harmless. He said it tasted strong, so I used to put in extra herbs, and pepper—"

"Did you give it to Lady Harriet when I was away in Chiba?"

"Yes, yes, but why do you look like that? It was nothing, a drop or two, and then a little sickness—the pain was not bad—and afterwards she was always so quiet and good."

The bowl shook in Grafton's hands, as Halide glowered defiantly at him. "*Quiet and good!* Now I begin to see . . . Did this happen whenever I went away?"

"Sometimes—when she'd been too difficult. Oh, I wouldn't have harmed her, you know that! Only a few drops I gave her, and then I would nurse her through it, and afterwards there would be peace for a few days."

"And she would be grateful. Clever girl, Halide! So then she gave you the ring—and what else?"

"Many things, and you shall not take them from me—because I gave them to my father and brother to keep. When I become an English lady—"

He spoke between his teeth. "You killed the old woman."

Her voice was shrill with rage. "How can you say this? It was only medicine, from the box the Lady's husband took on his expeditions. John said it was a purge, made from the seed of a—a spurge plant, and—"

Grafton sniffed at the bowl and gave a gasp. "Spurge plant! It's croton oil. Used only for camels! Twenty drops and you'd kill a healthy horse. . . . And you gave that stuff to an old woman who had had a coronary just this February!" His voice began to shake. "If you'd kept your stupid fingers out of the pie she'd be alive today, one fortune made and time to collect another at harvest. But you—you—"

He dashed the soup, bowl and all, in her face in an access of blinding rage. The greasy stuff took her full across the eyes, and the bowl smashed across her cheekbone. Her scream choked as the slimy stuff went down her throat. Then Grafton swung his arm back as if to strike her, and I gave a cry of protest and grabbed it. He wrenched away and I went reeling back.

Suddenly there was a flash of a knife in Halide's hand. She came away from the wall of crates like a cat, raking claws and knife, and went for his face. He leaped clear and snatched for a whip that lay on a pile of camel harness; but his hand missed it, and what he lifted and lashed down with was not the whip but the heavy, cruel goad.

It caught the girl full across the temple. She lurched forward, the knife missing his throat by inches as her body slithered down and collapsed at his feet, her head hitting the stone with a small and quite final little crack. In the silence, I heard the lamp fluttering again like a caught moth.

My knees felt as if they didn't belong as I tried to go to Halide. I said weakly, "Is she dead?"

Grafton was already down beside her on one knee. When he got to his feet he didn't need to speak. I'd never seen a dead body before, but no one could ever mistake death for anything but death, once he's seen it.

Grafton turned round on me, the goad still in his hand.

Of course, he hadn't meant to kill Halide. But she was dead, and I had seen it. And something else got through to me. He had never killed before, but he saw now how simple it had been. Whatever soothing lies he had been telling himself about Charles and me, now he knew. He had taken the first step . . . And behind those dilated black eyes, he might be high as a paid Middle Eastern assassin on drugs.

The doorway was clear, and I was nearer to it than he was. I turned and ran.

The Prince's Divan was the only way to go. I couldn't hope to get down from the Seraglio window, the postern was locked, and Jassim was guarding the main door. Besides, the rifle was in the Divan.

I was a third of the way up the stairs when Lethman hurtled down them, shouting, "Grafton! Grafton!" and ran into me. He gave a grunt of surprise and held me fast. I made no attempt to get away. Some instinct made me see him almost as a rescuer; corruptible, but not corrupt, a man who could not stand aside and watch me killed.

"How did you get out?" he snapped. "What's happened?"

I pointed at the storeroom as Henry Grafton erupted into the corridor with the goad raised in his hand. At the sight of us he stopped dead, and the goad slowly sank to the floor. There was a pause; then Lethman dragged me down the staircase to the storeroom door.

"It was an accident," Grafton said. "She went for me." Then, savagely, to me: "Tell him what happened, you little fool!"

"Oh, he never meant to kill her," I said, and told Lethman what had happened. "And I can't pretend I'm very sorry. She killed Great-Aunt Harriet."

Lethman kept his grip on me as he swung on Grafton. "She what?"

Grafton stared down at the goad as if he'd never seen it before. "She'd been treating her to doses of croton oil."

"Doses of— Good grief, I remember her asking about the stuff." Lethman looked sick. "But what could she hope to gain?"

"She didn't mean to kill her; that was ignorance. She was just clever enough to choose the times when I was away . . . it never entered my head. It was one of those simple, stupid schemes one might expect from that mentality—she just wanted the old lady periodically ill so she could nurse her with devotion and get her due reward. She wanted a—a dowry."

Lethman was biting his lip. Behind the slack lines of the addict I could see the ghost of the pleasant-faced boy who had been pulled into Grafton's orbit. And I saw, too, the shamed ghost of a boy now relieved of a burden. He turned abruptly away, dragging me with him up the stairs.

Grafton dropped the goad and followed. "Hang on to the girl." His voice was harsh. "Lord knows I'm sorry about what happened, John, but we'd better get back on the job. There isn't long to go. We'll have to shift the body, and somehow stall Nasirulla off. Stop gawping at me! And shove that girl in the cell with the man. She looks as if she's going to pass out on us."

It was quite true that I wasn't feeling well. I collapsed into the red chair, fighting back alternating feelings of icy nausea and heat. Through the waves of nausea I heard a sharp and urgent exchange of words.

"*What?* That's not possible!"

"It's true. The man's gone. I was coming to tell you," Lethman said. "I found Jassim knocked out, and the main gate open. Of course he didn't know the girl was here, or—"

"Tell Nasirulla to get the dogs out," snapped Grafton, "and to take his gun. That will get Nasirulla away while we clear up down below, and the dogs'll find the man all right. Hurry. And get back here as fast as you can to help me with the job below."

I grabbed at Lethman's sleeve as he turned to go. "Don't leave me with that swine! Can't you see he's gone overboard? Halide, and now Charles . . . Can't you see *you* haven't a chance?" I shook his arm. It was like pleading with a zombie. "Look, I know you've only done what he made you do! If you let Charles and me go, I'll stand up for you later and—"

"Get going," said Grafton, and Lethman pulled free and went.

Grafton jerked his head at me. "Come on. Back to your cage. You have the official dungeon this time."

The nausea had cleared. I got slowly to my feet, helping myself by the chair arms. Then I shoved myself suddenly upright, and sent the heavy chair skating across the marble tiles between Grafton and myself. I ran the other way, up the steps to the dais, jumped onto the bed and yanked the rifle down from the wall. I swung round and leveled it at him before he had taken three strides after me.

He checked. "Put that damned thing down. It isn't loaded."

The hounds bayed wildly from the court where Nasirulla was presumably loosing them. I laughed in Grafton's face. "Come and get me," I invited. He didn't move. I laughed again, and keeping the rifle ready, stepped down from the bed.

And suddenly there it was again, the wave of heat, then the choking nausea. I hung on to the arras, only dimly aware of the rifle sinking in my hands, of Grafton hesitating momentarily, of the wild baying of the dogs. . . .

Someone was shouting. I pulled myself upright—too late. He snatched the rifle from my hands, checked the empty magazine and, with a vicious swing of the hand, sent me sprawling across the bed just as the gray cat, spitting furiously, erupted from the blankets like a rocket at blast-off, and jumped over me.

I screamed. Grafton shouted something and grabbed for me, but I struck out at him with my feet as I jackknifed away towards the far side of the bed.

From the garden outside came another hoarse shout, a scrabble of racing paws, then the inhuman yell of a terrified cat, drowned in the wild tumult of hounds sighting a kill. The cat shot back into the room, a hissing gray streak, and after it the Salukis, in full cry, with Nasirulla in pursuit.

The cat leaped for the bed hangings and the hounds hurled themselves after it. The heavy chair went flying and crashed into a table, toppling and smashing a lamp in a sprayed arc of oil. Flame ran along the oil like ball lightning. Grafton dragged a blanket from the bed and jumped down the dais steps; but he slipped in the burning oil and went down, striking his head hard on the stone table. Over my head the cat leaped like a silver bird for the high windowsill and was gone.

It had all happened in seconds. The flames now went licking up the bed hangings in lapping gulps of flame. I rolled off the bed and hurled myself into the corridor beyond the arras. The last thing I saw was Nasirulla dragging Grafton towards the other door.

The hounds came with me, whining with fear. We raced down

the steps and ran on, past the room where poor Halide lay, through air already sharp with smoke, to the Prince's Door. My hands shook as I lifted the heavy latch and opened it. I slammed it shut behind us, only to find that there was fire here as well. . . .

Or so I thought, for one heart-stopping moment. Then I saw that the ancient brackets by the Prince's Door held makeshift torches, ready for the night's work. I stood irresolute while the hounds whined and shivered. The drug caravan was due soon, presumably by the postern door. But I had heard Halide say that the postern was locked and the key out of it. I would have to chance the main gate.

I ran up the passage toward it; but then I heard a turmoil of shouts from the midan. I stopped dead. Of course they would all be there: Grafton, Lethman, Nasirulla, Jassim. What was more, they would come back here at any moment now for their precious cargo.

I ran back to the door for the Seraglio stairs, and we tumbled through. Darkness dropped over us like a velvet curtain, stifling, silent, terrifying. I shut the door, took a few hesitating steps and fell over the bottom stair, hurting my shin. "Show me the way, mates," I whispered to the dogs, getting to my feet and holding on to a collar; and they thrust upwards so eagerly that I wondered if they smelled the bright, cool promise of that great sheet of water above our heads. Then Sofi, leaping ahead, pushed open the painted doorway, and the three of us ran out into smoky night air, and leaping red and gold light.

Fire ran through all the buildings to the west of the lake; the place was as bright as day. I had hoped to get the rope from the junk room and sling it down from the window before the flames took hold, but flakes of blazing straw or rags had blown onto the roof. As I watched, dismayed, the dry wooden shingles went up like straw and all along the arcade burning fragments were blown like fire arrows to start fresh buds of flame. Even the garden was burning, and the smoke was aromatic with blazing herbs.

The noise the flames made was like galloping wild horses, but the smoke streamed mercifully away from the island in a light wind. We were safe enough for the time being; I sat down with the hounds on the pavilion steps, and had time to be afraid.

The hounds huddled close to me for comfort, and I put an arm round each of them. The lake was a sheet of melted copper now, rippling and beating with flame until the very water seemed alive.

I rubbed my stinging eyes to dispel the illusion. But when I looked again I saw that it was true. The water was moving, alive with spearhead ripples as the creatures of the garden, driven by the fire, came arrowing towards the island.

The peacocks came first. The two hens flew in panic, from stone to stone of the broken bridge, but the cock, weighted by the magnificence of his tail, came yelling across the open lake, half paddling, half flying. Then the three big birds raced with hunched feathers up the rocky shore and clucked to an uneasy roost near the hounds and me.

Seven little rock partridges flew more easily to my feet, fluffy with fear, their bright eyes winking like rubies. One of them quivered warm against my ankle. A squirrel slid up the steps beside me and sat up, chittering, by Star. Then the water was full of little heads, black arrow tips making for the island: lizards, voles, shrews, snakes, house mice. And rats, gray, black and brown, who eyed me with bright intelligent eyes, then streaked for the shadows. I hadn't room for fear of them, or they of me; all of us had a right to this island until the danger was past. The hounds never even moved when one rat went clear across my feet and brushed its way through Sofi's tail.

A dove fell out of the sky, a wing singed, to flutter between my feet. I lifted it and held it gently. The water nearest the island boiled with fish as the carp crowded in from the bright edges of the lake. Above the noise of the galloping flames the dogs whined, the peacocks vented their harsh cry, the partridges crooned in panic, the rats and squirrels chittered and squealed. And I kept saying, "Oh, Charles . . . *Charles* . . ."

There was a heavy splash from the northeast corner of the lake and a ripple of the melted-gold wake as a black head speared

through the water. The creature reached the island, broke from the water, tossed a black lock of hair, and heaved itself ashore. Then it stood upright and resolved itself into my cousin, dripping, plastered with water weeds, and dressed in a pair of baggy Arab trousers, a gilt belt, a pair of soggy Arab sandals, and nothing else at all.

He regarded me and the menagerie. "Eve in the Garden of Eden. Hullo, love. Did you *have* to set the place on fire to fetch me back?"

"The dogs did it. They knocked a lamp over," I said rather waveringly. "And they said you were gone. They—they had me locked up. . . . Oh, Charles. Charles, darling . . ."

"Christy." He was down beside me on the marble floor, and Star was elbowed out of the way, and Charles's arms were round me and he was kissing me in an intense, starving, furious way that somehow seemed part of the fire. Then we were thrust apart by the wet jealous head of Star, and Charles, laughing, rolled aside from Sofi's eager paws and tongue.

"Hey, will you call your dogs off? . . . Shove over, mate, will you? I've only known this girl twenty-two years—you might give me a chance. When did I last kiss you, Christabel?"

"You'd be about ten. You've changed."

A lizard, dropping from the dome, shook us apart this time. Charles swore, swiped at it as it shot away unhurt. "Christy," he said, "I love you, and I could spend the rest of my life making love to you, and probably will, but the sooner we go the better."

"Yes. I love you, too. Did I say?"

"You made it plain," he said. "Oh, Christy, love . . . Darling, we've *got* to get out of here while there's still a chance!"

I sat up and blinked at the leaping flames. "But how? Oh, you've nearly squashed my pigeon . . . No, there it goes, thank goodness; it must have been doped with smoke. But mind the squirrel."

"And the dear little rats?" He laughed and pulled me to my feet. "We're safe enough here, but it might get a bit hot. The postern is the one way out. The shaft back there—" nodding at the painted door "—would act as a chimney if the underground passage were going up, and it shows no sign of it." He pulled the door open cautiously. The shaft was dark. "Was the bronze door to the Prince's corridor shut?"

"Yes, I shut it. I thought it would seal off the draft."

"You have your moments. Anyway, we'll have to try it."

"But the postern is locked. Halide said so."

"I've got the key." He grinned, fished somewhere in the Arab trousers, and then rattled a key ring. "I snitched it off poor old Jassim when I made a break for it. If one of these fits the postern . . ." He stopped short. "Before we go down, dip something in the lake to hold over your mouth if the smoke's bad. Half a trouser leg will do if I can tear the beastly things. . . . There, that's it."

We ran down the steps to the water. "Where *did* you get that Carnaby Street rig?"

"Tell you later. Splash some water over yourself."

The water was cool and sharply restorative. Its flickering reflections caught Charles's laughing face and brilliant eyes. I laughed back at him. An almost wild exhilaration possessed me, the aftermath of a more powerful drug than any Grafton had given me.

"This way, my lovely Christabel," Charles said. "Give me your wet little hand. If anyone had told me twenty years ago . . ." A pause while we negotiated the threshold of the painted door. This was made no easier by the fact that he held me all the time, and I him. "Though as a matter of fact I don't think I had any doubt even then. It's just been a case of taking the air here and there for a few years till the true north pulled. D'you feel like that?"

"When we were at the El Sal'q Source the bells went off like a burglar alarm. I thought, Well, really, here he is at last."

"As easy as that. Are you all right? There is a bit of smoke after all."

There was a great deal. The heat grew palpable as we crept down the spiral stair in the dark, and smoke met us, acrid and heavy. The dogs whined at our heels. "Hold it, here's the door."

He pulled it open cautiously. More smoke came wreathing in, and with it a red, flickering light. He craned through and I heard his grunt of relief. "It's only the torches. Smoke's seeping under the Prince's Door like floodwater, but no fire." He pulled me through and let the door swing shut after the dogs. "Come on, we'll run for it."

"Let's just hope we don't run smack into the dope caravan."

"The camels are coming yo-ho, yo-ho . . . Don't worry, love, our luck's in—and it's going to hold."

Some minutes later, after a terrifying run along a passageway, choking and blind with smoke, we reached the postern, and while Charles fumbled with the lock I dragged back the heavy bolts. Then the key clicked sweetly and he pulled the door open. The hounds brushed past us into the clear air. Charles's arm came round me and scooped me up the rocky ramp and onto the clean rock under the trees. The postern door clanged to behind us, and shut us out of Dar Ibrahim.

XI

AT ONCE, I heard the shouting of an excited crowd at the main gate. With the hounds trotting beside us, we ran below the Seraglio into the sycamore groves above the Nahr el Sal'q. There was smoke, thin and stinging, in the air, but it smelled fresh after the garden. Charles held me close.

"Charles," I said. "The shouting—ought we go and help?"

"I don't care if Grafton and Lethman are crisped to a cinder," he said shortly, "and anyway, half the village is there already, by the sound of it. But what were *you* doing back in there? You were supposed to be miles away."

As briefly as I could I told him my story, cutting through his shocked comments with a quick: "But what made you come back for me? How did you know I was there?"

"Darling, I heard you screeching like a diesel train just before the place went up in smoke. I had pretended to be stoned with their filthy hashish, and poor old Jassim fell for it; so I clobbered him, took his keys, and got out. The only trouble was that they'd taken my clothes, I can't imagine why."

"Lethman probably wanted them to wear. He drove your car away, and he'd want to look like you if anyone saw him."

"I suppose so. Well, I grabbed a few garments from the gatehouse and ran. I knew anyone following me would go straight down to the ford, so I doubled round the back under the Seraglio windows, stark naked, pants in hand, and leaping like a grasshopper every time I trod on a thistle."

"My poor lamb."

"I stopped under these trees to put the pants on. There was a shirt and a kaffiyeh as well." He cast about under the trees and pounced on something. "Here they are. . . . Then, when I heard you scream, I tore into the pants and shoes and belted back to the main gate, but they'd barred it again. Chaos broke loose inside the palace and I smelled smoke. So I ran round to that window below the Seraglio and climbed in. Now let me tie Jassim's headcloth round your shoulders: at least it's dry. What's this round your neck?"

"Oh. I'd forgotten it. It's a charm I got for you against the Evil Eye. You wanted one for your car, you said."

"For my love, I said. You'd better keep it. You look wonderful, Christy. That dress looks as if it had been poured over you out of a dirty jug, and your eyes are as big as mill wheels and as black as outer space."

"I've been smoking their filthy hashish, that's why. Oh, Charles, they're dealing in the stuff. They're planning—"

"Darling, I know. Lethman told me more than he realized. And I know Aunt Harriet is dead."

I stared. "How did you find out about her?"

"Guessed, to begin with. Didn't you know that she had your cat phobia?"

"*Did* she? We never had a cat at home, and I don't remember ever hearing her speak of it. I see. As soon as I told you 'she' had a cat in her room you knew something was wrong. But Grafton would know, surely?"

"He probably never even thought about it. In Aunt H's day, no cat would have invaded her room because of her dogs. They always slept on her bed."

We began to pick our way along the stony cliff top.

"Well, I made up my mind to find out what had happened to her. The fact that Lethman and Company let you wander around the place indicated that she wasn't hidden at Dar Ibrahim. Then when I saw the way that Koran and the dogs of Fu were left lying about, and that Samson had not been properly buried, I was sure she was dead. So after you'd gone off to bed that night I went snooping back. I got caught and locked up and that was that. Here we are, steady. Good Lord!"

We had reached the corner now and could see the front of the palace. The walls towered black and jagged against the leaping flames behind them. Windows pulsed with light, and one high roof was nothing but a burning grid of beams. With every gust of breeze, clouds of spark-filled smoke rolled down over the crowd at the main gate. The Arabs scattered, shouting with excitement, only to bunch again near the gate as the cloud dispersed. Men came and went through the general melee, so some salvage work was going on—though Grafton would be lucky if he saw any of the salvaged goods again.

Then I saw the bright chestnut horse, and John Lethman astride it. It was whirling, terrified, as he tried to get it clear of the crowd and past the Seraglio wall to the hillside track and freedom. The crowd scattered in front of the animal—all but Nasirulla. He ran in under the vicious hoofs and jumped for the headrope. He was shouting, and Lethman pointed back to the blazing building, and he yelled something, his voice suddenly clear above the roar of the crowd. Then Lethman brought his whip slashing down on Nasirulla, and drove the chestnut towards us at full gallop.

Nasirulla rolled clean over and came unhurt to his feet. A man by him was yelling and waving a shotgun. Nasirulla snatched it from him, whirled and shot.

But the chestnut was already out of range. It went by within a few feet of us. Lethman was just a crouching shadow against the bright mane, gone with a crash of hoofs. And at that moment Star and Sofi left us, vanishing in the horse's dust.

Henry Grafton emerged now from the gatehouse, his arms loaded. Nasirulla yelled something, ran forward, still yelling, and as Grafton turned to face him, fired again at a range of perhaps ten yards. Grafton fell.

I was shaking so much I could only cling to Charles and say through chattering teeth, "Was that because of Halide?"

"Sure to be. Lethman must have told him. And that's our cue to leave, love; Arab mobs are not my favorite thing. I think we can get down to the ford the back way." He took my hand, and together, by the light of the fire, we made our way down, and crossed the river still running scarlet for Adonis.

It was noon next day. The only memory I retained of the night before was of the smell of goat as, from some invisible corner, the faun tore himself from a grandstand view of the fire to offer his help as escort up to the village.

It was he who piloted us to a house near the far end. No light showed, but a woman was peering half fearfully out of the door at the fire, which still spurted among the smoking ruins across the valley. The boy shouted something—I was too tired to care what. Charles's arms half lifted me up the steep rough steps into the house. There, behind a curtain which divided the single room, I wrapped myself in some cotton garment which smelled clean, lay down on a bed of blankets, and was almost immediately asleep. The last thing I remember was my cousin's voice, talking Arabic, and waiting—as I found out later—for the headman, the woman's husband, to come from the fire.

Now we sat on the graveyard wall in the hot sun, hoping for a car to take us to Beirut. Charles still wore the grubby trousers and a shirt which exposed more than it covered of his brown chest. My dress was filthy, and my legs were scratched and bruised.

All the explanations had been made now. Henry Grafton had died instantly from the shot, and Lethman had vanished clear away into the High Lebanon. I never heard or cared very much what happened to him. Halide's body had been recovered. Some freak of fire had left the storeroom more or less undamaged. The police, arriving at dawn, found the contents depleted but still well worth investigation.

We had answered a round of questions this morning, and now the police were back at the smoking ruins, like a blackened tooth on the crag. We could see the scurrying movement as looters, presumably dodging the police with ease, prodded about in the wreckage.

I said, "I wonder if she'd have liked to know we were here?"

"From what I remember of the old dear," said Charles crisply, "she'd be delighted to know that she's taken the whole place up with her. Talk about a funeral pyre! Nobody in the Lebanon will ever forget her now."

"It looks as if most local households will have a souvenir or two," I said drily. "And your own Gabriel Hounds, Charles? They may still be there."

"I'm not going to compete with those jackals. Someday I'll buy another pair in memory of her."

Some small children came running by, kicking a tin can, and stopped to play in the dirt under the graveyard wall. Two or three thin dogs followed, and a tiny boy threw a stone at the smallest of them. It dodged behind a rusty oil drum. Charles clicked his fingers at it and said something in Arabic, and it came slinking to hide behind his legs.

"Here's a car coming," he said. "Looks like a taxi."

A big glossy car slid to a stop at the far end of the village street. The driver dismounted to open the rear door, and a tall man got out, unmistakably English as to tailoring, and unmistakably self-assured as to bearing.

We uncurled from the wall. "Father!" exclaimed Charles.

"Daddy!" I cried at the same moment.

"It's my father, not yours," said Charles.

The newcomer came our way, not hurrying.

"Give you twenty to one?" said Charles in my ear.

"N-no." Whichever it was, he had come. I felt a rush of relief and pleasure.

The man stopped in front of us. If he felt relief and pleasure, he concealed it very well. "I have never seen either of you look worse," he said, "but I take it it's nothing that a bath won't put right?" His eyes went to Dar Ibrahim. "So that's the place?" He watched the distant scene a moment, without comment. Then he turned back to us. "You can tell me the whole thing later on, but I'll get you back to Beirut now, and into those baths. I've squared the police. They'll see you again later."

"I suppose you know what's happened?" said Charles.

"Nobody's talking about anything else in Beirut. Why the devil did you let Christy in for that, Charles?"

"Unjust, unjust," said Charles, without heat. "The stupid girl got herself into a jam and I rescued her. Wait till her own father hears the story! Incidentally, settle a bet for us. Tell her it's only you."

He smiled. "Actually, I don't particularly want to lay claim to either of you at the moment."

My cousin said, "You're going to have to lay claim to both. One of us wants your consent and the other your blessing."

"So? I'm very glad. Welcome, darling." He hugged me. "Congratulations, boy. Far more than you deserve!"

My cousin grinned at me. "Well?"

"You win, Charles. You always do. Oh, Uncle Chas, it's wonderful to see you! And it's true Charles looked after me."

"This seems the right moment to tell you," said Charles, "that I lost the Porsche."

"So I gather. It's at the Phoenicia."

"Efficient devil you are!" said his son. "How did you do that?"

"Christy's driver brought it back. It seems that the man who stole it ran it off the road at a bend— No, Charles, it's all right, a scratch or two, that's all. Hamid was right on its tail and managed to lay the man out before he'd quite realized what had happened. You'll be able to thank him yourself—he drove me up."

"Oh, that's marvelous!" I said. "Can we go now?"

"Why not?" He turned to look again at Dar Ibrahim. The children had abandoned us to go talk to Hamid, and now the little dog ventured to creep to my uncle's feet. Uncle Chas turned. "Well, that's the end of a long story. Come along, now . . . What in the world—?" As he started to go, he had almost tripped over the dog, tangled and shapeless as a dirty mop, crouching flat at his feet. Through the filthy hair an eye shone eagerly. An apology for a tail wagged furiously. "Not yours, surely?"

"Just one of these miserable village dogs." Charles stooped to pull it aside and then exclaimed, "It's got a collar on." He disentangled the collar and a tag from the dirty hair. "There's something engraved here: *Thy life hath had some smatch of honour in it* . . . Any dog in *this* country that achieves a collar must be one of the aristoc—" He stopped dead.

Then I saw the name on the collar: SAMSON.

I knew Charles felt as moved as I did. " 'Some smatch of honour'! He must have run away after she died, or else that swine threw him out to starve." He tucked the little creature under one arm. "Father, do you remember Aunt Harriet's Samson? This is her wedding present to me. My personal Gabriel Hound."

Hamid, all smiles, was at the door of the car. I got into the back seat between the two men. Charles's arm held me close and my head went down on his shoulder. The little dog and I were both fast asleep before the car had covered the first mile to Beirut.

Mary Stewart

"Mary Stewart is magic," writes *New York Times* reviewer Anthony Boucher about the attractive but retiring Edinburgh housewife who has cast her spell on a huge international following of enchanted readers. Her new novel, *The Gabriel Hounds,* follows nine previous best sellers. The last one was *Airs Above the Ground* (Reader's Digest Condensed Books, Autumn 1965).

Even in her childhood, in her clergyman father's rectory in Durham, England, Mary Stewart was writing stories. But her professional career did not start until 1954, with *Madam, Will You Talk?* After finishing that novel, she could not bring herself to send it to a publisher, and it lay around the house until her husband insisted that she try her luck. The first publisher it went to accepted it, but when Mrs. Stewart saw proofs she tried to stop publication. "A novel is such an intensely personal thing," she says. "I couldn't stand the thought of thousands of eyes reading my private thoughts." Fortunately, husband and publisher overruled her.

Such reserve is more customary in the academic world, where Mrs. Stewart spent some years as a lecturer on English literature at her alma mater, Durham University. During World War II, she not only continued to teach and write but worked as an aircraft observer at night. (What time she had left, she divided, she says, between producing college plays and riding racehorses.) She met her husband—a professor at Durham—on V-E night; they were married three months later. Professor Stewart is now head of the geology department at Edinburgh University. His career often takes him abroad, and such shared trips soon led to Mrs. Stewart's creative interest in the romantic backgrounds so characteristic of her novels.

Success somewhat frightens Mrs. Stewart: she is afraid that she may be robbed of the things she values most—her quiet life in Edinburgh, her friends and her gardening, her leisurely travels. Her financial success has changed her life only by the addition of one Balmain dress and a Jaguar car—she likes to drive and is a fair mechanic. "Basically," she says, "my ambition is simply to go on living as quietly and happily as I do now."